The Design
and Analysis
of Experiments

To
VALDA MARIE -

The Design
and Analysis
of Experiments

OSCAR KEMPTHORNE
Professor of Statistics
Iowa State College

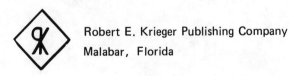
Robert E. Krieger Publishing Company
Malabar, Florida

Publisher's Note

The reader may notice a slight variation in type color on certain pages. This is caused by the resetting for over 170 corrections which have been incorporated in this edition.

ORIGINAL EDITION 1952
REPRINT 1973 (FROM 6TH PRINTING 1967)
(with corrections), 1975, 1979, 1983
Printed and Published by
ROBERT E. KRIEGER PUBLISHING CO. INC.
KRIEGER DRIVE, MALABAR, FLORIDA 32950

© *Copyright 1952 by*
JOHN WILEY & SONS, INC.
Reprinted by arrangement

Library of Congress Catalog Card Number: 51-13460
I.S.B.N. Number: 0-88275-105-0

PRINTED IN THE UNITED STATES OF AMERICA

PREFACE TO REPRINTED EDITION

This book was written in the years 1948-1950, when there were only two books devoted to the topic, The *Design of Experiments* by R.A. Fisher and *Experimental Designs* by W.G. Cochran and G.M. Cox, both of which retain their original utility and are completely basic. I felt then that there was a need for a book which presented some of the theory of the subject at a fairly simple mathematical level.

In the past twenty years the subject has expanded tremendously. Many books have been written on the theory of least squares, linear models and on the design of experiments. For advanced and specialized training these many recent books should be consulted. Also there have been many developments in combinatorics of designs, investigation of response relations, optimum seeking, and optimality of designs.

But the present book appears to have real value still as one which introduces the student and reader to the basic ideas of the design and analysis of comparative experiments. The exposition of the method of least squares for statistical linear models is useful as a short introductory account. The basic ideas of randomization, replication and blocking are not covered as deeply, it appears, in any of the books written since 1950. The role of randomization in experiments that are critical for society has been increasingly recognized in recent years. The present book presents some basis for the force of randomization, and seems alone in presenting the basic ideas of randomization analysis of randomized experiments. The treatment given of factorial designs, confounding and fractional replication is a necessary and good basis for general understanding, and is a necessary introduction to much of the more recent literature. The treatment of split-plot designs and incomplete block designs seems to have a similar status, though there is perhaps a bit too much emphasis on lattice designs. Even in this case, however, the presentation of the problem of combining different types of information which occurs with structured error contains basic essential ideas. Also, lattice designs are very widely used in some areas, particularly plant breeding.

These aspects have resulted in the book being used as the prescribed text for a course on the design of experiments at the MS level and as a basis for more advanced work in the design of experiments at Iowa State University and some other universities.

The book was aimed at readers of two classes, those in experimental science who wished to gain understanding of the basic mathematical, statistical and logical ideas, and those in statistics who wished to gain some understanding of the formal subject *and* of the uses of the ideas in experimental science. It appears that this aim was met and is still of value.

For the above reasons, it has been deemed appropriate to reprint the text. The opportunity has been taken to correct a rather large number of minor but irritating errors that were unfortunately present in the original printing. I am particularly indebted to G.L. Ghai and T.E. Emigh for aid in this correction process.

13 June 1973   Oscar Kempthorne

Preface

THE SUBJECT OF THE DESIGN OF EXPERIMENTS HAS BEEN BUILT UP
largely by two men, R. A. Fisher and F. Yates. The contributions of
R. A. Fisher to mathematical statistics form a major portion of the
subject as we now know it. His contributions to the logic of the scientific method and of experimentation are no less outstanding, and his
book *The Design of Experiments* will be a classic of statistical literature.
The contributions of F. Yates to the field of the design of experiments
are such that nearly all the complex designs of value were first put
forward by him in a series of papers since 1932. Both Fisher and Yates
have also made indirect contributions through the staff of the statistical
department of Rothamsted Experimental Station, since its founding in
1920. It is not surprising that the contributions originated from Rothamsted, because Rothamsted was probably the first place in the world
to incorporate a statistical department as a regular part of its research
staff, and the design of experiments is a subject that must grow through
stimulation by the needs of the experimental sciences. A third group
that has made considerable contributions since about 1937 is the Cal-
cutta school, under the leadership of P. C. Mahalanobis.

The first steps toward writing this book were taken about 1949, when
the only books dealing specifically with the design of experiments were
R. A. Fisher's *Design of Experiments* and F. Yates's *Design and Analysis
of Factorial Experiments*. At that time I felt the need, particularly in
teaching and also in consultation, for a book that would combine the
very considerable literature on the design of experiments into a systematic account of the subject from the point of view of both the user
of the designs and the statistician whose duties are to consult in this
field. The basic requirements of the user of experimental designs have
been satisfied by the book of Cochran and Cox entitled *Experimental
Designs*. There remains, however, the relationship of the experimental
designs to least squares and general linear hypothesis theory, the
enumeration of designs, and various other topics which arise with considerable frequency. The proportion of instances in which the needs
of the experimenter are satisfied entirely by an experimental plan, the
analysis of variance and standard errors, I have found to be comparatively low. The aim of this book has been to give a description

of the design of experiments from as broad a view as possible and to relate the subject matter of this field of statistics to the general theory of statistics and to the general problem of experimental inference.

These remarks are the basis for the general structure of the book. Chapters 1 to 3 are entirely introductory and contain an attempt to give the place of experimental design in the whole field of statistics and a statement of the statistical theory which is basic to the interpretation of experimental data. Chapter 4 contains a very short introduction to the principle of least squares, an elementary understanding of which is essential to the experimenter, no matter how little he is interested in the basis of experimental designs. Chapters 5 and 6 are an attempt to cover in a systematic way general linear hypothesis theory and the least squares treatment of linear models, together with some closely allied problems such as the estimation of components of variance. In these chapters the processes can be described in fairly simple language, but a description of the proofs would be unduly long without the use of matrix notation. It is not particularly important to the user of experimental designs to be familiar with these proofs so long as he understands the processes and their theoretical basis, and the proofs are therefore given in matrix notation. The time is coming rapidly when workers in many fields of science will find a knowledge of the elementary properties of matrices essential to an understanding of the theory of their fields. Chapters 7 and 8 are concerned with the function of randomization and an attempt to give a complete account of the basis of the experimental designs with which the main body of the book is concerned. Chapters 9 and 10 comprise an elementary description of the two basic designs, randomized blocks and Latin squares, and Chapters 11 and 12 a discussion of plot technique and the sensitivity of experiments. All the material up to and including Chapter 12 is in a sense introductory, and, these matters having been disposed of, the remainder of the book is concerned with the development of designs in a logical order. This development is hinged fairly completely, with the exception of partially balanced incomplete block designs, on factorial systems, and this is the main reason for the somewhat long discussion of the 2^n factorial system. The last two chapters of the book are concerned with the analysis of groups of experiments and with designs for sequences of treatments.

In a broad sense, practically all schemes of taking observations are part of the subject of the design of experiments. In this book attention is confined to experiments in which two or more treatments are being compared with preassigned replication. For example I have not discussed the general problem of maximizing information which is described by Fisher in *The Design of Experiments*, or the possibilities of sequential analysis.

The relationship of the material in the book to the content of courses at Iowa State College is possibly of some interest. For the last few years I have given a two-quarter course in the design of experiments to a rather heterogeneous group of students, all of whom had been exposed to courses in statistical methods and some of whom had taken an elementary course in the theory of statistics. The problems of teaching this group were an impetus toward writing this book. The analysis of variance is in many respects the most powerful tool that theoretical statistics provides; it is a comparatively simple technique from the point of view of computation and is of apparently wide applicability. The student of statistical methods tends to be one of two types; either he accepts the technique in its entirety and applies it to every conceivable situation, or he is more intelligent and questions the applicability at all. It is therefore necessary to discuss in some detail the basis of the technique and its scope of validity. It is also necessary to examine the inferences that are drawn from analysis of variance tests. As a result the course in experimental design consists of Chapters 1 to 16 excluding the more mathematical portions, 19, 20, 22, and parts of the later chapters. There is little point in spending time in the classroom to describe computational processes for the complex designs, for, even if the student remembers them for his examination, he will soon forget them and have recourse to a text setting out the processes systematically. In writing this book I could have restricted myself to material that should be given in such courses, but it seemed preferable to attempt a more complete coverage, so that the interested student can pursue the subject to any desired extent. The course which covers the above material of the book is supplemented by problems, some of which consist of filling in simpler parts of derivations, and by a large number of sets of experimental data, chosen to illustrate particular points in the development. This is an essential part of the course, and it is preferable that the instructor provide sets of data with which he is familiar, so that the class can be given a picture of the motivation behind the experiment, the reason for the choice of design, and so on.

The remainder of the book, apart from standard statistical theory, supplemented by the reading of papers, constitutes a course in experimental design for students whose aim is to become consulting statisticians with emphasis towards experimentation. I hope that the book will be of use not only to statisticians and prospective statisticians but also to biological scientists in general.

Some chapters are not elementary, though none of the material can be regarded as difficult from the mathematical point of view. It would perhaps have been desirable to give a more elementary treatment of some of the topics, but this would have lengthened the book unduly. There is no intention to make simple matters complex, and, conversely, it is hoped that difficult matters have not been simplified to the extent of giving a false picture. There are several points that I regard as part of general statistical theory, such as the non-central χ^2 distribution, and there is little point in including such matters in a book on experimental design.

With reference to the method of treatment of experimental designs, there is always the possibility of making the assumptions of the procedures in Chapters 5 and 6, and everything then follows in logical order. It was considered desirable, however, to examine the validity of these assumptions and the possibility of making less restrictive assumptions. Chapter 8 is concerned with this matter, and as a result the later treatment is based on a model that is termed the finite model. The results that are obtained are essentially the same as with normal law theory, except that randomization tests are assumed to be approximated closely by normal law theory tests. In other words, the weight of the assumptions is shifted from the experimentalist to the statistician, the onus being on the statistician to show that normal theory tests are reasonably valid under wider circumstances.

The help I have obtained from the general statistical literature is obvious, and, in addition to the writings of Fisher and Yates, the papers of Cochran, Neyman, Bose, Bartlett, Welch, and Pitman have been particularly useful in formulating the pattern of development that is followed in the book. I have developed the subject in a way that seemed logical to me and have attempted to give acknowledgment for the original formulations. The proofs of general linear hypothesis processes in Chapter 5 are based on a development of the subject presented by Dr. G. W. Brown in a course of lectures at Iowa State College.

I am indebted to Professor Ronald A. Fisher, Cambridge; to Dr. Frank Yates, Rothamsted; and to Messrs. Oliver and Boyd, Ltd., Edinburgh, for permission to reprint parts of Table V from their book *Statistical Tables for Biological Agricultural Research*. I am indebted to Professor E. S. Pearson, London, for permission to reprint the tables of the power of the analysis of variance test from Volume II of the *Statistical Research Memoirs*.

I wish to thank J. Wishart and J. O. Irwin for introducing me to statistics. My debt to F. Yates as regards the material of the book will be clear, but it is difficult to express completely my gratitude for the opportunity to work under him for some years. Without that experience and contact this book would certainly never have been written.

Acknowledgment is due to former graduate students at Iowa State College, particularly A. M. Dutton, D. J. Thompson, M. R. Mickey, J. F. Hofmann, O. P. Aggarwal, and L. J. Tick, for reading parts of the book and going over some of the examples. In conclusion, I wish to thank Miss June Duffield for her patience and diligence in preparing the manuscript for publication.

OSCAR KEMPTHORNE

December 1951

Contents

CONTENTS

CONTENTS

CONTENTS

CHAPTER 1

Introduction

1.1 THE SCIENTIFIC METHOD

The design of experiments must be regarded as an aspect of the scientific method, and we therefore start with a review of this method. It is not at all easy to give a concise definition of the "scientific method." Some have debated whether there is *a* method, rather than methods. The question of scientific methodology is not a trivial one, since the distinguishing feature of science is its method. Much has been written on this general topic, and it is not proposed to take up this question here in any detail; rather a few of the most general and least controversial features of the scientific method will be given.

A brief though adequate definition of scientific method would be the application of logic and objectivity to the understanding of phenomena. The essential feature of the scientific method is the examination of what is already known and the formulation therefrom of hypotheses which may be put to experimental test. The word "experimental" is the crux of the entire matter, for any question whose answer may not be obtained by planned observations is not in the realm of science. The ability to formulate hypotheses appears to be an individual characteristic, and, although many rules may be stated on the nature of appropriate hypotheses, the determination of the relevant aspects of the whole situation and the actual formulation of the hypotheses are a matter of intuition or genius. The next step is the examination of the hypotheses for consequences that are verifiable, and finally comes the objective verification. Verification of a theory cannot be absolute; we can only show that the observations are compatible with the theory within the limits of error to which the observations are subject. This somewhat negative approach, i.e., being able only to prove a hypothesis false, is the major reason for the use of the null hypothesis in statistics. Science searches for a pattern which will embrace as many facts as possible; that a theory may be used to give verifiable predictions in a wide range of circumstances is one of the bases on which it is accorded sup-

1

port. To use the words of Einstein: "The grand aim of all science
. . . is to cover the greatest possible number of empirical facts by logical deduction from the smallest possible number of hypotheses or
axioms." [1]

The circularity of the scientific method is perhaps not so widely
recognized as it should be. This may be brought out by noting that
it is only on the basis of hypotheses and theories that the scientist
knows what to observe. Facts and theories are intimately intermingled
and cannot be logically separated. That is to say, a fact is such only
on the basis of some theory, and vice-versa. This statement holds
very obviously in the physical sciences; in the social sciences the connection is not always clear but careful analysis shows it to exist. Herein
lies the reason why science at any finite point in its development
does not claim to provide the final answer. In the light of present
theories new facts will almost certainly be discovered in the future.
This will cause the abandonment or revision of these theories which in
turn will render "facts" under the old theory no longer "true." New-
tonian mechanics was able, in theory at least, to supply the answer to
all mechanical problems for some 150 to 200 years, but a new theory,
the general theory of relativity, was necessary to explain observations
made with finer instruments, these very instruments being products of
changing theories.

The situation may be represented diagrammatically as shown in
Figure 1.

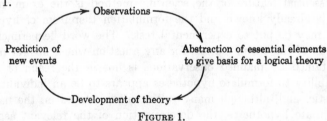

FIGURE 1.

Statistics enters at two places:

1. The taking of observations.
2. The comparison of the observations with the predictions from the
   theory.

Statistics cannot on its own bring about new scientific theories, except
in subject-matter fields that have a statistically formulated logical
theory. Unless accompanied by the deductively formulated theory,
statistics can only provide us with so-called empirical laws to which
exceptions will be found immediately the laws are stated.

This pattern of the development of a subject-matter field is well exemplified by genetics. Starting from the theory of independent segregation of genes, events could be predicted, and these led in turn to linkage theories, chromosome maps, and so on.

It may reasonably be asked what other methods there are by which adjustment to nature may be achieved or for which such claims are made. In their book, Cohen and Nagel [2] list the following: the method of tenacity in which a theory or proposition is believed by closing the mind to all contradictory evidence, the method of authority in which appeal is made to some highly respected source—a person or a book—and the method of intuition in which obvious truth is claimed for propositions. Whether this classification of other methods has any value may be doubted, but it can be used to determine how many so-called truths have originated. The essential point is that these "methods" do lead to the formulation of hypotheses, but the hypotheses cannot be accepted without experimental verification. They also lead, however, to belief in theories that cannot be verified at all.

1.2   THE FORMULATION AND TESTING OF HYPOTHESES

The formulation and testing of hypotheses are the important features of the scientific method, and some general ideas on this process may be given. In the first place, familiarity with the subject matter of the problem under investigation is absolutely essential, and, on the basis of previous knowledge, which may deal with situations that seem to be analogous, certain elements in the subject matter are regarded as significant and relevant. These elements are chosen because the investigator is aware of theories dealing with these elements. Without some theories or ideas, the investigator will be unable to choose which elements in the situation to observe. A formal condition for a hypothesis is that it must be formulated in such a way that verification or lack of it may be achieved by direct observation with an experimental procedure, or that deductions made from the hypothesis lead to predictions that may be verified. We shall make the distinction throughout this book between verification and proof. The idea of proof by prediction is, of course, fallacious; the basis of such proof is: If A (hypothesis), then B (prediction); B is observed, therefore A is true. By verification of a hypothesis, we mean the taking of observations and satisfying ourselves that the observations could have arisen from a population specified by the hypothesis. We shall avoid the term "proof," except in a mathematical argument, for the above reason, and because of the fact that a hypothesis can only be disproved.

A hypothesis must provide the answer for the practical problem for which it was formulated and, in addition to providing an explanation of already-known facts, must give predictions of observations that can be verified. It is of course essential, though frequently not realized, that the hypotheses and their outcomes should be formulated before verification is attempted. Hypotheses that are formulated from or modified by the observations are always suspect, and it is one of the elementary notions of statistical tests that probability statements cannot be made about statistical tests suggested by the data to which they are applied. It is possible that two or more hypotheses can give predictions that are experimentally indistinguishable, and in such cases appeal has to be made to notions of simplicity, that a simple hypothesis is in general to be preferred to a more complex one, and to esthetic appeal, though the simplicity or complexity of a hypothesis may not be obvious and may depend on the frame of reference in which it is formulated.

1.3 THE ROLE OF STATISTICS

Reasoning is usually classified into one of the two types: deductive and inductive. Deductive reasoning is the determination of the consequences involved in a set of premises. It cannot therefore of itself add to knowledge of natural phenomena but can be used to aid the verification of theories based on a set of premises. Consequences inherent in the premises may be deduced, and these consequences may be verified by observation and experimentation. Induction is the process of generalization, of drawing general conclusions from a particular set of instances. Such inferences depend on the particular set of instances being a fair sample of the population about which we make statements. It need not be emphasized that results obtained by induction are not certain to be correct; they are probable, relative to a certain body of evidence. The theory of statistics, which is entirely deductive, provides the basis for the inductive process.

The role of statistics in the scientific method has been aptly summarized by Cramér.[3] He states that statistics has three functions: *description, analysis,* and *prediction.* By description is meant the reduction of a mass of data, say, the ages of all the individuals of the United States, to as small a set of numbers as possible. For this purpose we have quantities such as the mean, variance, skewness of the distributions, each quantity being called a statistic. The purpose of this condensation is not only to enable description of the population as concisely and briefly as possible, but also to enable comparison between populations. The description of populations may be entirely deductive, in the sense that we have all the relevant information for the whole population, or may be inductive, in that we have the information only for a sample of the population. The latter is of course the more frequent and is included by Cramér in the second function: namely, analysis. A second aspect of analysis is that, given a sample of observed values of a variable, we are asked if it could have arisen from a particular distribution, or, given two samples which are differentiated in some way other than the measured characteristic, we are asked whether they could both have arisen from the same population. Some criterion must be used by which the possible difference in the two populations can be tested, and mathematical statistics provides a rationale for choosing between criteria. Also included in the analysis function of statistics is the estimation of population characteristics from samples. It is assumed that the sample values have originated from a population that is specified mathematically in terms of certain quantities called parameters which, if known, enable the complete distribution to be specified. The problem is to obtain the best estimates of the parameters, where a mathematical definition of "best" must be specified. In the broadest sense, of course, estimation may be regarded as an aspect of the testing of hypotheses in which we have to choose from a number of hypotheses specified by the unknown values of the parameters. The third function of statistics given by Cramér is that of prediction, which is in fact the main aim of the application of the scientific method to phenomena.

1.4 THE DESIGN OF EXPERIMENTS

The general procedure in scientific research is to formulate hypotheses and then to verify them directly or by their consequences. This verification necessitates the collection of observations, and the design of the experiment is essentially the pattern of the observations to be collected. The consideration of the design of an experiment to provide evidence for a hypothesis necessitates careful consideration of whether the hypothesis is, in fact, capable of being verified or not. That the observations to be made are relevant to the hypothesis and capable of giving an unambiguous answer must be verified. Observations obtained in one way may be completely useless for testing the hypothesis, whereas those obtained in another way can be used for verification. For example, the hypothesis that the correlation between two characters in a population has a particular non-zero value cannot be tested unless a random sample of the population is examined; whereas a sample selected according to the values of one of the characteristics may be used to test whether the correlation takes the particular value of zero, but not other values.

The appropriate meanings of the word "experiment" as given in Webster's Dictionary are: "a trial or special *observation* made to confirm or disprove something doubtful, especially one under conditions determined by the experimenter; an act or operation undertaken in order to discover some unknown principle or effect or to test, establish, or illustrate some suggested or known truth." For some purposes it is useful to distinguish two types of experiments: absolute and comparative experiments.[4] An example of an absolute experiment is the determination of, say, the electric charge on an electron. It was for such experiments as these that the theory of errors was originally devised. Repeated observations do not agree exactly with each other, and the problems considered were to obtain the best estimate and a measure of its reliability from a set of observations. The field of sample surveys is included by some writers as a branch of the design of experiments, and a sample survey may be regarded as an absolute experiment, the determination for a specified population of a particular characteristic.

A comparative experiment, on the other hand, is an experiment in which two or more treatments are compared in their effects on a chosen characteristic of the population. In such an experiment the value of the characteristic under either treatment separately for the population is of no particular interest. The observations may not in fact be members from a single distribution, but we may have a different distribution for each observation on each treatment, and the hypothesis may be that the distributions are the same regardless of treatment, or we may assume the distributions to be of the same form regardless of treatment and wish to estimate the constant displacement of those for one treatment relative to those for the other treatment. This book is concerned mainly with comparative experiments which may be described as the taking of controlled observations, where control is effected on all variables by the experimenter, either in actually fixing the variables, or controlling statistically by the process of randomization which will be discussed in detail later.

We may say that, in brief, the purpose of the theory of the design of experiments is to ensure that the experimenter obtains data relevant to his hypothesis in as economical a way as possible. The economic aspect of experimentation cannot be emphasized too strongly. The experimenter is always in the position of being able to, or wishing to, spend only a certain amount of time, labor, money, etc., on his investigation, and it is certain that there are more and less efficient ways of using these resources. No inductive inference is certain so that every statement drawn from experimental data is subject to some error, an error about which probability statements may be made with the aid of mathematical statistics. A measure of accuracy is therefore obtainable, and it is necessary as in all phases of practical life to consider the cost of obtaining a particular accuracy, whether it is worth this cost, and at what stage the cost of obtaining increased accuracy is too great.

The real distinction between two of the applications of statistics, the design of experiments and sample surveys, is that, in the design of experiments applied to a problem, the populations that are studied are formed by the experimenter in a specified way, whereas, in a sample survey dealing with the same problem, the population under study has arisen from a set of forces, the relation of which to the forces under consideration is unknown. A survey of a population tells us only about the objects observed and with suitable sampling schemes can tell us about a population of objects. It can demonstrate the existence of associations between characteristics in the population, but the value that may be attached to a statement, for example, that attributes X and Y have a correlation of, say, 0.45 is somewhat dubious except as a description of the population. All science is eventually concerned with the problem of how to make particular attributes of a population take on certain desired values. The existence of an association between attributes X and Y in the population in no way suggests that attribute X can be altered to a specified value by altering attribute Y in a particular way. In an experiment we determine whether altering attribute X has an effect on attribute Y, and this is the knowledge that is necessary for any action program. It is considerations of this type that nullify the value of much of the survey work that is done in fields where experimentation is extremely difficult. Survey work can be very useful in cases in which a deductively formulated theory exists and it is desired to estimate some parameters in the theory. It is however difficult to visualize how a theory can be started without some experimentation on which to base the original abstractions.

1.5 THE USE OF PRIOR INFORMATION

Up to several decades ago problems of estimation and testing of hypotheses were solved only by utilizing assumptions about the distribution of the unknown parameters. Starting with the work of Fisher of about 1920, the emphasis was completely in the opposite direction, the governing rule being that the sample data and only the sample data should be used in these statistical processes. For example, in estimating the mean of a normal distribution, it was taken to be completely incorrect to assume an *a priori* distribution of the mean, since no such distribution exists; in general, the unknown parameter has a particular fixed value, and it is incorrect to assume a distribution of the value. This led to the small sample theory of modern statistics.

This theory is certainly more realistic for the purposes of inference. It should, however, be realized that, if we are not prepared to make some *a priori* assumptions, we can ascertain nothing: We do not in fact know what characteristics to observe and have no reason to expect them to behave in any ordered way. Even when the use of *a priori* information was rejected, the experimenter had to produce his hypotheses so to speak "out of the hat."

The trend at the present time is then toward a more realistic approach. There are considerable difficulties in the use of *a priori* information. Every experimenter will have different *a priori* information, and there is therefore no "objective" answer. We may say that one of the functions of statistical techniques is to abstract according to recognized rules the new experimental data. The experimenter then combines, by a process that is very little understood, this new information with his own *a priori* information. With the new information presented according to recognized rules any experimenter can reach his own conclusions. Naturally, as the body of new information increases, the experimenter relies to an increasing extent on this information and this only. This situation is realized best, perhaps, when the experimental data lead to conclusions that the experimenter feels are entirely erroneous; frequently, he will reject the data though sometimes he will be wrong in doing so.

This branch of statistical inference is still very much in its infancy, and little can be said about it. The general position should, however, be recognized and realized by everyone.

1.6   THE DECISION FUNCTION APPROACH

In any discussion of scientific method and inference mention should be made of a new approach to the problem, originated by Wald [5] within the past few years.

The starting point of this approach is the idea that we perform experiments or take observations only to give us a basis for further action. It is appropriate then to consider the possible types of actions, the risks involved in taking each action, and the probabilities of our data and statistical techniques leading to the various actions. Our aim will be always to minimize the expectation of our risk (or possibly in more complicated situations to minimize our maximum risk). In the simple situation of testing hypotheses, we would not then consider separating the frequencies of type-I errors of rejecting the hypothesis when it is true and of type-II errors of accepting the hypothesis when it is false. We would specify the losses involved in each of these errors and minimize the expectation of our loss. This approach is obviously the best one in any technological problem, for example, in the production and utilization of a manufactured product, and for this type of problem some useful results are being obtained. A difficulty in the application of this approach to scientific research is the specification of weights or risk functions for incorrect decisions. It is interesting to note, however, that the choice of randomization procedure for an experiment amounts to the choice of a decision function.

REFERENCES

1. EINSTEIN, A. *The world as I see it.* Covici, Friede, New York. 1934.
2. COHEN, M., and NAGEL, E. *An introduction to logic and scientific method.* Harcourt, Brace, New York. 1934.
3. CRAMÉR, H. *Mathematical methods of statistics.* University Press, Princeton. 1946.
4. ANSCOMBE, F. J. The validity of comparative experiments. *Jour. Roy. Stat. Soc. A*, **61**, 181–211, 1948.
5. WALD, A. *Statistical decision functions.* John Wiley & Sons, New York. 1950.
6. CHURCHMAN, C. WEST. *Theory of experimental inference.* Macmillan, New York. 1948.
7. NORTHROP, F. S. C. *The logic of the sciences and humanities.* Macmillan, New York. 1948.
8. EDDINGTON, A. S. *The nature of the physical world.* Macmillan, New York. 1940.

CHAPTER 2

The Principles of Experimental Design

2.1 INTRODUCTION

In this chapter we shall indicate the general principles of experimentation without becoming deeply involved in statistical theory. A statistically designed investigation may be said to consist of the following steps:

1. Statement of the problem.
2. Formulation of hypotheses.
3. Devising of experimental technique and design.
4. Examination of possible outcomes and reference back to the reasons for the inquiry to be sure the experiment provides the required information to an adequate extent.
5. Consideration of the possible results from the point of view of the statistical procedures which will be applied to them, to ensure that the conditions necessary for these procedures to be valid are satisfied.
6. Performance of experiment.
7. Application of statistical techniques to the experimental results.
8. Drawing conclusions with measures of the reliability of estimates of any quantities that are evaluated, careful consideration being given to the validity of the conclusions for the population of objects or events to which they are to apply.
9. Evaluation of the whole investigation, particularly with other investigations on the same or similar problems.

2.2 AN ILLUSTRATIVE EXAMPLE

Some of these steps may be illustrated by the following simple inquiry. Suppose a person comes to us one day and says that he can predict whether a penny that we toss will fall heads or tails; we are naturally very skeptical of this claim and decide to test his ability. We

10

assume that he is talking about an unbiased penny, that is, one for which the probability is $\frac{1}{2}$ that the penny will fall with heads up and $\frac{1}{2}$ with tails up. Considering next the formulation of the hypothesis or hypotheses, we have to analyze the person's claims further. Does he mean that he will always be correct? If he does, our experimental procedure is quite simple; we toss pennies successively by some process, which we believe is random and which has been found to give results in accordance with random theory, and we stop the process when he makes a mistake. It should be noted that this hypothesis can never be proved, and it is true of all hypotheses that they can only be disproved. As a second example of this point, the law of gravitation states that the attractive force between two bodies of masses, m_1 and m_2 at distance r apart is $\gamma \dfrac{m_1 m_2}{r^2}$, where γ is a constant, but it cannot be proved that the power of r should be 2. If anyone suggested a value different from 2, it would presumably be possible to take sufficient observations to disprove the suggested value, but a limit on human resources is reached such that, for example, the powers of 2 and 2.0000001 are indistinguishable. The matter is resolved further on the basis of simplicity and practicality; for all practical purposes it may be sufficiently accurate to use a power of 2, even though the true power may be slightly different from that value.

Suppose the person claims that he can predict correctly more than 50 percent of times. Our first reaction to the person's claim is that it is completely false and that his predictions will be randomly related to the actual results of the tosses. In this case we would set up the null hypothesis that his predictions have an equal chance of being right or wrong. To test this hypothesis, we have to decide on the size of the experiment, or the number of tosses. If we use 8 tosses we know that in the long run the number of correct answers out of 8, by chance, will be distributed according to the binomial distribution with $n = 8$, and $P = \frac{1}{2}$:

8 correct	$\frac{1}{256}$	4 correct	$\frac{70}{256}$
7 correct	$\frac{8}{256}$	3 correct	$\frac{56}{256}$
6 correct	$\frac{28}{256}$	2 correct	$\frac{28}{256}$
5 correct	$\frac{56}{256}$	1 correct	$\frac{8}{256}$
		0 correct	$\frac{1}{256}$

If the person gives 8 correct answers, we have a considerable reason for rejecting the hypothesis that his predictions are, in fact, random, for the probability of his doing as well as this under this hypothesis is just 1 in 256. Two courses are open to us. We can decide either that an event with probability 1 in 256 has actually happened on a single trial and the person cannot predict correctly, or we can decide that our original hypothesis was wrong.   If we decide to reject the null hypothesis, or give credence to the person's claims, if he scored 8 successes we would, in statistical terminology, be using a significance level of 1 in 256.

It should be noted that the level of significance has no relation to the probability of the hypothesis being true, and, in fact, no such probability exists.   We may well decide that a level of significance of 1 in 256 is too high: if this level is used, the person cannot make any mistakes, whereas his claim is that he can predict better than at random. We see that, if we allow him to make not more than one error, the probability of getting this result by chance is 9 in 256 or about 1 in 28.4.   It is a matter for the experimenter to decide what level of significance he should use, depending on the purpose to which his experimental results will be put and the importance of decisions based on them.   If, for example, we are producing a drug that is dangerous in doses of greater than a certain amount, we shall require a high level of significance for the difference between the actual quantity and the specified amount.   Experimenters in biology and agronomy frequently use levels of significance of 1 in 20 and 1 in 100.   The evaluation of levels of significance is highly important, but the tendency for uncritical use of 5 percent and 1 percent levels should be avoided.   The choice of a level of significance in a particular investigation should depend on the null hypothesis and the alternatives, and on the cost to the experimenter of making erroneous decisions.   Usually it is difficult to give these costs concrete values and a 1-in-20 or 1-in-100 significance test has some intuitive appeal.   Levels of significance are a guide to the interpretation of experiments but do not give the actual interpretation.   They can, of course, be used absolutely in cases where experiments are performed very frequently and rapid objective decisions have to be made, but these circumstances do not usually pertain in the fields to which the design of experiments has been applied in the past.

So far we have considered only the null hypothesis, that the person cannot predict the results of the tosses.   Alternatively he may claim that he will be correct in a proportion P of cases.   If we assume that for each toss the probability of the person giving the correct answer is constant, we may examine whether the results he has obtained after a particular number of trials are in reasonable agreement with his claims.   We know that in n trials where n is large his actual percentage score should be in the range $P - 1.96\sqrt{P(1 - P)/n}$ to $P + 1.96\sqrt{P(1 - P)/n}$, unless he has been unlucky to the extent of a 1-in-20 chance event happening. (The quantity 1.96 is the normal deviate which will be exceeded in absolute magnitude 1 in 20 times by a random observation from a normal distribution with mean zero and variance unity.) We note that the probable range within which the actual result will be depends on the true proportion and on the number of trials. The relation to the true proportion is not of particular interest at this stage of the discussion, though in other cases it is of fundamental importance, and so we will concern ourselves only with n, the number of trials. The actual result will lie with probability of 95 percent within a range of $2 \times 1.96\sqrt{P(1-P)/n}$, which decreases inversely with the square root of n. The number of trials may be regarded as the size of the experiment, and the value of our information about the true proportion depends on this size. When the size is increased, the range becomes narrower. This serves to illustrate one aspect of experimental design: namely, that the experimenter must decide what accuracy he requires in his estimates and determine the size of the experiment accordingly. These concepts will be developed in detail later.

The essential part of the above argument is the formulation of the null hypothesis, which is couched in statistical terms. This hypothesis gives by mathematical arguments the distribution of the proportion of correct answers, and the actual result is compared with this distribution. It should be noted that many tests of the hypothesis may be formed. For example, a specification of the probability of a correct answer with an assumption of independent tosses may be used to examine the whole set of answers for chance deviations from what would be expected. This would involve what is called in mathematical texts the theory of runs.

Exact statement of the null hypothesis is essential because this is the basis of the distribution of the observed results from which the test of significance is derived. A statement on the alternatives which the experimenter considers possible is also necessary because without some specification of alternatives it is difficult to show that a particular test is a good one to use. For example, in the penny tossing we can think of no mechanism by which the person could get consistently less than 50 percent of correct results, and therefore we use a test that is designed to discover percentages greater than 50: namely, the test based on the upper tail of the distribution.

While we are discussing this simple example, it might be well to emphasize the necessity of formulating the hypothesis *before* the experimental results are examined. Tests can be found, if one is sufficiently ingenious, which will, when applied to a particular set of random numbers, indicate a deviation from randomness. Some of the results that one finds popularized on extrasensory perception appear to be subject to the criticism that the statistical tests were evolved in the light of the data and are therefore suspect.   On the other hand, it would be foolish to adhere too strictly to this rule.   It is often difficult to formulate the null hypothesis in strict terms without the data to which the statistical test is to be applied.   Again, when the problem is one of estimation, the model or distribution that the observations are presumed to follow may be difficult to specify without examination of the data (cf. transformations).

2.3   AN EXAMPLE ON FLAVOR DISCRIMINATION

A second example which is very similar to the example given by Fisher in *The Design of Experiments* [1] is the following, of which use is actually made in some food industries.   A manufacturer is producing a drink according to some long-used procedure, and his technical staff discovers a method by which the procedure may be shortened.   We suppose also that the modification of the procedure does not affect the constituents of the drink and that the important criterion is whether people can detect any difference in taste (or flavor) between the two products.   It would be possible to broaden the inquiry and bring in the matter of preference, but this is a secondary question.   A procedure that is frequently used is to present each of a panel of observers or tasters with 3 glasses of the drink, 2 of them being of one type and 1 of the other, and to observe whether each observer picks out the 1 drink that is different from the 2 like drinks.   The null hypothesis that we are interested in testing is that no differences are detectable and that the odd one will be chosen at random in relation to the treatment.   In order that the null hypothesis be satisfied when no difference exists, it is necessary that the association between the drinks, on the one hand, and the glasses in which they are placed and the order in which they are presented to the taster be zero: i.e., that these characteristics be chosen at random. This will be sufficient to ensure that on the average in the absence of a perceptible difference $\frac{1}{3}$ of the trials will result in a correct selection of the odd drink.   The random order is essential because the taster may tend for some reason to pick out the odd one just on the basis of order in which the 3 drinks are presented.

A single trial does not provide any information of value, and so the test has to be repeated several times.   If, for example, it is repeated 6 times, the possible results with their probabilities are given by the binomial distribution with $n = 6$ and $P = \frac{1}{3}$, namely:

6 correct	$\frac{1}{729}$	2 correct	$\frac{240}{729}$
5 correct	$\frac{12}{729}$	1 correct	$\frac{192}{729}$
4 correct	$\frac{60}{729}$	0 correct	$\frac{64}{729}$
3 correct	$\frac{160}{729}$		

If then a taster picks out the odd drink in each of 6 trials, there is very strong evidence against the hypothesis that the 2 types of drink have the same taste; and also if he picks out the odd drink correctly in 5 out of the 6 trials, because this result or the one possible better result could be achieved by chance in only 13 times out of 729 or 1 out of 56 times. Any smaller number of successes would not be regarded as indicating a difference, even though a small difference may exist. The smaller the difference in taste, the more trials will be necessary to detect it because errors will be more frequent.

As mentioned previously, in all experimental designs it is necessary to consider the hypotheses alternative to the null hypothesis. If the difference is such that it is detected by the taster in 50 percent of cases on the average, will the test of significance based on the null hypothesis indicate that the null hypothesis is incorrect? We therefore consider the above test with regard to the alternative hypothesis that $P = \frac{1}{2}$. If the probability of being correct on any one trial is $\frac{1}{2}$, the probabilities of the various results for 6 trials are:

6 correct	$\frac{1}{64}$	3 correct	$\frac{20}{64}$
5 correct	$\frac{6}{64}$	2 correct	$\frac{15}{64}$
4 correct	$\frac{15}{64}$	1 correct	$\frac{6}{64}$
		0 correct	$\frac{1}{64}$

For the null hypothesis we decided that 5 or 6 correct results gave an indication of a difference in taste, and from the above it is seen that the chances of getting this result when the true probability of being correct is $\frac{1}{2}$ are only 7 in 64 or about 1 in 9. We would therefore, on the basis of 6 trials, fail very frequently to notice a taste difference of the magnitude considered, and we may describe the experiment as lacking sensitivity. If the number of trials or replications is increased, the sensitivity will be increased. The experimenter must decide beforehand what differences he wishes the experiment to indicate and plan an experiment of such size that these differences have a high probability of being realized.

This example serves well to bring out the concept of the power of a test. Our possible results may be represented by the points 0 to 6 on a straight line, say:

$$\dot{0} \quad \dot{1} \quad \dot{2} \quad \dot{3} \quad \dot{4} \quad \dot{5} \quad \dot{6}$$

On the basis of the null hypothesis we select the results 5 and 6 correct as forming a critical region: that is, a region of the space of possible results on which we decide to reject the null hypothesis. If the observed value falls in this region, we reject the null hypothesis. The chance of our result falling into this region is a simple function of P, the probability of a correct result on one trial, and we may evaluate the probability of the observed result falling in this region for various values of P. The resulting relationship of this probability to P is called the power function of the test based on this critical region. In industrial statistics the same relationship is called the operating characteristic of the test. This relationship tells us the possibilities of our test discriminating between the null hypothesis and other hypotheses. Obviously in constructing a test we should consider the alternative hypotheses and the chances of our picking out these over the null hypothesis.

One way of increasing the accuracy and the sensitivity of an experiment is to increase the number of replicates or repetitions of the single trial. Broadly speaking, there are two other ways: (1) by changing the structure of the individual trial or replicate, and (2) by refinements in the experimental technique.

So far the individual trial consists of 3 glasses of drink, 1 of one type and 2 of the other. We can visualize a whole series of possibilities, a total of 4 glasses with 2 of each kind of drink, of 4 glasses with 3 of one type of drink and 1 of the other, of 5 glasses with 3 and 2 glasses, respectively, of the two types of drink. If we have 2 glasses of each type of drink presented randomly, the probability of matching them correctly by chance is $\frac{1}{3}$, as before. With 3 glasses of one kind and 1 of the other, the probability of being correct by chance is $\frac{1}{4}$; with a given number of replications then the taster can afford to make more mistakes and still indicate a difference. With 3 glasses of one type and 2 of the other, the taster will be correct by chance in $\frac{1}{10}$, and such a trial is considerably more sensitive to departures from the null hypothesis. Changes in design of the above type may be regarded as structural. This particular example is not, however, a good one for evaluation of structural changes, for we have no knowledge of the relative discriminatory ability in terms of proportion of successful choices for the various types of design.

What we mean by refinement of techniques is the removal by the experimenter of differences between the two types of glass and drink that may confuse the taster and lower his discriminatory power. Thus, it is reasonable to specify that one type of drink should not be drunk out of the bottle while the other is drunk out of a glass and also, insofar as possible, the drinks, when presented to the taster, should have been poured in the same way and for the same period. There is no limit to the number of possible ways in which the experimental conditions could be made more nearly constant, and the experimenter must decide how far he is prepared to go in this respect.

REFERENCE

1. FISHER, R. A. *The design of experiments.* Oliver and Boyd, Edinburgh, 4th ed., 1947.

CHAPTER 3

Elementary Statistical Notions

It is not intended to give here a complete description of elementary statistical theory, but it is worth while to note briefly the elementary statistical concepts and theory that are essential to the design and analysis of experiments. It is assumed that the reader will have met these concepts before; if not, what follows may be used as a guide for study. The text of Mood [1] may be mentioned as an excellent introductory mathematical one, or Hoel [2] at a slightly lower level.

3.1 POPULATIONS, DISTRIBUTIONS, PARAMETERS

The first concept is that of a population. By a population we mean an assemblage of individuals, each of which may be an actual individual or an attribute of an individual: for example, the height of a corn stalk in a field of corn. The individuals of this population may be arranged according to the magnitude of a characteristic, and the function giving the relative frequencies of the different measurements is called the distribution of the individuals. From this distribution we may obtain, for example, the proportion with measurements less than a particular chosen value or the proportion lying in any chosen interval of values. A distribution may be discrete or continuous: for example, the height of corn stalks will be a continuous measurement and will give a continuous distribution, whereas the number of kernels per ear must be an integer and would have a discrete distribution. In most problems we envisage a population with a corresponding theoretical distribution. A discrete distribution is specified by the probability of each possible value: e.g., for an unbiased penny, the probability of heads and the probability of tails are both equal to $\frac{1}{2}$. A continuous distribution is specified by the frequency function, $f(x)$, say, in which the probability of the variable lying in the infinitesimal range x to $x + \Delta x$ is equal to $f(x) \Delta x$.

Distribution curves should be quite familiar to readers of this book, and so an example will not be given. Measures of central tendency or general position of distributions are the mean, i.e., the average value of

18

the attribute, and the median, i.e., the value of the attribute such that exactly 50 percent of the population have a measurement less than this value and 50 percent a measurement greater than this value.   The mean is the more useful measure of central tendency, but the median has several important advantages over the mean, and the extent to which it is used is increasing gradually: for example, the median of a distribution is independent of the scale of measurement or rather varies exactly with the scale of measurement, so that the median of the square roots will be the square root of the median of the actual values.   If the distribution is symmetrical, the mean and median coincide.   Another measure of central tendency of which little use is made is the mode, roughly, that value which is most frequent.   The measure of spread of distribution that is almost universally used in experimental work is the variance, which is the mean square distance of the population elements from the mean.   The distribution will not be specified entirely by its mean and variance, unless it is a normal distribution.   Occasionally we may be interested in the mean rth power distance from the mean, that is, the moment of the rth order, usually denoted by μ_r.   Also of use occasionally are the skewness or the extent to which the measurements are distributed unequally about the mean, usually measured by $\mu_3/\mu_2^{3/2}$, and the kurtosis which determines the extent to which observations are piled up around the mean, measured by $(\mu_4/\mu_2^2) - 3$.

Any theoretical distribution is characterized by a mathematical form containing some quantities called parameters, and, when the values of these parameters are known, the distribution can be specified completely.   The estimation of these parameters from sample data is one of the most important functions of statistical theory.   A second important function of mathematical statistical theory is the derivation of what may be called derived distributions: that is, distributions of functions of sample observations from known distributions: for example, the distribution of the mean of a random sample of size n from a normal population and the distribution of the estimated variance.   These distributions will, of course, also be describable in terms of the parameters of the original distribution.

3.2   THE NORMAL DISTRIBUTION AND DERIVED DISTRIBUTIONS

The most important distribution in statistical theory is the normal distribution which has the frequency function

$$f(x) = \frac{1}{\sqrt{2\pi}\sigma} e^{-\frac{(x-\mu)^2}{2\sigma^2}} \tag{1}$$

In this case the parameters are μ, the mean, and σ, the standard deviation. We can determine several quantities which may be used to estimate the parameters of a frequency distribution, and we generally wish to use, as the estimator of a parameter, that one which is subject to the least sampling variance. The quantity that best estimates the mean μ of a population from a random sample of size n is the mean of the sample, $\bar{x}$, and this estimate is itself normally distributed about μ with a variance of σ^2/n.

The function of the observations which is an unbiased estimate of σ^2 and which is used in connection with tests and estimation is

$$\frac{1}{n-1} \Sigma(x-\bar{x})^2$$

where n is the size of the sample. This is usually denoted by s^2, and $(n-1)s^2/\sigma^2$ is distributed according to the χ^2 distribution with $(n-1)$ degrees of freedom. The sample mean $\bar{x}$ and s^2 are distributed independently; that is, their joint distribution is the product of their individual distributions. The explicit form of the χ^2 distribution is

$$f(\chi^2) = \frac{1}{2^{\frac{n-1}{2}} \Gamma\left(\frac{n-1}{2}\right)} e^{-\frac{1}{2}\chi^2} (\chi^2)^{\frac{n-3}{2}} \tag{2}$$

This is also the distribution of the sum of squares of $(n-1)$ variates distributed independently according to the normal distribution with mean zero and unit variance.

Tests of significance on two means of normal populations are based on Student's distribution. If x is a quantity normally distributed about a mean of zero with a variance of σ^2, and we have an estimate s^2 of σ^2, such that ns^2/σ^2 follows the χ^2 distribution with n degrees of freedom, independently of x, the quantity $t = x/s$ follows the t distribution, the explicit form of which is

$$f(t) = \frac{\Gamma\left(\frac{n+1}{2}\right)}{\sqrt{n\pi}\,\Gamma\left(\frac{n}{2}\right)} \left(1 + \frac{t^2}{n}\right)^{-\frac{n+1}{2}} \tag{3}$$

The distribution by which the means of several normal distributions with the same variance or independent estimates of variance of a normal distribution are compared is the F distribution. If ms^2_1/σ^2 and ns^2_2/σ^2 follow the χ^2 distributions with m and n degrees of freedom independently, so that s^2_1 and s^2_2 are two independent estimates of the population variance σ^2 based, respectively, on m and n degrees of freedom, the ratio $F = s^2_1/s^2_2$ is distributed as the F distribution, the form of which is

$$f(F) = \frac{\Gamma\left(\dfrac{m+n}{2}\right) m^{m/2} n^{n/2} F^{\frac{m-2}{2}}}{\Gamma\left(\dfrac{m}{2}\right)\Gamma\left(\dfrac{n}{2}\right)(n+mF)^{\frac{m+n}{2}}} \tag{4}$$

In a similar way we have a test to determine whether several estimated variances may be estimates of the same common variance. This is known as Bartlett's test, which states that if s^2_i, $i = 1, 2, \cdots, k$, are independent estimates of the same true variance, based on n_i degrees of freedom, the quantity

$$\frac{1}{1 + \dfrac{1}{3(k-1)}\left(\displaystyle\sum_{i=1}^{k}\dfrac{1}{n_i} - \dfrac{1}{n}\right)}\left(n \log_e \frac{\Sigma n_i s^2_i}{n} - \Sigma n_i \log_e s^2_i\right) \tag{5}$$

where $n = \Sigma n_i$ is distributed approximately as χ^2 with $(k-1)$ degrees of freedom.

3.3   LINEAR FUNCTIONS OF NORMALLY DISTRIBUTED VARIATES

If $x_1, x_2, \cdots, x_n$ are normally and independently distributed about means $\mu_1, \mu_2, \cdots, \mu_n$ with variances $\sigma^2_1, \sigma^2_2, \cdots, \sigma^2_n$, then any linear function of the x's, say,

$$\lambda_1 x_1 + \lambda_2 x_2 + \cdots + \lambda_n x_n \tag{6}$$

is normally distributed about a mean of

$$\lambda_1 \mu_1 + \lambda_2 \mu_2 + \cdots + \lambda_n \mu_n \tag{7}$$

with a variance of

$$\lambda^2_1 \sigma^2_1 + \lambda^2_2 \sigma^2_2 + \cdots + \lambda^2_n \sigma^2_n \tag{8}$$

This rule is the basis of estimation of errors in most analysis of variance work, as we shall see later. The simplest example of its use is to give the distribution of the mean $\bar{x}$ of a random sample $x_1, \cdots, x_n$ from a normal distribution of mean μ and variance σ^2. For then $\bar{x} = \dfrac{1}{n}\Sigma x$ and

$\mu_1 = \mu_2 = \cdots = \mu_n = \mu, \lambda_1 = \lambda_2 = \cdots = \lambda_n = 1/n$, so that $\bar{x}$ is normally distributed around μ with variance $\dfrac{\sigma^2}{n}$. Substituting s^2 for σ^2, we have that $\dfrac{\bar{x} - \mu}{s/\sqrt{n}}$ is distributed as t with $(n-1)$ degrees of freedom. Similarly the difference between the mean $\bar{x}_1$ of an independent sample of size n_1 from a population with variance $\sigma^2{}_1$ and the mean $\bar{x}_2$ of an independent sample of size n_2 from a population with variance $\sigma^2{}_2$ has a variance $\dfrac{\sigma^2{}_1}{n_1} + \dfrac{\sigma^2{}_2}{n_2}$. If the variances are the same, σ^2, say, the variance of the difference is $\sigma^2\left(\dfrac{1}{n_1} + \dfrac{1}{n_2}\right)$. From this we may derive the t test for this difference when the common variance is unknown, because the total sum of squares within samples is distributed independently of $\bar{x}_1$ and $\bar{x}_2$ according to $\chi^2\sigma^2$, with $n_1 + n_2 - 2$ degrees of freedom, so that

$$t = \frac{\bar{x}_1 - \bar{x}_2}{\sqrt{\Sigma(x_1 - \bar{x}_1)^2 + \Sigma(x_2 - \bar{x}_2)^2}} \sqrt{\frac{(n_1 + n_2 - 2)n_1 n_2}{(n_1 + n_2)}} \qquad (9)$$

is distributed as Student's t with $(n_1 + n_2 - 2)$ degrees of freedom. Tests of significance and estimated errors of regression coefficients may be obtained in the same way; the usual linear regression coefficient b is a linear function of the observed values: namely,

$$b = \Sigma\left[\frac{(x_i - \bar{x})y_i}{\Sigma(x_i - \bar{x})^2}\right]$$

so that its variance is $\sigma^2/\Sigma(x - \bar{x})^2$, and so on.

3.4 ORTHOGONALITY

The concept of orthogonality of contrasts is essential. Suppose we are given a random sample of n observations from a normal distribution, say, $x_1, x_2, \cdots, x_n$. Any linear contrast among these observations may be represented by the function

$$A = \lambda_1 x_1 + \lambda_2 x_2 + \cdots + \lambda_n x_n$$

with

$$\lambda_1 + \lambda_2 + \cdots + \lambda_n = 0$$

The variance of this function is, of course, $(\Sigma\lambda_i^2)\sigma^2$. Suppose we have another linear contrast B given by

$$B = \mu_1 x_1 + \mu_2 x_2 + \cdots + \mu_n x_n$$

Then the variance of B is $(\Sigma\mu_i^2)\sigma^2$, and the covariance of A and B is $(\Sigma\lambda_i\mu_i)\sigma^2$. The correlation r between A and B is given by

$$r^2 = \frac{(\Sigma\lambda_i\mu_i)^2}{(\Sigma\lambda_i^2)(\Sigma\mu_i^2)} \tag{10}$$

and the correlation is zero if $\Sigma\lambda_i\mu_i = 0$. The contrasts are then said to be orthogonal. In simple terms, this means that A and B will be distributed independently, and, if we use A to estimate one parameter and B to estimate another parameter, the errors in the estimation of the one parameter will not be related to the errors of estimation of the other parameter. The estimates are then said to be orthogonal. If the distribution is not normal, the quantities A and B will be uncorrelated if the condition is satisfied, but not necessarily independent. Further definitions and ramifications of orthogonality will be dealt with later.

3.5 OTHER DISTRIBUTIONS

The binomial, Poisson, and negative binomial distributions merit mention, as discrete experimental data frequently conform approximately to one of these distributions.

The binomial distribution gives the distribution of the number of successes in a number of independent trials, say, n; the chance of a success being constant, p, say. The probability of r successes is

$$P_r = \frac{n!}{r!(n-r)!} p^r q^{n-r} \quad \text{where} \quad q = 1 - p$$

The mean of this distribution is np, and the variance is npq. It is important to note that the variance depends on the mean. With large n, we may regard the number of successes as being normally distributed around np with variance npq. Even for moderately small n, the probability of a number r or less of successes is closely approximated by the probability of a variate less than $(r + \frac{1}{2})$ from a normal distribution with mean np and variance npq. We have used Yates's correction for continuity in inserting the $\frac{1}{2}$.

For the Poisson distribution the probability of the observation r is

$$P_r = e^{-m} \frac{m^r}{r!}$$

The mean of the population is m, and the variance of the distribution is also m. It may be noted that the binomial distribution tends to the Poisson distribution as n becomes large and p small, the mean np remaining constant and equal to m. This distribution is realized in practice when the underlying variation is binomial with low probability p, and a constant large number of binomial events is observed in a single trial.

The negative binomial distribution has been found to occur in many biological situations and can come about as a result of clustering (or contagion) among the "successes" of an otherwise binomial population: e.g., deaths of insects, number of insect bites per apple. It has the formula

$$P_x = \binom{x + k - 1}{k - 1} p^k q^x, \qquad q = 1 - p$$

and has a mean of kq/p and a variance of kq/p^2. This distribution also arises in inverse sampling from a binomial population and as a weighted average of Poisson distributions.

When these distributions occur, it is not correct to treat the observed values as having a constant variance and, hence, treat them by the analysis of variance. For this reason transformations of the data, which are discussed in a later chapter, are performed.

3.6 ESTIMATION

The main purpose of statistical techniques is to estimate properties of distributions and to test hypotheses about these properties. By the estimation of a property is meant the calculation from sample data of a quantity that will be taken as the value of the property for the population. There are, in general, many possible estimates of a property. Suppose, for example, we wish to estimate the mean ·of a normal distribution, which is also the median. We can take the mean of the sample; the mean of the extreme members of the sample, i.e., the mid-range; or the median of the sample. There are, of course, many other possibilities, and each of these functions of the sample observations is known as an estimator. We decide to use one estimator rather than another on the basis of considerations given below.

Estimation problems may be divided into two classes: parametric estimation, which deals with the estimation of parameters of a distribution, and non-parametric estimation, which deals with the estimation of properties of a distribution, the form of which is unspecified. In the latter case the methods are called distribution free. A possible non-parametric estimation problem would be estimating from a sample the shortest range in a distribution of unspecified form that contains, say, 95 percent of the probability. Sometimes a property of the distribution given by a parameter can be estimated non-parametrically; for example, in symmetrical distributions with finite variance the mean and median coincide, and we can estimate the population mean parametrically by the sample mean or some other function of the sample values and non-parametrically by the sample median. Parametric estimates are, of course, obtainable only when the form of the distribution is known, in distinction to non-parametric estimates for which this is not the case. Most of the methods of estimation in current use are parametric, but increasing use is being made of non-parametric methods, because less specification or none at all of the parent distribution is necessary for their use. We shall be concerned mainly with parametric methods based on distributions of assumed form, or specified sufficiently to allow a solution.

Estimators can be classified according to various criteria, the principal ones being:

1. *Consistency:* the estimate tends to the true value with increasing size of sample.
2. *Unbiased:* the expectation of the estimate is the true value.
3. *Sufficiency:* the estimate contains all the information, in a particular sense, in the sample on the value of the parameter.
4. *Efficiency:* the variance of the distribution of the estimate relative to some standard.

In experimentation, by and large, we like to have properties 1 and 2 and then obtain as efficient estimates as possible. This procedure is reasonable in that the comparison and averaging of results from different experiments are of considerable importance. Various methods of estimation are available, but we shall mention only three: the method of maximum likelihood, the method of least squares, and the method of minimum χ^2.

The method of maximum likelihood briefly is as follows: Suppose the frequency function of an observation x is

$$f(x; \theta_1, \theta_2, \cdots)$$

where θ_1, θ_2, $\cdots$, are the parameters to be estimated. Then the likelihood of a sample of values, x_1, x_2, $\cdots$, x_n, is defined to be equal to

$$\prod_{i=1}^{n} f(x_i; \theta_1, \theta_2, \cdots)$$

The estimates of θ_1, θ_2, $\cdots$, are those that maximize the likelihood, or, what amounts to the same thing, that maximize the logarithm of the likelihood. This method is asymptotically efficient, and the asymptotic variances and covariances of the estimates may be obtained.

The method of least squares consists of taking, as estimates of the parameters, those values of the parameters that minimize the sum of squares of deviations of the actual values from their expected values in terms of the parameters: i.e., to minimize

$$\Sigma[x_i - E(x_i)]^2$$

The method of least squares is intuitively reasonable when the deviations of the observations from their expectations are independent or at least uncorrelated and are subject to approximately the same variance. If the deviations are subject to different variances, whose relative magnitudes are known, the method is modified by weighting each squared deviation inversely as its relative variance. In other cases the method of least squares can lead to entirely erroneous results, particularly in the presence of correlations of the deviations. If the deviations are in fact normally and independently distributed, this method is essentially the same as that of maximum likelihood.

The method of minimum χ^2 is used for frequency data, when we observe that n_i of a sample of size n have the ith attribute, $i = 1, 2, \cdots, r$, and we postulate a law for the true proportions P_i. The law will contain parameters, and to estimate them we minimize the quantity

$$\chi^2 = \sum_i \frac{(n_i - nP_i)^2}{nP_i}$$

with respect to variations over the parameters. This method is, like maximum likelihood, asymptotically efficient. For large samples the minimum χ^2 is distributed according to the χ^2 distribution with degrees of freedom equal to the number of classes minus the number of parameters estimated.

We shall give no illustrations of these methods at present. For most purposes of experimental design the method which is used is that of least squares because of certain properties of the problems. In these cases the least squares theory is closely allied to the topic in mathematical statistics known as general linear hypothesis theory. A brief introduction to least squares theory is contained in the next chapter.

3.7 THE TESTING OF HYPOTHESES

We have already covered the elementary ideas on the testing of hypotheses, which briefly amount to the following: We formulate our hypotheses, consider the possible experimental results we can obtain, and divide these into classes, and to each class we attach a conclusion. In the case of the null hypothesis we have two classes: If our results fall into one of the classes we accept the null hypothesis, and if they fall into the other class we reject the null hypothesis. Corresponding to the general procedures by which estimation is performed, we have a general procedure for testing hypotheses: namely, the likelihood ratio test. For this test, we maximize the likelihood over all the possible values of the parameters, obtaining $L(\Omega_{max})$, and also over the possible values of the parameters specified by the hypothesis under test, obtaining $L(\omega_{max})$. The ratio $L(\omega_{max})/L(\Omega_{max})$ is used as a test criterion, and, when its distribution has been obtained, the upper to lower p percent tail is used to give a p percent test. Many of the usual tests can be derived in this manner, even though they may have originated from estimation considerations.

The ideal situation described above rarely exists. In spite of tests of significance, the experimenter tends to use at least three classes: If the results are in class A, say, he accepts the null hypothesis, if they are in class B, he rejects it, and, if they are in class C, he says he cannot make a decision and must perform another experiment. Such multiple-decision problems have been formulated and examined in recent years primarily by Wald,[3] but except in rather simple (from the point of view of the experimenter) cases the theory has not reached the stage where it can be applied readily. Furthermore, it is roughly true to say that the experimenter is less frequently interested in tests of hypothesis and is much more concerned with problems of estimation. In comparing two treatments, for example, the situation is usually that, if a sufficiently accurate trial were performed, a significant difference would be found. A difference between the two treatments may be assumed to exist, and the relevant question to the experimenter is how big this difference is, and this raises the problem of estimation. This should not be interpreted as meaning that the experimenter has no interest in the testing of hypotheses, merely that the greater emphasis is on estimation. As we shall see, an examination of the sensitivity of experiments, which is an aspect of the theory of testing hypotheses, is very important.

3.8 INTERVAL ESTIMATION

With the theory of estimation described earlier we obtain a point estimate with an estimated measure of its accuracy. The point estimate alone is of little value because we are in the position of having a sample of one from a population of which we do not know the spread. We do not know, therefore, how close we are likely to be to the true value. An estimate of the variance of estimates is then essential for all investigational purposes, because, in general, small variance of the estimate implies closeness of the estimate to the true value for the situations we shall consider.

However, we are more frequently concerned with making an interval estimate, by which we mean the calculation from the data of an interval such that we know the probability of this interval containing the true value. Such an interval is known as a confidence interval. It is possibly worth while presenting here in simple terms the arguments by which a confidence interval on the mean of a normal population is obtained from a sample of n values. We know that, if

$$\bar{x} = \frac{\Sigma x_i}{n} \quad \text{and} \quad s^2 = \Sigma \frac{(x_i - \bar{x})^2}{n - 1}$$

the quantity $\dfrac{\bar{x} - \mu}{s/\sqrt{n}}$ is distributed as Student's t with $(n - 1)$ degrees of freedom.

We can then find the probability that the inequality $-t \leq \dfrac{\bar{x} - \mu}{s/\sqrt{n}} \leq t$ is satisfied: namely, the percentage point p corresponding to the value of t in the table of the t distribution with $(n - 1)$ degrees of freedom.

Now this inequality can be written as $\bar{x} - ts/\sqrt{n} \leq \mu \leq \bar{x} + ts/\sqrt{n}$, and the probability that the inequality in this form is satisfied is also p. If then, having drawn a sample, we construct the interval

$$\bar{x} - ts/\sqrt{n} \quad \text{to} \quad \bar{x} + ts/\sqrt{n}$$

and say that the true mean lies within this interval, the probability that our statement is correct is equal to p. It should be noted that the probability is not of the true mean lying in the interval, because the true mean is a fixed unknown value and has no distribution, but the probability is the probability of the interval, which is the random variable, containing the true value. If we draw the conclusion that the true mean is in the calculated interval for each case we examine, we shall be wrong on the average in $(1 - p)$ of cases. This, then, is a confidence interval on the true mean.   Most of the estimates that are obtained in the analysis of experiments are linear estimates, which are distributed with a variance that may be estimated, and for which Student's distribution may be assumed to hold.   Examples will be given as they arise.

REFERENCES

1. Mood, A. M.   *Introduction to the theory of statistics.*   McGraw-Hill, New York. 1950.
2. Hoel, P. G.   *Introduction to mathematical statistics.*   John Wiley & Sons, New York.   1947.
3. Wald, A.   *Sequential analysis.*   John Wiley & Sons, New York.   1947.

CHAPTER 4

An Introduction to the Theory of Least Squares

4.1 INTRODUCTION

In this chapter we shall give an elementary discussion of least squares theory. This theory is basic to the subject of the design of experiments, and the material of this chapter is given with the hope that readers who are not mathematically minded will obtain sufficient insight into the process to appreciate the two succeeding chapters.

As we have noted in earlier chapters, the basis of the analysis of observational data is the formulation of hypotheses, or what really amounts to the same thing, the postulation of a mathematical model. This mathematical model in the simpler cases gives a value for each observed result in terms of various quantities which are unknown parameters or "constants" (hence, the term "fitting of constants"). For example, suppose we have two treatments and have subjected several experimental units to them. We might have as our mathematical model that the yields y under treatment 1 are given by

$$y_{1j} = t_1 + e_{1j} \qquad (1)$$

The subscript 1 denotes treatment 1, and j denotes the jth experimental unit that receives this treatment, t_1 the true yield from the treatment, and e_{1j} the deviation of the actual yield from the true yield. This deviation is due to the use of a particular experimental unit and the fact that our observation is subject to environmental or other uncontrolled causes of variation. Similarly, for treatment 2 we might have the model

$$y_{2j} = t_2 + e_{2j} \qquad (2)$$

the symbols being defined likewise.

In order to specify our model completely, we must have some knowledge about the e_{ij}'s: namely, how they are distributed. Suppose they are distributed normally and independently about zero with the same

30

variance σ^2, which is unknown. The quantities we wish to estimate are t_1, t_2, and to do this we use the principle of least squares: namely, to find the values of t_1 and t_2, say, $\hat{t}_1$ and $\hat{t}_2$, such that the sum of squares of deviations of the observed values from these values is a minimum. That is, we find the values $\hat{t}_1$ and $\hat{t}_2$ which minimize

$$\Sigma(y_{1j} - \hat{t}_1)^2 + \Sigma(y_{2j} - \hat{t}_2)^2 \tag{3}$$

where Σ denotes summation over the observed values. The values are, of course,

$$\hat{t}_1 = y_1. = \frac{1}{n_1}\Sigma y_{1j} \tag{4}$$

and

$$\hat{t}_2 = y_2. = \frac{1}{n_2}\Sigma y_{2j} \tag{5}$$

Furthermore, from least squares theory, an estimate s^2 of σ^2 is given by

$$\frac{1}{n_1 + n_2 - 2}\left[\sum_j (y_{1j} - y_1.)^2 + \sum_j (y_{2j} - y_2.)^2\right] \tag{6}$$

Finally, we can say that $\hat{t}_1 = \dfrac{1}{n_1}\Sigma y_{1j}$ will be distributed normally around its true value with variance σ^2/n_1, that $\hat{t}_2 = \dfrac{1}{n_2}\Sigma y_{2j}$ will be distributed normally around its true value with a variance of σ^2/n_2, and, as these are independently distributed, that $\hat{t}_1 - \hat{t}_2$ is distributed normally around its true value with variance $\sigma^2\left(\dfrac{1}{n_1} + \dfrac{1}{n_2}\right)$. Replacing σ^2 by its estimate s^2, we know that

$$\frac{\hat{t}_1 - \hat{t}_2 - d}{s\sqrt{\dfrac{1}{n_1} + \dfrac{1}{n_2}}} \tag{7}$$

where d is the true difference, is distributed according to the t distribution with $n_1 + n_2 - 2$ degrees of freedom, this being the number of degrees of freedom on which s^2 is based. This is the t test given in the previous chapter and is, of course, well known. We may therefore test the hypothesis that d takes on any value, and, in particular, if we put d equal to zero, we may test the null hypothesis that there is no difference between the treatments. We may also obtain a confidence interval on d: namely, that the interval

$$\hat{t}_1 - \hat{t}_2 \pm t_{n_1+n_2-2,95\%}\, s\sqrt{\frac{1}{n_1} + \frac{1}{n_2}}$$

has a probability of 95 percent of containing the true value d, $t_{n_1+n_2-2,95\%}$ being Student's t for $n_1 + n_2 - 2$ degrees of freedom and 95 percent.

4.2 THE MARKOFF THEOREM

The above is a particularly simple example of general linear hypothesis theory. In general, the situation is given by a theorem due to Markoff. Suppose we have observations y_α, $\alpha = 1$ to n, say, which are distributed with constant variance and uncorrelated errors around a linear function, say, $b_{\alpha1}p_1 + b_{\alpha2}p_2 + \cdots + b_{\alpha s}p_s$ of unknown constants $p_1, \cdots, p_s$, the coefficients $b_{\alpha i}$ being known; the best linear unbiased estimates of the unknown constants $p_1, \cdots, p_s$ are those that minimize the sum of squares

$$\sum_\alpha (y_\alpha - b_{\alpha1}p_1 - b_{\alpha2}p_2 - \cdots - b_{\alpha s}p_s)^2 \tag{8}$$

The term "best linear unbiased estimate" should be explained. A linear estimate of a parameter is a linear function of the observations, which is used to estimate the unknown parameter. Any function of the observations that estimates a parameter will be distributed in a particular way, as, for example, we can calculate the distribution of the mean of a sample from a normal population. This distribution will have a mean value, and, if this mean value is the true unknown value of the parameter, the estimate is called "unbiased." The average of a number of independent unbiased estimates will tend with increasing number to the true value. We mean by "best" that the estimate will be distributed around the true value with a variance less than that of any other linear unbiased estimate. Finally, if the parameters $p_1, \cdots, p_s$ are not connected by any relationships, we know that the quantity

$$\frac{1}{n-s} \Sigma(y_\alpha - b_{\alpha1}\hat{p}_1 - b_{\alpha2}\hat{p}_2 - \cdots - b_{\alpha s}\hat{p}_s)^2 \tag{9}$$

is an estimate of σ^2.

As an example, consider the case of simple regression, where the model is

$$y_i = \alpha + \beta x_i + e_i \tag{10}$$

the e_i's being normally and independently distributed with a constant variance σ^2. We minimize

$$\Sigma(y_i - \alpha - \beta x_i)^2 \tag{11}$$

and, by differentiation with respect to α and β, we get the two equations:

$$\Sigma y_i = n\hat{\alpha} + \hat{\beta}\Sigma x_i$$

or

$$y. = \hat{\alpha} + \hat{\beta}x. \tag{12}$$

and

$$\Sigma x_i y_i = \hat{\alpha}\Sigma x_i + \hat{\beta}\Sigma x^2_i$$

Expressing $\hat{\alpha}$ in terms of $\hat{\beta}$ and substituting the result in the second equation, we get

$$\Sigma x_i y_i = (\Sigma x_i)y. - \hat{\beta}(\Sigma x_i)x. + \hat{\beta}\Sigma x^2_i$$

or

$$\hat{\beta} = \frac{\Sigma x_i y_i - (\Sigma x_i)y.}{\Sigma x^2_i - (\Sigma x_i)x.} = \frac{\Sigma(x_i - x.)(y_i - y.)}{\Sigma(x_i - x.)^2} \tag{13}$$

where

$$y. = \frac{1}{n}\Sigma y_i, \qquad x. = \frac{1}{n}\Sigma x_i$$

Also $\hat{\alpha} = y. - \hat{\beta}x.$, and the variance σ^2 is estimated by

$$s^2 = \frac{1}{n-2}\Sigma(y_i - \hat{\alpha} - \hat{\beta}x_i)^2$$

$$= \frac{1}{n-2}\Sigma[(y_i - y.) - \hat{\beta}(x_i - x.)]^2 \tag{14}$$

$$= \frac{1}{n-2}[\Sigma(y_i - y.)^2 - \hat{\beta}\Sigma(x_i - x.)(y_i - y.)]$$

The estimated variance of $\hat{\beta}$ is $s^2/\Sigma(x_i - x.)^2$, and confidence intervals on $\hat{\beta}$ are given by

$$\hat{\beta} \pm \frac{ts}{\sqrt{\Sigma(x_i - x.)^2}} \tag{15}$$

As a second example, suppose we have the situation that we have observations y, assumed to be made up as follows:

$$y_1 = a_1 + e_1$$

$$y_2 = a_1 + a_2 + e_2 \tag{16}$$

$$y_3 = a_2 + e_3$$

where a_1, a_2 are unknown and the e's are normally and independently distributed around zero with constant variance σ^2. What are the best estimates of a_1 and a_2? We have to minimize

$$(y_1 - a_1)^2 + (y_2 - a_1 - a_2)^2 + (y_3 - a_2)^2$$

Differentiating with regard to a_1 and equating the result to zero, we have

$$y_1 - \hat{a}_1 + y_2 - \hat{a}_1 - \hat{a}_2 = 0$$

or

$$y_1 + y_2 = 2\hat{a}_1 + \hat{a}_2 \tag{17}$$

Likewise, we have for a_2 the equation

$$y_2 + y_3 = \hat{a}_1 + 2\hat{a}_2 \tag{18}$$

The estimates are then as follows:

$$\hat{a}_1 = \tfrac{1}{3}(2y_1 + 2y_2 - y_2 - y_3)$$
$$= \tfrac{1}{3}(2y_1 + y_2 - y_3) \tag{19}$$
$$\hat{a}_2 = \tfrac{1}{3}[-(y_1 + y_2) + 2(y_2 + y_3)]$$
$$= \tfrac{1}{3}(-y_1 + y_2 + 2y_3)$$

The minimum value of the sums of squares of deviations is

$$(y_1 - \hat{a}_1)^2 + (y_2 - \hat{a}_1 - \hat{a}_2)^2 + (y_3 - \hat{a}_2)^2 \tag{20}$$

and this divided by unity (equals $3 - 2$): i.e., this quantity itself is an estimate of σ^2, which as usual we denote by s^2.

It may be noted that this minimum sum of squares may be calculated very simply as $\Sigma y^2 - \hat{a}_1(y_1 + y_2) - \hat{a}_2(y_2 + y_3)$. The corresponding general statements are given in the following two chapters. In brief the situation is that our equations for estimating the parameters are of the form:

$$l_1(y) - g_1(a) = 0$$
$$l_2(y) - g_2(a) = 0$$

etc.

$$l_p(y) - g_p(a) = 0$$

where each of the functions $l_i(y)$ are linear functions of the y's, and $g_i(a)$ of the parameters $a_1, a_2, \cdots, a_p$. Then the minimum sum of squares is

$$\Sigma y^2{}_i - \hat{a}_1 l_1(y) - \hat{a}_2 l_2(y) - \cdots - \hat{a}_p l_p(y)$$

Finally let us consider the accuracy of our estimates. Each estimate, $\hat{a}_1$ and $\hat{a}_2$, is a linear function of the observations, and its error is therefore a linear function of variates, each normally and independently distributed around zero with a variance σ^2. The variances are then

$$\text{var } (\hat{a}_1) = \tfrac{1}{9}(4 + 1 + 1)\sigma^2 = \tfrac{6}{9}\sigma^2 = \tfrac{2}{3}\sigma^2 \tag{21}$$

$$\text{var } (\hat{a}_2) = \tfrac{1}{9}(1 + 1 + 4)\sigma^2 = \tfrac{6}{9}\sigma^2 = \tfrac{2}{3}\sigma^2 \tag{22}$$

and the covariance is

$$\text{cov } (\hat{a}_1, \hat{a}_2) = \tfrac{1}{9}(-2 + 1 - 2)\sigma^2 = -\tfrac{3}{9}\sigma^2 = -\tfrac{1}{3}\sigma_2 \tag{23}$$

Estimated variances are obtained by putting s^2 in place of σ^2, and we may then obtain confidence intervals on a_1 and on a_2. It is occasionally necessary to make use also of a linear function of the parameters, say, $\alpha_1 a_1 + \alpha_2 a_2$. This function will be estimated by $\alpha_1 \hat{a}_1 + \alpha_2 \hat{a}_2$, and its variance will be

$$\alpha^2_1 \text{ var } (\hat{a}_1) + \alpha^2_2 \text{ var } (\hat{a}_2) + 2\alpha_1\alpha_2 \text{ cov } (\hat{a}_1, \hat{a}_2) \tag{24}$$

The subject of design of experiments is concerned to a considerable extent with situations analogous to the examples above, and a proper appreciation of the subject can hardly be attained without an understanding of the process used. In the second example, the reader may find it instructive to examine other estimates of a_1 and a_2. For example, the quantity $y_2 - y_1$ estimates a_2 for

$$y_2 - y_1 = a_1 + a_2 + e_2 - a_1 - e_1$$

$$= a_2 + e_2 - e_1$$

The variance of this estimate of a_2 is clearly $2\sigma^2$, whereas the estimate we obtained by least squares has a variance of $\tfrac{2}{3}\sigma^2$. Similarly, $\tfrac{1}{2}(y_3 + y_2 - y_1)$ estimates a_2, and the variance of this estimate is $\tfrac{3}{4}\sigma^2$, which again is greater than the variance of the least squares estimate.

4.3 A NON-LINEAR EXAMPLE

The examples we have discussed are all of a certain type, in that the observation is a *linear* function of the parameters and the error. This is a rather specialized situation, though it is the one that occurs most frequently in the analysis of the basic designs.

To illustrate a different situation, we shall discuss the fitting of the relationship

$$y_i = a + bc^{x_i} + e_i \tag{25}$$

where y_i is the observation associated with x_i (greater than or equal to zero), the quantities a, b, and c are unknown constants, the e_i's are uncorrelated with a mean zero and constant unknown variance σ^2, and i

runs from 1 to n. Many examples exist of responses to amounts of a stimulus following this relationship in one form or another. The procedure is to minimize the quantity

$$\sum_{i=1}^{n} (y_i - a - bc^{x_i})^2$$

with respect to a, b, and c. Differentiating with respect to a and equating the derivative to zero, we have the equation

$$\sum_{i=1}^{n} (y_i - a - bc^{x_i}) = 0 \tag{26}$$

Similarly, differentiating with respect to b, we get the equation

$$\sum_{i=1}^{n} c^{x_i}(y_i - a - bc^{x_i}) = 0 \tag{27}$$

and, differentiating with regard to c, we obtain the equation

$$\sum_{i=1}^{n} x_i bc^{x_i-1}(y_i - a - bc^{x_i}) = 0 \tag{28}$$

where, if x_i equals zero, we put c^{x_i-1} equal to zero. These equations may be written in the form:

$$na + b(\Sigma c^{x_i}) = \Sigma y_i \tag{29}$$

$$a(\Sigma c^{x_i}) + b(\Sigma c^{2x_i}) = \Sigma y_i c^{x_i} \tag{30}$$

$$a(\Sigma x_i c^{x_i-1}) + b(\Sigma x_i c^{2x_i-1}) = \Sigma y_i x_i c^{x_i-1} \tag{31}$$

These equations are very tedious to solve, and some ingenuity may be required. If there is a small number of integral values of the x_i, say, 0, 1, 2, and 3, the following procedure may be used. The equations to be solved will then be:

$$4a + b(1 + c + c^2 + c^3) = \Sigma y_i \tag{32}$$

$$a(1 + c + c^2 + c^3) + b(1 + c^2 + c^4 + c^6) = y_0 + y_1 c + y_2 c^2 + y_3 c^3 \tag{33}$$

$$a(1 + 2c + 3c^2) + b(c + 2c^3 + 3c^5) = y_1 + 2y_2 c + 3y_3 c^2 \tag{34}$$

By plotting the observed values we can make a guess of c. Inserting this guessed value, c_0, say, in equations 33 and 34, we shall obtain two linear equations in a and b, of which the solution is $a = a_0$ and $b = b_0$. We may insert these values for a and b in equation 32 and then solve this equation for c, giving, say, c_1. The whole cycle of operations is then repeated until the estimated values for a, b, and c do not change appreciably. These final values will be the estimates of a, b, and c from the data. This procedure does not converge unduly slowly if the data conform reasonably to the law 25. Alternatively, we may consider the quantity

$$Q = \sum_i (y_i - a - bc^{x_i})^2 \qquad (35)$$

and note that the least squares estimates a_0, b_0, and c_0, satisfy

$$\frac{\partial Q}{\partial a} = 0, \qquad \frac{\partial Q}{\partial b} = 0, \qquad \frac{\partial Q}{\partial c} = 0 \qquad (36)$$

Now,

$$\frac{\partial Q}{\partial a}\bigg|_{a_0 b_0 c_0} = \frac{\partial Q}{\partial a}\bigg|_{abc} + (a_0 - a)\frac{\partial^2 Q}{\partial a^2}\bigg|_{abc} + (b_0 - b)\frac{\partial^2 Q}{\partial a\,\partial b}\bigg|_{abc}$$

$$+ (c_0 - c)\frac{\partial^2 Q}{\partial a\,\partial c}\bigg|_{abc}$$

approximately, with similar equations for $\dfrac{\partial Q}{\partial b}\bigg|_{a_0 b_0 c_0}$ and $\dfrac{\partial Q}{\partial c}\bigg|_{a_0 b_0 c_0}$, where

$\dfrac{\partial Q}{\partial a}\bigg|_{a_0 b_0 c_0}$ is the value taken by $\dfrac{\partial Q}{\partial a}$, when $a = a_0$, $b = b_0$, and $c = c_0$,

and so on. Guessing values a, b and c, we may evaluate $\dfrac{\partial Q}{\partial a}$, $\dfrac{\partial^2 Q}{\partial a^2}$, $\dfrac{\partial^2 Q}{\partial a\,\partial b}$,

etc., for these guessed values, and we shall then have three equations in the three unknowns $(a - a_0)$, $(b - b_0)$, and $(c - c_0)$. If the solutions are a', b', and c', then a closer approximation to the estimates a_0, b_0, and c_0 will be $a_0 = a + a'$, $b_0 = b + b'$, and $c_0 = c + c'$. The process is continued with these new values, until a cycle of operations produces little change. Approximate variances of the estimates can be obtained in a way analogous to that which will be described in the next chapter for linear regression models.

The reader will find that, if he wishes to fit this law, the fitting process is very laborious. Fortunately we shall not meet problems of such complexity computationally as this one for the bulk of this book, though one cannot avoid the problems in general.

FURTHER READING

1. DEMING, W. E. *The statistical adjustment of data.* John Wiley & Sons, New York. 1943.

CHAPTER 5

The General Linear Hypothesis
or Multiple Regression
and the Analysis of Variance

5.1 DESCRIPTION OF STATISTICAL PROCEDURES

The basis of most parametric analyses of experiments is closely related to the theory of the general linear hypothesis or, in other words that are probably more familiar to the readers, the theory of multiple regression. Simple cases were dealt with in the previous pages, and we now present a general description.

Our assumption is that the observations y are expressible as linear functions of some known variables $x_1, \cdots, x_p$, with residual errors which are normally and independently distributed around zero with constant variance. The model is then

$$y_\alpha = \beta_1 x_1 + \beta_2 x_2 + \cdots + \beta_p x_p + e_\alpha \qquad (1)$$

where $x_1, x_2, \cdots, x_p$ take on particular known values for each y_α, say, $x_{1\alpha}, x_{2\alpha}, \cdots, x_{p\alpha}$. Frequently we would let $x_1 = 1$ for all α.

Throughout this book we shall be concerned not only with the derivation of estimates, designs, and so on for particular mathematical models but also with the applicability of these models to the real world. There are always certain relationships inherent in the mathematical model, which are clearly apparent to the mathematician though not necessarily realized when the model is applied to a set of data. We shall endeavor to keep the two aspects distinct from each other without ignoring either. The model we are discussing here is an example to illustrate these points. This model states that the regression of y on any one x_i is linear with constant slope when the other variables $x_j (j \neq i)$ are kept constant, and also that the slope of the regression of y on x_i is the same for all choices of the other variables. Suppose, for example,

38

that we had two independent variables x_1 and x_2, then for constant x_2 the relationship of y to x_1 is given by Figure 2, the lines corresponding to different values of x_2 being parallel, of positive or negative slope, of course. Similarly, the relationship of y to x_2 is given by Figure 3, the

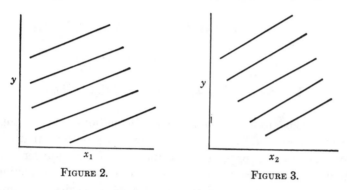

FIGURE 2.   FIGURE 3.

lines corresponding to different values of x_1 being parallel. In applying the model

$$y = \beta_1 x_1 + \beta_2 x_2 + e$$

to a set of data, we are then excluding from the start the situation represented by Figure 4. If we apply the above model to a situation such as this, we shall obtain an unreliable if not completely faulty picture of what is happening. In all the discussion of models that we shall give, we shall be speaking in terms of the experimenter's aims, that is, what effects factors have, and so on, and not in terms of obtaining a representation of some population. A more complicated model could be used to deal with the situation described: e.g., one involving the product $x_1 x_2$ possibly.

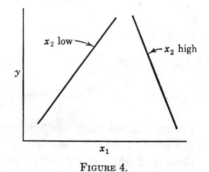

FIGURE 4.

To estimate the β's, we use the method of least squares: that is, we minimize the sum of squares of deviations:

$$\sum_\alpha (y_\alpha - \beta_1 x_{\alpha 1} - \beta_2 x_{\alpha 2} - \cdots - \beta_p x_{\alpha p})^2$$

Differentiating with regard to β_1 and equating to zero, we obtain the first equation below, and, with regard to β_2, β_3, $\cdots$, β_p, the succeeding equations:

$$\beta_1 \Sigma x^2_{\alpha1} + \beta_2 \Sigma x_{\alpha1} x_{\alpha2} + \cdots + \beta_p \Sigma x_{\alpha1} x_{\alpha p} = \Sigma y_\alpha x_{\alpha1}$$

$$\beta_1 \Sigma x_{\alpha i} x_{\alpha2} + \beta_2 \Sigma x^2_{\alpha2} + \cdots + \beta_p \Sigma x_{\alpha2} x_{\alpha p} = \Sigma y_\alpha x_{\alpha2}$$

$$\cdots \cdots \cdots \cdots \cdots \cdots \cdots \cdots$$

$$\beta_1 \Sigma x_{\alpha1} x_{\alpha p} + \beta_2 \Sigma x_{\alpha2} x_{\alpha p} + \cdots + \beta_p \Sigma x^2_{\alpha p} = \Sigma y_\alpha x_{\alpha p}$$

$$(2)$$

These equations are known as the normal equations. Let us suppose, also, as will be generally the case in regression problems, that our x_i's are not such that one or more linear functions of them are zero (for example, it is not the case that $x_1 + x_2 = $ a constant). Then a unique solution to the above set of p simultaneous equations exists. In order to solve them, the following procedure is usually best. We first solve p sets of p equations, the first set of which we write as follows, using $S_{ij} = S_{ji}$ as an abbreviation for $\displaystyle\sum_\alpha x_{\alpha i} x_{\alpha j}$:

$$c_1 S_{11} + c_2 S_{12} + \cdots + c_p S_{1p} = 1$$

$$c_1 S_{12} + c_2 S_{22} + \cdots + c_p S_{2p} = 0$$

$$\cdots \cdots \cdots \cdots \cdots \cdots$$

$$c_1 S_{1p} + c_2 S_{2p} + \cdots + c_p S_{pp} = 0$$

$$(3)$$

Denote the solutions of these equations by c_{11}, c_{12}, $\cdots$, c_{1p}, the first subscript indicating that this is the solution for the first set of equations and the second subscript denoting the particular c solution. Now we solve these equations with the numbers 0, 1, 0, 0, $\cdots$, 0 on the right-hand side: i.e., unity on the right-hand side of the second equation and zero on the right-hand side for all the other equations, the solution being denoted by c_{21}, c_{22}, $\cdots$, c_{2p}. Similarly we solve the equations with unity at the right-hand side of the third equation, the fourth equation, and so on to the pth equation, in each case the right-hand side of all the other equations being zero.

Arranging all our solutions we have a set of p^2 numbers which are arranged in a $p \times p$ square, the whole array being known as a matrix:

$$c_{11}c_{12} \cdots c_{1p}$$

$$c_{21}c_{22} \cdots c_{2p}$$

$$\cdot \quad \cdot \quad \cdot \quad \cdot \quad \cdot \quad \cdot$$

$$c_{p1}c_{p2} \cdots c_{pp}$$

This matrix is the inverse of the matrix with S_{ij} in place of c_{ij} and may be obtained by other computational procedures. It will be found that $c_{ij} = c_{ji}$: that is, that the array of c's is symmetrical about the leading diagonal. Then our solutions for β_1, β_2, $\cdots$, β_p are as follows:

$$\hat{\beta}_1 = c_{11}P_1 + c_{12}P_2 + \cdots + c_{1p}P_p$$

$$\hat{\beta}_2 = c_{12}P_1 + c_{22}P_2 + \cdots + c_{2p}P_p$$

$$\cdot \quad \cdot \quad \cdot \quad \cdot \quad \cdot \quad \cdot \quad \cdot \quad \cdot \quad \cdot \quad \cdot \quad \cdot \quad \cdot \quad \cdot$$

$$\hat{\beta}_p = c_{1p}P_1 + c_{2p}P_2 + \cdots + c_{pp}P_p$$

$$(4)$$

where P_i is $\displaystyle\sum_\alpha y_\alpha x_{\alpha i}$

We note that the c_{ij}'s are derived entirely from the x_{ij}'s; that is, they are a function of the structure of our observational setup and are not related to the y's or to the e's. The quantities estimating β_1, $\cdots$, β_p are linear functions of the y's, for example:

$$\hat{\beta}_1 = y_1(c_{11}x_{11} + c_{12}x_{21} + \cdots + c_{1p}x_{p1})$$

$$+ y_2(c_{11}x_{12} + c_{12}x_{22} + \cdots + c_{1p}x_{p2})$$

$$\cdot \quad \cdot \quad \cdot \quad \cdot \quad \cdot \quad \cdot \quad \cdot \quad \cdot \quad \cdot \quad \cdot \quad \cdot \quad \cdot$$

$$+ y_n(c_{11}x_{1n} + c_{12}x_{2n} + \cdots + c_{1p}x_{pn})$$

The expectations of the $\hat{\beta}$'s are easily found to be the corresponding β's. Furthermore the variance of $\hat{\beta}_i$ is $c_{ii}\sigma^2$, and the covariance of any two $\hat{\beta}$'s, say, $\hat{\beta}_i$ and $\hat{\beta}_j$ is $c_{ij}\sigma^2$. It should be noted that, for estimation purposes *only*, the assumption of normality and independence of the e's may be relaxed to the assumption that they are uncorrelated, retaining the assumption of zero mean and constant variance.

An estimate of σ^2 is derived from the sum of squares of deviations about the estimated values, in fact, by

$$s^2 = \frac{1}{n-p} \sum_\alpha (y_\alpha - \hat{\beta}_1 x_{\alpha 1} - \hat{\beta}_2 x_{\alpha 2} - \cdots - \hat{\beta}_p x_{\alpha p})^2 \qquad (5)$$

This quantity is substituted in the expressions for the variances and co-variances of the estimates of the regression coefficients. The quantity s^2 is more simply calculated as

$$\frac{1}{n-p} (\Sigma y^2_\alpha - \hat{\beta}_1 P_1 - \hat{\beta}_2 P_2 - \cdots - \hat{\beta}_p P_p)$$

or

$$\frac{1}{n-p} [\Sigma y^2_\alpha - R(\beta_1, \beta_2, \cdots, \beta_p)] \qquad (6)$$

where

$$R(\beta_1, \beta_2, \cdots, \beta_p) = \Sigma \hat{\beta}_i P_i$$

is the sum of squares removed by the regression on $x_1, x_2, \cdots, x_p$. The results may be expressed in terms of the analysis of variance as shown in Table 5.1.

TABLE 5.1

Variation Due to	df	Sum of Squares	Mean Square
Regression	p	$\sum_1^p \hat{\beta}_i P_i$	$(\Sigma \hat{\beta}_i P_i)/p = s^2_r$
Remainder	$n - p$	Difference	(Difference)$/n - p = s^2$
Total	n	$\sum_1^n y^2_\alpha$	

To test the significance of the regression coefficients jointly we evaluate the mean squares in the analysis of variance table and compute a variance ratio s^2_r/s^2. Under the null hypothesis that the true regression coefficients are all zero, this ratio is distributed according to the F distribution with p and $n - p$ degrees of freedom. Alternatively, to test the hypothesis that the β's are, say, β_{i0}, we compute the ratio

$$\sum_{i=1}^p \frac{(\hat{\beta}_i - \beta_{i0})(P_i - \sum_j \beta_{j0} S_{ij})}{ps^2}$$

and this is distributed again according to the F distribution if the true β's are the β_{i0}'s.

The above analysis is not exactly the same as that usually appearing in books on statistical methods, and the reason will appear shortly.

A frequent problem in regression analysis is the following. We wish to test whether certain of the regression coefficients are zero without making any assumptions about the remaining coefficients. Suppose we rename our regression coefficients $\beta_1, \cdots, \beta_q, \beta_{q+1}, \beta_{q+2}, \cdots, \beta_p$, and we wish to test whether $\beta_{q+1}, \beta_{q+2}, \cdots, \beta_p$ could be zero.

The procedure is simple: namely, to estimate the regression coefficients in the model

$$y_\alpha = \beta_1 x_1 + \beta_2 x_2 + \cdots + \beta_q x_q + e$$

obtaining, say, $\beta^*_1, \beta^*_2, \cdots, \beta^*_q$.

These β^*'s will be the solutions of the following set of equations:

$$\beta_1 S_{11} + \beta_2 S_{12} + \cdots + \beta_q S_{1q} = P_1$$

$$\beta_1 S_{12} + \beta_2 S_{22} + \cdots + \beta_q S_{2q} = P_2$$

$$\cdots \cdots \cdots \cdots \cdots \cdots \cdots$$

$$\beta_1 S_{1q} + \beta_2 S_{2q} + \cdots + \beta_q S_{qq} = P_q$$

$$(7)$$

The sum of squares removed by the regression $x_1, \cdots, x_q$ is equal to

$$R(\beta_1, \beta_2, \cdots, \beta_q) = \beta^*_1 P_1 + \beta^*_2 P_2 + \cdots + \beta^*_q P_q \qquad (8)$$

We can then construct the analysis of variance given in Table 5.2.

TABLE 5.2

Variation Due to	df	Sum of Squares	Mean Square
Regression on $x_1, \cdots, x_q$	q	$\sum_1^q \beta^*_i P_i$	s^2_q
Regression on $x_{q+1}, \cdots, x_p$ after fitting $x_1, \cdots, x_q$	$p - q$	$\sum_1^p \hat{\beta}_i P_i - \sum_1^q \beta^*_i P_i$	s^2_a
Regression on $x_1, \cdots, x_p$	p	$\sum_1^p \hat{\beta}_i P_i$	s^2_p
Remainder	$n - p$	Difference	s^2
Total	n	Σy^2	

To test the hypothesis that $\beta_{q+1}, \cdots, \beta_p$ are zero we utilize the fact that, under the hypothesis that they are zero, the mean squares s^2_a and s^2 are independent estimates of the same variance each distributed like $\chi^2 \sigma^2$, where σ^2 is the true variance around the regression equation in $x_1, \cdots, x_q$, and the degrees of freedom for χ^2 are $p - q$ and $n - p$, respectively. The ratio s^2_a/s^2 will therefore be distributed as F with $p - q$ and $n - p$ degrees of freedom, and the test is made by reference to the F table.

From the previous paragraph we may obtain the usual regression test. This test is devised to test whether deviations about the mean have a regression on the independent variates. Our complete hypothesis is that

$$y_\alpha = \beta_1 x_1 + \beta_2 x_2 + \cdots + \beta_p x_p + e_\alpha$$

and our restricted hypothesis that

$$y_\alpha = \beta_1 x_1 + e$$

where x_1 is unity for all the observations. The estimate β^*_1 is $\bar{y}$, the average y, and, with the complete model, we estimate the relationship to be

$$y_\alpha = (\bar{y} - \hat{\beta}_2 \bar{x}_2 - \cdots - \hat{\beta}_p \bar{x}_p) x_1 + \hat{\beta}_2 x_2 + \cdots + \hat{\beta}_p x_p$$

where x_1 is always unity, and $\hat{\beta}_1$ is equal to

$$(\bar{y} - \hat{\beta}_2 \bar{x}_2 - \hat{\beta}_3 \bar{x}_3 - \cdots - \hat{\beta}_p \bar{x}_p)$$

The analysis of variance corresponding to these two hypotheses is then as shown in Table 5.3.

TABLE 5.3

Variation Due to	df	Sum of Squares
Regression on x_1 (i.e., sum of squares due to mean)	1	$\bar{y}\Sigma y$
Regression $x_2, \cdots, x_p$ of deviations about mean	$p - 1$	$\hat{\beta}_2(P_2 - \bar{x}_2\Sigma y) + \hat{\beta}_3(P_3 - \bar{x}_3\Sigma y)$ $+ \cdots + \hat{\beta}_p(P_p - \bar{x}_p\Sigma y)$
Regression on $x_1, \cdots, x_p$	p	$(\bar{y} - \hat{\beta}_2\bar{x}_2 - \cdots - \hat{\beta}_p\bar{x}_p)(\Sigma y)$ $+ \hat{\beta}_2 P_2 + \cdots + \hat{\beta}_p P_p$
Remainder	$n - p$	Difference
Total	n	Σy^2

The "correction for the mean," $\bar{y}\Sigma y$, with 1 degree of freedom, may be deducted from the total, and we are left with the analysis in Table 5.4,

TABLE 5.4

Variation Due to	df	Sum of Squares
Regression on $x_2, \cdots, x_p$	$p - 1$	$\hat{\beta}_2 P_{2c} + \hat{\beta}_3 P_{3c} + \cdots + \hat{\beta}_p P_{pc}$
Remainder	$n - p$	Difference
Total	$n - 1$	$\Sigma y^2 - \bar{y}\Sigma y$

which is the more usual form, where we write P_{2c}, for example, instead of $P_2 - \bar{x}_2\Sigma y$, to denote the sum of products around the mean.

5.2 EXTENSION

The above process may be extended in the following obvious way. Suppose we have a series of hypotheses, each nested within the succeeding one, the models being

$$y_\alpha = \beta_1 x_1 + \beta_2 x_2 + \cdots + \beta_q x_q + e_\alpha$$

$$y_\alpha = \beta_1 x_1 + \beta_2 x_2 + \cdots + \beta_q x_q + \beta_{q+1} x_{q+1} + \cdots + \beta_{q+r} x_{q+r} + e_\alpha$$

$$y_\alpha = \beta_1 x_1 + \beta_2 x_2 + \cdots + \beta_q x_q + \beta_{q+1} x_{q+1} + \cdots + \beta_{q+r} x_{q+r}$$
$$+ \beta_{q+r+1} x_{q+r+1} + \cdots + \beta_{q+r+s} x_{q+r+s} + e_\alpha$$

and so on.

Corresponding to these hypotheses we shall have a partition of our degrees of freedom as shown in Table 5.5.

TABLE 5.5

Variation Due to	df	Sum of Squares
Regression on $x_1, \cdots, x_q$	q	$R(\beta_1, \beta_2, \cdots, \beta q)$
Regression on $x_{q+1}, \cdots, x_{q+r}$ after $x_1, \cdots, x_q$	r	Difference ($= R$, say)
Regression on $x_1, \cdots, x_q, x_{q+1}, \cdots, x_{q+r}$	$q + r$	$R(\beta_1, \beta_2, \cdots, \beta_{q+r})$
Regression on $x_{q+r+1}, \cdots, x_{q+r+s}$ after $x_1, \cdots, x_{q+}$,	s	Difference ($= S$, say)
Regression on $x_1, \cdots, x_q, x_{q+1}, \cdots,$ $x_{q+r}, x_{q+r+1}, \cdots, x_{q+r+s}$	$q + r + s$	$R(\beta_1, \beta_2, \cdots, \beta_{q+r+s})$
. . . .	. . . .	. . . .
. . . .	. . . .	. . . .
Remainder	n_e	E
Total	n	T

Of the various hypotheses that can be envisaged, only a few can, in general, be tested. We can test the following, for example, supposing we have only the three groups of parameters given above and have obtained the above analysis of variance:

1. All β's are zero: i.e., $\beta_1 = \beta_2 = \cdots = \beta_{q+r+s} = 0.$
2. $\beta_{q+1} = \beta_{q+2} = \cdots = \beta_{q+r+s} = 0.$
3. $\beta_{q+r+1} = \beta_{q+r+2} = \cdots = \beta_{q+r+s} = 0.$

The test of the hypothesis

$$\beta_1 = \beta_2 = \cdots = \beta_{q+r+s} = 0$$

is obtained by comparing the mean square for regression on $x_1, x_2, \cdots,$ x_{q+r+s}, namely,

$$\frac{R(\beta_1, \beta_2, \cdots, \beta_{q+r+s})}{q + r + s}$$

with the remainder mean square, E/n_e, by the F test with $(q + r + s)$ and n_e degrees of freedom.

To test the hypothesis

$$\beta_{q+1} = \beta_{q+2} = \cdots = \beta_{q+r+s} = 0$$

we compare the mean square

$$\frac{R(\beta_1, \beta_2, \cdots, \beta_{q+r+s}) - R(\beta_1, \beta_2, \cdots, \beta_q)}{r + s}$$

with E/n_e by the F test with $(r + s)$ and n_e degrees of freedom. To test the hypothesis

$$\beta_1 = \beta_2 = \cdots = \beta_q = 0$$

we would have to make a different order of subdivision of the analysis of variance in which the independent variates $x_1, \cdots, x_q$ are the last ones to be included.

We can make any test of the following form: Is the regression on x_i, x_j, $\cdots$, x_k significant after we allow, say, x_a, x_b, $\cdots$, x_c to account for as much variability as they can? Alternatively we can test whether the regression on x_a, x_b, $\cdots$, x_c is significant after we allow x_i, x_j, $\cdots$, x_k to account for as much variability as they can. We can also test whether the sets of regression coefficients take particular values. As will be seen in the later section giving the proofs of these results, we cannot test for regression on x_i, x_j, $\cdots$, x_k merely by disregarding the other x's. Also, in general, we cannot say that a certain proportion of the variability of the y's is attributable to x_a, x_b, $\cdots$, x_c and a certain proportion to x_i, x_j, $\cdots$, x_k, and so on. If we characterize groups of the parameters, the β's, by γ_1, γ_2, etc., we shall find, in general, that our estimates for any one group depend on assumptions made with regard to the other groups. For instance, if it is found that the regression on a set of the independent variates x_i, x_j, $\cdots$, x_k is not significant, it might seem to be correct to calculate the regression on the remaining variates by ignoring x_i, x_j, $\cdots$, x_k. This amounts to assuming that the regression on x_i, x_j, $\cdots$, x_k is, in fact, zero. If this regression is not zero, the procedure mentioned would lead to biased estimates of the regression on the variates included. Only insofar as the bias introduced is negligible will the estimates be satisfactory. The bias may be evaluated in particular cases.

There is also a difficulty in the interpretation of the regression coefficients. Suppose we wish to estimate, from a set of observations of rainfall, altitude, latitude and longitude, and the yield of a crop, the effect of varying independently each of these first 4 factors on the yield of the crop. It may well happen that in our data, rainfall and altitude, are very highly correlated so that errors in the estimation of the effect of rainfall are highly correlated with errors in the estimation of the effect of altitude and vice-versa. The extent to which this is important depends on the population to which the statistical results are to be applied. If in this population the same correlation exists, the correlation of errors of estimates *may* be unimportant.

5.3 THE LIKELIHOOD RATIO TEST

The tests of hypotheses which we have discussed are all derivable from the likelihood ratio test procedure. In the case of testing for regression on $x_{q+1}, \cdots, x_p$, the maximum of the likelihood under the original hypothesis is equal to: constant $(s^2)^{-n/2}$. Under the hypothesis that the regression on $x_{q+1}, \cdots, x_p$ is actually zero, the maximum of the likelihood is equal to

$$\text{Constant } [(n-p)s^2 + (p-q)s^2_a]^{-n/2}$$

The ratio $\dfrac{L(\omega_{\max})}{L(\Omega_{\max})}$ is then equal to

$$\text{Constant } \left[\frac{(n-p)s^2 + (p-q)s^2_a}{s^2} \right]^{-n/2}$$

This leads to the variance ratio test on s^2_a/s^2 already given.

In all cases of the linear hypothesis, the test criterion becomes the ratio of the minimum sum of squares of deviations under the hypothesis to be tested to the minimum sum of squares of deviations under the original hypothesis. The analysis of variance provides a convenient means of obtaining these minimum sums of squares and, hence, the mean squares. The mean squares are obtained so that we can use the tabulated F distribution.

5.4 REDUCTION OF OTHER CASES OF REGRESSION

Practically all cases of the testing of hypotheses on regressions may be reduced to the form already described. We shall give one example: namely, the testing of heterogeneity of several linear regressions. In this case we suppose that we have r sets of data, each set, denoted by i,

consisting of a number of observations on y and x.   For the ith set we
have the model
$$y_{ij} = z_i + \beta_i x_{ij} + e_{ij}$$
where y_{ij} and x_{ij} are the jth ($j = 1, 2, \cdots, n_i$) observations of the dependent and independent variables, respectively, in the ith set.   We
may wish to test equality of the α's, of the β's or of both for the sets of
data.   Suppose we wish to test the equality of the β's, making no assumptions about the α's.   The model may be written

$$y_{11} = z_1\alpha_1 + 0\alpha_2 + \cdots + 0\alpha_r + x_{11}\beta_1 + 0\beta_2 + \cdots + 0\beta_r + e_{11}$$
$$\vdots$$
$$y_{1n_1} = z_1\alpha_1 + 0\alpha_2 + \cdots + 0\alpha_r + x_{1n_1}\beta_1 + 0\beta_2 + \cdots + 0\beta_r + e_{1n_1}$$

$$y_{21} = 0\alpha_1 + z_2\alpha_2 + \cdots + 0\alpha_r + 0\beta_1 + x_{21}\beta_2 + \cdots + 0\beta_r + e_{21}$$
$$\vdots$$
$$y_{2n_2} = 0\alpha_1 + z_2\alpha_2 + \cdots + 0\alpha_r + 0\beta_1 + x_{2n_2}\beta_2 + \cdots + 0\beta_r + e_{2n_2}$$
$$\vdots$$
$$y_{r1} = 0\alpha_1 + 0\alpha_2 + \cdots + z_r\alpha_r + 0\beta_1 + 0\beta_2 + \cdots + x_{r1}\beta_r + e_{r1}$$
$$\vdots$$
$$y_{rn_r} = 0\alpha_1 + 0\alpha_2 + \cdots + z_r\alpha_r + 0\beta_1 + 0\beta_2 + \cdots + x_{rn_r}\beta_r + e_{rn_r}$$

where $\alpha_1 = 1$ for observations in the 1st set
        $= 0$ for all other sets
    $\alpha_2 = 1$ for observations in the 2nd set
        $= 0$ for all other sets
    and so on.

We wish to test the hypothesis $\beta_1 = \beta_2 = \cdots = \beta_r$, and this will proceed as in the general case.

It may be verified that the test reduces to an analysis of variance of
the form shown in Table 5.6.

TABLE 5.6

Due to	df
Separate α's and a common β	$r + 1$
Difference	$r - 1$
Individual regressions	$2r$
Remainder	$\Sigma n_i - 2r$
Total about zero	Σn_i

TABLE 5.7

Due to	df
Common β	1
Difference	$r - 1$
Individual β's	r
Remainder	$\Sigma n_i - 2r$
Total within sets	$\Sigma n_i - r$

This analysis may be reduced further to the form given in Table 5.7, where

$$\text{Total within sets} = \sum_{ij} (y_{ij} - y_{i\cdot})^2$$

Sum of squares due to individual regressions

$$= \sum_i \frac{\left[\sum_j (y_{ij} - y_{i\cdot})(x_{ij} - x_{i\cdot}) \right]^2}{\sum_j (x_{ij} - x_{i\cdot})^2}$$

Sum of squares due to common regression

$$= \frac{\left[\sum_i \sum_j (y_{ij} - y_{i\cdot})(x_{ij} - x_{i\cdot}) \right]^2}{\sum_i \sum_j (x_{ij} - x_{i\cdot})^2}$$

$y_{i\cdot}$ being $\dfrac{1}{n_i} \sum_j y_{ij}$, and $x_{i\cdot}$ being $\dfrac{1}{n_i} \sum_j x_{ij}$. Other cases may be examined easily by the same procedure, though the reduction to analysis of variance form is not always immediately obvious without some practical experience.

5.5 ORTHOGONALITY

If our data conform to a certain pattern, we do not become involved in the difficulties of estimation and testing of hypotheses about the parameters mentioned earlier. This is so when the estimate of any one parameter of one group is uncorrelated with that of any parameter of any other group. In other words our c matrix, which when multiplied by σ^2 gives the variance-covariance matrix of our estimates, may be arranged so that it is of the form:

$$
\begin{array}{c}
\quad\quad \overbrace{\gamma_1} \quad\quad \overbrace{\gamma_2} \quad\quad \overbrace{\gamma_3} \quad\quad \cdots\cdots \\[2pt]
\gamma_1 \left\{ \begin{array}{c} x\,x\,\cdot\,x \\ x\,x\,:\,x \\ x\,x\,\cdot\,x \end{array} \right. \quad 0 \quad\quad 0 \quad\quad 0 \\[18pt]
\gamma_2 \left\{ \quad 0 \quad \begin{array}{c} x\,x\,\cdot\cdot\,x \\ x\,x\,\cdot\cdot\,x \\ x\,x\,\cdot\cdot\,x \end{array} \quad 0 \quad\quad 0 \right. \\[18pt]
\gamma_3 \left\{ \quad 0 \quad\quad 0 \quad \begin{array}{c} x\,x\,\cdot\cdot\,x \\ \cdot\,:\,\cdot\cdot\cdot \\ x\,x\,\cdot\cdot\,x \end{array} \quad 0 \right.
\end{array}
$$

Here γ_1, γ_2, $\cdots$ denote the groups of parameters, and the matrix is such that, when the rows and columns are arranged so that those corresponding to γ_1 are contiguous, those for γ_2 contiguous, and so on, the elements of the matrix are zero, apart from the elements corresponding to each group of parameters.

If this is the case, it is easily proved that the estimate of γ_1, say, is unaffected by whether we first estimate the parameters of any or of all of the other groups. The proof is, in fact, obvious when we consider the equations for estimating all the parameters. The matrix of the coefficients in the least squares equations will be of identical form with the c matrix, so that we get the same equations for estimating the parameters of the group γ_1, regardless of whether we also have equations for estimating the other groups. Likewise, the total sum of squares removed by the regression may be partitioned to give an analysis of variance of the form shown in Table 5.8.

TABLE 5.8

Due to	df	Sum of Squares	Mean Square
γ_1	p_1	S_1	s^2_1
γ_2	p_2	S_2	s^2_2
.	.	.	.
.	.	.	.
.	.	.	.
Total due to $\gamma_1, \gamma_2, \cdots$	p	S_p	s^2_p
Remainder	$n-p$	S_e	s^2_e
Total	n	$\displaystyle\sum_{ijk} y^2_{ijk}$	

The expectation of each of the mean squares under the hypothesis that all the β's are zero is equal to σ^2, the expectation of the remainder mean square. If some of the parameters of the group γ_i, say, are not equal to zero, the expectation of s^2_i will be σ^2 plus a quadratic expression in the parameters of γ_i, while the expectations of all the other mean squares will be σ^2. So, when the null hypothesis is false, the expectations of the mean squares are:

$$E(s^2_1) = \sigma^2 + Q(\gamma_1)$$

$$E(s^2_2) = \sigma^2 + Q(\gamma_2)$$

$$\cdot \quad \cdot \quad \cdot \quad \cdot \quad \cdot \quad \cdot \quad \cdot \quad \cdot$$

$$E(s^2_e) = \sigma^2$$

Each of the quantities $Q(\gamma_i)$, etc., is positive, except when all the parameters of the group γ_i are zero, when $Q(\gamma_i)$ is equal to zero. Each of these mean squares under the null hypothesis that the β's of its group are zero is distributed independently of each other as $\chi^2\sigma^2$, where χ^2 has the appropriate number of degrees of freedom. We may, therefore, test any of the groups using the F test with appropriate degrees of freedom. Our tests will not of course be independent because we shall be using the same denominator in all, and whatever deviation s^2_e has from σ^2 will affect all the F tests in the same way.

When the above situation exists, the pattern of observations is said to be *orthogonal* for these groups of parameters. In passing we note that:

1. The orthogonality relates to the model we assume, in particular the assumption that the residuals of each y are uncorrelated (or independently normal) with the same variance.

2. As a rough generalization, the importance of orthogonality decreases with increasing quantities of data, providing the correlations are not close to unity.

3. In many situations we wish to predict the result of increasing the level of one factor: The fact that we have independent estimates of each of the regression coefficients will be of no help, if we cannot alter the level of the one factor without altering the level of other factors. This tends to vitiate, more or less completely, the results obtained from the analysis by ordinary regression methods of many survey data. For the research worker usually resorts to the analysis of survey data when he is unable to perform experiments: that is, when he is unable to vary the factors himself at will. Consider for example the problem in farm management economics of assessing output y in terms of size of

farm x_1, capital invested x_2, and labor used x_3, for a particular type of farming region. (We suppose the economic terms to be defined adequately.) Analysis of survey data by farms by the usual methods may result in an equation of the form

$$y = \alpha + \beta_1 x_1 + \beta_2 x_2 + \beta_3 x_3$$

but the interpretation of this equation is in many cases almost entirely a matter of guesswork. Can we estimate, for instance, from this equation the effect for an individual farmer of increasing the capital invested? On the other hand, it may be said in extenuation of the fairly frequent use of this method that it is of value in demonstrating the existence of relationships in the population studied, and this may be of real value to the research worker. The difficulties mentioned above have led in economics to the development of structural equations, which take account of the interrelationship of the so-called independent variables.

5.6 QUANTITY OF INFORMATION

Emphasis has been made in several places on the economic aspect of experimentation. It is fairly easy to visualize the way in which the cost of an experiment could be calculated, though it might be difficult in particular instances to assess the cost of the various resources on the same scale, in terms of dollars, say. For to do this we have to put some value on the time of the experimenter as well as on the materials and hired labor. It might be a rather difficult decision to assess the value of a week's work by the experimenter on an experiment. If he were not doing the experiment, what else would he be doing, and what would that be worth? Usually he is on a payroll and his salary will be paid, within limits, whether he performs the experiment or not.

Supposing, however, that a reasonable cost function has been devised, what measure can we have of the value of his experiment? There are two aspects of the value of an experiment, to only one of which a measure of quantity of information can be attached. The aspect that cannot be evaluated except perhaps by the market value of the experimenter is whether he has good hypotheses, good in the sense of leading to advances in knowledge. Suppose for example one is studying the nutrition of a child. Anyone with the vaguest of ideas on nutrition would be able to suggest various factors that might be varied in an experiment so that their effects could be estimated. The experimenter with the more original mind will suggest a more valuable set of factors to be tested and will devise techniques for their measurement. Nothing in statistical reasoning however suggests a method of ascribing a measure to this value, except in the sense that the better experimenter will be able in the long run to predict a variable affected by many factors with greater accuracy.

The other aspect is this: Supposing the experimenter has decided on the factors to be investigated, is it possible to ascribe a measure of value to the various possible designs that are available? To make the discussion more concrete, suppose the function of the experiment is to estimate a single parameter. The only requirement that our measure of information should satisfy is that the information on a parameter provided by, say, two independent samples from the distribution should be equal to the sum of the information contained in the two samples considered separately. This implies of course that the information is directly proportional to the size of the sample. The generally adopted measure of quantity of information is that originated by Fisher.[1]

Fisher defined the quantity of information, stated completely in mathematical terms, as follows: Suppose we wish to estimate the parameter θ for a distribution $f(x, \theta)$, then the amount of information in a sample of size n is equal to

$$nI = n \int_{-\infty}^{\infty} \left(\frac{\partial \log f}{\partial \theta} \right)^2 f \, dx$$

In the case of the normal distribution where we are estimating the mean μ,

$$f(x) = \frac{1}{\sqrt{2\pi}\sigma} e^{-\frac{1}{2} \frac{(x-\mu)^2}{\sigma^2}}$$

then

$$\log f = \frac{1}{2} \log (2\pi) - \log \sigma - \frac{1}{2} \frac{(x - \mu)^2}{\sigma^2}$$

and

$$\frac{\partial \log f}{\partial \mu} = \frac{x - \mu}{\sigma^2}$$

so that

$$nI = n \int_{-\infty}^{\infty} \frac{(x - \mu)^2}{\sigma^4} \frac{1}{\sqrt{2\pi}\sigma} e^{-\frac{1}{2} \frac{(x-\mu)^2}{\sigma^2}} \, dx$$

$$= \frac{n}{\sigma^2}$$

The information per observation is therefore $1/\sigma^2$. In the case of an estimate that is normally distributed around its expected value, we use then the reciprocal of the variance of the estimate as a measure of the information given by the estimate. It is obvious that this measure of information has the required property, and intuitively this seems a reasonable measure. For the variance of a mean of a normal sample of size n_1 is σ^2/n_1, and of another sample of size n_2 is σ^2/n_2, while the variance of the mean of the combined sample is $\sigma^2/(n_1 + n_2)$. The information about the mean of the population is obviously contained entirely in the variance of the estimate, and the only function of this variance that is additive for independent samples is the reciprocal.

In the case of the general linear hypothesis, it was stated earlier in this chapter that the variance-covariance matrix of the estimates of the parameters was the c matrix multiplied by σ^2, and the obvious analogue for information in this case is the matrix which was inverted to give the c matrix: that is, the matrix of the coefficients of the linear equations which give the estimates. This matrix is often referred to as the information matrix. In general, we would use a volume based on this information matrix, usually that of the ellipsoid of concentration. We saw above that it was desirable both for testing hypothesis and estimation that the c matrix be diagonal and, therefore, that the information matrix be diagonal. Our estimates are then uncorrelated, and we may consider the information contained in each estimate independently.

Another measure of quantity of information is given by Wiener [2] in his recent remarkable book *Cybernetics*. This measure relates however to *a priori* and *a posteriori* distributions of the parameters and therefore appears of little value in the present context, though, when an *a priori* distribution exists, it would be useful.

5.7 PROOF OF THE RESULTS OF THIS CHAPTER

In the proofs we assume that the reader is familiar with matrix notation, which enables a considerably shorter presentation. The observations and parameters are connected by the relation

$$\mathbf{y} = \mathbf{X}\boldsymbol{\beta} + \mathbf{e} \tag{9}$$

where

$$
\mathbf{y} = \begin{bmatrix} y_1 \\ \cdot \\ \cdot \\ \cdot \\ y_\alpha \\ \cdot \\ \cdot \\ \cdot \\ y_n \end{bmatrix}, \quad
\mathbf{X} = \begin{bmatrix} x_{11}\,x_{12} \cdots x_{1p} \\ \cdot \quad \cdot \quad\quad \cdot \\ \cdot \quad \cdot \quad\quad \cdot \\ \cdot \quad \cdot \quad\quad \cdot \\ x_{\alpha 1}\,x_{\alpha 2} \cdots x_{\alpha p} \\ \cdot \quad \cdot \quad\quad \cdot \\ \cdot \quad \cdot \quad\quad \cdot \\ \cdot \quad \cdot \quad\quad \cdot \\ x_{n1}\,x_{n2} \cdots x_{np} \end{bmatrix}, \quad
\boldsymbol{\beta} = \begin{bmatrix} \beta_1 \\ \beta_2 \\ \cdot \\ \cdot \\ \cdot \\ \cdot \\ \cdot \\ \beta_p \end{bmatrix}, \quad \text{and} \quad
\mathbf{e} = \begin{bmatrix} e_1 \\ \cdot \\ \cdot \\ \cdot \\ e_\alpha \\ \cdot \\ \cdot \\ \cdot \\ e_n \end{bmatrix}
$$

The e_i's are assumed to be normally and independently distributed around a mean of zero with variance σ^2. The sum of squares which is to be minimized is

$$
\begin{aligned}
e'e &= (y - X\beta)'(y - X\beta) \\
&= y'y - \beta'X'y - y'X\beta + \beta'X'X\beta \qquad (10) \\
&= y'y - 2y'X\beta + \beta'X'X\beta
\end{aligned}
$$

Differentiating with regard to β_i, and denoting $X'X$ by S, we get the equations

$$
S\hat{\beta} = X'y
$$

Note that S is certainly non-negative, for any quadratic form $u'Su = u'X'Xu = (Xu)'(Xu)$, which cannot be negative.

If S is non-singular,

$$
\hat{\beta} = S^{-1}X'y \qquad (11)
$$

It is readily verified that the $\hat{\beta}_i$'s are unbiased, for

$$
\begin{aligned}
E(\hat{\beta}) &= E(S^{-1}X'y) \\
&= E[S^{-1}X'(X\beta + e)] \\
&= E(S^{-1}S\beta + S^{-1}X'e) \qquad (12) \\
&= \beta
\end{aligned}
$$

The variance-covariance matrix of the estimates is equal to

$$
E[(\hat{\beta} - \beta)(\hat{\beta} - \beta)'] = E(S^{-1}X'ee'XS^{-1})
$$
since $S = X'X$ is symmetric: i.e., $S = S'$

$$
= S^{-1}X'\sigma^2 I_p XS^{-1}
$$
where I_n is the $n \times n$ unit matrix, since the e_i's have zero mean and constant variance and are uncorrelated

$$
\begin{aligned}
&= \sigma^2 S^{-1}X'XS^{-1} \\
&= \sigma^2 S^{-1}SS^{-1} \qquad (13) \\
&= \sigma^2 S^{-1}
\end{aligned}
$$

It should be noted that S^{-1} is the matrix c_{ij} described earlier.

Now we prove the property of "best linear unbiasedness." If the linear functions Ay are to estimate β unbiasedly, we must have

$$
E(Ay) = E(AX\beta + Ae) = \beta \qquad (14)
$$

so, since $E(e) = 0$, the matrix A must satisfy

$$
AX = I \qquad (15)
$$

The matrix $(S^{-1}X' + B)$ will satisfy this relation in place of A if

$$BX = O_p \tag{16}$$

where O_p is a $p \times p$ matrix, all of whose elements are zero.

$$(S^{-1}X' + B)y$$

is an arbitrary unbiased estimator of β, subject to this condition on B. The variance-covariance matrix of the estimates is equal to

$$E[(S^{-1}X' + B)ee'(XS^{-1} + B')] = \sigma^2(S^{-1}X' + B)(XS^{-1} + B')$$

$$= \sigma^2(S^{-1} + S^{-1}X'B' + BXS^{-1} + BB')$$

$$= \sigma^2(S^{-1} + BB') \tag{17}$$

But BB' is such that the ith diagonal element is the sum of the squares of the elements of the ith row of B. Any diagonal element of BB' is therefore positive, unless all the elements of the row are zero. Any unbiased linear estimate of each β_i other than the one we obtained in equation 11 has therefore a greater variance. It should be noted that in this derivation we have made use only of the assumptions that the e's have zero mean and constant variance and are uncorrelated. For tests of significance we use normal distribution theory, so that normality is also required. This, with zero correlation, implies independence of the e's. It is easily proved that the best linear unbiased estimate of a linear function of the parameters is the same linear function of the estimates of the parameters.

To obtain the test of significance we note that

$$(y - X\beta_0)'(y - X\beta_0) = (y' - \beta'_0 X')(y - X\beta_0)$$

$$= [y' - \hat{\beta}'X' + (\hat{\beta}' - \beta'_0)X'][y - X\hat{\beta} + X(\hat{\beta} - \beta_0)]$$

$$= (y' - \hat{\beta}'X')(y - X\hat{\beta}) + (y' - \hat{\beta}'X')X(\hat{\beta} - \beta_0)$$

$$+ (\hat{\beta}' - \beta'_0)X'(y - X\hat{\beta})$$

$$+ (\hat{\beta}' - \beta'_0)X'X(\hat{\beta} - \beta_0) \tag{18}$$

where β_0 is an arbitrarily chosen set of β_i's. Utilizing the fact that $S\hat{\beta} = X'y$, or $y'X = \hat{\beta}'S$, we note that the second and third terms (which are equal) are zero. The identity in β_0

$$(y - X\beta_0)'(y - X\beta_0) = (y - X\hat{\beta})'(y - X\hat{\beta}) + (\hat{\beta}' - \beta'_0)S(\hat{\beta} - \beta_0) \tag{19}$$

therefore holds. The first term on the right-hand side is the sum of squares about the fitted regression equation. We found above that

$$\hat{\beta} = \beta + S^{-1}X'e$$

so

$$y - X\hat{\beta} = X\beta + e - X\beta - XS^{-1}X'e = (I - XS^{-1}X')e \qquad (20)$$

This term is equal then to

$$e'(I - XS^{-1}X')'(I - XS^{-1}X')e = e'(I - XS^{-1}X')e \qquad (21)$$

and is a quadratic form in the errors e, regardless of the true β and β_0. The second term on the right-hand side is similar to $R(\beta_1, \beta_2, \cdots, \beta_p)$ of the first section of this chapter and equals

$$[(\beta - \beta_0) + S^{-1}X'e]'S[(\beta - \beta_0) + S^{-1}X'e]$$

$$= (\beta - \beta_0)'S(\beta - \beta_0) + 2(\beta - \beta_0)'X'e + e'XS^{-1}X'e \qquad (22)$$

Now consider the two cases:

1. *Suppose $\beta_0 = \beta$*: i.e., the β_{0i}'s are the true values of β_i's. Then,

$$(y - X\beta_0) = e$$

and

$$e'e = e'(I - XS^{-1}X')e + e'XS^{-1}X'e \qquad (23)$$

or

$$\sum_1^n e^2{}_\alpha = Q_1 + Q_2 \qquad (24)$$

where Q_1 and Q_2 are non-negative quadratic forms in the e's. Q_1 is non-negative because it is equal to $(y - X\hat{\beta})'(y - X\hat{\beta})$, and Q_2 is non-negative because it may be written $(X'e)'S^{-1}(X'e)$. The rank of the left-hand side is certainly n: the rank of Q_2 is less than or equal to the rank of S, and the rank of Q_1 is less than or equal to $n - p$, for Q_1 is the sum of squares of the quantities

$$(y - X\hat{\beta})_\alpha$$

which are connected by p linear relations, since $X'(y - X\hat{\beta}) = 0$. Because the rank of the sum of quadratic forms is less than or equal to the sum of the ranks, it must be the case that

$$r(Q_1) = n - p$$

and

$$r(Q_2) = p$$

We now use Cochran's theorem (see for example Cramér [3]):

If $\sum_1^n x^2{}_i = Q_1 + Q_2 + \cdots + Q_k$ where $Q_1, Q_2, \cdots, Q_k$ are non-negative quadratic forms of ranks $r_1, r_2, \cdots, r_k$ and $\sum_1^k r_i = n$, then there exists an orthogonal transformation $x = \mathbf{O}y$, such that

$$Q_1 = \sum_1^{r_1} y^2_i, \qquad Q_2 = \sum_{r_1+1}^{r_1+r_2} y^2_i, \quad \text{etc.}$$

This is a theorem in algebra, and its value in statistics arises because, if $x_1, x_2, \cdots, x_n$ are normally and independently distributed around a mean of zero with variance σ^2, then $y_1, \cdots, y_n$, where $x = \mathbf{O}y$, $\mathbf{O}$ being orthogonal, are also normally and independently distributed around a mean of zero with variance σ^2. The quadratic forms Q_1 and Q_2 have then the distributions,

$$Q_1 = \chi^2_{n-p}\sigma^2, \qquad Q_2 = \chi^2_p\sigma^2$$

and the ratio $\dfrac{Q_2}{p} \Big/ \dfrac{Q_1}{n-p}$ is distributed as F with p and $(n-p)$ degrees of freedom.

The properties of the estimates and the fact that $E(Q_1) = (n-p)\sigma^2$ are known as the Markoff theorem, and it may be noted that the assumption of normality is not necessary for this theorem. The necessary conditions on the errors are that they have expectation zero, are uncorrelated, and have the same variance.

2. Suppose $\boldsymbol{\beta} \neq \boldsymbol{\beta}_0$. Then,

$$(\mathbf{y} - \mathbf{X}\boldsymbol{\beta}_0)'(\mathbf{y} - \mathbf{X}\boldsymbol{\beta}_0) = Q_1 + Q_2(\boldsymbol{\beta}_0) \tag{25}$$

Now Q_1 is exactly the same expression as before and is therefore distributed as $\chi^2_{n-p}\sigma^2$. The quantity $Q_2(\boldsymbol{\beta}_0)$ has an expectation of

$$p\sigma^2 + (\boldsymbol{\beta} - \boldsymbol{\beta}_0)'\mathbf{S}(\boldsymbol{\beta} - \boldsymbol{\beta}_0) \tag{26}$$

and, since $\mathbf{S}$ is positive definite, this expectation is greater than $p\sigma^2$, if $\boldsymbol{\beta} \neq \boldsymbol{\beta}_0$. The ratio $F = \dfrac{Q_2(\boldsymbol{\beta}_0)}{p} \Big/ \dfrac{Q_1}{n-p}$ is then distributed as F, if $\boldsymbol{\beta} = \boldsymbol{\beta}_0$, and, if $\boldsymbol{\beta} \neq \boldsymbol{\beta}_0$, the numerator will on the average be greater than the denominator. The ratio F may therefore be used to test the hypotheses $\boldsymbol{\beta} = \boldsymbol{\beta}_0$, for deviations from the hypothesis will tend to make F large. The upper tail of the F distribution must be used as a critical region. From the point of view of computations, it is worth noting that equation 19,

$$(\mathbf{y} - \mathbf{X}\boldsymbol{\beta}_0)'(\mathbf{y} - \mathbf{X}\boldsymbol{\beta}_0) = (\mathbf{y} - \mathbf{X}\hat{\boldsymbol{\beta}})'(\mathbf{y} - \mathbf{X}\hat{\boldsymbol{\beta}}) + (\hat{\boldsymbol{\beta}}' - \boldsymbol{\beta}'_0)\mathbf{S}(\hat{\boldsymbol{\beta}} - \boldsymbol{\beta}_0)$$

may be put in the form

$$(\mathbf{y} - \mathbf{X}\hat{\boldsymbol{\beta}})'(\mathbf{y} - \mathbf{X}\hat{\boldsymbol{\beta}})$$

$$= (\mathbf{y} - \mathbf{X}\boldsymbol{\beta}_0)'(\mathbf{y} - \mathbf{X}\boldsymbol{\beta}_0) - (\hat{\boldsymbol{\beta}}' - \boldsymbol{\beta}'_0)\mathbf{X}'(\mathbf{y} - \mathbf{X}\boldsymbol{\beta}_0) \quad (27)$$

In words this says:

> Sum of squares of deviations from fitted regression = sum of squares about hypothesized true regression $- \sum_i [(\hat{\beta}_i - \beta_{0i}) \{\text{right hand side}$
>
> of ith normal equation - its hypothesized value}]

The test of the hypothesis $\boldsymbol{\beta} = \boldsymbol{\beta}_0$ has been obtained essentially by use of the likelihood ratio test. It has been proved by Hsu, Simaika, Wald, and Wolfowitz that the test given above has optimum properties (see Wolfowitz [4]).

5.8 THE TESTING OF A SUBHYPOTHESIS

We now suppose that the parameters $\beta_1, \cdots, \beta_p$ are divided into two groups $\gamma_1, \cdots, \gamma_{p-q}$ and $\delta_1, \cdots, \delta_p$ so that $\mathbf{y} = \mathbf{X}\boldsymbol{\beta} + \mathbf{e} = \mathbf{X}_1\boldsymbol{\gamma} + \mathbf{X}_2\boldsymbol{\delta} + \mathbf{e}$, where $\mathbf{X}_1$ is the matrix composed of the first $p-q$ columns of $\mathbf{X}$, and $\mathbf{X}_2$ of the last (q) columns, and

$$\boldsymbol{\gamma} = \begin{bmatrix} \gamma_1 \\ \vdots \\ \gamma_{p-q} \end{bmatrix} \quad \boldsymbol{\delta} = \begin{bmatrix} \delta_1 \\ \vdots \\ \delta_q \end{bmatrix} \quad (28)$$

Suppose we wish to estimate $\boldsymbol{\gamma}$ and to test the hypothesis that $\boldsymbol{\gamma} = \boldsymbol{\gamma}_0$. We could assume $\boldsymbol{\delta} = \boldsymbol{\delta}_0$, and we would then have the hypothesis

$$\mathbf{y} - \mathbf{X}_2\boldsymbol{\delta}_0 = \mathbf{X}_1\boldsymbol{\gamma} + \mathbf{e}$$

and, from the previous section, we would estimate $\boldsymbol{\gamma}$ by

$$\hat{\boldsymbol{\gamma}}(\boldsymbol{\delta}_0) = (\mathbf{X}'_1\mathbf{X}_1)^{-1}\mathbf{X}'_1(\mathbf{y} - \mathbf{X}_2\boldsymbol{\delta}_0)$$

This estimate is biased unless $\boldsymbol{\delta}_0$ equals the true value $\boldsymbol{\delta}$, for

$$E[\hat{\boldsymbol{\gamma}}(\boldsymbol{\delta}_0)] = (\mathbf{X}'_1\mathbf{X}_1)^{-1}\mathbf{X}'_1[\mathbf{X}_1\boldsymbol{\gamma} + \mathbf{X}_2(\boldsymbol{\delta} - \boldsymbol{\delta}_0)]$$

$$= \boldsymbol{\gamma} + (\mathbf{X}'_1\mathbf{X}_1)^{-1}\mathbf{X}'_1\mathbf{X}_2(\boldsymbol{\delta} - \boldsymbol{\delta}_0) \quad (29)$$

Since, in general, we do not know $\boldsymbol{\delta}$, we must estimate both $\boldsymbol{\gamma}$ and $\boldsymbol{\delta}$, and our estimates will then be unbiased. If, however, we know $\boldsymbol{\delta}$, we would be foolish not to use this information, for the variance of $\hat{\boldsymbol{\gamma}}(\boldsymbol{\delta})$ is less than the variance of $\hat{\gamma}$ (except with orthogonality of γ and δ). This follows from the basic theorem on the best linear unbiased estimate and can be verified easily by noting that

$$\text{var } (\hat{\gamma}_i) = \text{var } [\hat{\gamma}_i(\delta)] + \text{var } [\hat{\gamma}_i - \hat{\gamma}_i(\delta)] + 2 \text{ cov } [\hat{\gamma}_i, \hat{\gamma}_i - \hat{\gamma}_i(\delta)]$$

and that it is easily found that

$$\text{cov } [\hat{\gamma}_i, \hat{\gamma}_i - \hat{\gamma}_i(\delta)] = 0$$

the subscript i denoting any component of $\hat{\gamma}$ or $\hat{\gamma}(\delta)$.

The procedure for testing $\gamma = \gamma_0$ can be obtained by the likelihood ratio criterion. Under the original hypothesis,

$$H_0 : y = X_1\gamma + X_2\delta + e$$

and, under the restricted hypothesis (or subhypothesis),

$$H_1 : y = X_1\gamma_0 + X_2\delta + e$$

where γ_0 is known. The minimum sum of squares under H_0 is

$$(y - X_1\hat{\gamma} - X_2\hat{\delta})'(y - X_1\hat{\gamma} - X_2\hat{\delta})$$

where

$$\begin{pmatrix} \hat{\gamma} \\ \hat{\delta} \end{pmatrix} = S^{-1}(X_1 \mid X_2)'y$$

The minimum sum of squares under H_1 is

$$[y - X_1\gamma_0 - X_2\hat{\delta}(\gamma_0)]'[y - X_1\gamma_0 - X_2\hat{\delta}(\gamma_0)]$$

where

$$\hat{\delta}(\gamma_0) = (X'_2X_2)^{-1}X'_2(y - X_1\gamma_0)$$

The column matrix $\hat{\delta}(\gamma_0)$ denotes the estimate of δ, assuming that $\gamma = \gamma_0$, so that

$$\hat{\delta}(\gamma_0) = (X'_2X_2)^{-1}X'_2(y - X_1\gamma_0)$$

$$= (X'_2X_2)^{-1}X'_2[X_1(\gamma - \gamma_0) + X_2\delta + e]$$

$$= (X'_2X_2)^{-1}X'_2X_1(\gamma - \gamma_0) + \delta + (X'_2X_2)^{-1}X'_2e \qquad (30)$$

But, from the identity 19, we have

$$(y - X_1\gamma_0 - X_2\delta_0)'(y - X_1\gamma_0 - X_2\delta_0)$$

$$= [y - X_1\gamma_0 - X_2\hat{\delta}(\gamma_0)]'[y - X_1\gamma_0 - X_2\hat{\delta}(\gamma_0)]$$

$$+ [\hat{\delta}(\gamma_0) - \delta_0]'X'_2X_2[\hat{\delta}(\gamma_0) - \delta_0] \qquad (31a)$$

and also

$$[\mathbf{y} - \mathbf{X}_1\boldsymbol{\gamma}_0 - \mathbf{X}_2\hat{\boldsymbol{\delta}}(\boldsymbol{\gamma}_0)][\mathbf{y} - \mathbf{X}_1\boldsymbol{\gamma}_0 - \mathbf{X}_2\hat{\boldsymbol{\delta}}(\boldsymbol{\gamma}_0)]$$

$$= (\mathbf{y} - \mathbf{X}_1\hat{\boldsymbol{\gamma}} - \mathbf{X}_2\hat{\boldsymbol{\delta}})'(\mathbf{y} - \mathbf{X}_1\hat{\boldsymbol{\gamma}} - \mathbf{X}_2\hat{\boldsymbol{\delta}})$$

$$+ \begin{bmatrix} \hat{\boldsymbol{\gamma}} - \boldsymbol{\gamma}_0 \\ \hat{\boldsymbol{\delta}} - \hat{\boldsymbol{\delta}}(\boldsymbol{\gamma}_0) \end{bmatrix}' \mathbf{S} \begin{bmatrix} \boldsymbol{\gamma} - \boldsymbol{\gamma}_0 \\ \hat{\boldsymbol{\delta}} - \hat{\boldsymbol{\delta}}(\boldsymbol{\gamma}_0) \end{bmatrix} \quad (31)$$

so that we have the identity in $\boldsymbol{\gamma}_0$ and $\boldsymbol{\delta}_0$,

$$(\mathbf{y} - \mathbf{X}_1\boldsymbol{\gamma}_0 - \mathbf{X}_2\boldsymbol{\delta}_0)'(\mathbf{y} - \mathbf{X}_1\boldsymbol{\gamma}_0 - \mathbf{X}_2\boldsymbol{\delta}_0)$$

$$= (\mathbf{y} - \mathbf{X}_1\hat{\boldsymbol{\gamma}} - \mathbf{X}_2\hat{\boldsymbol{\delta}})'(\mathbf{y} - \mathbf{X}_1\hat{\boldsymbol{\gamma}} - \mathbf{X}_2\hat{\boldsymbol{\delta}}) + \begin{bmatrix} \hat{\boldsymbol{\gamma}} - \boldsymbol{\gamma}_0 \\ \hat{\boldsymbol{\delta}} - \hat{\boldsymbol{\delta}}(\boldsymbol{\gamma}_0) \end{bmatrix}' \mathbf{S} \begin{bmatrix} \hat{\boldsymbol{\gamma}} - \boldsymbol{\gamma}_0 \\ \hat{\boldsymbol{\delta}} - \hat{\boldsymbol{\delta}}(\boldsymbol{\gamma}_0) \end{bmatrix}$$

$$+ [\hat{\boldsymbol{\delta}}(\boldsymbol{\gamma}_0) - \boldsymbol{\delta}_0]'\mathbf{X}'_2\mathbf{X}_2[\hat{\boldsymbol{\delta}}(\boldsymbol{\gamma}_0) - \boldsymbol{\delta}_0] \quad (32)$$

or

$$(\mathbf{y} - \mathbf{X}_1\boldsymbol{\gamma}_0 - \mathbf{X}_2\boldsymbol{\delta}_0)'(\mathbf{y} - \mathbf{X}_1\boldsymbol{\gamma}_0 - \mathbf{X}_2\boldsymbol{\delta}_0) = Q_1 + Q_2 + Q_3 \quad (33)$$

As before, we now consider the various possible cases.

1. *Suppose* $\boldsymbol{\gamma}_0 = \boldsymbol{\gamma}$ *and* $\boldsymbol{\delta}_0 = \boldsymbol{\delta}$. Then

$$\hat{\boldsymbol{\delta}}(\boldsymbol{\gamma}_0) = (\mathbf{X}'_2\mathbf{X}_2)^{-1}\mathbf{X}'_2(\mathbf{y} - \mathbf{X}_1\boldsymbol{\gamma}_0)$$

$$= (\mathbf{X}'_2\mathbf{X}_2)^{-1}\mathbf{X}'_2(\mathbf{X}_2\boldsymbol{\delta} + \mathbf{e})$$

$$= \boldsymbol{\delta} + (\mathbf{X}'_2\mathbf{X}_2)^{-1}\mathbf{X}'_2\mathbf{e} \quad (34)$$

and

$$\hat{\boldsymbol{\delta}}(\boldsymbol{\gamma}_0) - \boldsymbol{\delta} = (\mathbf{X}'_2\mathbf{X}_2)^{-1}\mathbf{X}'_2\mathbf{e}$$

Also,

$$\begin{bmatrix} \hat{\boldsymbol{\gamma}} - \boldsymbol{\gamma}_0 \\ \hat{\boldsymbol{\delta}} - \hat{\boldsymbol{\delta}}(\boldsymbol{\gamma}_0) \end{bmatrix} = \begin{pmatrix} \hat{\boldsymbol{\gamma}} - \boldsymbol{\gamma} \\ \hat{\boldsymbol{\delta}} - \boldsymbol{\delta} \end{pmatrix} - \begin{bmatrix} 0 \\ \hat{\boldsymbol{\delta}}(\boldsymbol{\gamma}_0) - \boldsymbol{\delta} \end{bmatrix}$$

$$= \mathbf{S}^{-1}(\mathbf{X}_1 \mid \mathbf{X}_2)'\mathbf{e} - \begin{bmatrix} 0 \\ (\mathbf{X}'_2\mathbf{X}_2)^{-1}\mathbf{X}'_2\mathbf{e} \end{bmatrix} \quad (35)$$

So Q_2 and Q_3 are quadratic forms in the e's. The rank of Q_1 we know from before to be $n - p$, and the rank of Q_3 is less than or equal to q. The quadratic form Q_2 is equal to

$$\left\{ \mathbf{S}^{-1}(\mathbf{X}_1 \mid \mathbf{X}_2)'\mathbf{e} - \begin{bmatrix} 0 \\ (\mathbf{X}'_2\mathbf{X}_2)^{-1}\mathbf{X}'_2\mathbf{e} \end{bmatrix} \right\}'$$

$$\times \mathbf{S} \left\{ \mathbf{S}^{-1}(\mathbf{X}_1 \mid \mathbf{X}_2)'\mathbf{e} - \begin{bmatrix} 0 \\ (\mathbf{X}'_2\mathbf{X}_2)^{-1}\mathbf{X}'_2\mathbf{e} \end{bmatrix} \right\}$$

But

$$(\mathbf{X}_1 \mid \mathbf{X}_2)'\mathbf{e} - \mathbf{S}\left[\frac{\mathbf{0}}{(\mathbf{X}'_2\mathbf{X}_2)^{-1}\mathbf{X}'_2\mathbf{e}}\right]$$

$$= \left(\frac{\mathbf{X}'_1\mathbf{e}}{\mathbf{X}'_2\mathbf{e}}\right) - \left(\frac{\mathbf{X}'_1\mathbf{X}_1 \mid \mathbf{X}'_1\mathbf{X}_2}{\mathbf{X}'_2\mathbf{X}_1 \mid \mathbf{X}'_2\mathbf{X}_2}\right)\left(\frac{\mathbf{0}}{(\mathbf{X}'_2\mathbf{X}_2)^{-1}\mathbf{X}'_2\mathbf{e}}\right)$$

$$= \left(\frac{\mathbf{X}'_1\mathbf{e}}{\mathbf{X}'_2\mathbf{e}}\right) - \left[\frac{\mathbf{X}'_1\mathbf{X}_2(\mathbf{X}'_2\mathbf{X}_2)^{-1}\mathbf{X}'_2\mathbf{e}}{\mathbf{X}'_2\mathbf{e}}\right]$$

$$= \left[\frac{\mathbf{X}'_1\mathbf{e} - \mathbf{X}'_1\mathbf{X}_2(\mathbf{X}'_2\mathbf{X}_2)^{-1}\mathbf{X}'_2\mathbf{e}}{\mathbf{0}}\right] \qquad (36)$$

so Q_2 is a quadratic form in only $(p - q)$ linear functions of the e's and is therefore of rank less than or equal to $p - q$. Since the rank of a sum of quadratic forms is less than or equal to the sum of the ranks, the rank of Q_2 must be $(p - q)$, and of Q_3 must be q.

We may therefore apply Cochran's theorem to give the result that

$$Q_1 \text{ is distributed as } \chi^2{}_{n-p}\sigma^2,$$

$$Q_2 \text{ is distributed as } \chi^2{}_{p-q},$$

and

$$Q_3 \text{ is distributed as } \chi^2{}_q\sigma^2,$$

independently of each other.

As a result, if we know the true values for $\boldsymbol{\gamma}$ and $\boldsymbol{\delta}$ and compute Q_1, Q_2, and Q_3, any ratio of two of them adjusted according to their degrees of freedom follows the F distribution.

2. *Suppose* $\boldsymbol{\gamma}_0 \neq \boldsymbol{\gamma}$ *and* $\boldsymbol{\delta}_0 \neq \boldsymbol{\delta}$. Then, analogously to equation 35, using equation 30 gives

$$\begin{bmatrix} \hat{\boldsymbol{\gamma}} - \boldsymbol{\gamma}_0 \\ \hat{\boldsymbol{\delta}} - \boldsymbol{\delta}(\boldsymbol{\gamma}_0) \end{bmatrix} = \mathbf{S}^{-1}(\mathbf{X}_1 \mid \mathbf{X}_2)'\mathbf{e} - \begin{bmatrix} \mathbf{0} \\ (\mathbf{X}'_2\mathbf{X}_2)^{-1}\mathbf{X}'_2\mathbf{e} \end{bmatrix}$$

$$+ \begin{bmatrix} \boldsymbol{\gamma} - \boldsymbol{\gamma}_0 \\ -(\mathbf{X}'_2\mathbf{X}_2)^{-1}\mathbf{X}'_2\mathbf{X}_1(\boldsymbol{\gamma} - \boldsymbol{\gamma}_0) \end{bmatrix} \qquad (37)$$

The expectation of Q_2 is equal to

$$(p - q)\sigma^2 + \begin{bmatrix} \boldsymbol{\gamma} - \boldsymbol{\gamma}_0 \\ -(\mathbf{X}'_2\mathbf{X}_2)^{-1}\mathbf{X}'_2\mathbf{X}_1(\boldsymbol{\gamma} - \boldsymbol{\gamma}_0) \end{bmatrix}'$$

$$\times \mathbf{S}\begin{bmatrix} \boldsymbol{\gamma} - \boldsymbol{\gamma}_0 \\ -(\mathbf{X}'_2\mathbf{X}_2)^{-1}\mathbf{X}'_2\mathbf{X}_1(\boldsymbol{\gamma} - \boldsymbol{\gamma}_0) \end{bmatrix}$$

and, since S is positive definite, this expectation is greater than $(p - q)\sigma^2$ unless $\gamma_0 = \gamma$. The quantity $R(\beta_1, \cdots, \beta_p) - R(\beta_{p-q+1}, \beta_{p-q+2}, \cdots, \beta_p)$ of the previous section equals Q_2.

The ratio $\dfrac{Q_2(\gamma_0)}{(p - q)} \bigg/ \dfrac{Q_1}{n - p}$ may therefore be used to test the hypothesis that $\gamma = \gamma_0$. This is true, regardless of whether $\delta_0 = \delta$ or not, because Q_2 is distributed as χ^2_{p-q} in either case. For computational purposes we note that Q_1 is the minimum sum of squares with no restrictions on γ and δ, and $Q_1 + Q_2$ is the minimum sum of squares with $\gamma = \gamma_0$. The quadratic form Q_3 which equals

$$[\hat{\delta}(\gamma_0) - \delta_0]'X'_2X_2[\hat{\delta}(\gamma_0) - \delta_0]$$

contains residual errors and the differences $(\gamma - \gamma_0)$ and $(\delta - \delta_0)$, because $\hat{\delta}(\gamma_0) - \delta_0$ is equal to

$$(X'_2X_2)^{-1}X'_2X_1(\gamma - \gamma_0) + (\delta - \delta_0) + (X'_2X_2)^{-1}X'_2e$$

If γ_0 and δ_0 are the true values of γ and δ, the form Q_3 is distributed as $\chi^2_q\sigma^2$, but Q_3 is not distributed as $\chi^2_q\sigma^2$ if $\delta_0 = \delta$, but $\gamma_0 \neq \gamma$.

Under one other condition the quadratic form will not contain terms in $(\gamma - \gamma_0)$, and that is when $X'_2X_1 = O$, for $(X'_2X_2)^{-1}$ is non-singular. If this condition holds,

$$\hat{\delta}(\gamma_0) = \delta + (X'_2X_2)^{-1}X'_2e$$

and is the same as $\hat{\delta}$, so that our estimate of $\hat{\delta}$ is constant, regardless of assumptions about γ. The converse statement also holds. Under these circumstances the quadratic form Q_3 has an expectation of

$$q\sigma^2 + (\delta - \delta_0)'X'_2X_2(\delta - \delta_0)$$

which will be greater than $q\sigma^2$ unless $\delta_0 = \delta$. The ratio $\dfrac{Q_3}{q} \bigg/ \dfrac{Q_1}{n - p}$ may be used therefore to test the hypothesis $\delta = \delta_0$ if $X'_2X_1 = 0$. This test will not be independent of the test $\gamma = \gamma_0$ already given, because the denominators in the two F values are identical.

If the relation $X'_2X_1 = 0$ holds, the parameters γ and δ are said to be orthogonal. This property is, of course, a property of the data, and one of the functions of the design of experiments is to formulate a pattern of observations so that the condition holds.

The extension to cases of a breakdown of β into more than two parts is obvious. The model will then be of the form

$$y = X_1\gamma + X_2\delta + X_3\rho + X_4\pi + \cdots + e \tag{38}$$

and the groups of parameters are orthogonal if all products X'_iX_j are zero matrices.

These proofs can be easily adapted to deal with the situation when the e_i's are assumed to be normally and independently distributed around zero with variances $k_i\sigma^2$, the k_i's being known. For, let

$$
K = \begin{bmatrix}
\dfrac{1}{\sqrt{k_1}} & 0 & 0 & \cdots & 0 \\
0 & \dfrac{1}{\sqrt{k_2}} & 0 & \cdots & 0 \\
\cdot & & \cdot & & \cdot \\
\cdot & & & \cdot & \cdot \\
\cdot & & & & \cdot \\
0 & \cdots & \cdots & 0 & \dfrac{1}{\sqrt{k_n}}
\end{bmatrix}
\tag{39}
$$

then,

$$
Ky = KX\beta + \eta \tag{40}
$$

where the η's are normally and independently distributed around zero with the same variance σ^2. In non-matrix terms, if the model is

$$
y_\alpha = \beta_1 x_{\alpha 1} + \beta_2 x_{\alpha 2} + \cdots + \beta_p x_{p\alpha} + e_\alpha
$$

and the e_α's have expectation zero, are uncorrelated, and have variances of $k_\alpha\sigma^2$, when the k_α's are known, the best linear unbiased estimates are obtained by minimizing

$$
\sum_\alpha \frac{1}{k_\alpha} (y_\alpha - \beta_1 x_{\alpha 1} - \beta_2 x_{\alpha 2} - \cdots - \beta_p x_{\alpha p})^2 \tag{41}
$$

The solution may be obtained by either matrix manipulation on equation 40 or ordinary differentiation of equation 41. A simple example of this case is the model

$$
y = \beta x + e
$$

where the e's have expectation zero, are uncorrelated, and have a variance of $x\sigma^2$. We minimize

$$
\sum \frac{1}{x} (y - \beta x)^2
$$

giving the estimate $\beta = \Sigma y / \Sigma x$, and so on.

These results may also be extended simply to the case when the e'_αs have a *known* variance-covariance matrix $\mathbf{A}$ say, for we can then find a matrix $\mathbf{P}$ such that $\mathbf{P'AP}$ is the unit matrix.

5.9 THE CANONICAL FORM OF THE GENERAL LINEAR HYPOTHESIS

If the e_α's of the model

$$\mathbf{y} = \mathbf{X\beta} + \mathbf{e}$$

are normally and independently distributed with mean zero and variance σ^2, the joint distribution of the y's may be transformed into the canonical form

$$\left(\frac{1}{\sqrt{2\pi}\sigma}\right)^n \exp\left\{-\frac{1}{2}\left[\sum_{i=1}^{p}(z_i + \delta_i)^2 + \sum_{i=p+1}^{n} z^2{}_i\right]\right\} \prod_{i=1}^{n} dz_i$$

We have seen that

$$(\mathbf{y} - \mathbf{X\beta})'(\mathbf{y} - \mathbf{X\beta}) = (\mathbf{y} - \mathbf{X\hat{\beta}})'(\mathbf{y} - \mathbf{X\hat{\beta}}) + (\hat{\beta} - \beta)'\mathbf{S}(\hat{\beta} - \beta)$$

$$= Q_1 + Q_2$$

Let β_0 be the hypothesized value of β. Then,

$$\hat{\beta} - \beta = \mathbf{S}^{-1}\mathbf{X'e} + \beta_0 - \beta$$

Also,

$$(\mathbf{y} - \mathbf{X\hat{\beta}})'(\mathbf{y} - \mathbf{X\hat{\beta}}) = \mathbf{e}'(\mathbf{I} - \mathbf{XS}^{-1}\mathbf{X'})\mathbf{e}$$

There exists an orthogonal $p \times p$ matrix $\mathbf{O}$ such that

$$\mathbf{OSO'} = \begin{bmatrix} \lambda^2{}_1 & 0 & 0 & \cdots & 0 \\ 0 & \lambda^2{}_2 & 0 & \cdots & \cdot \\ \cdot & \cdot & \cdot & & \cdot \\ & & & \cdot & \\ \cdot & \cdot & \cdot & & \cdot \\ \cdot & \cdot & \cdot & & \cdot \\ 0 & \cdots & \cdots & \cdots & \lambda^2{}_p \end{bmatrix} = \Lambda^2$$

where $\lambda^2{}_1, \lambda^2{}_2, \cdots, \lambda^2{}_p$ are the characteristic roots of $\mathbf{S}$.   Then

$$(\hat{\boldsymbol{\beta}} - \boldsymbol{\beta})'S(\hat{\boldsymbol{\beta}} - \boldsymbol{\beta}) = \{O[S^{-1}X'e + (\boldsymbol{\beta}_0 - \boldsymbol{\beta})]\}'\Lambda^2\{O[S^{-1}X'e + (\boldsymbol{\beta}_0 - \boldsymbol{\beta})]\}$$

$$= \Sigma\lambda^2{}_i\eta^2{}_i = \sum_{i=1}^{p} (\xi_i + \delta_i)^2$$

where

$$\boldsymbol{\xi} = \Lambda OS^{-1}X'e, \qquad \boldsymbol{\delta} = \Lambda O(\boldsymbol{\beta}_0 - \boldsymbol{\beta})$$

Suppose we fill out the $(p \times n)$ matrix $\Lambda OS^{-1}X'$ to an orthogonal matrix $P = \left(\dfrac{\Lambda OS^{-1}X'}{T}\right)$. This is easily seen to be possible. Then if $z = Py$,

we have that $Q_1 = \displaystyle\sum_{i=p+1}^{n} z^2{}_i, Q_2 = \sum_{i=1}^{p} (z_i + \delta_i)^2$, and the Jacobian of the transformation is unity. The canonical form is therefore obtained.

REFERENCES

1. FISHER, R. A. Theory of statistical estimation. *Proc. Camb. Phil. Soc.*, **22**, 700–725, 1925.
2. WIENER, N. *Cybernetics.* John Wiley & Sons, New York. 1948.
3. CRAMÉR, H. *Mathematical methods of statistics.* University Press, Princeton, 1946.
4. WOLFOWITZ, J. The power of the classical tests associated with the normal distribution. *Ann. Math. Stat.*, **20**, 540–551, 1949.

FURTHER READING

There does not appear to be a complete presentation of all the material in this chapter anywhere in the literature. The tests were given by Fisher [5,6] and have been used continuously since that time. To understand the proofs given herein it is necessary to know the elementary properties of matrices and their manipulation. Any good text on higher algebra may be consulted, for example, Birkhoff and Mac-Lane [7] or a text specifically on matrices such as Aitken.[8] The reader may also refer to Mood [9] and Wilks [10] for other descriptions of the material. Reference 11 is concerned with least squares theory and its application. Reference 12 gives a detailed discussion of the problem from the point of view of Neyman-Pearson theory. This list, of course, is by no means complete.

5. FISHER, R. A. The goodness of fit and regression formulae, and the distribution of regression coefficients. *Jour. Roy. Stat. Soc.*, **85**, Part IV, 597–612, 1922, and reprinted in *Contributions to mathematical statistics.* John Wiley & Sons, New York. 1950.
6. FISHER, R. A. *Statistical methods for research workers.* Oliver and Boyd, Edinburgh. 1st ed., 1925; 11th ed., 1950.
7. BIRKHOFF, G., and MACLANE, S. *A survey of modern algebra.* Macmillan, New York. 1947.
8. AITKEN, A. C. *Determinants and matrices.* Oliver and Boyd, Edinburgh. 3rd ed., 1944.

9. Mood, A. M. *Introduction to the theory of statistics.* McGraw-Hill, New York. 1950.
10. Wilks, S. S. *Mathematical statistics.* University Press, Princeton. 1943.
11. Deming, W. E. *Statistical adjustment of data.* John Wiley & Sons, New York. 1943.
12. Kolodziejczyk, St. On an important class of statistical hypotheses. *Biometrika,* **27,** 161–190, 1935.

FURTHER NOTES

It may be proved easily that least squares also has the property of giving a set of estimators with minimum generalized variance in the case of a linear model. The distribution of Q_2/Q, in the non-null case follows directly from the canonical form, the derivation being indicated in Chapter 12.

CHAPTER 6

The Analysis
of Multiple Classifications

Frequently experimental results consist of data arranged according to a multiple classification. The methods of Chapter 5 are quite general and apply to this situation also. There are, however, several facets that require separate examination, and the more frequent cases of classification data will be discussed in this chapter. In addition, the problems of the estimation of components of variance will be considered.

6.1 THE 2-WAY CLASSIFICATION WITH ONE OBSERVATION PER CELL

For the 2-way classification the model is

$$y_{ij} = \mu + b_i + t_j + e_{ij}, \qquad i = 1, 2, \cdots, r, \qquad j = 1, 2, \cdots, s \quad (1)$$

where μ, b_i, and t_j are the parameters, $\mu + b_i + t_j$ is the expected value of y_{ij}, and the e_{ij}'s are normally and independently distributed around a mean of zero with variance σ^2. We wish to estimate the b's and t's and to test hypotheses about them. We may write the model as a multiple regression hypothesis in the following way,

$$y_{ij} = \mu x_0 + b_1 x_1 + b_2 x_2 + \cdots + b_r x_r + t_1 z_1 + t_2 z_2 + \cdots + t_s z_s + e_{ij}$$

$$(1a)$$

where

$\qquad x_0 = 1$ for all y_{ij}

$\qquad x_1 = 1$ for all y_{ij} with $i = 1$, and $= 0$ for all other y_{ij}

$\qquad x_2 = 1$ for all y_{ij} with $i = 2$, and $= 0$ for all other y_{ij}

and so on, and

$$z_1 = 1 \text{ for all } y_{ij} \text{ with } j = 1, \text{ and } = 0 \text{ for all other } y_{ij}$$

$$z_2 = 1 \text{ for all } y_{ij} \text{ with } j = 2, \text{ and } = 0 \text{ for all other } y_{ij}$$

and so on. In this formulation there are $1 + r + s$ parameters. The difficulty with this approach is that the matrix of coefficients has rank $1 + r + s - 2$, because $x_1 + x_2 + \cdots + x_r = 1$, and $z_1 + z_2 + \cdots + z_s = 1$, for all y_{ij}'s. The matrix of coefficients of the normal equations is singular and, therefore, does not have an inverse. The hypothesis is said to be a hypothesis not of full rank. We do not need, of course, to have recourse to matrix theory to see that we have only $r + s - 1$ independent parameters, for we can alter μ by an arbitrary quantity, the b_i's by adding another arbitrary quantity the same for all b_i's and likewise the t_j's, providing that these three arbitrary quantities add to zero, without altering the expectation of the observations. Unique solutions for the original parameters can only be obtained by imposing conditions on the parameters.

The linear hypothesis which is singular may be avoided from the beginning, but this results in the loss of the symmetry of the usual statement of the model and would lead to clumsy formulas.

One way out of the difficulty is the following. We wish to test the existence of differences of the b's and differences of the t's, and whether, for example, taking account of μ, the b's and the t's makes the estimates of the yield y_{ij}, namely, $\mu + b_i + t_j$, significantly closer to the observed value than taking account of μ only. This leads us automatically to suitable linear conditions to impose on the b's, because, with no restrictions, the mean over the whole is an estimate of

$$\mu + b. + t.$$

We, therefore, regard this quantity as μ', and then have

$$b'_i = b_i - b$$

$$t'_j = t_j - t.$$

with

$$\Sigma b'_i = 0$$

and

$$\Sigma t'_j = 0$$

and

$$y_{ij} = \mu' + b'_i + t'_j + e_{ij} \qquad (2)$$

This process will be called a reparametrization of the model.

Straightforward application of least squares leads then to the following equations, where for the rest of this section the primes are omitted:

$$\text{For } \mu: \quad rs\hat{\mu} = Y_{..}$$

$$\text{For } b_i: \quad s\hat{\mu} + s\hat{b}_i = Y_{i.} \tag{3}$$

$$\text{For } t_j: \quad r\hat{\mu} + r\hat{t}_j = Y_{.j}$$

where

$$Y_{i.} = \sum_j y_{ij}, \quad Y_{.j} = \sum_i y_{ij}, \quad Y_{..} = \sum_{i,j} y_{ij}$$

We shall attempt to adhere always to the rule of notation that the sum over some subscripts of, say, $y_{ijk\cdots}$ is denoted by the capital letter, say, Y with the subscripts over which summation is made replaced by dots. Thus,

$$\sum_{i,k} y_{ijkl} = Y_{.j.l}$$

We shall denote corresponding means by a small letter: e.g., $y_{.j.l}$. The equations (3) are not independent, because the μ equation can be obtained by adding the equations for the b's or the t's, since $\Sigma \hat{b}_i = \Sigma \hat{t}_j = 0$.

To exhibit the orthogonality present in this situation, we must substitute for one of the b_i's, say b_r, in terms of the others by the relation

$$b_1 + b_2 + \cdots + b_r = 0$$

in the model, and in the normal equations 3, and likewise for one of the t_j's, say t_s. If now we subtract the b_r equation from each of the other b equations, and the t_s equation from each of the other t equations, we obtain the following set of equations:

$$rs\hat{\mu} = Y_{..}$$

$$s\hat{b}_i + s\sum_1^{r-1} \hat{b}_k = Y_{i.} - Y_{r.}, \qquad i = 1, 2, \cdots, r-1 \tag{4}$$

$$r\hat{t}_j + r\sum_1^{s-1} \hat{t}_k = Y_{.j} - Y_{.s}, \qquad j = 1, 2, \cdots, s-1$$

of which the matrix of coefficients is

	$\hat{\mu}$	$\hat{b}_1$	$\hat{b}_2$	·	·	$\hat{b}_{r-1}$	$\hat{t}_1$	$\hat{t}_2$	·	·	$\hat{t}_{s-1}$
$\hat{\mu}$	rs	0	0	·	·	0	0	0	·	·	0
$\hat{b}_1$	0	$2s$	s	·	·	s	0	0	·	·	0
$\hat{b}_2$	0	s	$2s$	·	·	s	0	0	·	·	0
·		·	·	·	·	·	·	·	·	·	·
·		·	·	·	·	·	·	·	·	·	·
$\hat{b}_{r-1}$	0	s	s	·	·	$2s$	0	0	·	·	0
$\hat{t}_1$	0	0	0	·	·	0	$2r$	r	·	·	r
$\hat{t}_2$	0	0	0	·	·	0	r	$2r$	·	·	r
·		·	·	·	·	·	·	·	·	·	·
·		·	·	·	·	·	·	·	·	·	·
$\hat{t}_{s-1}$	0	0	0	·	·	0	r	r	·	·	$2r$

These new parameters fall into three groups:

$$\gamma_1 \text{ consisting of } \mu$$
$$\gamma_2 \text{ consisting of } b_1, b_2, \cdots, b_{r-1}$$
$$\gamma_3 \text{ consisting of } t_1, t_2, \cdots, t_{s-1}$$

such that the groups are orthogonal.

Estimates of the parameters are easily seen to be

$$\hat{\mu} = \frac{Y_{..}}{rs}$$

$$\hat{b}_i = \frac{Y_{i\cdot}}{s} - \frac{Y_{..}}{rs} \tag{5}$$

$$\hat{t}_j = \frac{Y_{\cdot j}}{r} - \frac{Y_{..}}{rs}$$

The sum of squares accounted for by the parameters, which we may denote by $R(\mu, b, t)$, is

$$\hat{\mu} Y.. + \sum_i \hat{b}_i Y_i. + \sum_j \hat{t}_j Y._j$$

which equals

$$\frac{Y^2..}{rs} + \left(\sum_i \frac{Y^2_i.}{s} - \frac{Y^2..}{rs} \right) + \left(\sum_j \frac{Y^2._j}{r} - \frac{Y^2..}{rs} \right) \qquad (6)$$

We therefore have the analysis of variance given in Table 6.1.

TABLE 6.1

Due to	df	Sum of Squares	Mean Square
Mean	1	$Y^2../rs$	
b's	$r - 1$	$\sum Y^2_i./s - Y^2../rs$	
t's	$s - 1$	$\sum Y^2._j/r - Y^2../rs$	
Remainder	$(r - 1)(s - 1)$	By difference	
Total about zero	rs	$\sum y^2_{ij}$	

Usually the term due to mean is subtracted from the total about zero to give what is then called the total sum of squares.

So far this analysis of variance is an algebraic identity and can be made, regardless of assumptions about the origin and nature of the data.

Supposing now that the b_i's refer to groups and the t_j's to treatments, then we are interested in testing whether there are differences among the groups or among the treatments. To make tests of significance we must use the assumption that the e_{ij}'s are normally and independently distributed with the same variance σ^2 around a mean of zero.

Under this assumption we examine the portions of the analysis of variance table:

1. *Due to mean:* This quantity is equal to

$$\frac{Y^2..}{rs} = \left(rs\mu + \sum_{ij} e_{ij} \right)^2 \bigg/ rs$$

The expected value of this quantity is then

$$rs\mu^2 + \sigma^2$$

2. *Due to b's:* This sum of squares is equal to

$$\sum_i \frac{Y^2_{i\cdot}}{s} - \frac{Y^2_{\cdot\cdot}}{rs}$$

The quantity $\sum_i \dfrac{Y^2_{i\cdot}}{s}$ is equal to

$$\Sigma[(s\mu + sb_i) + \sum_j e_{ij}]^2/s$$

and has expectation

$$\sum_i s(\mu + b_i)^2 + r\sigma^2 = rs\mu^2 + s \sum_i b^2_i + r\sigma^2$$

The expectation of the sum of squares due to the b's is then

$$(r - 1)\sigma^2 + s \sum_i b^2_i$$

If we define the variance of our original *finite* population of r b's as

$$\sum_i \frac{(b_i - b_{\cdot})^2}{(r - 1)} = \sigma^2_b$$

the expectation is $(r - 1)(\sigma^2 + s\sigma^2_b)$. The expectation of the mean square is then $(\sigma^2 + s\sigma^2_b)$.

3. *Due to t's:* Similarly the expectation of the mean square due to the t's is $\sigma^2 + r\sigma^2_t$, where σ^2_t is defined by

$$\sigma^2_t = \frac{1}{s - 1} \sum_j (t_j - t_{\cdot})^2$$

4. *Remainder:* This by the Markoff theorem has expectation

$$(r - 1)(s - 1)\sigma^2$$

as may be verified easily by noting that it is equal to

$$\sum_{ij} (y_{ij} - y_{i\cdot} - y_{\cdot j} + y_{\cdot\cdot})^2$$

Finally the following distribution theory holds because of Cochran's theorem and of the presence of orthogonality:

1. The remainder sum of squares is distributed as $\chi^2\sigma^2$, regardless of whether the b's and t's are zero.
2. The sum of squares due to the b's is distributed as $\chi^2\sigma^2$ if the b's are zero, regardless of the values of the t's.
3. The sum of squares due to the t's is distributed as $\chi^2\sigma^2$ if the t's are zero, regardless of the values of the b's.

In each case χ^2 has the degrees of freedom corresponding to those in the analysis of variance table, and the χ^2's are independent. If σ^2 were known, tests based of χ^2 could be made. This can sometimes be done, for example, with data arising by transformation on binomial data to angles (Chapter 8).

If we call the mean squares B, T, and E, it follows that

1. B/E is distributed as F with $(r-1)$ and $(r-1)(s-1)$ degrees of freedom if the b's are zero. If the b's are not zero, the value of B/E will be larger than would be expected with the b's zero, so that, if the observed value is one that will be exceeded by chance in a proportion p of times if the b's were zero, we say that the b's are significantly different from zero at the p percentage level. If the value of p is at or below the chosen significance level, we reject the hypothesis that the b's are zero.

2. T/E is distributed as F with $(s-1)$ and $(r-1)(s-1)$ degrees of freedom if the t's are zero. We have a similar test and interpretation for the t's: i.e., for treatment differences.

Finally, we note that our test of the t's is not affected by any assumptions about the values of the b's, because of the orthogonality of the b's and t's. The variance of any difference of two $\hat{t}$'s is constant and equal to $2\sigma^2/r$.

6.2 ALTERNATIVE APPROACH TO HYPOTHESES NOT OF FULL RANK

The foregoing approach is satisfactory in most instances but is not complete in the sense that it does not indicate exactly what functions of the parameters can be estimated. Clearly it is impossible to estimate μ or any b_i, say, in the original model. It is preferable then to start from the beginning with the linear hypothesis not of full rank. In this section matrix notation will be used.

We have then the hypothesis

$$\mathbf{y} = \mathbf{X}\boldsymbol{\beta} + \mathbf{e} \qquad (7)$$

where

$$\mathbf{y} = \begin{bmatrix} y_1 \\ y_2 \\ . \\ . \\ . \\ y_n \end{bmatrix}, \quad \boldsymbol{\beta} = \begin{bmatrix} \beta_1 \\ \beta_2 \\ . \\ . \\ . \\ \beta_p \end{bmatrix}, \quad \mathbf{X} = \begin{bmatrix} x_{11} & x_{12} & \cdots & x_{1p} \\ x_{21} & x_{22} & \cdots & x_{2p} \\ . & . & & . \\ . & . & & . \\ x_{n1} & x_{n2} & \cdots & x_{np} \end{bmatrix}, \quad \text{and} \quad \mathbf{e} = \begin{bmatrix} e_1 \\ e_2 \\ . \\ . \\ . \\ e_n \end{bmatrix}$$

The β's are fixed unknown parameters, and the e_i's are normally and independently distributed around zero with a variance of σ^2. The rank of $\mathbf{X}$ (the number of linearly independent columns or rows) is supposed to be r, where r is less than p.

Consider the estimation of $\boldsymbol{\lambda}'\boldsymbol{\beta}$, where

$$\boldsymbol{\lambda} = \begin{bmatrix} \lambda_1 \\ \lambda_2 \\ \cdot \\ \cdot \\ \cdot \\ \lambda_p \end{bmatrix}$$

Suppose we use to estimate $\boldsymbol{\lambda}'\boldsymbol{\beta}$, the linear function of the observations $\mathbf{a}'\mathbf{y}$, where

$$\mathbf{a} = \begin{bmatrix} a_1 \\ a_2 \\ \cdot \\ \cdot \\ \cdot \\ a_n \end{bmatrix}$$

Then, if this estimate is to be unbiased, we must have

$$\mathbf{a}'\mathbf{X} = \boldsymbol{\lambda}' \quad \text{or} \quad \mathbf{X}'\mathbf{a} = \boldsymbol{\lambda} \tag{8}$$

We then consider of all the estimates satisfying this condition the one that has minimum variance. The error of the estimate is

$$\mathbf{a}'\mathbf{e}$$

and the variance of the estimate is

$$\mathbf{E}(\mathbf{a}'\mathbf{e}\mathbf{e}'\mathbf{a}) = (\Sigma a^2_i)\sigma^2$$

We must find the minimum value of Σa^2_i subject to the condition $\mathbf{X}'\mathbf{a} = \boldsymbol{\lambda}$. Using the method of Lagrange multipliers, we differentiate with regard to the a_i the quantity

$$\Sigma(a^2_i) - 2 \sum_{j=1}^{p} \rho_j \left(\sum_k x_{kj}a_k - \lambda_j \right) \tag{9}$$

where the ρ_j's are Lagrange multipliers. This gives the equations,

$$a_i - \sum_{j=1}^{p} \rho_j x_{ij} = 0 \tag{10}$$

or

$$\mathbf{a} = \mathbf{X}\boldsymbol{\rho}$$

But

$$\mathbf{X}'\mathbf{a} = \boldsymbol{\lambda}$$

so

$$\mathbf{X}'\mathbf{X}\boldsymbol{\rho} = \boldsymbol{\lambda}$$

or

$$\mathbf{S}\boldsymbol{\rho} = \boldsymbol{\lambda} \quad \text{where} \quad \mathbf{S} = \mathbf{X}'\mathbf{X}$$

If then $\boldsymbol{\rho}$ is a solution of the equations

$$\mathbf{S}\boldsymbol{\rho} = \boldsymbol{\lambda} \tag{11}$$

the best linear unbiased estimate of $\boldsymbol{\lambda}'\boldsymbol{\beta}$ is given by

$$\widehat{\boldsymbol{\lambda}'\boldsymbol{\beta}} = \boldsymbol{\rho}'\mathbf{X}'\mathbf{y} \tag{12}$$

The estimate is the same function of the observations for any solution $\boldsymbol{\rho}$ of the equations $\mathbf{S}\boldsymbol{\rho} = \boldsymbol{\lambda}$. For let $\boldsymbol{\rho}_1$ be another solution of the equations; then this leads to the estimate

$$\boldsymbol{\rho}'_1\mathbf{X}'\mathbf{y}$$

The system of equations in $\hat{\boldsymbol{\beta}}$

$$\mathbf{S}\hat{\boldsymbol{\beta}} = \mathbf{X}'\mathbf{y}$$

is consistent, so that

$$\boldsymbol{\rho}'_1\mathbf{X}'\mathbf{y} = \boldsymbol{\rho}'_1\mathbf{S}\hat{\boldsymbol{\beta}} = \boldsymbol{\rho}'\mathbf{X}'\mathbf{y}$$

The variance of the estimate is

$$\begin{aligned}
E(\boldsymbol{\rho}'\mathbf{X}'\mathbf{ee}'\mathbf{X}\boldsymbol{\rho}) &= \sigma^2(\boldsymbol{\rho}'\mathbf{X}'\mathbf{X}\boldsymbol{\rho}) \\
&= \sigma^2(\boldsymbol{\rho}'\mathbf{S}\boldsymbol{\rho}) \\
&= \sigma^2\boldsymbol{\rho}'\boldsymbol{\lambda} \tag{13}
\end{aligned}$$

This, of course, is constant for all solutions $\boldsymbol{\rho}$ of $\mathbf{S}\boldsymbol{\rho} = \boldsymbol{\lambda}$, for, if $\mathbf{S}\boldsymbol{\rho}_1 = \boldsymbol{\lambda}$ also,

$$\boldsymbol{\rho}'\mathbf{S}\boldsymbol{\rho} = \boldsymbol{\rho}'\mathbf{S}\boldsymbol{\rho}_1 = \boldsymbol{\rho}'_1\mathbf{S}\boldsymbol{\rho}_1$$

The general procedure then for the hypothesis not of full rank is to write down the equations

$$\mathbf{S}\hat{\boldsymbol{\beta}} = \mathbf{X}'\mathbf{y}$$

If any linear combination of the left-hand sides of the equations, say $\boldsymbol{\rho}'\mathbf{S}\hat{\boldsymbol{\beta}}$, is equal to $\boldsymbol{\lambda}'\hat{\boldsymbol{\beta}}$, then the estimate of $\boldsymbol{\lambda}'\boldsymbol{\beta}$ is the same linear combination of the right-hand sides, and the variance of the estimate is equal to $\rho'\lambda\sigma^2$.

With the 2-way classification,

$$y_{ij} = \mu + b_i + t_j + e_{ij}; \qquad i = 1, 2, \cdots, r; \qquad j = 1, 2, \cdots, s$$

the equations $S\hat{\beta} = X'y$ are:

$$rs\hat{\mu} + s\hat{b}_1 + s\hat{b}_2 + \cdots + s\hat{b}_r + r\hat{t}_1 + r\hat{t}_2 + \cdots + r\hat{t}_s = Y_{..}$$

$$s\hat{\mu} + s\hat{b}_1 \qquad\qquad + \hat{t}_1 + \hat{t}_2 + \cdots + \hat{t}_s = Y_{1.}$$

$$s\hat{\mu} + \qquad s\hat{b}_2 \qquad + \hat{t}_1 + \hat{t}_2 + \cdots + \hat{t}_s = Y_{2.}$$

$$\cdots\cdots\cdots\cdots\cdots\cdots\cdots\cdots\cdots$$

$$r\hat{\mu} + \hat{b}_1 + \hat{b}_2 + \cdots + \hat{b}_r + r\hat{t}_1 \qquad\qquad = Y_{.1}$$

$$r\hat{\mu} + \hat{b}_1 + \hat{b}_2 + \cdots + \hat{b}_r + \qquad r\hat{t}_2 \qquad = Y_{.2}$$

$$\cdots\cdots\cdots\cdots\cdots\cdots\cdots\cdots\cdots$$

The estimate of $\hat{t}_1 - \hat{t}_2$ is then $\dfrac{1}{r}(Y_{.1} - Y_{.2})$, and the variance of the estimate is

$$\rho'\lambda\sigma^2 = \left(0, \overbrace{0, \cdots, 0}^{r \text{ times}}, \frac{1}{r}, -\frac{1}{r}, \overbrace{0, \cdots, 0}^{s-2 \text{ times}}\right) \begin{bmatrix} 0 \\ 0 \\ \vdots \\ \vdots \\ 0 \\ 1 \\ -1 \\ 0 \\ \vdots \\ \vdots \\ 0 \end{bmatrix} \left.\begin{array}{c} \\ \\ \\ \\ \end{array}\right\} r \text{ times} \qquad \sigma^2 = \frac{2}{r}\sigma^2 \qquad \left.\begin{array}{c} \\ \\ \\ \\ \end{array}\right\} (s-2) \text{ times}$$

Any linear function of the parameters $\lambda'\beta$, such that there exists a solution to the equations

$$S\rho = \lambda$$

may be said to be estimable. The condition that these equations have a solution is equivalent to the condition that

$$E(\rho'X'y) = \lambda'\beta$$

This states that there exists an estimate for any function of the parameters which is a linear function of the expectations of the observations. Clearly only such functions can be estimated by linear functions of the observations.

It is virtually obvious and may easily be proved that, for the hypothesis of rank r:

1. There exist only r linearly independent estimable functions.
2. Any reparametrization leads to the same estimate of an estimable function.
3. The best estimate of a linear function of estimable functions is the same linear function of the estimates of the estimable functions.
4. The hypothesis may be expressed as an hypothesis of full rank on a set of r linearly independent estimable functions.
5. It is possible to test hypotheses only about estimable functions.

Finally we need a definition of orthogonality of estimable functions. If $\lambda'_1\beta$ and $\lambda'_2\beta$ are estimable, their estimates are

$$\rho'_1 X'y \quad \text{and} \quad \rho'_2 X'y$$

The covariance of these estimates is

$$E(\rho'_1 X'ee'X\rho_2) = \sigma^2\rho'_1 S\rho_2$$
$$= \sigma^2(\rho'_1\lambda_2)$$

which is zero if $\rho'_1\lambda_2$ equals zero. Clearly any block comparison is orthogonal to any treatment comparison in the 2-way classification with equal numbers.

In addition there are certain invariance properties which hold and which enable the analysis of variance to be constructed easily by the imposition of linear conditions on the set of equations

$$S\hat{\beta} = X'y$$

If $\hat{\beta}$ is a solution of these equations, obtained by the imposition of any conditions, then $\hat{\beta}'S\hat{\beta}$ is invariant, for, if $\hat{\beta}_1$ and $\hat{\beta}_2$ are two solutions,

$$\hat{\beta}'_1 S\hat{\beta}_1 = \hat{\beta}'_1 S\hat{\beta}_2 = \hat{\beta}'_2 S\hat{\beta}_2$$

Also, since

$$y'y = (y - X\hat{\beta})'(y - X\hat{\beta}) + \hat{\beta}'S\hat{\beta}$$

and $y'y$ is clearly invariant, the quantity $(y - X\hat{\beta})'(y - X\hat{\beta})$ is invariant and is distributed as $\chi^2_{n-r}\sigma^2$. Invariance is also obvious from the fact that $X\beta$ is estimable, and therefore $X\hat{\beta}$ is unique.

It is possible only to test hypotheses about estimable functions. It is not, however, necessary to go through any algebra to obtain the tests, for, from Chapter 5, all we have to do is to find the minimum sum of squares of deviations under the various hypotheses, and this leads to the usual tests of significance.

For instance, in the 2-way classification, the hypothesis is H_0, that

$$y_{ij} = \mu + b_i + t_j + e_{ij}; \qquad i = 1, 2, \cdots, r; \qquad j = 1, 2, \cdots, s$$

We may test $t_j - t_{j'} = 0$, for all $j \neq j'$, since every $t_j - t_{j'}$ is estimable. The minimum sum of squares under H_0 is obtained by taking any solution of the normal equations derived by imposing linear restrictions on the estimates. This gives

$$\sum_{ij} (y_{ij} - y_i. - y._j + y..)^2 = Q_1$$

The minimum with the hypothesis under test H_1, say, that

$$y_{ij} = \mu + b_i + t + e_{ij}$$

is likewise obtained to be

$$\sum_{ij} (y_{ij} - y_i.)^2$$

which equals $Q_1 + Q_2$. (The notation for Q_1, Q_2 is that of the previous chapter.)

Therefore,

$$Q_2 = r \sum_j (y._j - y..)^2$$

and the F test is

$$\frac{Q_2}{s - 1} \bigg/ \frac{Q_1}{(r - 1)(s - 1)}$$

The most useful part of this exposition is the definition of an estimable function, its estimate, and the variance of the estimate. These we shall have occasion to use in several places throughout this book.

6.3 THE 2-WAY CLASSIFICATION WITH UNEQUAL NUMBERS AND NO INTERACTION

The model is

$$y_{ijk} = \mu + b_i + t_j + e_{ijk}; \qquad i = 1, 2, \cdots, r; \qquad j = 1, 2, \cdots, s \quad (14)$$

with the usual assumptions, and the number of observations in the (ij) cell is n_{ij}: i.e., the range of k is 0, 1, 2, $\cdots$, n_{ij}. We shall refer to the i classification as blocks and the j classification as treatments.

The normal equations are:

$$N_{..}\hat{\mu} + \sum_i N_{i.}\hat{b}_i + \sum_j N_{.j}\hat{t}_j = Y_{...}$$

$$N_{i.}\hat{\mu} + N_{i.}\hat{b}_i + \sum_j n_{ij}\hat{t}_j = Y_{i..} \qquad (15)$$

$$N_{.j}\hat{\mu} + \sum_i n_{ij}\hat{b}_i + N_{.j}\hat{t}_j = Y_{.j.}$$

As usual the replacement of a dot for a subscript letter indicates a total (capital letter) or a mean (small letter) over the possible values of the subscript. To solve these equations, we may determine each $(\mu + b_i)$ in terms of observational results and the t_j's, thus:

$$\hat{\mu} + \hat{b}_1 = \frac{1}{N_{1.}}\left(Y_{1..} - \sum_j n_{1j}\hat{t}_j\right)$$

$$\hat{\mu} + \hat{b}_2 = \frac{1}{N_{2.}}\left(Y_{2..} - \sum_j n_{2j}\hat{t}_j\right) \qquad (16)$$

and so on.

Substituting in the t equations, we get the equations,

$$\left(N_{.j} - \sum_i \frac{n^2_{ij}}{N_{i.}}\right)\hat{t}_j - \sum_{k \neq j}\left(\sum_i \frac{n_{ij}n_{ik}}{N_{i.}}\right)\hat{t}_k = Q_j \qquad (17)$$

where

$$Q_j = Y_{.j.} - \sum_i \frac{n_{ij}Y_{i..}}{N_{i.}} \qquad (18)$$

These equations are not independent, it being easily verified that the sum of left-hand and of right-hand sides are both identically zero. To obtain a unique solution we may impose any condition, the simplest one (generally) being $\qquad \Sigma\hat{t}_j = 0$

A convenient method of solving these equations is to augment the equations $\qquad \Sigma\lambda_{kj}\hat{t}_k = Q_j \qquad (17a)$

by introducing another unknown, say, z, and making up the set of equations:

$$\lambda_{11}\hat{t}_1 + \lambda_{12}\hat{t}_2 + \cdots + \lambda_{1s}\hat{t}_s + z = Q_1$$

$$\lambda_{21}\hat{t}_1 + \lambda_{22}\hat{t}_2 + \cdots + \lambda_{2s}\hat{t}_s + z = Q_2$$

$$\cdot\;\cdot\;\cdot\;\cdot\;\cdot\;\cdot\;\cdot\;\cdot\;\cdot\;\cdot\;\cdot\;\cdot\;\cdot\;\cdot \qquad (19)$$

$$\lambda_{s1}\hat{t}_1 + \lambda_{s2}\hat{t}_2 + \cdots + \lambda_{ss}\hat{t}_s + z = Q_s$$

$$\hat{t}_1 + \hat{t}_2 + \cdots + \hat{t}_s \qquad\quad = 0$$

Denoting the matrix of the coefficients by Λ, we find the inverse of Λ, say, C, and the solution of the equations is

$$
\begin{bmatrix} \hat{t}_1 \\ \hat{t}_2 \\ \cdot \\ \cdot \\ \hat{t}_s \\ z \end{bmatrix} = C \begin{bmatrix} Q_1 \\ Q_2 \\ \cdot \\ \cdot \\ Q_k \\ 0 \end{bmatrix} \tag{20}
$$

As a result of the imposition of the chosen condition, any $\hat{t}_i$ is the estimate, in fact, of $(t_i - \bar{t}.)$. This procedure is useful in that it produces as a by-product the variances and covariances of the $\hat{t}$'s, for the variance of $\hat{t}_i$ is $c_{ii}\sigma^2$ and the covariance of $\hat{t}_i$ and $\hat{t}_j$ is $c_{ij}\sigma^2$. As far as estimation is concerned, we now have to obtain estimates of μ, b_i which may be done by substitution back into the equations 15 and imposing the condition, say, that $\Sigma \hat{b}_i = 0$. The reduction in sum of squares due to fitting μ, b_i, and t_j is $R(\mu, b, t)$, which is given by

$$
R(\mu, b, t) = \hat{\mu} Y \ldots + \sum_i \hat{b}_i Y_i \ldots + \sum_j \hat{t}_j Y_{.j}.
$$

The residual mean square which equals

$$
\frac{1}{[N.. - (r + s - 1)]} \left[\sum_{ijk} y^2_{ijk} - R(\mu, b, t) \right]
$$

is an unbiased estimate of σ^2.

We now set up the two hypotheses,

$$
H_0 : y_{ijk} = \mu + b_i + t_j + e_{ijk}
$$

$$
H_1 : y_{ijk} = \mu + b_i + t + e_{ijk}
$$

and we may omit t in the H_1 equation. Under H_1 the normal equations lead to $\tilde{\mu} + \hat{b}_i = y_i..$, so that the reduction in sum of squares is

$$
R(\mu, b) = \sum_i \frac{Y^2_{i..}}{N_i.}
$$

The reduction in sum of squares due to fitting μ, b_i, and t_j, i.e., under H_0, is

$$
R(\mu, b, t) = \hat{\mu} Y \ldots + \sum_i \hat{b}_i Y_i \ldots + \sum_j \hat{t}_j Y_{.j}.
$$

and this equals

$$\sum_i (\hat{\mu} + \hat{b}_i)Y_i.. + \sum_j \hat{t}_j Y._j.$$

$$= \sum_i \frac{Y_i..}{N_i.} (Y_i.. - \sum_j n_{ij}\hat{t}_j) + \sum_j \hat{t}_j Y._j.$$

$$= \sum_i \frac{Y^2_i..}{N_i.} + \sum_j \hat{t}_j(Y._j. - \sum_i \frac{n_{ij}}{N_i.} Y_i..)$$

$$= y...Y... + \sum_i (y_i.. - y...)Y_i.. + \sum_j \hat{t}_j Q_j.$$

$$= R(\mu, b) + \sum_j \hat{t}_j Q_j$$

For testing treatments then, we have the analysis of variance shown in Table 6.2.

TABLE 6.2

Due to	df	Sum of Squares	Mean Square
Fitting μ, b_i	r	$\sum_i \frac{Y^2_i.}{N_i.}$	
Fitting t_j	$s - 1$	$\sum_j \hat{t}_j Q_j$	T
Error	$N.. - r - s + 1$	By subtraction	E
Total about zero	$N..$	$\sum_{ijk} y^2_{ijk}$	

The test of the hypothesis $t_j = t$ is made by comparing T/E with the appropriate F distribution.

An alternative form of the analysis of variance which is more frequently used is the one in Table 6.3.

TABLE 6.3

Due to	df	Sum of Squares	Mean Square
Blocks ignoring treatments	$r - 1$	$\sum_i \frac{Y^2_i..}{N_i.} - \frac{Y^2...}{N..}$	
Treatments eliminating blocks	$s - 1$	$\sum_j \hat{t}_j Q_j$	T
Error	$N.. - r - s + 1$	By subtraction	E
Total	$N.. - 1$	$\sum_{ijk} y^2_{ijk} - \frac{Y^2...}{N..}$	

The relationship between the two forms is obvious. It should be noted that the mean square for blocks ignoring treatments may not be used to test the hypothesis that $b_i = b$, because it will contain treatment effects. With orthogonality, of course, this is not the case.

6.3.1 A Numerical Example

For the benefit of the less mathematically minded reader, we will work through an example with artificial data in full.

Suppose the data are as shown in Table 6.4, being fleece weight of

TABLE 6.4

		Age in months			
		12	13	14	15
Type of birth	$j =$ \ $i =$	1	2	3	4
Single	1	8 7	8 9	10	
Twin	2	6 7	8 6		9

sheep. The model is

$$y_{ijk} = \mu + a_i + t_j + e_{ijk}$$

the e_{ij}'s being normally independently distributed around zero with the same variance σ^2. Then:

$$n_{11} = 2, \qquad n_{12} = 2, \qquad N_1. = 4$$

$$n_{21} = 2, \qquad n_{22} = 2, \qquad N_2. = 4$$

$$n_{31} = 1, \qquad n_{32} = 0, \qquad N_3. = 1$$

$$n_{41} = 0, \qquad n_{42} = 1, \qquad N_4. = 1$$

$$N._1 = 5, \qquad N._2 = 5, \qquad N.. = 10$$

$$Y_{11}. = 15, \qquad Y_{12}. = 13, \qquad Y_1.. = 28$$

$$Y_{21}. = 17, \qquad Y_{22}. = 14, \qquad Y_2.. = 31$$

$$Y_{31}. = 10, \qquad Y_{32}. = 0, \qquad Y_3.. = 10$$

$$Y_{41}. = 0, \qquad Y_{42}. = 9, \qquad Y_4.. = 9$$

$$Y._1. = 42, \qquad Y._2. = 36, \qquad Y... = 78$$

The normal equations are:

$$10\hat{\mu} + 4\hat{a}_1 + 4\hat{a}_2 + \hat{a}_3 + \hat{a}_4 + 5\hat{t}_1 + 5\hat{t}_2 = 78$$

$$4\hat{\mu} + 4\hat{a}_1 \qquad\qquad\qquad + 2\hat{t}_1 + 2\hat{t}_2 = 28$$

$$4\hat{\mu} \qquad + 4\hat{a}_2 \qquad\qquad + 2\hat{t}_1 + 2\hat{t}_2 = 31$$

$$\hat{\mu} \qquad\qquad + \hat{a}_3 \qquad + \hat{t}_1 \qquad = 10$$

$$\hat{\mu} \qquad\qquad\qquad + \hat{a}_4 \qquad + \hat{t}_2 = 9$$

$$5\hat{\mu} + 2\hat{a}_1 + 2\hat{a}_2 + \hat{a}_3 \qquad + 5\hat{t}_1 \qquad = 42$$

$$5\hat{\mu} + 2\hat{a}_1 + 2\hat{a}_2 \qquad + \hat{a}_4 \qquad + 5\hat{t}_2 = 36$$

or

$$
\begin{bmatrix}
10 & 4 & 4 & 1 & 1 & 5 & 5 \\
4 & 4 & 0 & 0 & 0 & 2 & 2 \\
4 & 0 & 4 & 0 & 0 & 2 & 2 \\
1 & 0 & 0 & 1 & 0 & 1 & 0 \\
1 & 0 & 0 & 0 & 1 & 0 & 1 \\
5 & 2 & 2 & 1 & 0 & 5 & 0 \\
5 & 2 & 2 & 0 & 1 & 0 & 5
\end{bmatrix}
\begin{bmatrix}
\hat{\mu} \\ \hat{a}_1 \\ \hat{a}_2 \\ \hat{a}_3 \\ \hat{a}_4 \\ \hat{t}_1 \\ \hat{t}_2
\end{bmatrix}
=
\begin{bmatrix}
78 \\ 28 \\ 31 \\ 10 \\ 9 \\ 42 \\ 36
\end{bmatrix}
$$

Substituting for $\hat{\mu} + \hat{a}_1$, $\hat{\mu} + \hat{a}_2$, $\cdots$, in the t equations, we get:

$$[5 - \tfrac{2}{4}^2 - \tfrac{2}{4}^2 - \tfrac{1}{1}^2 - \tfrac{0}{1}^2]\hat{t}_1 - (\tfrac{4}{4} + \tfrac{4}{4} + \tfrac{0}{1} + \tfrac{0}{1})\hat{t}_2 = Q_1$$

$$-(\tfrac{4}{4} + \tfrac{4}{4} + \tfrac{0}{1} + \tfrac{0}{1})\hat{t}_1 + [5 - \tfrac{2}{4}^2 - \tfrac{2}{4}^2 - \tfrac{0}{1}^2 - \tfrac{1}{1}^2]\hat{t}_2 = Q_2$$

where

$$Q_1 = Y_{\cdot 1 \cdot} - \frac{n_{11}}{N_{1 \cdot}} Y_{1 \cdot \cdot} - \frac{n_{21}}{N_{2 \cdot}} Y_{2 \cdot \cdot} - \frac{n_{31}}{N_{3 \cdot}} Y_{3 \cdot} - \frac{n_{41}}{N_{4 \cdot}} Y_{4 \cdot \cdot}$$

$$= 42 - \tfrac{2}{4} \times 28 - \tfrac{2}{4} \times 31 - \tfrac{1}{1} \times 10 - \tfrac{0}{1} \times 9$$

$$= 42 - 14 - 15.5 - 10 = 42 - 39.5 = 2.5$$

$$Q_2 = 36 - \tfrac{2}{4} \times 28 - \tfrac{2}{4} \times 31 - \tfrac{0}{1} \times 10 - \tfrac{1}{1} \times 9$$

$$= 36 - 14 - 15.5 - 9 = -2.5$$

So the t equations are

$$2\hat{t}_1 - 2\hat{t}_2 = 2.5$$

$$-2\hat{t}_1 + 2\hat{t}_2 = -2.5$$

The solution in this case is obvious: Imposing the condition,

$$\hat{t}_1 + \hat{t}_2 = 0 \quad \text{or} \quad \hat{t}_2 = -\hat{t}_1$$

we get

$$4\hat{t}_1 = 2.5$$

or

$$\hat{t}_1 = 0.625$$

So

$$\hat{t}_1 = 0.625$$

$$\hat{t}_2 = -0.625$$

Substituting back in the normal equations, we have:

$$4\hat{\mu} + 4\hat{a}_1 = 28 \quad \text{or} \quad \hat{\mu} + \hat{a}_1 = 7$$

$$4\hat{\mu} + 4\hat{a}_2 = 31 \quad \text{or} \quad \hat{\mu} + \hat{a}_2 = 7.75$$

$$\hat{\mu} + \hat{a}_3 = 9.375$$

$$\hat{\mu} + \hat{a}_4 = 9.625$$

Adding, we get

$$4\hat{\mu} + \hat{a}_1 + \hat{a}_2 + \hat{a}_3 + \hat{a}_4 = 33.75$$

and we then impose the condition

$$\hat{a}_1 + \hat{a}_2 + \hat{a}_3 + \hat{a}_4 = 0$$

This gives

$$\hat{\mu} = 8.4375$$

and then

$$\hat{a}_1 = -1.4375$$

$$\hat{a}_2 = -0.6875$$

$$\hat{a}_3 = 0.9375$$

$$\hat{a}_4 = 1.1875$$

It follows that

$$R(\mu, a, t) = 8.4375 \times 78 + (-1.4375) \times 28$$

$$+ \quad (-0.6875) \times 31 + 0.9375 \times 10$$

$$+ \quad 1.1875 \times 9 + 0.625 \times 42 + (-0.625) \times 36$$

$$= 620.375$$

The analysis of variance is then as shown in Table 6.5.

TABLE 6.5

Due to	df	Sum of Squares	Mean Square
Fitting constants for μ, a_i, t_j	5	620.375	
Remainder	5	3.625	0.725
Total	10	624	

The estimate of σ^2 is 0.725. Suppose now we wish to test the hypothesis: $t_1 = t_2$. We need to calculate the additional quantity, $\Sigma \hat{l}_j Q_j$. In this case it equals

$$0.625 \times 2.5 + (-0.625) \times (-2.5) = 3.125$$

As a check we may obtain

$$R(\mu, a) = \frac{1}{N_1.} Y^2_1.. + \frac{1}{N_2.} Y^2_2.. + \frac{1}{N_3.} Y^2_3.. + \frac{1}{N_4.} Y^2_4..$$

$$= (\tfrac{1}{4})28^2 + (\tfrac{1}{4})31^2 + (\tfrac{1}{1})10^2 + (\tfrac{1}{1})9^2$$

$$= 617.25$$

and note that
$$620.375 - 617.25 = 3.125$$

The analysis of variance for testing $t_1 = t_2$ is then as presented in Table 6.6.

TABLE 6.6

Due to	df	Sum of Squares	Mean Square
Fitting μ and a_i	4	617.25	
Difference	1	3.125	3.125
Fitting μ, a_i, t_j	5	620.375	
Remainder	5	3.625	0.725
Total	10	624.00	

We compare $F = 3.125/0.725$ with the F distribution with 1 and 5 degrees of freedom. A test for the hypothesis, $a_1 = a_2 = a_3 = a_4$ may be made similarly.

Finally, to exemplify the calculation of variances we augment the t equations to give us three equations:

$$2\hat{t}_1 - 2\hat{t}_2 + z = 2.5$$

$$-2\hat{t}_1 + 2\hat{t}_2 + z = -2.5$$

$$\hat{t}_1 + \hat{t}_2 \quad\;\; = 0$$

or, in matrix form,

$$\begin{bmatrix} 2 & -2 & 1 \\ -2 & 2 & 1 \\ 1 & 1 & 0 \end{bmatrix} \begin{bmatrix} t_1 \\ t_2 \\ z \end{bmatrix} = \begin{bmatrix} 2.5 \\ -2.5 \\ 0 \end{bmatrix}$$

The inverse of the matrix,

$$\begin{bmatrix} 2 & -2 & 1 \\ -2 & 2 & 1 \\ 1 & 1 & 0 \end{bmatrix}$$

is

$$\begin{bmatrix} \frac{1}{8} & -\frac{1}{8} & \frac{1}{2} \\ -\frac{1}{8} & \frac{1}{8} & \frac{1}{2} \\ \frac{1}{2} & \frac{1}{2} & 0 \end{bmatrix}$$

It follows then that

For $\hat{t}_1$, which, in fact, equals $\left(\hat{t}_1 - \dfrac{\hat{t}_1 + \hat{t}_2}{2}\right)$, the variance is $\frac{1}{8}\sigma^2$.

For $\hat{t}_2$, which, in fact, equals $\left(\hat{t}_2 - \dfrac{\hat{t}_1 + \hat{t}_2}{2}\right)$, the variance is $\frac{1}{8}\sigma^2$.

For $(\hat{t}_1 - \hat{t}_2)$, the variance is $[\frac{1}{8} + \frac{1}{8} - 2 \times (-\frac{1}{8})]\sigma^2 = \frac{1}{2}\sigma^2$.

The variance of $(\hat{t}_1 - \hat{t}_2)$ is estimated to be $\frac{1}{2}(0.725) = 0.362$. Our conclusion on the effect of type of birth is then that the difference is $\hat{t}_1 - \hat{t}_2 = 1.25 \pm 0.60$.

6.4 THE CASE OF PROPORTIONAL FREQUENCIES

In certain situations, for example, when a randomized block is replicated twice on one set of experimental material and three times on another set, the inequality of the frequencies may be of a special type: namely, that the n_{ij}'s may be expressed as kr_is_j, or, in words, that the frequencies are proportional. Under these circumstances we would have

$$N_{i\cdot} = kr_i S_\cdot \quad \text{where} \quad S_\cdot = \sum_j s_j$$

$$N_{\cdot j} = kR_\cdot s_j \quad \text{where} \quad R_\cdot = \sum_i r_i$$

and

$$N_{\cdot\cdot} = kR_\cdot S_\cdot.$$

The normal equations 15 then become:

$$kR_\cdot S_\cdot \hat{\mu} + kS_\cdot \left(\sum_i r_i \hat{b}_i\right) + kR_\cdot \left(\sum_j s_j \hat{t}_j\right) = Y_{\cdot\cdot\cdot}$$

$$kr_i S_\cdot \hat{\mu} + kr_i S_\cdot \hat{b}_i + kr_i \left(\sum_j s_j \hat{t}_j\right) \qquad = Y_{i\cdot\cdot} \qquad (15\text{a})$$

$$kR_\cdot s_j \hat{\mu} + ks_j \left(\sum_i r_i \hat{b}_i\right) + kR_\cdot s_j \hat{t}_j \qquad = Y_{\cdot j\cdot}$$

Imposition of the conditions,

$$\sum_i r_i \hat{b}_i = 0$$

$$\sum_j s_j \hat{t}_j = 0$$

leads immediately to the solution:

$$\hat{\mu} = y_{\cdot\cdot\cdot}$$

$$\hat{b}_i = y_{i\cdot\cdot} - y_{\cdot\cdot\cdot}$$

$$\hat{t}_j = y_{\cdot j\cdot} - y_{\cdot\cdot\cdot}$$

Orthogonality of the b's and t's now holds, and the analysis is easily completed.

6.5 MORE COMPLEX CLASSIFICATIONS

We shall deal below with a few other cases of the analysis of multiple classification data with unequal numbers. We shall also consider models with interaction. These cases do not occur very frequently when the experiment is completely under the control of the experimenter, but they do arise, for example, in genetical research. They are important for the student of experimental design also in that they provide examples of the change in the analysis and interpretation brought about by the inclusion of an interaction term in the model.

6.5.1   The 2-Way Classification with Interaction

The model that we will assume for this case is

$$y_{ijk} = \mu + a_i + t_j + h_{ij} + e_{ijk} \tag{21}$$

in which the terms μ, a_i, t_j are defined as before, and the term h_{ij} is a measure of the interaction contribution to individuals in the (i,j)th cell, and e_{ijk} is a deviation or error. Note that, with the non-interaction model:

$$y_{ijk} - y_{i'jk} = a_i - a_{i'} + \text{error}$$

$$y_{i'jk} - y_{i'j'k} = t_j - t_{j'} + \text{error}$$

and

$$y_{i'j'k} - y_{i'jk} - y_{ij'k} + y_{ijk}$$

$$= (\mu + a_{i'} + t_{j'}) - (\mu + a_{i'} + t_j) - (\mu + a_i + t_{j'})$$

$$+ (\mu + a_i + t_j) + \text{errors}$$

$$= 0 + \text{errors}$$

In the case of the new model,

$$y_{i'j'k} - y_{i'jk} - y_{ij'k} + y_{ijk} = h_{i'j'} - h_{i'j} - h_{ij'} + h_{ij} + \text{errors}$$

so that the effect of a change in the first classification (factor) depends on the level of the second classification (factor).

The estimation of effects and interactions proceeds as in previous cases. By assuming that the deviations e_{ijk} have an expectation of zero, have the same variance σ^2, and are uncorrelated, we may apply least squares. It is a simple matter to show that for this case the best estimate of the true cell mean, namely,

$$\mu + a_i + t_j + h_{ij}$$

is, in fact,

$$y_{ij\cdot} = \frac{Y_{ij\cdot}}{n_{ij}}$$

Any function of the true cell means is estimated by the corresponding function of the observed cell means.

The analysis of variance which provides an estimate of σ^2 is the well-known one (Table 6.7).

TABLE 6.7

Due to	df	Sum of Squares	Mean Square
Mean or correction	1	$\dfrac{Y^2\ldots}{N..}$	
Between cells	$rs - 1$	$\sum_{ij} \dfrac{Y^2_{ij.}}{n_{ij}} - \dfrac{Y^2\ldots}{N..}$	
Within cells	$N.. - rs$	$\sum_{ijk} (y_{ijk} - y_{ij.})^2$	E
Total	$N..$	$\sum_{ijk} y^2_{ijk}$	

The number of degrees of freedom for "between cells" will be $rs - 1$ if all the cells are occupied by at least one individual. Otherwise it is the number of occupied cells minus one. The mean square within cells, E, say, gives an unbiased estimate of σ^2. The variance of an observed cell mean is

$$\frac{\sigma^2}{n_{ij}}$$

which is estimated by E/n_{ij}. The variance of any linear function of the cell means may be obtained easily and, hence, the variance of any function of the parameters that can, in fact, be estimated.

As in all cases of a linear model, we test a hypothesis by obtaining the minimum sum of squares under the original hypothesis, and also under the hypothesis to be tested. The sum of squares removed with the hypothesis under test is $R(\mu, a, t)$.

We may then make up the subdivision of the analysis of variance shown in Table 6.8.

TABLE 6.8

Due to	df	Sum of Squares	Mean Square
Fitting μ, a_i, t_j	$r + s - 1$	$R(\mu, a, t)$	
Difference	$rs - r - s + 1$	Difference	I
Fitting μ, a_i, t_j and interaction	rs	Previous table	
Within cells	$N.. - rs$		E
Total	$N..$	$\sum_{ij} y^2_{ijk}$	

The test of zero interaction is to compare I/E with the F distribution with appropriate degrees of freedom.

Now to consider hypotheses about effects. It is necessary for us to be more specific about what we mean by effects when there are interactions than when there are not. When we wish to test the effects of the i classification, we must specify over what set of conditions given by the j classification we wish to consider this effect. We noted previously that the functions that could be estimated are the true cell means and, hence, any function of these true cell means. So we can consider the effects of the i classification averaged over the set of conditions given by the j classification, assuming these conditions occur equally frequently, or alternatively as they occurred in our data, or again according to some preassigned frequencies. There appear to be no difficulties once the set of conditions has been specified. In the presence of interaction, the existence of cells with no observations prevents the estimation of effects without further assumptions.

6.5.2   The General p-Way Classification without Interaction

In this case each individual is classified in n different ways, say, according to age, breed, year, sire, dam, and so on, if the observation unit is a cow, for example. We are assuming that there are no interactions, so that the model can be written

$$y_{ijkl}\cdots = \mu + a_i + b_j + c_k + d_l + \cdots + e_{ijkl}\cdots \qquad (22)$$

Here the effect of a change in position with regard to one classification is assumed to be the same, regardless of the position of the individual with respect to the other classifications. The contributions in the model have an interpretation similar to that for the 2-way classification. Again assuming that the e_{ijkl}'s have an expectation of zero, have the same variance σ^2, and are uncorrelated, we may use least squares.

With regard to notation we adopt the following rules: The last of the $(p + 1)$ subscripts on the symbol $y_{ijkl}\cdots$ will denote the order number of the individual in the cell given by $(i, j, k, \cdots)$. The number of individuals in this cell will be denoted by $n_{ijk}\cdots$, there being p subscripts. Sums over all the groups of a classification will be denoted by capital letters with the subscript for the classifications over which addition is performed replaced by a dot. Thus with a 4-way classification, we shall have y_{ijklm}, and m is the order number of the individual in the $(ijkl)$ class, there being n_{ijkl} individuals in this cell: the quantity $Y_{i\cdot k\cdot\cdot}$, for example, is equal to $\sum\limits_{j,l,m} y_{ijklm}$. The normal equations will be as follows

for the case of a 3-way classification with $i = 1, 2, \cdots, r$; $j = 1, 2, \cdots, s$; $k = 1, 2, \cdots, t$, only typical equations being given:
Equation for:

μ $N_{\cdots}\hat{\mu}+N_{1\cdots}\hat{a}_1 \quad +\cdots+N_{r\cdots}\hat{a}_r+N_{\cdot1\cdot}\hat{b}_1+\cdots+N_{\cdot s\cdot}\hat{b}_s$

$\qquad +N_{\cdot\cdot1}\hat{c}_1+\cdots+N_{\cdot\cdot t}\hat{c}_t \qquad = Y_{\cdots}$.

a_1 $N_{1\cdots}\hat{\mu}+N_{1\cdots}\hat{a}_1 \qquad +N_{11\cdot}\hat{b}_1+N_{12\cdot}\hat{b}_2+\cdots+N_{1s\cdot}\hat{b}_s$

$\qquad +N_{1\cdot1}\hat{c}_1+\cdots+N_{1\cdot t}\hat{c}_t \qquad = Y_{1\cdots}$

a_2 $N_{2\cdots}\hat{\mu} \qquad +N_{2\cdots}\hat{a}_2 \qquad +N_{21\cdot}\hat{b}_1+N_{22\cdot}\hat{b}_2+\cdots+N_{2s\cdot}\hat{b}_s$

$\qquad +N_{2\cdot1}\hat{c}_1+\cdots+N_{2\cdot t}\hat{c}_t \qquad = Y_{2\cdots}$

b_1 $N_{\cdot1\cdot}\hat{\mu}+N_{11\cdot}\hat{a}_1+N_{21\cdot}\hat{a}_2+\cdots+N_{r1\cdot}\hat{a}_r+N_{\cdot1\cdot}\hat{b}_1$ \hfill (23)

$\qquad +N_{\cdot11}\hat{c}_1+N_{\cdot12}\hat{c}_2+\cdots+N_{\cdot1t}\hat{c}_t = Y_{\cdot1\cdot}$

b_2 $N_{\cdot2\cdot}\hat{\mu}+N_{12\cdot}\hat{a}_1+N_{22\cdot}\hat{a}_2+\cdots+N_{r2\cdot}\hat{a}_r+N_{\cdot2\cdot}\hat{b}_2$

$\qquad +N_{\cdot21}\hat{c}_1+N_{\cdot22}\hat{c}_2+\cdots+N_{\cdot2t}\hat{c}_t = Y_{\cdot2\cdot}$

c_1 $N_{\cdot\cdot1}\hat{\mu}+N_{1\cdot1}\hat{a}_1+N_{2\cdot1}\hat{a}_2+\cdots+N_{r\cdot1}\hat{a}_r+N_{\cdot11}\hat{b}_1+N_{\cdot21}\hat{b}_2+\cdots+N_{\cdot s1}\hat{b}_s$

$\qquad +N_{\cdot\cdot1}\hat{c}_1 \qquad = Y_{\cdot\cdot1}$.

c_2 $N_{\cdot\cdot2}\hat{\mu}+N_{1\cdot2}\hat{a}_1+N_{2\cdot2}\hat{a}_2+\cdots+N_{r\cdot2}\hat{a}_r+N_{\cdot12}\hat{b}_1+N_{\cdot22}\hat{b}_2+\cdots+N_{\cdot s2}\hat{b}_s$

$\qquad +N_{\cdot\cdot2}\hat{c}_2 \qquad = Y_{\cdot\cdot2}$.

A procedure we may follow for solving the equations is the following. Let us suppose that r is greater than s or t. Then we may solve the a equations for $(\hat{\mu} + \hat{a}_i)$ in terms of the $\hat{b}$'s and $\hat{c}$'s. These expressions may be substituted in the b and c equations to give equations only in the $\hat{b}$'s and $\hat{c}$'s. These equations can then, if desired, be reduced further by solving for the $\hat{b}$'s in terms of the $\hat{c}$'s, and so on. Thus, for the above equations,

$$\hat{\mu} + \hat{a}_1 = \frac{1}{N_{1\cdots}} \left(Y_{1\cdots} - \sum_j N_{1j\cdot}\hat{b}_j - \sum_k N_{1\cdot k}\hat{c}_k\right)$$

$$\hat{\mu} + \hat{a}_2 = \frac{1}{N_{2\cdots}} \left(Y_{2\cdots} - \sum_j N_{2j\cdot}\hat{b}_j - \sum_k N_{2\cdot k}\hat{c}_k\right)$$

etc. So, substituting in the b_j equation, we get

$$\left(N_{\cdot j\cdot} - \sum_i \frac{N^2_{ij\cdot}}{N_{i\cdots}}\right)\hat{b}_j - \sum_{j'\neq j}\left(\sum_i \frac{N_{ij\cdot}\cdot N_{ij'\cdot}}{N_{i\cdots}}\right)\hat{b}_{j'}$$

$$+ \sum_k\left(N_{\cdot jk} - \sum_i \frac{N_{ij\cdot}\cdot N_{i\cdot k}}{N_{i\cdots}}\right)\hat{c}_k = Y_{\cdot j\cdot} - \sum_i \frac{N_{ij\cdot}}{N_{i\cdots}}Y_{i\cdots} \quad (24)$$

$$j = 1, 2, \cdots, s$$

Similarly, the equation for c_k becomes, on substitution for $(\hat{\mu} + \hat{a}_i)$ in terms of the $\hat{b}$'s and $\hat{c}$'s,

$$\sum_j \left(N_{\cdot jk} - \sum_i \frac{N_{ij} \cdot N_{i \cdot k}}{N_{i \cdot \cdot}} \right) \hat{b}_j + \left(N_{\cdot \cdot k} - \sum_i \frac{N^2_{i \cdot k}}{N_{i \cdot \cdot}} \right) \hat{c}_k$$

$$- \sum_{k' \neq k} \left(\sum_i \frac{N_{i \cdot k} N_{i \cdot k'}}{N_{i \cdot \cdot}} \right) \hat{c}_{k'} = Y_{\cdot \cdot k \cdot} - \sum_i \frac{N_{i \cdot k}}{N_{i \cdot \cdot}} Y_{i \cdot \cdot \cdot} \quad (25)$$

$$k = 1, 2, \cdots, t$$

By substituting in this fashion, we retain the symmetry present in the original equations: namely, that the coefficient of $\hat{c}_k$ in the b_j equation is equal to the coefficient of $\hat{b}_j$ in the c_k equation.

The next step could be done in the following way:

Consider the matrix of the coefficients of the b's in the b equations, namely:

$$N_{\cdot 1 \cdot} - \sum_i \frac{N^2_{i1 \cdot}}{N_{i \cdot \cdot}} \qquad - \sum_i \frac{N_{i1} \cdot N_{i2 \cdot}}{N_{i \cdot \cdot}} \quad \cdots \quad - \sum_i \frac{N_{i1} \cdot N_{is \cdot}}{N_{i \cdot \cdot}}$$

$$- \sum_i \frac{N_{i2} \cdot N_{i1 \cdot}}{N_{i \cdot \cdot}} \qquad N_{\cdot 2 \cdot} - \sum_i \frac{N^2_{i2 \cdot}}{N_{i \cdot \cdot}} \quad \cdots \quad - \sum_i \frac{N_{i2} \cdot N_{is \cdot}}{N_{i \cdot \cdot}}$$

$$\vdots \qquad\qquad \vdots \qquad\qquad \vdots$$

$$- \sum_i \frac{N_{is} \cdot N_{i1 \cdot}}{N_{i \cdot \cdot}} \qquad - \sum_i \frac{N_{is} \cdot N_{i2 \cdot}}{N_{i \cdot \cdot}} \quad \cdots \quad N_{\cdot s \cdot} - \sum_i \frac{N^2_{is \cdot}}{N_{i \cdot \cdot}}$$

Let us augment this matrix $\Lambda = (\lambda_{pq})$, say, $p, q = 1, 2, \cdots, s$, by adding a column of 1's and a row of 1's except for the $(s + 1, s + 1)$th element which is zero. Suppose this gives Λ', which is then

$$\Lambda' = \begin{bmatrix} N_{\cdot 1 \cdot} - \sum_i \frac{N^2_{i1 \cdot}}{N_{i \cdot \cdot}} & \cdots & - \sum_i \frac{N_{i1} \cdot N_{is \cdot}}{N_{i \cdot \cdot}} & 1 \\[2em] - \sum_i \frac{N_{i2} \cdot N_{i1 \cdot}}{N_{i \cdot \cdot}} & \cdots & - \sum_i \frac{N_{i2} \cdot N_{is \cdot}}{N_{i \cdot \cdot}} & 1 \\[2em] \vdots & \vdots & \vdots \\[2em] - \sum_i \frac{N_{is} \cdot N_{i1 \cdot}}{N_{i \cdot \cdot}} & \cdots & N_{\cdot s \cdot} - \sum_i \frac{N^2_{is \cdot}}{N_{i \cdot \cdot}} & 1 \\[2em] 1 & \cdots & 1 & 0 \end{bmatrix}$$

Let the inverse of this matrix which will be symmetrical be $\mathbf{D}$, where

$$
\mathbf{D} = \begin{bmatrix}
d_{11} & \cdots & d_{1s} & d_{1,s+1} \\
d_{21} & \cdots & d_{2s} & d_{2,s+1} \\
\cdot & \cdots & \cdot & \cdot \\
d_{s1} & \cdots & d_{ss} & d_{s,s+1} \\
d_{s+1,1} & \cdots & d_{s+1,s} & d_{s+1,s+1}
\end{bmatrix} \tag{26}
$$

Then

$$
\begin{bmatrix}
\hat{b}_1 \\
\hat{b}_2 \\
\cdot \\
\cdot \\
\hat{b}_s
\end{bmatrix} = \begin{bmatrix}
d_{11}d_{12} & \cdots & d_{1s} \\
\cdot & & \cdot \\
\cdot & & \cdot \\
d_{s1}d_{s2} & \cdots & d_{ss}
\end{bmatrix} \begin{bmatrix}
Y_{\cdot 1 \cdots} - \sum_i \dfrac{N_{ij\cdot}}{N_{i\cdot\cdot}} Y_{i\cdots} - \sum_k f_{1k}\hat{c}_k \\
\cdot \\
\cdot \\
Y_{\cdot s \cdots} - \sum_i \dfrac{N_{is\cdot}}{N_{i\cdot\cdot}} Y_{i\cdots} - \sum_k f_{sk}\hat{c}_k
\end{bmatrix} \tag{27}
$$

where f_{jk} is the matrix of coefficients of the c_k's in the b equations. We may then substitute for the $\hat{b}$'s in terms of the $\hat{c}$'s and known quantities in the equations for the $\hat{c}$'s, thus obtaining a set of t equations in the $\hat{c}$'s. These again may be solved by adding a row and a column of 1's except for the lowest diagonal element which is zero, giving, say, a matrix G. This matrix may be inverted to give, say, h_{uv}, u, $v = 1, 2, \cdots, t+1$, and the estimates obtained in the usual way. The variance-covariance matrix of the $\hat{c}_k$'s is

$$(h_{uv})\sigma^2$$

The other parameters may then be estimated by substitution.

The sum of squares attributable to μ, a_i, b_j, c_k is $R(\mu, a, b, c)$ equal to

$$\hat{\mu}Y_{\cdots} + \Sigma\hat{a}_i Y_{i\cdots} + \Sigma\hat{b}_j Y_{\cdot j\cdots} + \Sigma\hat{c}_k Y_{\cdot\cdot k\cdot}.$$

that is, the sum of products of the estimates and the right-hand sides of the normal equations.

The analysis of variance is then as shown in Table 6.9.

TABLE 6.9

Due to	df	Sum of Squares	Mean Square
Fitting constants for			
μ, a_i, b_j, c_k	$r + s + t - 2$	$R(\mu, a, b, c)$	
Remainder	$N_{\cdots} - r - s - t + 2$	By subtraction	E
Total	$N_{\cdots}$	$\sum_{ijkl} y^2_{ijkl}$	

The mean square E is an unbiased estimate of σ^2. Any estimate has an estimated variance obtained by replacing σ^2 in its true variance by E.

Suppose we wish to test the hypothesis that the c_k's are equal. We must assume as before that the e_{ijkl}'s are normally distributed, in addition to the previous assumptions. We fit the model in which the c_k's are replaced by a constant c (or put equal to zero). Thus, we fit the model

$$y_{ijkl} = \mu + a_i + b_j + e_{ijkl}$$

and obtain the sum of squares due to fitting constants for μ, a_i, and b_j, say, $R(\mu, a, b)$.

The analysis of variance is then as given in Table 6.10.

.TABLE 6.10

Due to	df	Sum of Squares	Mean Square
Fitting μ, a_i, b_j	$r + s - 1$	$R(\mu, a, b)$	
Difference	$t - 1$	By subtraction	C
Fitting μ, a_i, b_j, c_k	$r + s + t - 2$	$R(\mu, a, b, c)$	
Remainder	$N.. - r - s - t + 2$	By subtraction	E
Total	$N...$	$\sum_{ijkl} y^2_{ijkl}$	

The ratio C/E is compared with the F distribution with appropriate degrees of freedom. If the procedure given above for eliminating μ, a_i, and b_j from the c equations is followed and the right-hand sides of the resulting c equations are called $Q_1, \cdots, Q_t$, the sum of squares due to "difference" above is $\Sigma \hat{c}_k Q_k$.

Tests for the following hypotheses may be obtained in a similar way:

$$a_i = a, \qquad b_j = b, \qquad c_k = c$$

$$a_i = a, \qquad b_j = b$$

$$a_i = a, \qquad c_k = c$$

$$b_j = b, \qquad c_k = c$$

$$a_i = a$$

$$b_j = b$$

It is unfortunate that the computations for these tests have little in common, so that one has almost to start from scratch with each hypothesis to be tested.

Tests for hypotheses such as $b_1 = b_2$, without specifying the other b's may be obtained by the same process: i.e., obtaining the difference in sum of squares due to fitting the full model and the sum of squares due to fitting the adjusted model. The mean square of the difference is tested against E by the F test.

6.5.3   The Case of Missing Observations in Planned n-Way Classifications

In the case of the n-way classification for which the experimental plan called for one observation per cell, it will occasionally happen that the observations for a few cells are missing. In this case some special devices are available. We shall discuss the 2-way classification: e.g., blocks and treatments for illustrative purposes.

The treatment of a 2-way classification without interaction with single observations per cell except for some cells with missing observations is a simple case of the 2-way classification without interaction and with unequal numbers, for we take $n_{ij} = 0$ for the cells in which observations are missing and $n_{ij} = 1$ for the cells with an observation. This method is quite general providing, of course, that no classification is missing entirely, in which case the model and normal equations must be revised. If several observations are missing, the procedure given for solving a set of equations for the t's is best. Alternatively, if the number of block parameters is less than the number of treatment parameters, an analogous set of equations for the block parameters may be obtained and solved and then the treatment parameters estimated by substitution of these estimates in the treatment equations. It is necessary to assume that the missing observations do not arise as the result of factors whose effects we wish to estimate.

6.5.4   The Alternative Method of Analyzing Incomplete Experiments

When only a few observations are missing, a simple method of estimating the t_j's is available, providing that all treatments and blocks are represented. We insert algebraic symbols x, y, etc., for the missing observations and perform the usual analysis of variance, supposing that x, y, etc., are numbers. The remainder or error sum of squares may be evaluated, and it will be a function of x, y, etc., and their squares and products. Estimates of x, y, etc., are obtained by minimizing this sum of squares with regard to x, y, etc. The estimates of x, y, etc., obtained are inserted in the 2-way table and the marginal means calculated. The deviation of the ith treatment mean from the general mean of this augmented table is then equal to $\hat{t}_i$. Furthermore, the remainder sum of squares in the correct analysis of variance for the data as actually obtained is equal to the remainder sum of squares in the analysis of variance of the augmented table. It is then a simple matter to calculate the total sum of squares of the original observations, the sums of squares due to the mean, and to blocks after taking account of the mean, and thus complete the analysis of variance in the following way, k being the number of missing plots (Table 6.11).

TABLE 6.11. EXACT TEST OF SIGNIFICANCE FOR TREATMENT DIFFERENCES

Due to	df	Sum of Squares	Mean Square
Mean and blocks	r	$B = \Sigma \dfrac{(\text{block total})^2}{\text{no. in block}}$	
Treatments	$s - 1$	$T - E - B$ (obtain by difference)	
Mean, blocks, and treatments	$r + s - 1$	$T - E$ (obtain by difference)	
Remainder	$(r - 1)(s - 1) - k$	E (obtain from analysis of augmented data)	
Total	$rs - k$	$T = \Sigma y^2_{ij}$ (summing over actual observations only)	

The order of computation is:

1. Obtain T.
2. Obtain E.
3. Obtain $T - E$.
4. Obtain B.
5. Obtain $T - E - B$.

An approximate test of significance is obtainable from the analyses of the augmented values by treating the augmented table as the actual yields except that the degrees of freedom for the remainder are reduced by the number of missing observations. It can be verified that the treatment mean square has an expectation of the form $k_1\sigma^2 + r\sigma^2_t$, where k_1 is greater than unity. It is this latter fact that results in the bias of this test. Furthermore, the treatment sum of squares so obtained is not distributed as $\chi^2\sigma^2$ under the null hypothesis that the t_j's are zero, nor is it distributed independently of the error sum of squares. The approximate test may be obtained quickly and suggests when it is desirable to calculate the exact significance level, since the significance level indicated by the approximate test is, in general, too large (i.e., instead of, say, 10 percent, the test may indicate a 5 percent level of significance).

As a method of estimation of treatment effects and block effects, the substitution of algebraic values is generally the simpler operationally, but the matter depends on the number of missing plots. For example, in an experiment with 20 blocks of 4 treatments with, say, more than

5 missing plots, it is simpler to solve the normal equations for the 4-treatment parameters, t_1, t_2, t_3, and t_4.

6.5.5 Proof of Alternative Procedure for Missing Plots

Algebraically the alternative procedure consists of performing the analysis of variance on the model

$$y_{ij} = \mu + b_i + t_j + e_{ij} \quad \text{for plots present}$$

and

$$x_{ij} = \mu + b_i + t_j$$

if the observation in the (i, j)th cell is missing and we substitute x_{ij} for it.   The estimation procedure is to minimize the error sum of squares over the x_{ij}'s.   The error sum of squares is the minimum of

$$\Sigma(y_{ij} - \mu - b_i - t_j)^2 + \Sigma(x_{ij} - \mu - b_i - t_j)^2$$

Taking the minimum of this sum of squares with respect to μ, b_i, t_j, and x_{ij} is obviously equivalent to taking the minimum of

$$\Sigma(y_{ij} - \mu - b_i - t_j)^2$$

where summation is over cells for which observations are present, because the minimization over the x_{ij} gives merely

$$\hat{x}_{ij} = \hat{\mu} + \hat{b}_i + \hat{t}_j$$

This then identifies the procedure of Section 6.5.4 with the general procedure.   Clearly the best estimates of differences amongst the b_i's or the t_j's are given by the corresponding differences of the marginal means of the augmented table.

6.6   THE ANALYSIS OF COVARIANCE

The analysis of covariance may be incorporated simply in the least squares approach given in this and the previous chapter.   Consider the 2-way classification with one observation per cell and no interaction. Suppose we have also an attribute x subject to variation over the experimental area or units.   In the absence of treatment effects, we might set up the hypothesis

$$y_{ij} = \mu + b_i + \beta(x_{ij} - \bar{x}) + e_{ij}; \qquad i = 1, 2, \cdots, r$$
$$j = 1, 2, \cdots, s$$

and wish to test with the model

$$y_{ij} = \mu + b_i + \beta(x_{ij} - \bar{x}) + t_j + e_{ij} \qquad (28)$$

whether the t's could be equal. It is convenient to measure the x_{ij}'s about their mean $\bar{x}$. We suppose, as before, that $\Sigma b_i = 0$, as we have an arbitrary choice at our disposal. We wish to have an analysis of variance of the form shown in Table 6.12.

TABLE 6.12

Due to	df	Sum of Squares	Mean Square
μ, b_i, and β	$r + 1$	$R(\mu, b_i, \beta)$	
Treatments after μ, b_i, and β	$s - 1$	Difference	
μ, b_i, β, and t_j	$r + 1 + s - 1$	$R(\mu, b_i, \beta, t_j)$	
Residual	$rs - r - s$	Difference	
Total	rs	Σy^2_{ij}	

Our equations for estimating $\mu(= \mu + t)$, b_i, β when we ignore treatments (i.e., assuming the t_j's are equal to t), which estimates we denote by $\tilde{\mu}$, $\tilde{b}_i$ and $\tilde{\beta}$, are, using the conditions, $\Sigma \tilde{b}_i = 0$:

$$rs\tilde{\mu} = Y..$$
$$s\tilde{\mu} + s\tilde{b}_i + \tilde{\beta}\left[\sum_j (x_{ij} - \bar{x})\right] = Y_i. \tag{29}$$

$$\sum_i \tilde{b}_i \left[\sum_j (x_{ij} - \bar{x})\right] + \tilde{\beta}\left[\sum_{ij}(x_{ij} - \bar{x})^2\right] = \sum_{ij} y_{ij}(x_{ij} - \bar{x})$$

It follows that

$$\tilde{\mu} = Y../rs$$
$$s\tilde{b}_i + \tilde{\beta}\sum_j (x_{ij} - \bar{x}) = (Y_i. - Y../r) \tag{30}$$

or

$$\tilde{b}_i = \frac{1}{s}(Y_i. - Y../r) - \frac{\tilde{\beta}}{s}\sum_j (x_{ij} - \bar{x})$$

so

$$\sum_i \left[\frac{1}{s}(Y_i. - Y../r) - \frac{\tilde{\beta}}{s}\sum_j (x_{ij} - \bar{x})\right]\left[\sum_j (x_{ij} - \bar{x})\right] + \tilde{\beta}\sum_{ij}(x_{ij} - \bar{x})^2$$
$$= \sum_{ij} y_{ij}(x_{ij} - \bar{x})$$

and

$$\tilde{\beta}\left\{\sum_{ij}(x_{ij} - \bar{x})^2 - \frac{1}{s}\sum_i\left[\sum_j (x_{ij} - \bar{x})\right]^2\right\}$$
$$= \sum_{ij} y_{ij}(x_{ij} - \bar{x}) - \sum_i\left[\frac{1}{s}\left(Y_i. - \frac{Y..}{r}\right)\sum_j (x_{ij} - \bar{x})\right] \tag{31}$$

Similarly, with the model

$$y_{ij} = \mu + b_i + \beta(x_{ij} - \bar{x}) + t_j + e_{ij}$$

the equations are, using the conditions, $\Sigma \hat{b}_i = 0$, $\Sigma \hat{t}_j = 0$:

$$rs\hat{\mu} \hspace{7cm} = Y..$$

$$s\hat{\mu} + s\hat{b}_i + \hat{\beta} \sum_j (x_{ij} - \bar{x}) \hspace{3.5cm} = Y_i.$$

$$r\hat{\mu} + r\hat{t}_j + \hat{\beta} \sum_i (x_{ij} - \bar{x}) \hspace{3.5cm} = Y._j \hspace{1cm} (32)$$

$$\sum_i \hat{b}_i \sum_j (x_{ij} - \bar{x}) + \sum_j \hat{t}_j \sum_i (x_{ij} - \bar{x})$$
$$+ \hat{\beta} \sum_{ij} (x_{ij} - \bar{x})^2 = \sum_{ij} y_{ij}(x_{ij} - \bar{x})$$

where we use the circumflex ($\wedge$) to differentiate these estimates from the previous ones.   It will be found that

$$\hat{\beta} \left\{ \sum_{ij} (x_{ij} - \bar{x})^2 - \frac{1}{r} \sum_j \left[\sum_i (x_{ij} - \bar{x}) \right]^2 - \frac{1}{s} \sum_i \left[\sum_j (x_{ij} - \bar{x}) \right]^2 \right\}$$

$$= \sum_{ij} \left[y_{ij} - \frac{Y_i.}{s} - \frac{Y._j}{r} + \frac{Y..}{rs} \right] \left[x_{ij} - \frac{X_i.}{s} - \frac{X._j}{r} + \frac{X..}{rs} \right] \quad (33)$$

and that

$$\hat{t}_j = \frac{Y._j}{r} - \frac{Y..}{rs} - \frac{\hat{\beta}}{r} \sum_i (x_{ij} - \bar{x}) \hspace{2cm} (34)$$

To bring these formulas into the form of the analysis of covariance, suppose that analyses of variance on y and x and an analysis of the products yx are performed to give the information in Table 6.13.

TABLE 6.13

Due to	y^2	xy	x^2
Mean	$\dfrac{Y^2..}{rs}$	$\dfrac{Y..X..}{rs}$	$\dfrac{X^2..}{rs}$
b's	B_{yy}	B_{yx}	B_{xx}
t's	T_{yy}	T_{yx}	T_{xx}
Remainder	E_{yy}	E_{yx}	E_{xx}
Total	$\sum_{ij} y^2_{ij}$	$\sum_{ij} y_{ij}x_{ij}$	$\sum_{ij} x^2_{ij}$

The symbols are as follows:

$$X.. = \sum_{ij} x_{rs}$$

$$B_{yy} = \frac{1}{s} \Sigma Y^2_{i\cdot} - \frac{Y^2..}{rs}$$

$$B_{yx} = \frac{1}{s} \Sigma Y_{i\cdot} . X_{i\cdot} - \frac{Y..X..}{rs}$$

$$B_{xx} = \frac{1}{s} \Sigma X^2_{i\cdot} - \frac{X^2..}{rs}$$

$$T_{yy} = \frac{1}{r} \Sigma Y^2_{\cdot j} - \frac{Y^2..}{rs}$$

$$T_{yx} = \frac{1}{r} \Sigma Y_{\cdot j} X_{\cdot j} - \frac{Y..X..}{rs}$$

$$T_{xx} = \frac{1}{r} \Sigma X^2_{\cdot j} - \frac{X^2..}{rs}$$

E_{yy}, E_{yx}, and E_{xx} being obtained by subtraction. With the above notation,

$$\tilde{\beta} = \frac{T_{yx} + E_{yx}}{T_{xx} + E_{xx}}$$

and

$$\hat{\beta} = \frac{E_{yx}}{E_{xx}}$$

For the fitting of $\tilde{\mu}$, $\tilde{b}_i$, and $\tilde{\beta}$, we can obtain with some algebraic manipulation the breakdown of sum of squares (Table 6.14).

TABLE 6.14

Due to	df	Sum of Squares	Mean Square
$\tilde{\mu}$, $\tilde{b}_i$, and $\tilde{\beta}$	$r + 1$	Difference D_1	
Remainder	$rs - r - 1$	$T_{yy} + E_{yy} - \dfrac{(T_{yx} + E_{yx})^2}{T_{xx} + E_{xx}}$	
Total	rs	Σy^2_{ij}	

For the fitting of $\hat{\mu}$, $\hat{b}_i$, $\hat{\beta}$, and $\hat{t}_j$, we can obtain the breakdown of the sum of squares (Table 6.15).

TABLE 6.15

Due to	df	Sum of Squares	Mean Square
μ, b_i, β, t_j	$r + s$	Difference D_2	
Remainder	$rs - r - s$	$E_{yy} - \dfrac{E^2_{yx}}{E_{xx}}$	
Total	rs	$\sum\limits_{ij} y^2_{ij}$	

For the null hypothesis that the t_j's are zero, we may test the mean square

$$\frac{1}{s-1}(D_2 - D_1)$$
$$= \frac{1}{s-1}\left\{\left[(T_{yy} + E_{yy}) - \frac{(T_{yx} + E_{yx})^2}{T_{xx} + E_{xx}}\right] - \left(E_{yy} - \frac{E^2_{yx}}{E_{xx}}\right)\right\}$$

against the mean square

$$\frac{1}{rs - r - s}\left(E_{yy} - \frac{E^2_{yx}}{E_{xx}}\right)$$

by the F distribution with $(s - 1)$ and $(rs - r - s)$ degrees of freedom.

It should be noted that we no longer have orthogonality of the $\hat{b}_i$'s and $\hat{t}_j$'s and that $\hat{\beta}$ is not orthogonal to the $\hat{t}_j$'s. That the test of significance of the hypothesis $t_j = t$ is valid follows from the general linear hypothesis theory given earlier.

The estimates of the t_j's are

$$\hat{t}_j = \left(\frac{Y_{\cdot j}}{r} - \frac{Y_{\cdot\cdot}}{rs}\right) - \hat{\beta}\left(\frac{X_{\cdot j}}{r} - \frac{X_{\cdot\cdot}}{rs}\right)$$

Any treatment difference is estimated by

$$\hat{t}_j - \hat{t}_k = \frac{1}{r}[(Y_{\cdot j} - Y_{\cdot k}) - \hat{\beta}(X_{\cdot j} - X_{\cdot k})]$$

and has a variance of

$$\frac{2\sigma^2}{r} + \frac{\sigma^2}{r^2 E_{xx}}(X_{\cdot j} - X_{\cdot k})^2$$

Thus, every treatment difference has a different variance. For purposes of presentation, it is often satisfactory to attach to each mean ad-

justed by the regression a variance equal to half the average variance
for a difference of

$$\frac{\sigma^2}{r}\left(1 + \frac{1}{s-1}\frac{T_{xx}}{E_{xx}}\right) \tag{35}$$

where σ^2 is estimated by

$$\frac{1}{rs-r-s}\left(E_{yy} - \frac{E^2_{yx}}{E_{xx}}\right)$$

6.7 COMPONENTS OF VARIANCE

The analysis of variance by which effects in the multiple classification
are tested is of identical form with the analysis of variance used for an
analogous problem of sampling. We need to consider this matter because it will arise in connection with certain types of experiment.

Suppose for example that we have an infinite population which may
be classified in two ways and that we have one observation in each cell.
The observation in the (i, j)th cell is assumed to be

$$y_{ij} = \mu + b_i + t_j + e_{ij}; \qquad i = 1, 2, \cdots, r; \qquad j = 1, 2, \cdots, s$$

where the e_{ij}'s are distributed with common variance σ^2, the b_i's with
variance $\sigma^2{}_b$, and the t_j's with variance $\sigma^2{}_t$, and where the e_{ij}'s, b_i's, t_j's
are uncorrelated, and have zero means. (In some sampling problems
these have a mean of zero by definition.)

The analysis of variance may be used to estimate σ^2, $\sigma^2{}_b$, and $\sigma^2{}_t$ by
equating observed mean squares to expected mean squares as indicated
in Table 6.16.

TABLE 6.16

Due to	df	Sum of Squares	Expectation of Mean Square
b's	$r - 1$	$\Sigma \dfrac{Y^2_{i\cdot}}{s} - \dfrac{Y^2_{\cdot\cdot}}{rs}$	$\sigma^2 + s\sigma^2{}_b$
t's	$s - 1$	$\Sigma \dfrac{Y^2_{\cdot j}}{r} - \dfrac{Y^2_{\cdot\cdot}}{rs}$	$\sigma^2 + r\sigma^2{}_t$
Residual	$(r - 1)(s - 1)$	Difference	σ^2
Total	$rs - 1$	$\Sigma y^2_{ij} - \dfrac{Y^2_{\cdot\cdot}}{rs}$	

The important point to note is that it is not necessary to make any
assumptions about the distributions of the e_{ij}'s, b_i's, t_j's except that
they are uncorrelated. To make tests of significance of differences of

$\sigma^2{}_b$ and $\sigma^2{}_t$ from zero, however, normal independent distributions of the e_{ij}'s are necessary.

In the general problem of the estimation of components of variance there are essentially two cases:

1. The hierarchal classification.
2. The multiple classification of the type we have been discussing in the early part of the present chapter.

We shall give a brief discussion of these cases and leave a mixture of the two cases for the reader to examine, except for a few cases of importance to experimental design.

6.7.1 The Hierarchal Classification

The simplest case is that of a 1-fold classification: say, individuals by families or observations by individual. The model used is the following:

$$y_{ij} = \mu + a_i + e_{ij}; \qquad i = 1, 2, \cdots, r$$

that is, that the observation for the jth individual in the ith group is made up of a portion μ common to all observations, a contribution a_i common to all individuals of the ith group, and a deviation e_{ij} particular to the jth individual of the ith group. By definition then, the expectation of any e_{ij} is zero. We assume that the e_{ij}'s have the same variance σ^2 and are uncorrelated. Suppose also that the a_i's are a random sample from a population with variance $\sigma^2{}_a$. Let the number in the ith group be n_i. We may then obtain estimates of μ, a_i as if they were fixed effects and construct the analysis of variance (Table 6.17), where

$$k = \frac{1}{r-1}\left(N. - \frac{\Sigma n^2{}_i}{N.}\right)$$

TABLE 6.17

Due to	df	Sum of Squares	Mean Square	Expectation of Mean Square
Fitting μ	1	$\dfrac{Y^2..}{N.}$		
Difference	$r-1$	Difference	A	$\sigma^2 + k\sigma^2{}_a$
Fitting μ, a_t	r	$\sum_i \dfrac{Y^2{}_{i\cdot}}{n_i}$		
Remainder	$N. - r$	By subtraction *	E	σ^2
Total	$N.$	$\sum_{ij} y^2{}_{ij}$		

* Equals sum of squares within groups.

The expectation of the sum of squares denoted by "difference" above is, in fact, the expectation of the sum of squares between families: i.e., of

$$\sum_i n_i (y_i. - y..)^2$$

Now,

$$y_i. = \mu + a_i + e_i.$$

$$y.. = \mu + \frac{\sum_i n_i a_i}{N.} + e..$$

so

$$y_i. - y.. = \left(a_i - \frac{\sum_i n_i a_i}{N.}\right) + e_i. - e..$$

$$= \frac{N. - n_i}{N.} a_i - \sum_{i' \neq i} \frac{n_{i'}}{N.} a_{i'}$$

$$+ \left(\frac{1}{n_i} - \frac{1}{N.}\right) \sum_j e_{ij} - \frac{1}{N.} \sum_{i' \neq i} \sum_j e_{i'j}$$

The expectation of the square of $(y_i. - y..)$ is then

$$\left[\left(\frac{N. - n_i}{N.}\right)^2 + \sum_{i' \neq i} \frac{n^2_{i'}}{N^2.}\right] \sigma^2_a + \left[n_i \frac{(N. - n_i)^2}{N^2.n^2_i} + \frac{(N. - n_i)}{N^2.}\right] \sigma^2$$

$$= \left(1 - \frac{2n_i}{N.} + \sum_i \frac{n^2_i}{N^2.}\right) \sigma^2_a + \frac{N. - n_i}{N.n_i} \sigma^2$$

Multiplying by n_i and adding over i, we get

$$\left[\sum_i n_i - 2\frac{\Sigma n^2_i}{N.} + \frac{(\Sigma n_i)\left(\sum_i n^2_i\right)}{N^2.}\right] \sigma^2_a + \sum_i \frac{N. - n_i}{N.} \sigma^2$$

$$= \left(N. - 2\frac{\Sigma n^2_i}{N.} + \frac{\Sigma n^2_i}{N.}\right) \sigma^2_a + (r - 1)\sigma^2$$

Dividing by $(r - 1)$ we find that the mean square has expectation

$$\sigma^2 + \frac{1}{r - 1}\left(N. - \sum_i \frac{n^2_i}{N.}\right) \sigma^2_a = \sigma^2 + k\sigma^2_a \qquad (36)$$

As unbiased estimates of σ^2 and σ^2_a, we may then use

$$\hat{\sigma}^2 = E$$

$$\hat{\sigma}^2_a = \frac{1}{k}(A - E)$$

In general, we shall also wish to have sampling errors of these estimates. The variance of these estimates may be obtained exactly in terms of the cumulants of the true parent populations. See for instance Kendall.[1]

For example, if the e_{ij}'s are independent, the variance of $\hat{\sigma}^2$ is

$$\frac{N. - r + \Sigma \dfrac{1}{n_i}}{(N. - r)^2} K_4 + 2 \frac{K^2_2}{(N. - r)}$$

where K_2, K_4 are, respectively, the second and fourth cumulant of the distribution of the e_{ij}'s. The formula for the variance of $\hat{\sigma}^2_a$ is more difficult to obtain, though the difficulty is entirely one of algebra.

If we make the assumptions that e_{ij} and a_i are normally distributed, then

$$\text{var} (\hat{\sigma}^2) = 2 \frac{\sigma^4}{n - 1}$$

and may be estimated unbiasedly by

$$2 \frac{(\hat{\sigma}^2)^2}{n + 1}$$

where $n - 1$ is the number of degrees of freedom for the remainder. If the n_i's are all equal to k, say (so that k above equals this k),

$$\text{var} (\sigma^2 \hat{+} k\sigma^2_a) = 2 \frac{(\sigma^2 + k\sigma^2_a)^2}{r - 1}$$

Furthermore, $\hat{\sigma}^2$ and $(\sigma^2 \hat{+} k\sigma^2_a)$ are independent, so that

$$\text{var} [(\sigma^2 \hat{+} k\sigma^2_a) - \hat{\sigma}^2] = \text{var} (\sigma^2 \hat{+} k\sigma^2_a) + \text{var} (\hat{\sigma}^2)$$

or

$$k^2 \text{var} (\hat{\sigma}^2_a). = 2 \frac{(\sigma^2 + k\sigma^2_a)^2}{r - 1} + 2 \frac{\sigma^4}{n - 1}$$

As an example of the use of these formulas, let us suppose that we are dealing, in fact, with material for which $\sigma^2 = 1.0$ and $\sigma^2_a = 1.0$. Then,

$$\text{var} (\hat{\sigma}^2) = \frac{2}{n - 1}$$

and

$$k^2 \text{var} (\hat{\sigma}^2_a) = 2 \frac{(1 + k)^2}{r - 1} + \frac{2}{n - 1}$$

Let
$$k = 5, \qquad r = 10$$
then
$$n - 1 = r(k - 1) = 40$$
and
$$\text{var } (\hat{\sigma}^2) = \frac{2}{40} \quad \text{or} \quad \text{SE } (\hat{\sigma}^2) = 0.22$$
and
$$\text{var } (\hat{\sigma}^2{}_a) = \frac{1}{25} \left(\frac{2 \times 36}{9} + \frac{2}{40} \right)$$
$$= 0.32$$
so that
$$\text{SE}(\hat{\sigma}^2{}_a) = 0.55$$

It is clear that the number of observations given by k and r is completely inadequate for this situation.

In the case of unequal numbers, corresponding results can be obtained after a lot of simple but laborious algebra.

6.7.2 The n-Fold Hierarchal Classification

We shall deal first with the case of equal numbers and suppose that we have groups A (a in all), groups B (b for each A group) within A, groups C (c for each B group) within groups B, and so on. We use the model

$$y_{ijk} = \mu + a_i + b_{ij} + c_{ijk} + \cdots + e_{ijk}\ldots$$

where

$$E(e_{ijk}\ldots) = 0, \quad E(a_i) = 0, \quad E(b_{ij}) = 0, \quad \text{etc.,}$$
$$E(a^2{}_i) = \sigma^2{}_a, \quad E(b^2{}_{ij}) = \sigma^2{}_b, \quad \text{etc.}$$

and all the terms are uncorrelated. This leads to the analysis of variance (Table 6.18) with groups A, B, C, D, and e individuals per ultimate D group.

TABLE 6.18

	df	Mean Square	Expectation of Mean Square
Between A groups	$a - 1$	A	$\sigma^2 + e\sigma^2{}_d + de\sigma^2{}_c + cde\sigma^2{}_b + bcde\sigma^2{}_a$
Between B groups within A groups	$a(b - 1)$	B	$\sigma^2 + e\sigma^2{}_d + de\sigma^2{}_c + cde\sigma^2{}_b$
Between C groups within B groups	$ab(c - 1)$	C	$\sigma^2 + e\sigma^2{}_d + de\sigma^2{}_c$
Between D groups within C groups	$abc(d - 1)$	D	$\sigma^2 + e\sigma^2{}_d$
Error	$abcd(e - 1)$	E	σ^2
Total (about mean)	$abcde - 1$		

The sums of squares are easily obtained.   The estimates of the components of variance are given by the linear functions of the mean squares the expectation of which is equal to the desired component.   If the residuals, the a_i's, the b_{ij}'s, etc., are normally and independently distributed, the mean squares are independently distributed.   The variance of each mean square is equal to

$$2 \frac{\text{(expectation of mean square)}^2}{\text{degrees of freedom}}$$

and these variances may be combined in the usual way to obtain the variance of a linear function.

In the case of unequal numbers the situation is more complex.   The analysis of variance has the same formal structure as before, the degrees of freedom depending on the number of individuals in each ultimate group.   It is possibly best obtained in a step-wise manner: Obtain the sum of squares within the ultimate groups, which is used as computed, then obtain the sum of squares within the penultimate groups, and obtain the sum of squares between ultimate groups by subtracting the former from the latter, and so on.

We shall take a 2-fold hierarchal classification as an example, the model being

$$y_{ijk} = \mu + a_i + b_{ij} + e_{ijk}$$

with

$$i = 1, 2, \cdots, \alpha$$

$$j = 1, 2, \cdots, \beta_i$$

$$k = 1, 2, \cdots, n_{ij}$$

The sums of squares are:

Within B groups: $\sum_{ijk} (y_{ijk} - y_{ij\cdot})^2$ with df $\sum_{ij} (n_{ij} - 1)$

Between B groups within A groups:

$$\sum_{ij} n_{ij}(y_{ij\cdot} - y_{i\cdot\cdot})^2 \text{ with df } \sum_{i} (\beta_i - 1)$$

Between A groups: $\sum_{i} N_{i\cdot}(y_{i\cdot\cdot} - y_{\cdots})^2$ with df $(\alpha - 1)$

The expectation of the within B groups sum of squares is easily verified to be equal to

$$\left[\sum_{ij} (n_{ij} - 1) \right] \sigma^2$$

By an argument identical to that for the 1-fold classification, the expectation of the sum of squares between B groups is

$$\left[\sum_i (\beta_i - 1)\right] \sigma^2 + \left(N.. - \sum_i \frac{\sum_j n^2_{ij}}{N_i.}\right) \sigma^2_b$$

The sum of squares between the A groups may be written

$$\sum_i \left(\frac{Y^2_i..}{N_i.}\right) - \frac{Y^2...}{N..}$$

Now,

$$y_{ijk} = \mu + a_i + b_{ij} + e_{ijk}$$

$$Y_{ij.} = n_{ij}\mu + n_{ij}a_i + n_{ij}b_{ij} + \sum_k e_{ijk}$$

$$Y_{i..} = N_i.\mu + N_i.a_i + \sum_j n_{ij}b_{ij} + \sum_{jk} e_{ijk}$$

$$\therefore E(Y^2_i..) = N^2_i.\mu^2 + N^2_i.\sigma^2_a + \left(\sum_j n^2_{ij}\right)\sigma^2_b + N_i.\sigma^2$$

Also

$$Y... = N..\mu + \Sigma N_i.a_i + \sum_{ij} n_{ij}b_{ij} + \sum_{ijk} e_{ijk}$$

$$\therefore E(Y^2...) = N^2..\mu^2 + (\Sigma N^2_i.)\sigma^2_a + \left(\sum_{ij} n^2_{ij}\right)\sigma^2_b + N..\sigma^2$$

The expectation of the sum of squares between A groups is then

$$\sum_i \left[N_i.\mu^2 + N_i.\sigma^2_a + \left(\frac{\sum_j n^2_{ij}}{N_i.}\right)\sigma^2_b + \sigma^2\right]$$

$$- \left[N..\mu^2 + \left(\frac{\Sigma N^2_i.}{N..}\right)\sigma^2_a + \left(\frac{\sum_{i,j} n^2_{ij}}{N..}\right)\sigma^2_b + \sigma^2\right]$$

which equals

$$(\alpha - 1)\sigma^2 + \left[\sum_i \left(\frac{\sum_j n^2_{ij}}{N_i.}\right) - \frac{\sum_{ij} n^2_{ij}}{N..}\right]\sigma^2_b + \left(N.. - \frac{\sum_i N^2_i.}{N..}\right)\sigma^2_a$$

This must be divided by $(\alpha - 1)$ to give the expectation of the mean square.

This process may be extended indefinitely with little difficulty. We have then dealt with the case of hierarchal classifications. Aspects that we have not considered are:

1. The variances of the estimates of components: This will proceed

in the usual way by virtue of the fact that the estimates are always quadratic functions of the observations.

2. The effect of inadequacies in the model: For instance, the variance of the e_{ijk}'s may change from one class to another. Again it is a matter of algebra, though somewhat tedious, to evaluate the expectations under some other model. It should be noted that the model includes not only the linear equation

$$y_{ijk} = \mu + a_i + b_{ij} + \text{etc.}$$

but also the statement of distributional properties of the quantities on the right-hand side of the equation.

These problems are virtually unsolved at the present time, though the procedure to be followed is simple. It is to be hoped that some progress will be made on them.

6.7.3   The Case of n-Way Classifications

The situation now becomes very complex. In fact there appears to be practically no theory at all on which to base the estimation in the general non-orthogonal case. As a beginning let us state the results for the orthogonal case: namely, when an equal number of observations, say, n, occurs in each cell of the classification.

Suppose that we have the model:

$$y_{ijkl} = \mu + a_i + b_j + c_k + e_{ijk}$$

$$i = 1, 2, \cdots, r$$

$$j = 1, 2, \cdots, s$$

$$k = 1, 2, \cdots, t$$

$$l = 1, 2, \cdots, n$$

With equal frequencies we obtain a simple procedure by the analysis of variance (Table 6.19).

TABLE 6.19

Due to	df	Sum of Squares	Expectation of Mean Square
Mean μ	1	$\dfrac{Y^2\cdots}{N\cdots}$	
Differences among a_i	$r - 1$	$S(a)$	$\sigma^2 + nst\sigma^2_a$
Differences among b_j	$s - 1$	$S(b)$	$\sigma^2 + nrt\sigma^2_b$
Differences among c_k	$t - 1$	$S(c)$	$\sigma^2 + nrs\sigma^2_c$
Remainder	$N.. - r - s - t + 2$	By subtraction	σ^2
Total	$N..(= nrst)$	$\sum_{ijkl} y^2_{ijkl}$	

Estimates of σ^2_a, σ^2_b, etc., may be obtained from the mean squares by equating observed and expected mean squares, and the estimated variances of the estimates are now given exactly, if normality holds, by the fact that

$$\text{var (mean square)} = 2\,\frac{(\text{true mean square})^2}{\text{degrees of freedom}}$$

The estimated variance of the estimate is obtained by substituting the observed mean square for the true mean square, and a divisor equal to (degrees of freedom $+ 2$). The true variances may be combined in the usual manner for the variance of a linear function. It should be noted that the combination of estimated variances raises some difficult problems, analogous to the Behrens-Fisher problem.

In a similar fashion one can write down the analysis of variance for the n-way classification with all possible interactions included: that is, for the model,

$$y_{ijkl} = \mu + a_i + b_j + (ab)_{ij} + c_k + (ac)_{ik} + (bc)_{jk} + (abc)_{ijk} + e_{ijkl}$$

$$i = 1, \cdots, r; \quad j = 1, \cdots, s; \quad k = 1, \cdots, t; \quad l = 1, \cdots, n$$

everything except μ having expectation zero, variances of the a_i's equal to σ^2_a, etc., of the $(ab)_{ij}$'s equal to σ^2_{ab}, etc., and all these random variables being uncorrelated (Table 6.20).

TABLE 6.20

Due to	df	Expectation of Mean Square
μ	1	
a	$r - 1$	$\sigma^2 + n\sigma^2_{abc} + nt\sigma^2_{ab} + ns\sigma^2_{ac} + nst\sigma^2_a$
b	$s - 1$	$\sigma^2 + n\sigma^2_{abc} + nt\sigma^2_{ab} + nr\sigma^2_{bc} + nrt\sigma^2_b$
(ab)	$(r-1)(s-1)$	$\sigma^2 + n\sigma^2_{abc} + nt\sigma^2_{ab}$
c	$t - 1$	$\sigma^2 + n\sigma^2_{abc} + ns\sigma^2_{ac} + nr\sigma^2_{bc} + nrs\sigma^2_c$
(ac)	$(r-1)(t-1)$	$\sigma^2 + n\sigma^2_{abc} + ns\sigma^2_{ac}$
(bc)	$(s-1)(t-1)$	$\sigma^2 + n\sigma^2_{abc} + nr\sigma^2_{bc}$
(abc)	$(r-1)(s-1)(t-1)$	$\sigma^2 + n\sigma^2_{abc}$
Remainder	$rst(n-1)$	σ^2
Total	$nrst$	

These expectations should be verified by the reader. The estimation of the components is again straightforward.

In the case of unequal frequencies, we can regard the terms in the model apart from the error term as being unknown constants and make up the analysis of variance described earlier in this chapter. If we could obtain the expectation of the mean squares in terms of variance components, the "constants" now being random variables, we could estimate the components by equating observed mean squares to expected mean squares and solving the resulting equations, which will be linear in the components.

As an example we will consider the 2-way classification with no interactions. In that case we make the analysis of variance, in which items obtained by subtraction are marked + (Table 6.21).

TABLE 6.21

Due to	df	Sum of Squares	Mean Square
μ	1	$R(\mu)$	
Difference	$r-1$	+	A
μ and a_i	r	$R(\mu, a)$	
Difference	$s-1$	+	B
μ, a_i, b_j	$r+s-1$	$R(\mu, a, b)$	
Remainder	$N.. - r - s + 1$	+	E
Total	$N..$	$\sum_{ijk} y^2{}_{ijk}$	

The expectation:

Of E is σ^2

Of B is $\sigma^2 + \dfrac{1}{s-1} \sum_j \left(N_{\cdot j} - \sum_i \dfrac{n^2{}_{ij}}{N_{i\cdot}} \right) \sigma^2{}_b = \sigma^2 + k_1 \sigma^2{}_b$

Of A is $\sigma^2 + k_2 \sigma^2{}_b + k_3 \sigma^2{}_a$

where

$$k_2 = \frac{1}{r-1} \left(\sum_j \sum_i \frac{n^2{}_{ij}}{N_{i\cdot}} - \sum_j \frac{N^2{}_{\cdot j}}{N..} \right)$$

$$k_3 = \frac{1}{r-1} \left(N.. - \frac{\sum_i N^2{}_{i\cdot}}{N..} \right)$$

So, to estimate σ^2, $\sigma^2{}_b$, and $\sigma^2{}_a$, we could solve the equations:

$$E = \hat{\sigma}^2$$

$$B = \hat{\sigma}^2 + k_1 \hat{\sigma}^2{}_b$$

$$A = \hat{\sigma}^2 + k_2 \hat{\sigma}^2{}_b + k_3 \hat{\sigma}^2{}_a$$

More complex cases have possibly been worked out, but the author has not found such in the literature.

Problems yet to be solved are:

1. The variance of estimates obtained in this way.

2. The efficiency of various estimation procedures: We should consider the estimation by obtaining sums of squares for each classification, which will not be orthogonal to each other, and equating observed values to expectations.

6.8 AN EXAMPLE OF THE ESTIMATION OF COMPONENTS OF VARIANCE IN A GENETIC PROBLEM

We conclude with a less common problem in the estimation of components of variance as an example of method. Suppose that we have a set of p inbred lines and make all possible *crosses* among these lines, using each as a male and a female parent. It is reasonable from some genetic points of view to assume the model

$$y_{ijk} = \mu + g_i + g_j + s_{ij} + r_{ij} + e_{ijk}$$

where

y_{ijk} = the observation of the kth offspring of line i as male and line j as female parent

μ = a contribution common to all observations

g_i = a contribution particular to line i

s_{ij} = a contribution particular to the cross of line i and line j, such that $s_{ji} = s_{ij}$

r_{ij} = a contribution arising from the difference between using line i as male and line j as a female parent rather than vice-versa, and is such that $r_{ij} = -r_{ji}$

e_{ijk} = a random deviation

It is assumed that we are dealing with a sample of lines from a population and that the e_{ijk}'s are uncorrelated, with mean zero and constant variance σ^2. The terms g_i, s_{ij}, r_{ij} are assumed to be random variables with mean zero and variance σ^2_g, σ^2_s, and σ^2_r, respectively. The aim is to estimate σ^2, σ^2_g, σ^2_s, and σ^2_r. We assume also that there are n offspring from each possible cross.

Our estimation procedure will be to regard the g_i's, s_{ij}'s, and r_{ij}'s as fixed variables and construct an analysis of variance. We shall then take expectations of mean squares in this analysis and equate them to the observed values. The estimates of μ, g_1, g_2, $\cdots$, s_{ij}, r_{ij} are obtained by minimizing the sum of squares:

$$\Sigma(y_{ijk} - \mu - g_i - g_j - s_{ij} - r_{ij})^2$$

The equations are:

$$p(p-1)n\hat{\mu} + 2(p-1)n\sum_i \hat{g}_i + 2n\sum_{\substack{ij \\ i<j}} \hat{s}_{ij} = Y\dots$$

$$2(p-1)n\hat{\mu} + 2(p-1)n\hat{g}_i + 2n\sum_{i'\neq i} \hat{g}_{i'} + 2n\sum_{\substack{j \\ j\neq i}} \hat{s}_{ij} = Y_{i}.. + Y_{\cdot i}.$$

$$2n\hat{\mu} + 2n\hat{g}_i + 2n\hat{g}_j + 2n\hat{s}_{ij} = Y_{ij\cdot} + Y_{ji\cdot}$$

$$2n\hat{r}_{ij} = Y_{ij\cdot} - Y_{ji\cdot}.$$

To obtain a solution, we impose the conditions,

$$\sum_i \hat{g}_i = 0, \qquad \sum_j \hat{s}_{ij} = 0 \quad \text{for each } i$$

The solutions to these equations are then

$$\hat{r}_{ij} = \frac{Y_{ij\cdot} - Y_{ji\cdot}}{2n}$$

$$\hat{\mu} = \frac{Y\dots}{np(p-1)}$$

$$2n(p-2)\hat{g}_i = Y_{i}.. + Y_{\cdot i}. - 2(p-1)n\hat{\mu}$$

$$2n\hat{s}_{ij} = Y_{ij\cdot} + Y_{ji\cdot} - 2n\hat{\mu} - 2n\hat{g}_i - 2n\hat{g}_j$$

where

$$\hat{\mu} + \hat{g}_i + \hat{g}_j$$

$$= \hat{\mu} + \left[\frac{Y_{i}.. + Y_{\cdot i}.}{2n(p-2)} - \frac{2n(p-1)\hat{\mu}}{2n(p-2)}\right] + \left[\frac{Y_{j}.. + Y_{\cdot j}.}{2n(p-2)} - \frac{2n(p-1)\hat{\mu}}{2n(p-2)}\right]$$

$$= \frac{1}{2n(p-2)}(-2np\hat{\mu} + Y_{i}.. + Y_{\cdot i}. + Y_{j}.. + Y_{\cdot j}.)$$

$$= \frac{1}{2n(p-2)}\left(Y_{i}.. + Y_{\cdot i}. + Y_{j}.. + Y_{\cdot j}. - \frac{2}{p-1}Y\dots\right)$$

It should be noted that we do not, in fact, estimate any g_i or s_{ij}; these quantities are not estimable. What we have estimated as g_1 is,

$$g_1 - \bar{g} + \frac{1}{(p-2)}\sum_\alpha s_{1\alpha} - \frac{1}{p(p-2)}\sum_{\alpha,\beta} s_{\alpha\beta}$$

The total sum of squares removed is equal to

$$R(\mu, g, s, r) = \hat{\mu}Y \ldots + \Sigma \hat{g}_i(Y_{i\cdot\cdot} + Y_{\cdot i\cdot}) + \sum_{i<j} \hat{s}_{ij}(Y_{ij\cdot} + Y_{ji\cdot})$$

$$+ \sum_{i<j} \hat{r}_{ij}(Y_{ij\cdot} - Y_{ji\cdot})$$

$$= \underbrace{\frac{Y^2 \ldots}{p(p-1)n}}_{(\alpha)} + \underbrace{\left[\sum_i \frac{(Y_{i\cdot\cdot} + Y_{\cdot i\cdot})^2}{2n(p-2)} - \frac{2Y^2 \ldots}{p(p-2)n} \right]}_{(\beta)}$$

$$+ \underbrace{\left[\sum_{i<j} \hat{s}_{ij}(Y_{ij\cdot} + Y_{ji\cdot}) \right]}_{(\gamma)} + \underbrace{\left[\sum_{i<j} \frac{(Y_{ij\cdot} - Y_{ji\cdot})^2}{2n} \right]}_{(\delta)}$$

If we fitted for μ, g_i, s_{ij}, we would have the same normal equations as the first three above, and the solutions of this set which would be denoted by $\tilde{\mu}$, $\tilde{g}_i$, $\tilde{s}_{ij}$ are the same as before if the same conditions are imposed. So

$$R(\mu, g, s) = \alpha + \beta + \gamma$$

Similarly,

$$R(\mu, g) = \alpha + \beta$$

$$R(\mu) = \alpha$$

We have the analysis of variance (Table 6.22).

TABLE 6.22

Due to	df	Sum of Squares	Expectation of Mean Square
μ	1	α	
g	$p - 1$	β	$\sigma^2 + 2n\sigma^2_s + 2(p-2)n\sigma^2_g$
s	$\dfrac{p(p-3)}{2}$	γ	$\sigma^2 + 2n\sigma^2_s$
r	$\dfrac{p(p-1)}{2}$	δ	$\sigma^2 + 2n\sigma^2_r$
Within cells	$p(p-1)(n-1)$	ϵ (say)	σ^2
Total	$p(p-1)n$		

The meanings of the components of variance are:

1. σ^2 is the variance between different progeny of the same cross, both male and female parents being specified.

2. σ^2_r is the average value of the square of the difference in means of two reciprocal crosses divided by 4. If the crossing is at random, the contribution to the progeny due to the fact that the male was of one

line and the female of the other rather than vice-versa will have variance $\sigma^2{}_r$.

3. $\sigma^2{}_s$ is the square of the deviation of the average yield of the two reciprocal crosses from what we would expect, given an estimate of the additive values of the two lines from an infinite sample of crosses with different lines.

4. $\sigma^2{}_g$ is defined conceptually as follows: Suppose each of the p lines is crossed with a very large number of others with equal frequency as male parent and female parent. This will give means of, say, x_1, x_2, $\cdots$, x_p, and $\sigma^2{}_g$ is equal to $\dfrac{1}{p-1} \Sigma(x_i - \bar{x})^2$. If we take a random line, its additive contribution is a variable with mean zero and expectation $\sigma^2{}_g$.

The practical value of knowledge of these components is a matter for the geneticist.

The expectation of the mean squares is obtained in the following manner.

1. δ:

$$Y_{ij\cdot} - Y_{ji\cdot} = 2nr_{ij} + \text{sum of } n \text{ different } e\text{'s} - \text{sum of } n \text{ different } e\text{'s}$$

$$E(Y_{ij\cdot} - Y_{ji\cdot})^2 = 2n\sigma^2 + 4n^2\sigma^2{}_r$$

and

$$E\left[\sum_{\substack{ij \\ i<j}} \frac{(Y_{ij\cdot} - Y_{ji\cdot})^2}{2np\,\dfrac{(p-1)}{2}}\right] = \sigma^2 + 2n\sigma^2{}_r$$

2. β:

$$(Y_{i\cdot\cdot} + Y_{\cdot i\cdot}) = 2(p-1)n\mu + 2(p-1)ng_i + 2n\sum_{\substack{i' \\ i'\neq i}} g_{i'} + 2n\sum_{\substack{j \\ j\neq i}} s_{ij}$$

$$+ \text{sum of } 2(p-1)n \text{ different } e\text{'s}$$

so

$$E\left[\sum_i \frac{(Y_{i\cdot\cdot} + Y_{\cdot i\cdot})^2}{2n(p-2)}\right]$$

$$= \frac{2p(p-1)^2 n\mu^2}{(p-2)} + \frac{2p^2(p-1)n\sigma^2{}_g}{(p-2)} + \frac{2np(p-1)\sigma^2{}_s}{(p-2)} + \frac{p(p-1)\sigma^2}{(p-2)}$$

Also,

$$Y\ldots = p(p-1)n\mu + 2(p-1)n\Sigma g_i + 2n \sum_{\substack{ij \\ i<j}} s_{ij}$$

$$+ \text{ sum of } np(p-1) \text{ different } e's$$

so

$$E\left[\frac{2Y^2\ldots}{p(p-2)n}\right] = \frac{2p^2(p-1)^2n^2\mu^2}{p(p-2)n} + \frac{8p(p-1)^2n^2\sigma^2_g}{p(p-2)n}$$

$$+ \frac{8n^2p(p-1)\sigma^2_s}{2p(p-2)n} + \frac{2np(p-1)\sigma^2}{np(p-2)}$$

Subtracting, we get, as the expectation of the sum of squares,

$$(p-1)\sigma^2 + 2n(p-1)\sigma^2_s + 2n(p-1)(p-2)\sigma^2_g$$

and, therefore, the expectation of the mean square is

$$\sigma^2 + 2n\sigma^2_s + 2n(p-2)\sigma^2_g$$

3. γ:

As regards experimental errors, we have the following in which we denote $\sum_k e_{ijk}$ by $e_{ij}.$: (It should be noted that this is not in accordance with our usual notation.) Then,

$$2n(p-2)\hat{s}_{12} = (p-2)(e_{12}. + e_{21}.) - e_{12}. - e_{21}. - e_{21}. - e_{12}.$$

$$+ \frac{2}{p-1}(e_{12}. + e_{21}.) + \text{other terms}$$

$$= \frac{(p-3)(p-2)}{p-1}(e_{12}. + e_{21}.) + \text{other terms}$$

and

$$Y_{12}. + Y_{21}. = (e_{12}. + e_{21}.)$$

Also:

$$E(e_{12}.)(e_{12}.) = n\sigma^2$$

$$E(e_{12}.)(e_{ij}.) = 0, \qquad (i, j) \neq (1, 2)$$

$$E(e_{21}.)(e_{21}.) = n\sigma^2 \quad \text{and so on}$$

So the expectation of $\hat{s}_{12}(Y_{12}. + Y_{21}.)$ is equal to

$$\frac{1}{2n(p-2)}\left[\frac{(p-3)(p-2)n}{(p-1)} + \frac{(p-3)(p-2)n}{(p-1)}\right]\sigma^2 = \frac{(p-3)}{(p-1)}\sigma^2$$

There are in all $p(p-1)/2$ such terms, giving as the expectation of the sum of squares $p(p-3)\sigma^2/2$ and as expectation of the mean square σ^2.

The term involving $\sigma^2{}_s$ is found by an identical argument to be $2n\sigma^2{}_s$. As a check we may prepare Table 6.23 of expectations of sums of squares.

TABLE 6.23

	μ^2	$\sigma^2{}_g$	$\sigma^2{}_s$	σ^2	$\sigma^2{}_r$
α	$np(p-1)$	$4n(p-1)$	$2n$	1	
ϵ				$(n-1)p(p-1)$	
δ				$\dfrac{p(p-1)}{2}$	$np(p-1)$
γ			$np(p-3)$	$\dfrac{p(p-3)}{2}$	
β		$2n(p-1)(p-2)$	$2n(p-1)$	$p-1$	
Total	$np(p-1)$	$2np(p-1)$	$np(p-1)$	$np(p-1)$	$np(p-1)$

The expectations of the individual items sum to the expectation of the total sum of squares (about zero), so that we have verified our calculations.

6.9 CONCLUSION

In this and the previous chapter we have dealt with the estimation from data assumed to conform to a particular class of models, of the parameters of the member of the class actually encountered.

We have not discussed, except briefly at the beginning, the problems of inference. The work we have described is entirely deductive in that we assumed random samples from partially specified populations.

There is one difficulty involved in the application of these methods to a set of data which can hardly be emphasized sufficiently. The results are obtained for conceptual populations which are formed according to simple specifications. The application of these theoretical results to a real population of experimental or observational units depends entirely on the validity of the correspondence between the actual population and the chosen theoretical population. If we have good reason to believe that the theoretical population does not correspond to the actual population, we are in no position to translate deduced results in the theoretical population into predictions of what would happen in the actual population. The correspondence is a matter of degree, and it is impossible to obtain a perfect correspondence. This should not, however, lull us into ignoring the risk that we may be on an erroneous path with the most complex model that we can handle.

The acid test (and the only one) of the reliability of a model, theoretical or otherwise, is the comparison of observations with predictions. The fact that observations agree with predictions does not prove the accuracy of the model but verifies that the model can predict within the range of error we desire at a particular moment. Later we shall be interested in smaller errors, and our model will be shown to be at best an approximation and at worst entirely erroneous.

We shall find, however, in the next chapters, that we can obtain a considerable amount of insurance against such risks by applying the method of randomization. Under this principle, the experimental units which occur in a particular cell of a treatment classification are chosen at random from a specified population.

REFERENCES

1. KENDALL, M. G. *The advanced theory of statistics.* Vol. I. Griffin, London. 1943.

FURTHER READING

2. YATES, F. The principles of orthogonality and confounding in replicated experiments. *Jour. Agr. Sci.*, **23**, 108–145, 1933.
3. YATES, F. The analysis of multiple classifications with unequal numbers in the different classes. *Jour. Amer. Stat. Assoc.*, **29**, 51–66, 1934.
4. WISHART, J., and SANDERS, H. G. *Principles and practice of field experimentation.* Empire Cotton Growing Corporation, London. 1935.
5. WISHART, J. Tests of significance in analysis of covariance. *Suppl. Jour. Roy. Stat. Soc.*, **3**, 79–82, 1936.
6. WILKS, S. S. The analysis of variance and covariance in non-orthogonal data. *Metron*, **13**, 141–154, 1938.
7. DANIELS, H. E. The estimation of components of variance. *Suppl. Jour. Roy. Stat. Soc.*, **6**, 186–197, 1939.
8. RAO, C. R. On the linear combination of observations and the general theory of least squares. *Sankhyā*, **7**, 237–256, 1946.
9. KENDALL, M. G. *The advanced theory of statistics.* Vol. II. Griffin, London. 1946.
10. CRUMP, S. L. The estimation of variance components in analysis of variance. *Biometrics*, **2**, 7–11, 1946.
11. CRUMP, S. L. The present status of variance component analysis. *Biometrics*, **7**, 1–16, 1951.
12. COCHRAN, W. G. Testing a linear relation among variances. *Biometrics*, **7**, 17–32, 1951.
13. TUKEY, J. W. Components in regression. *Biometrics*, **7**, 33–69, 1951.

CHAPTER 7

Randomization

7.1 THE PRINCIPLE OF RANDOMIZATION

Let us consider the basis of possible interpretations of data by methods that have so far been given. In all cases we have to assume that our experimental results conform to some mathematical distribution which is specified to a greater or lesser degree. For example, the assumption may be that y, the variable under study, is distributed around some function of the other variables independently according to a normal distribution with mean zero and constant variance. In the case of the tasting test, we have to assume that the taster will, in the absence of any difference detectable to him, choose the odd drink randomly unless he knows which one of the three is the odd one. The important question is then: Can we ever be sure that our observations will follow the appropriate distribution? Fisher [1] gives an excellent, and now classical, discussion of the problem, illustrating the points with the lady's tea-tasting experiment.

First, consider the triangular tasting experiment. Suppose there is no difference between the two processes for producing the drink, and that, in fact, they are identical as far as taste is concerned. Under these circumstances we wish the results to be in accord with the binomial distribution. Our taster will, each time, pick out one of the 3 drinks presented to him as the odd one. The processes by which he reaches a decision are unknown to us, but on tasting each drink he presumably scores it in some way and compares these scores. The score may, of course, be a composite of several characteristics and may exist only subconsciously in the taster's mind. Supposing then the decision is based on considerations other than the treatment, because we assume the treatment to have no effect, we can be sure that he will be correct, by chance, 1 in 3 times on the average if the association between the treatment and any other characteristic of the experimental material is zero. The notion of lack of association between treatments and characteristic of the experimental material is not difficult to visualize. One

120

can formalize it by an argument such as the following. We imagine that the experimental material can be classified, say, for the purposes of argument into discrete classes, thus:

Classification of Material (i)	Treatment (j)	
	1	2
1		
2		

We have a process by which treatments are allocated to the experimental material which will specify the number n_{ij} of experimental units in the (i, j)th cell. This number n_{ij} must have the same distribution over the i cells for all the treatments.

To develop a process that will have this property is a "tall" order, for the association must not exist for any characteristic of the experimental material. Furthermore, we do not know all these characteristics. The great contribution of Fisher to the scientific method was the notion of randomization. By this device, we can ensure that all the desirable conditions are met.

Many attempts have been made to define randomness, but the definitions tend to be circular. We adopt the axiomatic theory of probability, in which we regard probability as a function of sets of points with particular properties. One property is that, for any set (to be precise and possibly a little esoteric for this book, the sets must be Borel sets) of points, it is non-negative and additive, and, for the set of points consisting of the whole space, it is unity. From these axioms we deduce certain theorems, of which the most important in the present context is the central limit theorem. This is a theorem entirely in our conceptual theory. The theorem states that, almost regardless of the true distributions of successive random variables x_1, x_2, $\cdots$, their sum has a distribution which tends to a distribution of known form, depending on the means and variances of the distributions of the x_i's. As a special case, if we are sampling from a binomial distribution, the probability that the relative frequency deviates from a particular value by more than a certain amount tends to zero with increasing sample size. Note that all the terms in the previous sentences are in the *conceptual* theory: i.e., sample, binomial distribution, probability. Now phenomena are observed in nature, i.e., in the perceptual sphere, which appear to have this property. For example, if we toss a penny successively in the usual way and plot the relative frequency of heads obtained up to each toss, we shall get a graph that may look like Figure 5.

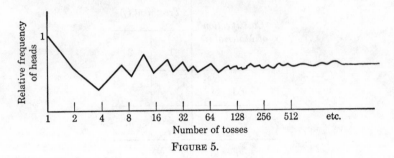

FIGURE 5.

This is precisely the sort of thing to which our conceptual framework leads us. It suggests to us that the theory in the conceptual sphere may be related to the phenomenon in the observed world by interpreting probability in the conceptual sphere as relative frequency in the perceptual sphere.

Again, we may examine the heights of the corn plants in a particular small area and obtain a histogram of these heights (Figure 6). We

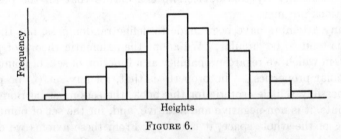

FIGURE 6.

realize that, with a large number of plants, finer observations, and smaller grouping intervals, this histogram will tend more and more closely to a smooth curve. It may never actually achieve a smooth curve because in the present stage of genetic knowledge the height of each plant is regarded as made up of the small effects of a large but finite number of genes plus environmental effects. But it will certainly approximate a smooth curve. It has been found, for example, in some cases that the histogram can be closely approximated by the normal or Gaussian curve. Now suppose we have a population whose distribution resembles the normal distribution and we draw samples in such a way that we know nothing about each individual: i.e., draw samples completely haphazardly, and examine the distribution of the means of these samples. We shall find that this distribution follows closely the distribution of means that we can derive for the normal distribution. The crucial word of this statement is "haphazardly." How can we draw samples without knowing anything about the individual members of the population? We need a process in the real world that will lead to results comparable to what we obtain in the conceptual world with equal probabilities. Here again we meet the difficulty of induction, that all we can show with a particular process is that it has worked in the past.

The situation grows more and more complicated the deeper we delve into it, and we may perhaps best conclude this discussion by saying that processes have been found that give "random" numbers, which have the property that, if the members of our population are assigned successively the numbers 1, 2, 3, etc., and we use the set of random numbers to draw samples, we obtain samples whose distribution in particular respects, e.g., the mean, is closely approximated by the corresponding theoretical distribution.

Given such a set of generated numbers, we are completely equipped for the drawing of random samples. We use a set of random numbers, because it is in most cases impossible for each and every one of us to carry a machine that we know will produce random numbers. In a sense, we can carry such a machine, for we are pretty sure that a new nickel, say, has the property of giving heads and tails with equal frequency in the long run and we could generate random numbers with it. If we wished, we could check that the nickel has this property. It is perhaps worth while to indicate how we would use such a "machine" to arrange, say, 20 items in random order. We would toss the nickel 5 times to obtain a random number between 0 and 31 by the following process: record heads as 1 and tails as 0; then we shall have 5 numbers which we write out in order as

$$a_1 \quad a_2 \quad a_3 \quad a_4 \quad a_5$$

each a_i being 0 or 1. From this we calculate the number as

$$a_5 + 2a_4 + 4a_3 + 8a_2 + 16a_1$$

If all the a's are unity, we get 5 heads and the corresponding number is 31, and, if all tails, the number is 0. If we repeat the process again and again, we shall eventually obtain all the numbers from 0 to 31 in some order, disregarding a number when we have obtained it before. We may then delete the numbers 0 and 21 to 31 and we have our numbers 1 to 20 arranged in random order.

Such a process is rather tedious, and so we use sets of random numbers prepared by someone else. There are some theoretical objections to the use by all of us of the same set of random numbers or to our using the same set of numbers for all our acts of randomizing. These, however, need not worry us here. The ordinary experimenter will not go wrong if he uses a table in order and when he has gone through the table starts again. But, if he does a large number of randomizations, he should use different sets of numbers, and he should not use a set of, say, 10,000 numbers to arrange the numbers 1 to 5000 in order. These ideas are intuitive but can probably be given some objective basis.

What we have done essentially is to push the justification for our procedure of randomization back a step. Any particular specified set of numbers may be random or not, depending on how they were obtained. In fact, the randomness of the numbers is not a property of the numbers but of the process that generated them. If they were obtained by a process which we believe to be random and the results of which have met successfully tests for randomness, we rely on the inference that these numbers have the desirable properties for our problems, and such an inference like all other inferences cannot be shown to be completely true. The sum total of our discussion is then that we put our faith in a set of random numbers. We have this to strengthen our belief in the process, that it has been found to work whenever it has been tested: for example, in sampling where we can compare our sample results with those obtained by complete enumeration. Furthermore, if this process does not work, it seems clear, though probably difficult to show, that no process of induction can work.

To return to the tasting experiment, suppose that our production process goes by steps 1, 2, 3, etc., to N, and that we introduced a change in the process at step n and wish to ascertain if this change has produced any effect perceptible to the taster. If we divide our material at step $(n - 1)$ into 3 portions and assign 1 of the 2 treatments at random to 1 of the 3 portions, and then continue the process from the $(n + 1)$th step to the Nth step, we know that the taster will, in the absence of any effect, pick out the odd one correctly by chance in $\frac{1}{3}$ of repeated trials, in the same way that we obtain results in our conceptual sphere with a binomial distribution with $p = \frac{1}{3}$. In order to validate the process completely, that is, to test the hypothesis that the change in the process only at the nth step has had no effect, we should apply processes $(n + 1)$ to N to the 3 portions at random also, or, less preferably, in some preassigned systematic way. Suppose that our taster is using some effect completely unconnected with the processes at the nth step in order to make his choice of the odd one. Then we have by our randomizing process given this effect a probability of $\frac{1}{3}$ of being associated with the odd drink, and this is all we require to validate our tests based on the binomial distribution. Now consider the stipulation that the processes after the nth are to be applied at random or in a preassigned systematic way to the 3 drinks and what happens if this is done. This stipulation will result in lack of association on the average of *any* external factors with the treatments.

Finally we should consider the extent to which we should endeavor to make all the processes apart from the one under test as alike as possible. It is obvious that, as far as our test of the null hypothesis is concerned, it does not matter how gross the differences are, but we have to consider what happens under our alternative hypotheses. In the present case our alternative hypotheses are that the difference is such that the taster will choose the odd one correctly in a proportion p of cases, p being greater than $\frac{1}{3}$. Gross differences occurring more or less haphazardly will lower the proportion of cases in which the differences will be detected correctly. In our discussion in Chapter 2 on the power of a test we considered only the case of p equal to $\frac{1}{2}$, and then only briefly. Suppose we are using a 5 percent test, and we wish to reject the null hypothesis 95 times out of 100 on the average when the true hypothesis is that p equals $\frac{1}{2}$. Then we shall require approximately 92 trials. If, on the other hand, the true hypothesis is that p equals $\frac{3}{4}$, the number required under the same conditions is approximately 13. The general effect of gross haphazard differences is obvious from these two cases. The removal of various haphazard effects will undoubtedly entail additional expenditure of resources and brings with it an increase in the sensitivity of the experiment. A final answer to the balance that is to be practiced in this situation, namely, that an increase in the sensitivity or accuracy of an experiment requires additional expenditure of effort and money, is obtained only by recourse to economic arguments.

Our general conclusion is the following. The experimenter must decide which of the various causes that he feels will produce variation in his results must be controlled experimentally. Those causes that he does not control experimentally, because he is not cognizant of them, he must control by the device of randomization. To reiterate the criticism of many so-called experiments in the various branches of science, particularly in the social sciences,* but also of some occurrence in other sciences (fortunately decreasing as the principles of statistical inference become more widely known), only when the treatments in the experiment are applied by the experimenter using the full randomization procedure

* See, for example, F. Chapin, *Experimental Designs in Sociological Research.*

is the chain of inductive inference sound. It is only under these circumstances that the experimenter can attribute whatever effects he observes to the treatment and to the treatment only. Under these circumstances his conclusions are reliable in the statistical sense.

7.2 RANDOMIZATION IN THE CASE OF CONTINUOUS VARIABLES

There is little need to discuss the effectiveness of randomization in the case of continuous variables. The same conclusions hold qualitatively as for the discrete case, but some additional remarks are necessary, in that, with the particular example discussed, the distributions of our results in the case of the null hypothesis were completely determinate from the hypotheses. For example, in the tasting experiment the null hypothesis was equivalent to stating that the results would be distributed according to the binomial distribution with p equal to $\frac{1}{3}$. For any special number of trials, then, the probabilities of the possible results could be evaluated. There can, of course, be cases in which the discrete distribution is not completely specified by the null hypothesis.

For the continuous case, consider the estimation of the differential effects of 2 treatments on a characteristic for which the possible measurements form a continuous set of numbers. Suppose that, with one treatment, the characteristic y is distributed for the population nearly according to the normal distribution

$$f(y) = \frac{1}{\sqrt{2\pi}\sigma} e^{-\frac{(y-\mu_1)^2}{2\sigma^2}}$$

and, with the other treatment,

$$f(y) = \frac{1}{\sqrt{2\pi}\sigma} e^{-\frac{(y-\mu_2)^2}{2\sigma^2}}$$

The hypothesis we wish to test is that μ_1 is equal to μ_2, no assumptions being made about the value of σ^2 other than that it is positive.

The situation is exactly analogous to the problem in the axiomatic theory of testing the differences between samples from two populations, and the same considerations as with the tasting experiment hold. We must select the members of the population that receive treatment 1 at random, and also the members that receive treatment 2. We must apply the treatments to the selected members individually and must randomize any stages in the process after the stage of applying the treatments. If the treatments have no differential effects, then our experimental results will belong to one distribution, with $\mu_1 = \mu_2$ in the above formulas.

The basis of our inferences in this case is that the experimental results for the population are arranged in distributions approximated closely by the corresponding theoretical distributions. Our randomization procedure by definition completes the reasoning process.

7.3 SAMPLING FROM FINITE POPULATIONS

The considerations that we have given above hold for particular sets of circumstances only. These may be stated briefly as follows: that we are sampling by a random process from an infinite population: e.g., of repetitions of the triangular taste trial. In any particular experimental situation it is difficult to specify any infinite population from which we are sampling, and, if this is possible, it is rarely permissible to assume that we are sampling at random from this infinite population, as regards the choice of experimental units which are attached to particular treatments. The case of field experiments is somewhat classical in that it has been subjected to more examination than other cases and also has been a subject of considerable controversy. Practically all the difficulties of interpretation of an experiment in any subject-matter field are exemplified by this case, and we shall therefore examine it in some detail.

Suppose we wish to compare 2 treatments on an area of land, and for the purpose we divide the area into plots, over which the treatments are distributed randomly. We know that, if we give the area of land a uniform treatment and harvest it in very small plots, we shall find that the yields are approximately normally distributed. In our experiment, however, we may perhaps divide the area into 20 plots, arrange these in pairs to make replicates, and assign the treatments at random within each pair. The plots then that receive a particular one of the treatments are a sample taken randomly without replacement from a finite population of 20 elements stratified into 10 strata, each of 2 elements, there being 1 element from each stratum. It is common sense that the yields of neighboring plots are correlated (probably approximately as some function of their distance apart), and we know that 2 random elements of a finite population of n elements have a correlation of $-1/(n-1)$, which with strata of 2 elements equals -1. In the absence of any further considerations, we could not possibly regard such sampling as being from an infinite population and could not therefore use the theory of previous chapters which is concerned with infinite populations.

7.4 RANDOMIZATION TESTS

Suppose we have performed an ordinary randomized block experiment with t treatments in r blocks of t plots, the treatments being assigned at random within each block. If the treatments have no differential effects, we can say that we have made a grouping of the rt plots into t groups of r plots which is a random one of the possible $(t!)^r$ groupings that we could have obtained. Any property of a grouping may be considered, such as the sum of squares between treatment totals or the range of the treatment totals (or some peculiar property such as the cube of the means of the cube roots of the treatment totals, though it is unlikely that this quantity would be of interest). A chosen property may be evaluated for the particular grouping and for all the other possible groupings, and we may then consider that we have a random sample of 1 from the possible $(t!)^r$ values that could have been obtained. Under the null hypothesis that the treatments have no differential effects on each individual plot, the value for the chosen grouping has an expectation of the average value for all the possible groupings. We may take any set of the values of possible groupings that has a probability of 5 percent and, if the actual grouping falls in this set, reject the null hypothesis. In this way we can be sure that we are using a 5 percent significance test; that is, under the null hypothesis we have a chance of 5 percent of rejecting the null hypothesis when it is true. We need not, of course, go through all this work to get a 5 percent significance test: We need merely to reject the null hypothesis with a probability of 5 percent according to some random device; in other words, we need not examine the observations at all.

In order that our testing procedure have value, it is necessary to examine the power of the test or the sensitivity of the test to departures from the null hypothesis. The criterion that we choose must be such that deviations from the null hypothesis tend to place the value of the criterion in a distinctive set of the possible values. It is with regard to the specification of alternatives that we encounter some difficulties. The simplest alternative that can be specified is that the effect of treatment i measured from some arbitrarily chosen base is t_i on any plot. The null hypothesis specifies that the t_i's are equal and the alternative that the t_i's are unequal. This suggests the criterion to be used, namely, the sum of squares between treatment means, for this sum of squares will contain $\Sigma(t_i - \bar{t})^2$. This is the simplest (mathematically) positive symmetric function of the differences of the t_i's. One could proceed in this fashion examining the distribution of the sum of squares between the treatment means, and it is only the labor of evaluating this sum of squares for all the possible groupings that militates against the procedure.

The way out of this difficulty is indicated by the theory based on normal distributions which we discussed in Chapter 6. For we know that, if normal theory and the additive hypothesis hold, we can test the hypothesis that the t_i's are equal against the alternative hypothesis that they are unequal by using the variance ratio criterion: namely, (treatment mean square)/(error mean square). It is natural, then, to examine the distribution over the possible randomizations of this quantity. This was done empirically by Eden and Yates [2] and theoretically by Welch,[3] Pitman,[4] and others. It is fairly easily shown that in the absence of treatment effects the expectation of the treatment mean square is equal to the expectation of the error mean square. It should be noted that the expectation is not with respect to some infinite population of repetitions of the experiment, but over the possible randomizations of the treatments. It was proved by Pitman [4] that in the case of randomized blocks the criterion (treatment mean square/error mean square) was distributed approximately according to the F distribution. We shall discuss these matters in the next chapter.

It follows that the F test may be used for testing the hypothesis that the treatments have had the same effect on each plot. There is, of course, the question of the closeness of the approximation to the distribution of the criterion by the F test, and more work needs to be done on this problem. Assuming, however, that the approximation is satisfactory, we may, as far as the test of the null hypothesis is concerned, regard the observations in a randomized block experiment as having arisen from a model

$$y_{ij} = \mu + b_i + t_j + e_{ij}$$

i, j being the block and treatment numbers, respectively; μ, b_i, and t_j being fixed unknown constants; and the e_{ij}'s being normally and independently distributed around a mean of zero with variance σ^2. We must regard the error component e_{ij} as measuring the deviation of the plot from the block mean, when a uniform treatment is used over the whole experimental area or material. It should be emphasized that so far we have considered the use of the analysis of variance for testing the null hypothesis. The analysis of variance has another use and one that is generally more important, the estimation of the error of treatment comparisons, and we shall deal with this in the next chapter.

7.4.1 An Example of a Randomization Test

Suppose we have 8 experimental objects, a, b, c, d, e, f, g, h, of which 4, a, b, c, d, have received treatment 1 and the other 4 treatment 2, and let the experimental results be:

a	18	e	9
b	13	f	16
c	3	g	17
d	17	h	17

There are 70 possible ways of assigning the 2 treatments to the 8 objects, of which 35 pairs lead to equal treatment differences except for sign. We enumerate the sets of 4 which include a, and evaluate the treatment differences in each case ignoring sign (Table 7.1).

TABLE 7.1

Set Involving a	Difference of Sets, R (plus or minus)	Set Involving a	Difference of Sets, R (plus or minus)
abcd	8	acdh	0
abce	24	acef	18
abcf	10	aceg	16
abcg	8	aceh	16
abch	8	acfg	2
abde	4	acfh	2
abdf	18	acgh	0
abdg	20	adef	10
abdh	20	adeg	12
abef	2	adeh	12
abeg	4	adfg	26
abeh	4	adfh	26
abfg	18	adgh	28
abfh	18	aefg	10
abgh	20	aefh	10
acde	16	aegh	12
acdf	2	afgh	26
acdg	0		

We find that in 25 cases out of the 35 (i.e., 71 percent of cases) a difference as large as 8 (the observed difference) or larger would have been found. There is, therefore, no evidence from the randomization test of a treatment effect.

If we applied the analysis of variance to this set of data we would have the results given in Table 7.2, where

TABLE 7.2

Due to	df	Sum of Squares	Mean Square	F
Between treatments	1	8	8	0.26
Within treatments	6	185.5	30.9	
Total	7	193.5		

Between-treatments sum of squares

$$= [(18 + 13 + 3 + 17) - (9 + 16 + 17 + 17)]^2/8 = (-8)^2/8 = 8$$

Within-treatments sum of squares $= 18^2 + 13^2 + 3^2 + 17^2$

$$- \frac{51}{4}^2 + 9^2 + 16^2 + 17^2 + 17^2 - \frac{59}{4}^2 = 185.5$$

and

Total sum of squares

$$= 18^2 + 13^2 \cdots + 17^2 - \frac{110}{8}^2 = 1706 - 1512.5 = 193.5$$

The F value is much less than unity, and its level of significance is approximately 0.63. The agreement between these two methods of analysis, the one with very broad assumptions, and the other assuming normality, is such that the use of the normality assumption will not mislead the experimenter. The results in Table 7.3 were obtained with a number of similar sets of artificially constructed data, where $p(F)$ is the probability of getting the value of F or a greater one according to the F distribution, and $p(R)$ is the probability of getting a more extreme value of R.

If we take into account the fact that $p(R)$ is restricted to changes of $\frac{1}{35}$ or 0.028, the agreement between the two values is surprising. It would appear that, in general, the asymptotic result is closely realized for the usual type of experiment.

TABLE 7.3

Set of Data	$p(F)$	$p(R)$
1	0.967	1.000
2	0.960	1.000
3	0.941	0.943
4	0.925	0.914
5	0.916	1.000
6	0.858	0.943
7	0.857	0.771
8	0.808	0.971
9	0.741	0.714
10	0.678	0.714
11	0.656	0.657
12	0.546	0.571
13	0.435	0.543
14	0.435	0.457
15	0.404	0.429
16	0.395	0.371
17	0.382	0.343
18	0.296	0.343
19	0.263	0.257
20	0.246	0.286
21	0.238	0.257
22	0.165	0.257
23	0.125	0.143
24	0.006	0.029

7.5   OTHER FORMULATIONS OF THE PROBLEM

The most important other formulation of the problem is that due to Neyman et al.[5] The difference arises in the formulation of the error of the yield of a particular plot with a particular treatment, and of the aim of the experimenter. Suppose a plot in a randomized block experiment is denoted by three subscripts, i, j, and k, the block, plot within the block, and treatment, respectively. The "true" yield of the plot (i, j) with treatment (object) k is denoted by $X_{ij}(k)$. The definition of "true" yield is based on the idea that the experiment could conceptually be repeated indefinitely without any change of experimental conditions or of arrangement so that the kth treatment is always tested on the plot (i, j). A population of yields for this plot would be generated, and $X_{ij}(k)$ is defined as the mean of this population. Any particular yield obtained is denoted by $x_{ij}(k)$, and the difference

$$x_{ij}(k) - X_{ij}(k) = e_{ij}(k)$$

is called the technical error of the particular yield $x_{ij}(k)$, since it is due to the inaccuracy of experimental technique. In addition to the technical error there is the "soil" error, or error due to the inherent variability of the experimental units. The true yield of the jth plot in the ith block may be represented as follows:

$$X_{ij}(k) = X..(k) + [X_i.(k) - X..(k)] + [X_{ij}(k) - X_i.(k)]$$
$$= X..(k) + B_i(k) + \eta_{ij}(k)$$

The observed yield is therefore given by

$$x_{ij}(k) = X..(k) + B_i(k) + \eta_{ij}(k) + e_{ij}(k)$$

Neyman assumed that our purpose is to compare numbers such as $X..(k)$, or the average yields the treatments will give when applied to the whole of the experimental material. In order to examine the bias of comparisons estimated by comparing observed yields, expectations are taken (1) over the population of repetitions envisaged in the definition of true yields and (2) over the population of possible randomizations. It is shown by Neyman that under these circumstances the estimates are unbiased.

Neyman proposed as the null hypothesis that the $X..(k)$'s do not depend on k, in other words that the average yield over the experimental area would be the same under all treatments. This null hypothesis is less restrictive than Fisher's in that it is satisfied when Fisher's null hypothesis is satisfied and also when the treatments have differing effects on the different plots but average to zero. The question is then which of the two null hypotheses is the more satisfactory, and it seems that this is a matter of the objectives of the experimenter. If the experimenter is interested in the more fundamental research work, Fisher's null hypothesis is more satisfactory, for one should be interested in discovering the fact that treatments have different effects on different plots and in trying to explain why such differences exist. It is only in technological experiments designed to answer specific questions about a particular batch of material which is later to be used for production of some sort that Neyman's null hypothesis appears satisfactory: for example, when the experiment is designed to test the hypothesis that there are no differences in yield between a certain set of varieties of wheat grown over the state of Iowa.

Neyman's hypothesis appears artificial in this respect, that a series of repetitions is envisaged, the experimental conditions remaining the same but the technical errors being different. It follows, from the above discussion of Fisher's null hypothesis that there is a test of the null hypothesis of zero differences between the effects of the treatments as actually applied, without the introduction of any conceptual population of repetitions, except the population inherent in the choice of a particular randomization.

On the other hand, it must be admitted that, when an experimenter applies a treatment, say, X units of a certain stimulus, we know that he does not apply exactly X units, but $X \pm \delta$ units, where δ is an error variable which may be due to measuring. If the circumstances of the experiment are such that this error variable has a distribution with appreciable spread, this fact should be utilized in the design. In the case of randomized blocks, for example, it may be suggested that under these circumstances the size of the block should be twice the number of treatments and each treatment should be represented twice at random within the block. The exact effect of such a modification in the design has not, however, been worked out. Such a modification is of value also for the examination of the other possible difficulty, that the treatments have different effects on the different plots. With this modification it would be possible to test whether there were differential effects between the blocks.

REFERENCES

1. FISHER, R. A. *The design of experiments.* Oliver and Boyd, Edinburgh. 4th ed., 1947.
2. EDEN, T., and YATES, F. On the validity of Fisher's z-test when applied to an actual sample of non-normal data. *Jour. Agr. Sci.*, **23**, 6–16, 1933.
3. WELCH, B. L. On the z-test in randomised blocks and Latin Squares. *Biometrika*, **29**, 21–52, 1937.
4. PITMAN, E. J. G. Significance tests which may be applied to samples from any population. III. The analysis of variance test. *Biometrika*, **29**, 322–335, 1937.
5. NEYMAN, J., IWASZKIEWICZ, K., and KOLODZIEJCZYK, ST. Statistical problems in agricultural experimentation. *Suppl. Jour. Roy. Stat. Soc.*, **2**, 107–154, 1935.

CHAPTER 8

The Validity of Analyses
of Randomized Experiments

8.1 INTRODUCTION

We noted in the previous chapter that there is good reason to expect that tests of significance of treatment effects obtained by the analysis of variance, when randomization is used, are reliable, regardless of the distributions involved. In this way we considered one aspect of the analysis of experiments, but there remains the question of the estimation of treatment effects. In many respects this is the more important aspect particularly as it is unlikely that 2 treatments that are not identical give exactly similar observations. The discussion of the previous chapter was largely qualitative, and we shall be concerned in this chapter with the analysis of experiments from the point of view of the effect of randomization on the estimation problem.

The simplicity of the testing of hypotheses lay in the fact that it was unnecessary to specify alternatives, the randomization test intuitively discriminating against any alternatives. There remains, of course, the question of the sensitivity of the test. As regards estimation, randomization ensures that any comparison of treatments is estimated without bias by the same comparison of the observed mean yields. Any experiment, then, in which randomization of treatments is used, gives a point estimate of the true difference, but the value of a point estimate without an indication of its reliability is low and, in most cases, questionable. It is therefore necessary to consider the circumstances under which an error may be attached to estimates, the distribution of this error following some known distribution.

There is also the further difficulty of defining exactly what we mean by a treatment effect. For example, suppose we consider a stimulus that adds a definite amount, say, 5 units, to the square root of the observation: then, letting y_c and y_t be the yields under the control and the stimulus, respectively, we could have results such as the following:

y_c	$\sqrt{y_c}$	$\sqrt{y_c} + 5 = \sqrt{y_t}$	y_t	$y_t - y_c$
25	5	10	100	75
64	8	13	169	105
100	10	15	225	125

On the actual scale of measurement the effect of the stimulus varies in the range of controls considered, from 75 to 125. If another experimenter is working with exactly the same stimulus on material for which the control yield is in the range 9 to 16, say, and the response law is identical in the two cases, he will observe an effect on the actual scale of measurement of 55 to 65 units. Under these circumstances both experimenters will agree only if they state their results in terms of effects on the square root of the observation. It is desirable then to express effects on a scale of measurement such that they are exactly additive. Such a procedure has its defects, for experimenters prefer to state effects on a scale of measurement that is used as a matter of custom or for convenience reasons. It is probably difficult, for instance, to communicate to a farmer the meaning of the statement that a certain dose of an insecticide reduces the square root of the number of corn borers. A statement on the effect on number of corn borers can be made but is more complex. These difficulties are not, however, in the realm of the experimenter. He should examine his data on a scale of measurement which is such that treatment effects are additive. The real difficulty, in general, is to determine the scale of measurement that has the desired property. The problem is identical with that which occurs in quantitative genetics, where heritabilities, genetic correlations, and so on may depend considerably on the scale of measurement that is used in their calculation.

8.2 THE ANALYSIS OF RANDOMIZED BLOCKS WHEN ADDITIVITY HOLDS

We shall use the randomized block design to illustrate a general process by which randomized designs may be examined. We shall denote the yield with treatment $k(= 1, 2, \cdots, t)$ on plot $j(= 1, 2, \cdots, t)$ of block $i(= 1, 2, \cdots, r)$ by y_{ijk}, and we then have the identity

$$y_{ijk} = y_{\cdots} + (y_{i\cdots} - y_{\cdots}) + (y_{ijk} - y_{ij\cdot}) + (y_{ij\cdot} - y_{i\cdots}) \qquad (1)$$

If we have additivity of treatment effects, we may write

$$y_{ijk} - y_{ij.} = t_k \quad \text{for all } i \text{ and } j \tag{2}$$

and we may then write the identity as

$$y_{ijk} = \mu + b_i + t_k + e_{ij} \tag{3}$$

where

$$\mu = y \ldots, \quad b_i = y_{i..} - y \ldots, \quad \text{and} \quad e_{ij} = y_{ij.} - y_{i..}$$

In fact, we do not observe the yield of treatment k on plot j but merely the yield of treatment k on a randomly chosen plot in the block. If we denote the observed yield of treatment k in block i by y_{ik}, we may write

$$y_{ik} = \mu + b_i + t_k + \sum_j \delta_{ij}^k e_{ij} \tag{4}$$

where δ_{ij}^k is equal to unity if treatment k occurs on plot j in the ith block and is zero otherwise. The random error attached to any observed yield is the whole expression $\sum_j \delta_{ij}^k e_{ij}$. Any particular e_{ij} is a fixed variable which we do not know. The random variable in the expression 4 is the term δ_{ij}^k, and its distribution is determined by the randomization procedure which is used in obtaining the particular experimental plan. The properties of the δ_{ij}^k's which are necessary for our purposes are as follows:

$$\text{Prob } (\delta_{ij}^k = 1) = \frac{1}{t} \quad \text{for any } i, j, k$$

Given that

$$\delta_{ij}^k = 1, \quad \text{then} \quad \delta_{ij'}^k = 0 \quad \text{for all } j' \neq j \quad \text{and} \quad \delta_{ij}^{k'} = 0 \quad \text{for all } k' \neq k$$

δ_{ij}^k and $\delta_{i'j'}^{k'}$ are independent if

$$i' \neq i \quad \text{for any } j, j', k, k'$$

Given that

$$\delta_{ij}^k = 1, \quad \text{prob } (\delta_{ij'}^{k'} = 1) = \frac{1}{t-1} \quad \text{for } j' \neq j, \ k' \neq k$$

These properties are an expression of the fact that we randomize the positions of the treatments in each block separately and, of course, that a treatment occurs on only 1 plot in a block and that any plot receives only 1 treatment.

Now let us examine the estimates of treatment effects. A treatment total $Y_{.k}$ or T_k is given by

$$T_k = r\mu + rt_k + \sum_i \sum_j \delta_{ij}^k e_{ij} \tag{5}$$

The expectation of δ_{ij}^k is $1/t$, and, because $\sum_j e_{ij} = 0$, the expectation of the treatment total is $r\mu + rt_k$. Similarly, the expectation of any comparison of observed treatment means is the same comparison of treatment effects. The variance of a treatment total is equal to the expectation of $\left(\sum_i \sum_j \delta_{ij}^k e_{ij} \right)^2$.

Now

$$\left(\sum_i \sum_j \delta_{ij}^k e_{ij} \right)^2 = \sum_i \sum_j (\delta_{ij}^k)^2 e^2_{ij} + \sum_i \sum_{j' \neq j} \delta_{ij}^k \delta_{ij'}^k e_{ij} e_{ij'}$$

$$+ \sum_{i' \neq i} \sum_j \sum_{j'} \delta_{ij}^k \delta_{i'j'}^k e_{ij} e_{i'j'} \quad (6)$$

Using $E(\theta)$ to denote the expectation of the quantity θ, we have

$$E(\delta_{ij}^k)^2 = \frac{1}{t}$$

$$E(\delta_{ij}^k \delta_{ij'}^k) = 0 \quad \text{for } j' \neq j$$

$$E(\delta_{ij}^k \delta_{i'j'}^k) = \frac{1}{t^2} \quad \text{for } i' \neq i \text{ and any } j, j'$$

Since $\sum_j e_{ij}$ equals zero, we have

$$E[T_k - E(T_k)]^2 = \frac{1}{t} \sum_{ij} e^2_{ij} \quad (7)$$

Similarly, we find that

$$E\{[T_k - E(T_k)][T_{k'} - E(T_{k'})]\} = -\frac{1}{t(t-1)} \sum_{ij} e^2_{ij} \quad (8)$$

that

$$E\{[(T_k - T_{k'})] - [E(T_k) - E(T_{k'})]\}^2 = \frac{2}{t-1} \sum_{ij} e^2_{ij} \quad (9)$$

and that

$$E\{(\overline{T}_k - \overline{T}_{k'}) - [E(\overline{T}_k) - E(\overline{T}_{k'})]\}^2 = \frac{2}{r^2(t-1)} \sum_{ij} e^2_{ij} \quad (10)$$

where $\overline{T}_k$ is the treatment mean: i.e., T_k/r.

The estimation problem is solved to an appreciable extent then if we can find a quantity whose expectation is a known multiple of $\sum_{ij} e^2_{ij}$ and if we can make statements about the joint distributions of the estimates and their errors. The method of estimating $\sum_{ij} e^2_{ij}$ is based on the analysis of variance, involving a division of the total sum of squares into portions for blocks, treatments, and error. For we have the identity

$$\sum_{ik} (y_{ik} - y_{..})^2 = t \sum_i (y_{i.} - y_{..})^2 + r \sum_k (y_{\cdot k} - y_{..})^2$$

$$+ \sum_{ik} (y_{ik} - y_{i.} - y_{\cdot k} + y_{..})^2$$

where as usual $y_{i.} = \dfrac{1}{t} \sum_k y_{ik}$, and so on. The expectations of the terms on the right-hand side are easily obtained. The first term, the block sum of squares, is a constant and equal to $t\Sigma b^2_i$. The second term, the treatment sum of squares, is also expressible as

$$\frac{1}{r} \sum_k T^2_k - \frac{(\Sigma T_k)^2}{rt}$$

and the quantity ΣT_k is equal to $rt\mu$ and contains no errors. The expectation of the treatment sum of squares is then $\dfrac{1}{r} \Sigma e^2_{ij} + r\Sigma t^2_k$. The total sum of squares, that is the quantity on the left-hand side, is equal to $\Sigma e^2_{ij} + r\Sigma t^2_k + t\Sigma b^2_i$, and the third term on the right-hand side may be obtained by subtraction. Thus we have the analysis of variance (Table 8.1).

TABLE 8.1

Due to	Sum of Squares	Expectation of Sum of Squares
Blocks	$t \sum_i (y_{i.} - y_{..})^2$	$t\Sigma b^2_i$
Treatments	$r \sum_k (y_{\cdot k} - y_{..})^2$	$\dfrac{1}{r} \sum_{ij} e^2_{ij} + r\Sigma t^2_k$
Remainder	$\sum_{ik} (y_{ik} - y_{i.} - y_{\cdot k} + y_{..})^2$	$\dfrac{r-1}{r} \sum_{ij} e^2_{ij}$
Total	$\sum_{ik} (y_{ik} - y_{..})^2$	$\sum_{ij} e^2_{ij} + r\Sigma t^2_k + t\Sigma b^2_i$

If we divide the remainder sum of squares by $(r - 1)(t - 1)$, we obtain a quantity whose expectation is $\dfrac{1}{r(t - 1)} \sum_{ij} e^2_{ij}$, and, if we denote this by σ^2, the variance of a treatment difference is $2\sigma^2/r$. We may introduce the degrees of freedom for the remainder or error sum of squares of $(r - 1)(t - 1)$ for this reason if we wish, though we usually justify this number because the error sum of squares is the sum of squares of $(r - 1)(t - 1)$ linearly independent quantities. Also, if we divide the treatment sum of squares by $(t - 1)$, its degrees of freedom, we see that the expectation of the treatment mean square is

$$\frac{1}{r(t - 1)} \sum_{ij} e^2{}_{ij} + \frac{r}{t - 1} \Sigma t^2{}_k$$

If there are no treatment effects, the expectation of the treatment mean square is equal to the expectation of the error mean square. This is the property of unbiasedness, which is an essential property of an experimental design.

We see, therefore, that any comparison of the treatment effects

$$\Sigma \lambda_k t_k \quad \text{with} \quad \Sigma \lambda_k = 0$$

is estimated unbiasedly by the same comparison of the observed treatment means, with a variance equal to

$$(\Sigma \lambda^2{}_k) \frac{\sigma^2}{r}$$

where σ^2 is the expectation of the error mean square. It should be noted that we have used no assumptions about the errors, except that there are fixed deviations of plot values from block means, which are attached at random to the treatment yields. We have used no assumption of homogeneity of errors, using the word "error" to denote the quantity $\sum_j \delta^k_{ij} e_{ij}$, which is the error of the observed yield, nor have we assumed that, for example, $\sum_j e^2{}_{ij}$ is the same for all values of i. It remains to us now to consider the distribution of estimates and errors.

We shall first consider the test of the hypothesis that there are no treatment effects: that is, that the t_k's are all zero. For this purpose it is necessary to obtain the distribution of the treatment sum of squares, the error sum of squares, or the criterion of (treatment mean square/error mean square) over the $(t!)^r$ possible randomizations in the absence of treatment effects. We note that, if we denote $\sum_{ij} e^2{}_{ij}$ by S, the sum of the treatment sum of squares and the error sum of squares is then equal to S. We have already found that the expectation of the treatment sum of squares T is S/r. After some straightforward but tedious algebra, it is found that the variance of T over the population of randomizations is

$$\frac{2}{(t-1)r^2}(S^2 - K) \tag{11}$$

where

$$K = \sum_i \left(\sum_j e^2_{ij}\right)^2 \tag{12}$$

If the errors of the blocks are homogeneous, then $\sum_j e^2_{ij} = S/r$ for each i, so that $K = S^2/r$, and the variance of T is

$$\frac{2(r-1)}{(t-1)r^3}S^2 \tag{13}$$

If the e_{ij}'s were normally and independently distributed, the quantity $\dfrac{T}{t-1}\bigg/\dfrac{S-T}{(r-1)(t-1)}$ would follow the F distribution (cf. Chapters 5 and 6), and the quantity T/S would follow the beta distribution,

$$f(x) = \frac{\Gamma\left(\dfrac{m+n}{2}\right)}{\Gamma\left(\dfrac{m}{2}\right)\Gamma\left(\dfrac{n}{2}\right)} x^{\frac{m}{2}-1}(1-x)^{\frac{n}{2}-1} \tag{14}$$

where $m = (t-1)$ and $n = (r-1)(t-1)$, the degrees of freedom, respectively, for T and $S-T$. The mean of this distribution is $\dfrac{m}{m+n}$, and the variance is

$$\frac{2mn}{(m+n)^2(m+n+2)}$$

If the distribution of T/S is to be representable by the beta distribution, the two distributions should at least have the same mean and variance. The mean of the distribution of T/S is $1/r$, and the mean of the beta distribution is $\dfrac{(t-1)}{(r-1)(t-1)+(t-1)}$, which equals $1/r$. The variance of the distribution of T/S we have found to be $2(r-1)/(t-1)r^3$, under certain specified conditions. The variance of the beta distribution is very closely approximated by

$$\frac{2(r-1)(t-1)^2}{[r(t-1)]^3} \quad \text{or} \quad \frac{2(r-1)}{(t-1)r^3}$$

if 2 is small compared to $r(t-1)$. The agreement is remarkable, and we may conclude that, if the error variance is the same for all the blocks, the distribution of T/S is fairly accurately represented by the beta distribution. It then follows that the distribution of the quantity $\dfrac{T}{t-1} \Big/ \dfrac{(S-T)}{(r-1)(t-1)}$ or, in words, of the criterion (treatment mean square/error mean square) is fairly accurately represented by the ordinary F distribution. This was proved by Welch [1] and Pitman,[2] the latter also making an examination of the third and fourth moments of T/S.

If we denote $\sum_j e^2{}_{ij}$ by S_i so that ΣS_i equals S, and $\dfrac{1}{r} S$ by $\bar{S}$, the variance of T/S over the population of randomizations is equal to

$$\frac{2}{(t-1)r^2S^2} \left[S^2 - \frac{S^2}{r} - \Sigma(S_i - \bar{S})^2 \right]$$

or

$$\frac{2(r-1)}{r^3(t-1)} \left[1 - \frac{r}{r-1} \frac{\Sigma(S_i - \bar{S})^2}{S^2} \right]$$

or

$$\frac{2(r-1)}{(t-1)r^3} \left[1 - \frac{\Sigma(S_i - \bar{S})^2}{r(r-1)\bar{S}^2} \right] \tag{15}$$

If the errors of the blocks are homogeneous, S_i equals $\bar{S}$, and we have the previous expression again.

Heterogeneity of the errors does not affect the mean of the distribution of T/S but reduces the variance. As an example of the effect of heterogeneity, let us suppose that we have an experiment in 4 blocks and that one of the blocks is 3 times as variable as the others. Then the variance of the distribution of T/S will be $\frac{1}{9}$ less than if the error variances were homogeneous. If, in addition, we suppose that there are 6 treatments, the parameters m and n of the beta distribution, which closely represents the randomization distribution, are given by the equations,

$$\frac{m}{m+n} = \frac{1}{r}, \qquad \frac{2mn}{(m+n)^3} = \frac{2(r-1)}{(t-1)r^3} \times \frac{8}{9}$$

or

$$\frac{m}{m+n} = \frac{1}{4}, \qquad \frac{2mn}{(m+n)^3} = \frac{1}{60}$$

The solution to these equations is $m = {}^{360}\!\!/_{64}$ and $n = 3m$. In order to obtain the level of significance by the randomization test, we should then compare the criterion (treatment mean square/error mean square) to the F distribution with about 6 and 17 degrees of freedom, instead of the F distribution with 5 and 15 degrees of freedom. The general effect of heterogeneity of errors will be that the ordinary use of the F distribution underestimates the level of significance of the randomization test. Just how much the underestimation will be in a particular situation may be calculated on the lines of the example above. Although there remains the problem of the accurate evaluation of the difference between the approximation and the true value and the size of experiment necessary for this difference to be small, we may rely on the F distribution to give us a sufficiently accurate evaluation of the level of significance except for very small experiments.

We found above that any treatment comparison

$$\sum_k \lambda_k l_k$$

is estimated by

$$\sum_k \lambda_k \overline{T}_k$$

with a variance equal to

$$\frac{(\Sigma\lambda^2_k)}{r} \frac{\displaystyle\sum_{ij} e^2{}_{ij}}{r(t-1)} \quad \text{or} \quad \frac{1}{r}(\Sigma\lambda^2_k)\frac{S}{r(t-1)}$$

The expectation of the error mean square E is $S/r(t-1)$, which we have called σ^2, and so we shall state that the estimated variance of the estimate of the comparison is $\dfrac{1}{r}(\Sigma\lambda^2_k)E$. In order that this statement may be of value to us, however, we need to be able to assume that the t distribution or some other easily handled distribution holds for the ratio of the error of the comparison to the estimated standard error of the comparison. In this connection we must note that the distribution of the error sum of squares has a mean of $(r-1)(t-1)\sigma^2$, and a variance equal to that of T, because S is a constant: that is, a variance of $\dfrac{2(r-1)S^2}{(t-1)r^3}$ or $\dfrac{2(r-1)(t-1)}{r}\sigma^4$. With the normal model theory of

Chapter 6 we noted that the error sum of squares was distributed as $\chi^2\sigma^2$ with $(r - 1)(t - 1)$ degrees of freedom. This distribution has a mean of $(r - 1)(t - 1)\sigma^2$, and a variance of $2(r - 1)(t - 1)\sigma^4$. The fact that the variance of the error sum of squares under randomization is less by a factor of r could have been expected from the fact that in a sense we are considering the sum of squares of a random sample of $(r - 1)(t - 1)$ deviates from a finite population of $r(t - 1)$ deviates. There does not appear to be a strict justification for using the t test for individual comparisons, but rather we rely on the general applicability of the t distribution to a wide range of problems.

We may note that we can construct a set of $(t - 1)$ normalized orthogonal comparisons of the treatments, say,

$$\gamma_p = \sum_k \lambda_{pk} t_k, \qquad p = 1, 2, \cdots, t - 1 \qquad (16)$$

with

$$\sum_k \lambda_{pk} = 0, \quad \sum_k \lambda^2_{pk} = 1, \quad \text{and} \quad \sum_k \lambda_{pk}\lambda_{p'k} = 0, \quad p' \neq p$$

Each of these comparisons may be estimated in each block by the corresponding comparison of yields, and it is easily verified that in block i the estimate, say, C_{pi}, has a variance of $\sum_j e^2_{ij}/(t - 1)$ and that the comparisons are uncorrelated. If we denote $\sum_j e^2_{ij}/(t - 1)$ by σ^2_i and consider any one comparison for all the blocks, we have r uncorrelated estimates of this comparison with variances $\sigma^2_1, \sigma^2_2, \cdots, \sigma^2_r$, respectively, for each estimate. The assumption of homogeneity of errror that we made above is the assumption that

$$\sigma^2_1 = \sigma^2_2 = \cdots = \sigma^2_r = \sigma^2$$

If this assumption is true and we make up a set of orthogonal comparisons and obtain an error sum of squares for each with $(r - 1)$ degrees of freedom, then we should find that the $(t - 1)$ sums of squares are homogeneous. It does not appear likely, however, that Bartlett's test of homogeneity of variances would apply to this case, because we noted above that the total sum of squares for error is not distributed approximately as $\chi^2\sigma^2$ over the possible randomizations.*

This brings to light an additional point in regard to estimation, that it is desirable that the variance within the blocks be constant, for we know that, if we have uncorrelated and unbiased estimates $\hat{\gamma}_i$ of a parameter γ with variance σ^2_i, $i = 1, 2, \cdots, n$, the best linear unbiased

---

* An empirical examination by W. D. Barclay (M.S. thesis Iowa State College) has indicated that t tests are satisfactory but that Bartlett's criterion does not have the appropriate distribution over randomizations.

estimate of γ is

$$\frac{\sum_i \frac{\hat{\gamma}_i}{\sigma^2_i}}{\sum_i \frac{1}{\sigma^2_i}}$$

which has a variance of

$$\frac{1}{\sum_i \frac{1}{\sigma^2_i}}$$

We shall always use arithmetic means in a randomized block experiment, and the variance of the arithmetic mean is

$$\frac{1}{n^2}\left(\sum_i \sigma^2_i\right)$$

If the σ^2_i's vary considerably, we may have very inefficient estimates. For example, if we have two estimates, $\hat{\gamma}_1$ and $\hat{\gamma}_2$, with variances of 1 and 11, respectively, the variance of the arithmetic mean is 3, which is 3 times the variance of the estimate $\hat{\gamma}_1$ *alone*. The variance of the weighted estimate is $11/12$, which is, of course, lower than the variance of $\hat{\gamma}_1$. It is desirable from the point of view of estimation therefore that the variances within blocks be approximately the same. We may expect that F tests will be more accurate in this case also, as we have seen earlier.

We have not given the results for the completely randomized design because they are essentially the same as in the randomized block case.

8.3 THE ANALYSIS OF RANDOMIZED BLOCKS WITH NON-ADDITIVITY

We now formulate a model in which additivity does not hold. Consider any block given by the subscript i, the plots within the block given by the subscript j, and the treatment given by the subscript k. Let y_{ijk} be the yield of plot j in block i under treatment k. In performing an experiment we obtain a balanced sample of the y_{ijk}'s. We may write

$$y_{ijk} = y\cdots + (y_{i}\cdots - y\cdots) + (y_{ij}\cdot - y_{i}\cdots) + (y\cdot_{\cdot k} - y\cdots)$$
$$+ (y_{i}\cdot_k - y_{i}\cdots - y\cdot_{\cdot k} + y\cdots) + (y_{ijk} - y_{ij}\cdot - y_{i}\cdot_k + y_{i}\cdots) \quad (17)$$

This is an algebraic identity, the replacement of a subscript by a dot indicating that an average over the values of that subscript has been taken. The terms on the right-hand side have practical meaning:

1. $y\ldots$: the mean over the whole experiment, if each treatment could be applied to each plot.

2. $y_{i\cdot\cdot} - y\ldots$: the deviation of the block mean from the over-all mean, averaging over all treatments.

3. $y_{ij\cdot} - y_{i\cdot\cdot}$: the deviation of the jth plot from the block mean, averaging over all treatments.

4. $y_{\cdot\cdot k} - y\ldots$: the deviation of the kth treatment from the over-all mean, averaging over all plots.

5. $(y_{i\cdot k} - y_{i\cdot\cdot} - y_{\cdot\cdot k} + y\ldots)$: the deviation of the effect of the kth treatment in block i from the effect over all blocks.

6. $(y_{ijk} - y_{ij\cdot} - y_{i\cdot k} + y_{i\cdot\cdot})$: the deviation of the effect of the kth treatment on the jth plot of the ith block from the average effect in the ith block.

We now take into account the fact that we observe, say, y_{ik}, which equals the yield of the kth treatment in the ith block and which occurs on a randomly chosen plot. It should be noted that we distinguish the members of the population of possible results y_{ijk} from the observed result y_{ik}, the latter containing only two subscripts, one for the block and one for the treatment.

Then,

$$y_{ik} = \mu + b_i + t_k + e_{ik} + (bt)_{ik} + \eta_{ijk} \qquad (18)$$

where

$$\mu = y\ldots, \qquad b_i = y_{i\cdot\cdot} - y\ldots, \qquad t_k = y_{\cdot\cdot k} - y\ldots$$

e_{ik} is the random variable which takes the values $y_{ij\cdot} - y_{i\cdot\cdot}$ if treatment k occurs on plot j,

$$(bt)_{ik} = (y_{i\cdot k} - y_{i\cdot\cdot} - y_{\cdot\cdot k} + y\ldots)$$

and is the same regardless of the plot to which treatment k happens to be allocated, and

$$\eta_{ijk} = (y_{ijk} - y_{ij\cdot} - y_{i\cdot k} + y_{i\cdot\cdot})$$

if treatment k occurs on plot j.

We note that the difference between this model and the one we had previously is that the present one contains two additional terms. The first, $(bt)_{ik}$, measures the extent to which effects differ from block to block and is not a random variable unless we consider that we have a random sample of some population of blocks. The second, η_{ijk}, measures the extent to which the effect of the kth treatment on plot (ij) is different from the effect of treatment k averaging over the plots in the ith block and is a random variable as far as treatment k is concerned.

A method of writing the model which exhibits the random variable nature of some of the terms is to use the symbol δ_{ij}^k of the previous section. The model then becomes

$$y_{ik} = \mu + b_i + t_k + (bt)_{ik} + \sum_j \delta_{ij}^k e_{ij} + \sum_j \delta_{ij}^k \eta_{ijk} \qquad (19)$$

It is instructive to examine what the usual estimates in fact estimate, if this is the true model. Since

$$E(\delta_{ij}^k) = \frac{1}{t}, \quad \sum_i (bt)_{ik} = \sum_k (bt)_{ik} = 0, \quad \sum_j e_{ij} = 0, \quad \text{and} \quad \sum_j \eta_{ijk} = 0 \qquad (20)$$

a treatment total $\sum_i y_{ik}$ has an expectation of

$$r\mu + rb. + rt_k$$

i.e., the observed treatment mean estimates the mean that would have been obtained had the whole of the experimental material been subjected to treatment k.

Now let us examine the usual analysis of variance (Table 8.2).

TABLE 8.2

Due to	df	Sum of Squares	Mean Square
Blocks	$r - 1$	$\frac{1}{t} \sum_i Y^2{}_i. - Y^2../rt$	
Treatments	$t - 1$	$\frac{1}{r} \sum_k Y^2._k - Y^2../rt$	
Error	$(r - 1)(t - 1)$	By subtraction	
Total	$rt - 1$	$\Sigma y^2_{ik} - Y^2../rt$	

It is a straightforward job to evaluate the expectation of the respective sums of squares and, hence, of the mean squares. As an example, consider $Y^2{}_i.$. Now,

$$Y_i. = t\mu + tb_i + \sum_k \sum_j \delta_{ij}^k e_{ij} + \sum_k \sum_j \delta_{ij}^k \eta_{ijk}$$

But

$$\sum_k \delta_{ij}^k = 1 \quad \text{and} \quad \sum_j e_{ij} = 0$$

so

$$Y_i. = t\mu + tb_i + \sum_k \sum_j \delta_{ij}^k \eta_{ijk}$$

and

$$Y^2{}_i. = t^2\mu^2 + t^2 b^2{}_i + 2t^2\mu b_i + 2t(\mu + b_i) \sum_k \sum_j \delta_{ij}^k \eta_{ijk} + \left(\sum_k \sum_j \delta_{ij}^k \eta_{ijk} \right)^2$$

Now,

$$E(\delta_{ij}^k) = \frac{1}{t} \quad \text{and} \quad \sum_j (\eta_{ijk}) = 0$$

so that

$$E[2t(\mu + b_i) \sum_k \sum_j \delta_{ij}^k \eta_{ijk}] = 0$$

Also,

$$\left(\sum_k \sum_j \delta_{ij}^k \eta_{ijk} \right)^2 = \sum_{kj} (\delta_{ij}^k)^2 \eta^2_{ijk} + \sum_{k' \neq k} \sum_j (\delta_{ij}^k)(\delta_{ij}^{k'}) \eta_{ijk}\eta_{ijk'}$$
$$+ \sum_k \sum_{j' \neq j} \delta_{ij}^k \delta_{ij'}^k \eta_{ijk}\eta_{ij'k} + \sum_{k' \neq k} \sum_{j' \neq j} \delta_{ij}^k \delta_{ij'}^{k'} \eta_{ijk}\eta_{ij'k'}$$

and, since

$$E[(\delta_{ij}^k)^2] = \frac{1}{t}$$

$$\delta_{ij}^k \delta_{ij}^{k'} = 0, \qquad k' \neq k$$

$$\delta_{ij}^k \delta_{ij'}^k = 0, \qquad j' \neq j$$

and

$$E(\delta_{ij}^k \delta_{ij'}^{k'}) = \frac{1}{t(t-1)}, \qquad j' \neq j, \quad k' \neq k$$

we find that

$$E\left(\sum_k \sum_j \delta_{ij}^k \eta_{ijk} \right)^2 = \frac{1}{t} \sum_{kj} \eta^2_{ijk} + \frac{1}{t(t-1)} \sum_{k' \neq k} \sum_{j' \neq j} \eta_{ijk}\eta_{ij'k'}$$

$$= \frac{1}{t} \sum_{kj} \eta^2_{ijk} - \frac{1}{t(t-1)} \sum_{k' \neq k} \sum_j \eta_{ijk}\eta_{ijk'}$$

$$= \frac{1}{t} \sum_{kj} \eta^2_{ijk} + \frac{1}{t(t-1)} \sum_{kj} \eta^2_{ijk}$$

$$= \frac{1}{t-1} \sum_{kj} \eta^2_{ijk} \tag{21}$$

The expectation of all the other terms may be evaluated similarly, and the result shown in Table 8.3 is obtained, where

$$\zeta_{ijk} = e_{ij} + \eta_{ijk}$$

TABLE 8.3   EXPECTATION OF MEAN SQUARES UNDER RANDOMIZATION

Due to	df	Expectation of Mean Square
Blocks	$r-1$	$\frac{1}{rt(t-1)} \sum_{ijk} \eta^2_{ijk} + \frac{t}{r-1} \Sigma b^2_i$
Treatments	$t-1$	$\frac{1}{rt(t-1)} \sum_{ijk} \zeta^2_{ijk} - \frac{1}{rt(t-1)^2} \sum_{ijk} \eta^2_{ijk} + \frac{r}{t-1} \sum_k t^2_k$
Error	$(r-1)(t-1)$	$\frac{1}{rt(t-1)} \sum_{ijk} \zeta^2_{ijk} - \frac{1}{rt(t-1)^2} \sum_{ijk} \eta^2_{ijk} + \frac{1}{(r-1)(t-1)} \sum_{ik} (bt)^2_{ik}$
Total	$rt-1$	

We have incidentally proved again the unbiased character of the randomized block design under the null hypothesis that the treatments have identical effects on all plots, for, in that case,

$$\eta_{ijk} = 0, \quad \text{all } i, j, k$$

$$(bt)_{ik} = 0, \quad \text{all } i, k$$

It should be noted that we are considering the estimation problem. The analysis of variance given in Table 8.3 is entirely irrelevant from the point of view of the testing of the hypothesis, that there are no treatment effects, for we have obtained the expectations over the population of possible experiments that we could have obtained. As regards the testing of the hypothesis, we shall obtain one experiment only, and we shall apply the randomization test procedure to that one experiment. This test procedure would consist of superimposing all the possible randomizations on the set of yields we would obtain in the particular experiment and evaluating some criterion for each randomization. If this criterion is in the critical region, we reject the hypothesis that there are no treatment effects. It is difficult to visualize the effect of non-additive treatment effects on the sensitivity of this test: that is, on the proportion of the possible experiments we could have obtained with particular non-additive treatment effects, which would have indicated by the randomization test that there are treatment effects.

If the treatment effects are not additive, the observed mean of a treatment will estimate the mean yield we would have obtained had the whole experimental area been subjected to that treatment. Comparisons of these means will be of value to the experimenter, because they give estimates of treatment differences over a well-defined population. It is necessary, however, to consider under what circumstances we may attach a standard error to these means which can be interpreted in the usual manner. If we write

$$y_{ik} = \mu + b_i + t_k + (bt)_{ik} + \epsilon_{ik} \tag{22}$$

it is easily found that

$$E(\epsilon^2_{ik}) = \frac{1}{t} \sum_j (y_{ijk} - y_{i \cdot k})^2$$

$$E(\epsilon_{ik}\epsilon_{ik'}) = \frac{1}{t(t-1)} \sum_j (y_{ijk} - y_{i \cdot k})(y_{ijk'} - y_{i \cdot k'}), \qquad k' \neq k$$

$$E(\epsilon_{ik}\epsilon_{i'k'}) = 0 \quad \text{for any } k, k' \quad \text{and} \quad i \neq i'$$

If we could assume that

$$\frac{1}{t} \sum_j (y_{ijk} - y_{i \cdot k})^2 = \sigma^2{}_{ik} \tag{23}$$

is constant for all blocks and treatments and equal to $\sigma^2{}_1$, say, and that

$$\frac{1}{t} \sum_j (y_{ijk} - y_{i \cdot k})(y_{ijk'} - y_{i \cdot k'}) = \rho \sigma^2{}_1 \tag{24}$$

for all i's and all k's and k''s, the variance of a treatment comparison

$$\sum_k \lambda_k y_{\cdot k}, \ \Sigma \lambda_k = 0$$

would be

$$(\Sigma \lambda^2{}_k) \frac{\sigma^2{}_1}{r} \left(1 + \frac{\rho}{t-1} \right) \tag{25}$$

Furthermore, if the terms $(bt)_{ik}$ are zero, the expectation of the error mean square is equal to $\sigma^2{}_1 \left(1 + \dfrac{\rho}{t-1} \right)$. If E is the observed mean square, the variance of the comparison would be estimated by $(\Sigma \lambda^2{}_k) E/r$, which is the usual process.

The above assumptions are, however, not easy to justify from a practical point of view. The constancy of $\sigma^2{}_{ik}$ appears fairly reasonable, though it is likely that $\sigma^2{}_{ik}$ depends on k unless the treatments are additive in their effects. The assumption of constant correlations is not entirely reasonable because, if 2 treatments k and k' are, in fact, identical in their effects, the assumption that

$$\frac{1}{t} \sum_j (y_{ijk} - y_{i \cdot k})(y_{ijk'} - y_{i \cdot k'}) = \rho \sigma^2{}_1$$

implies that

$$\frac{1}{t} \sum_j (y_{ijk} - y_{i \cdot k})^2 = \rho \sigma^2{}_1$$

whereas we have already assumed it to be equal to $\sigma^2{}_1$. Since, however, ρ cannot be greater than unity, the effect of the correlation term in the variance will be small if we have several treatments.

It appears therefore that we can justify the usual process of estimating the errors of treatment comparisons if we can assume that $\sigma^2{}_{ik}$ is constant and that there are no block-treatment interactions. If the assumption that the block-treatment interactions are not zero is incorrect, we shall overestimate the standard error of the treatment comparison, as an estimate of the true treatment comparison for the whole experimental area. The applicability of the t test when block-treatment interactions are not negligible, cannot be examined without postulating some distribution of the terms $(y_{ijk} - y_{i \cdot k})$. It may be suspected, however, as for the case when additivity holds, that the usual t test is somewhat conservative.

8.4   METHOD OF ANALYSIS USED IN SUBSEQUENT CHAPTERS

The methods of analysis of experimental data given in Chapters 5 and 6 are based on a model containing fixed environmental and treatment effects with an error which is normally and independently distributed around a mean of zero with constant variance (or known relative variances). The difficulty inherent in this approach is that the population of experimental units and repetitions of the experiment about which the inferences are made are unspecified. For this reason we considered it desirable to examine the possibilities of making inferences about the experimental units actually used. The analysis given above for the case when additivity holds is based only on the repetitions given by the set of possible randomization patterns. It provides a test of the effects of the treatments as actually applied on the experimental units used.

It should be noted, however, that the analysis given in section 8.2 concerns certain errors only, in that we suppose that, if treatment k is placed on plot (ij), the yield is given by

$$y_{ik} = x_{ij} + t_k$$

The quantity e_{ij} which we have used in earlier sections may be called the plot error, and the analysis of section 8.2 dealt only with these plot errors. In general, we may expect that there will be other errors due to variations in experimental technique, or extraneous factors. These variations should have small effects, and, if, for example, variations in experimental technique, such as the exact amount of stimulus applied to an experimental unit, cannot be considered small, further definition of the problem under investigation is necessary. From the point of view of estimation of treatment differences, we therefore adopt the model

$$y_{ik} = \mu + b_i + t_k + e_{ik} \tag{26}$$

where the error e_{ik} now contains the plot errors and the other errors. We have seen that orthogonal comparisons of treatments within the blocks have plot errors that have expectation zero, are uncorrelated, and have the same variance. We may assume that the errors due to extraneous factors are uncorrelated, with expectation zero and constant variance.

Therefore, in the model 26, the quantities μ, b_i, and t_k are fixed unknown constants, and the e_{ik}'s may be regarded as being uncorrelated, with expectation zero and constant variance, because, using this model, we shall estimate treatment comparisons by within-block comparisons. This model we shall term the finite model, and it is the one we shall use for most purposes. We prefer it to the infinite model which has the same components but in which the e_{ik}'s are assumed to be independently normally distributed, because the main component of the errors will usually be the plot errors, and these are not normally distributed. For tests of significance we shall rely on the approximation to the randomization test by the F test and on the assumption that the normal theory tests may be used for tests of individual comparisons and similar questions, realizing that they may possibly be somewhat in error if there are only plot errors. We shall regard the inferences that we make as being inferences about the experimental units actually used, the extrapolation of these to a broader population being a matter of judgment in the present state of knowledge. This is not, of course, the case when a broader population is introduced at the beginning of the investigation and random samples of it are used.

The main requirements on the use of the model are that we have additivity of treatment effects and that we have homogeneity of errors. The main device to obtain these is the use of a transformation, and this is discussed in a later section. The two requirements are not necessarily consistent, and it appears that additivity is the more important one, because we may expect plot errors to be the more important ones generally.

Occasionally, we may find that no simple transformation of the data appears to give a reasonable approximation to additivity. We may then consider orthogonal contrasts among the treatments and evaluate an error for each with $(r - 1)$ degrees of freedom. Such a procedure in a small experiment has doubtful value when the orthogonal contrasts are made up on the basis of the observed yields, for we are then using a procedure the operating characteristics of which would be very difficult to ascertain. If the interpretation made of the experiment depends at all markedly on the choice of orthogonal contrasts, we may conclude that the experiment is of little value.

There is considerable discussion in the literature of the problems we have examined, and we may refer the reader to the papers by Neyman et al.[3] and McCarthy [4] on the problem of tests of hypotheses that the average effects of treatments are identical. We may also refer the reader to the paper by Anscombe [5] for a discussion of the general problem of inference from experiments.

We may conclude this section with the observation that, even if our inferences from experimental designs are open to some criticism, we can take the position that we are following rules of action and interpretation of which we know the operating characteristics under perfect conditions and for which there appear to be no good substitutes. There are three separate parts of the whole procedure which can be altered.

First, we can decide to take observations according to some pattern other than a randomized pattern; that is, we can use a systematic design. There is an extensive discussion of this point in the literature, and we may refer the reader to Fisher,[6] Barbacki and Fisher,[7] Yates,[8] and Student.[9, 9a] Insofar as there is no possibility of estimating the errors of treatment comparisons for systematic designs even when additivity holds, without very considerable replication or prior knowledge, we shall not consider the systematic designs at all in this book. The joint probability distribution of the numbers δ^k_{ij} determines the pattern of observations to be taken, and, although it would perhaps be interesting to consider distributions other than the one that is generally used, it is clear from the derivation of the estimates and errors of estimates in section 8.2 that recourse to a distribution other than the one used would render the estimation of errors very difficult even with additivity.

Second, we may consider different tests and test criteria to be applied to the data of the individual experiment. The randomization test is preferred because no assumption of distributions is necessary. The use of the criterion (treatment mean square/error mean square) is deemed best because we can obtain reasonably accurate significance levels for this criterion very easily. The fact that the test based on this criterion has optimum properties with samples from normal populations is an additional reason of some force.

The third part of the process is the estimation of effects, and the procedure we follow does not appear to have a preferable substitute that is manageable and realistic.

8.5 TRANSFORMATIONS

We have mentioned the problem of the choice of scale of measurement, and we have seen that, if we can find a scale of measurement on which treatment effects are additive, the examination of the experiment and the presentation of the results are straightforward. Since we shall not usually be able to specify a scale on which effects will be additive, it is necessary to consider means of examining the experimental data to discover non-additivity. We shall in a later section describe Tukey's test for non-additivity, which is however based on normal or infinite model theory. As a rough test we may utilize the fact that we can partition the error sum of squares into $(t - 1)$ sums of squares, each with $(r - 1)$ degrees of freedom. It is unlikely that we can test these accurately by Bartlett's test as we have already noted. However, if they are markedly different we may need to examine some transformations. A better procedure, if there are small block differences, is to examine the range r for each treatment in relation to the mean m. If this examination suggests that $r = g(m)$, we may be fairly confident that the transformation given by

$$f(y) = \int \frac{dy}{g(y)} \tag{27}$$

will result in closer conformity to additivity. This procedure is suggested by normal theory, in that the range will be proportional approximately to the standard deviation. If $\sigma_y = g(y)$, then approximately $\operatorname{var}[f(y)] = [f'(y)]^2[g(y)]^2$, and, if the variance of the transformed variable $f(y)$ is to be constant, we must have

$$f'(y) \; : \; \frac{1}{g(y)} \quad \text{or} \quad f(y) \; : \; \int \frac{dy}{g(y)}$$

Thus, if the range appears to be proportional to the mean, a logarithmic transformation will be useful, and, if the (range)^2 is proportional to the mean, a square root transformation should be made.

It we use normal law theory in the analysis of experiments, the essential conditions for the applicability of the methods of Chapters 5 and 6 are that the yield be composed additively of environmental effects, treatment effects, and error, the errors being normally and independently distributed with mean zero and constant variance. If we are using a linear model, the minimum conditions for the application of least squares are that additivity holds as before and that the errors are uncorrelated with zero mean and known relative variances, preferably constant.

It is, perhaps, unnecessary to state that, if a transformation is used, the best estimates of the treatment means on the untransformed scale are obtained by transforming back the means of the transformed variate. Similarly, confidence intervals must be obtained on the transformed variate.

In general, in the analysis of experimental data, our procedure is to obtain a transformation that results in homogeneity of error variance and to assume that deviations from additivity on the transformed scale are small. Heterogeneity of error variance usually arises from a relationship of variance to mean and will often be due to non-additivity, so that our choice of transformation depends on the relation between variance and mean of observations. This relation must be determined generally from the actual data by a device such as that mentioned above of comparing the mean under treatments with the range. Another device which is occasionally helpful is to examine the deviations of observed values from what would be expected with additivity and constant variance. A plotting of

$$\left| x_{ik} - x_{i\cdot} - x_{\cdot k} + x_{\cdot\cdot} \right|$$

against x_{ik} will indicate whether a transformation has been reasonably successful.

A transformation may be suggested on the basis of the method of collection of the observations. If, for example, we are observing proportions by examining a random sample of individuals within each plot, we know that the variance of an observed p is

$$\frac{P(1 - P)}{n}$$

where P is the true proportion. It is easily verified that the appropriate transformation is $\sin^{-1} \sqrt{p}$, and, furthermore, if there is no heterogeneity between the plots, the variance of the transformed variate will be $0.25/n$ or $821/n$, according as $\sin^{-1} \sqrt{p}$ is measured in radians or degrees.

The term heterogeneity as used here should be defined more precisely. Suppose we are performing an experiment to determine the response curve of a biological population to some killing drug, and for the purpose we draw 4 random samples of, say, 20 individuals, these samples being exposed to doses of 0, 1, 2, 3 units of the drug, respectively. The number that die at each dose is recorded. Now it may possibly be (and is frequently) assumed that the distribution of the tolerance (the amount of drug that will just kill an individual) in the population is one of some specified family of distributions. It is possible that experimental conditions are so well under control that the only differences apart from treatment between the groups tested with various amounts of the drug arise because they are different random samples of the same population. In other words, it is possible that there are no extraneous forces that cause groups treated with the same amount to vary more than would be expected under the binomial law. If the groups were, for example, exposed to the drug on different days, one would expect that environmental forces would tend to cause greater variation. The statement "if there is no heterogeneity" is then interpreted as meaning in the absence of extraneous factors producing variation. Heterogeneity is essentially the same as the existence of plot errors, which we discussed earlier. The transformation obtained in the above way is not designed to deal with the extraneous variation, though it may well do so. In particular instances the effect of the heterogeneity may be small, but, on the other hand, it does not seem reasonable to assume that there are no plot errors. No transformation may be expected to work perfectly, and it is this fact more than any other that vitiates extensive computations to fit a computationally awkward transformation.

With these remarks in mind we list in Table 8.4 from Bartlett [10] transformations that have been found to have practical value.

TABLE 8.4

Variance in Terms of Mean m	Transformation	Approximate Variance on New Scale in Absence of Heterogeneity	Parent Distribution	Reference
$\left.\begin{array}{l} m \\ \lambda^2 m \end{array}\right\}$	$\sqrt{x}$ or $\sqrt{x+\frac{1}{2}}$ for small integers	$\left\{\begin{array}{l} 0.25 \\ 0.25\lambda^2 \end{array}\right.$	Poisson Empirical	11 ..
$\lambda^2 m^2$	$\left\{\begin{array}{l} \log_e x,\ \log_e (x+1) \\ \log_{10} x,\ \log_{10} (x+1) \end{array}\right.$	λ^2 $0.189\lambda^2$	 Empirical	 ..
$\dfrac{2m^2}{n-1}$	$\log_e x$	$\dfrac{2}{n-1}$	Sample variance	12
$\dfrac{m(1-m)}{n}$	$\left\{\begin{array}{l} \sin^{-1}\sqrt{x}\ \text{(degrees)} \\ \sin^{-1}\sqrt{x}\ \text{(radians)} \end{array}\right.$	$\left.\begin{array}{l} 821/n \\ 0.25/n \end{array}\right\}$	Binomial	13
$km(1-m)$	$\sin^{-1}\sqrt{x}\ \text{(radians)}$	$0.25k$	Empirical	..
$\lambda^2 m^2(1-m)^2$	$\log_e \left(\dfrac{x}{1-x}\right)$	λ^2	Empirical	..
$\dfrac{(1-m^2)^2}{n-1}$	$\frac{1}{2}\log_e \left(\dfrac{1+x}{1-x}\right)$	$\dfrac{1}{n-3}$	Sample correlation	14
$m + \lambda^2 m^2$	$\lambda^{-1}\sinh^{-1}(\lambda\sqrt{x})$ or $\lambda^{-1}\sinh^{-1}(\lambda\sqrt{x+\frac{1}{2}})$ for small integers	0.25	Negative binomial	15
$\mu^2(m + \lambda^2 m^2)$	$\lambda^{-1}\sinh^{-1}(\lambda\sqrt{x})$ or $\lambda^{-1}\sinh^{-1}(\lambda\sqrt{x+\frac{1}{2}})$ for small integers	$0.25\mu^2$	Empirical	..

In addition to these transformations, for which the transformed variate has constant variance if the basic distribution is as specified, there are 2 transformations that have been used extensively in biological assay which do not have this property: namely, the probit and logit transformations for variates which take values between 0 and 1.   In the probit transformation the variate which is a proportion is replaced by the deviate of the normal distribution equal to the variate below the deviate. The book *Probit Analysis* (by Finney [16]) contains a comprehensive account of applications of this transformation which have been used. In the case of logits, instead of the normal distribution, the distribution

$$f(x) \, dx = \tfrac{1}{2} \operatorname{sech}^2 x \, dx$$

is used, and the proportion p is replaced by $z = \tfrac{1}{2} \log \left(\dfrac{p}{1 - p} \right)$ The logit transformation is also indicated when the response of the experimental unit to the stimulus tends to behave as an autocatalytic reaction (Berkson [17]). This distribution and the normal distribution can be made virtually indistinguishable experimentally by suitable choices of scale.

A transformation that has some intuitive appeal has been used to apply the analysis of variance to ranked data (Fisher and Yates [18]). The observations are obtained by ranking objects given the various treatments in order of preference, say, 1, 2, $\cdots$, 10 if there are 10 treatments. The procedure is to replace the rank r, say, these running from 1 for the best to n for the worst, by the expected value of the rth largest of a sample of size n from a normal distribution of mean zero and unit variance. These quantities are tabulated by Fisher and Yates.[18] Such a procedure should, however, if possible, be preceded by investigation into the repeatability of ranks and additivity on the new scale.

A similar problem arises in experiments, particularly in food technology, on the effect of treatments on preferences for foods produced under different treatments. A common procedure is to ask a number of individuals (tasters) to give the product a rating between, say, 1 and 10. The resulting experimental data are obviously not susceptible to treatment by the analysis of variance without some *a priori* information about the statistical behavior of actual ratings and possibly a transformation. The *a priori* information on ratings by tasters which is necessary appears to be the same essentially as that required when we use any measuring device. When we use a measuring device such as a foot rule, we know that the rule we are using has been calibrated according to some standard and that it varies little over the range of environmental conditions for which we use it. We also know that, given an arbitrary measuring device, we can calibrate it according to some standard device. It might be desirable to obtain scores for each rating such that the variation due to the interaction of test materials with tasters is a minimum relative to the variation over repetitions. These scores would then have some properties of additivity. There are many problems in this field which are essentially untouched so far. An example of a similar technique was first given by Fisher.[19]

A final remark should be made. It is general experience that frequently it is very difficult to decide which transformation, if any, should be used and that under these circumstances the general conclusions are often little affected by the choice. This should not, however, be construed as a recommendation to ignore the whole problem.

8.6 AN EXAMPLE FOR THE READER

The data in Table 8.5 were obtained in an investigation of 2 grass mixtures (H and C), at 4 rates of application. The characteristic of

TABLE 8.5   GRASS EXPERIMENT: COUNTS OF PLANTS PER SQUARE YARD

Treatment	Replicate I	Treatment	Replicate II
H_1	94, 53, 57	H_4	431, 540, 551
C_3	371, 397, 295	C_2	180, 90, 120
H_4	604, 1890, 1570	H_3	404, 350, 234
C_1	25, 11, 18	C_3	332, 44, 150
C_4	865, 690, 1120	C_4	910, 880, 560
C_2	90, 59, 103	C_1	29, 11, 21
H_2	303, 271, 134	H_2	297, 199, 123
H_3	730, 261, 243	H_1	88, 81, 56

interest was the number of plants after a certain interval, and this was measured on 3 random samples of 1 square yard in each plot. The data are given in the table, and obviously a transformation is necessary. The rates of seeding denoted by 1, 2, 3, and 4 were in fact 1, 4, 16, and 64 seeds per unit area.

8.7 THE ANALYSIS OF COVARIANCE

In Chapter 6 we considered the addition of a concomitant variable to the linear hypothesis for a 2-way classification and gave the test that may be used.

The relationship of this material to that of the previous sections of the present chapter must be considered. We have adopted the criterion that the experiment be capable of giving estimates of the plot errors to which treatment comparisons are subject, and this amounted to the criterion that the expectation of the treatment mean square should equal the expectation of the error mean square (cf. Yates [20]). The expectation in these cases was taken over the possible randomizations of treatments that we could apply. The notion behind this is that an observed treatment comparison will be subject to errors because the treatments fell on some plots rather than on others, and the error of a treatment comparison is the deviation of what we actually observe from what we would have observed had it been possible to apply every treatment to every experimental unit. As far as estimation is concerned then, we visualize the experiment we have as a random one of a population, and we wish to estimate the deviation of this experiment from the whole population, the whole population estimating comparisons perfectly. If we can assume additivity, we have seen that the problem is solved, and the solution appears to be satisfactory.

When we utilize the analysis of covariance, we cannot adopt similar reasoning and therefore rely entirely on the validity of the model

$$y_{ij} = \mu + b_i + t_j + \beta x_{ij} + e_{ij} \tag{28}$$

where

y_{ij} = the observed yield

μ = a constant

b_i = the block effect

t = treatment effect

x_{ij} = the concomitant variable

e_{ij} = the error, these being normally and independently distributed with mean zero and variance σ^2

and

β = a regression coefficient

This model is very reasonable under some circumstances. For instance, if a plot yielded a known amount x_{ij} in the previous year, it is reasonable to assume that its yield in the present year will be equal to a constant plus βx_{ij} plus an error with the stated distributional properties. The advantage of using the above model is that we achieve greater accuracy in the comparison of treatments.

In the case when we use "arbitrary corrections" (Fisher,[6] pp. 178–179), we do not incur the difficulties of the assumptions of the normal law or infinite model above, if we are reasonably sure that the corrected observation is additive.

Our reason for making this remark is that, without the concomitant variable, we do not rely on the accuracy of a model for the test of the hypothesis that there are no treatment effects, whereas for the analysis of covariance we are entirely dependent on the accuracy of the model given above.

For this reason the analysis of covariance is less useful than one might at first think. If, for example, we have performed a randomized experiment on a field crop and have made plant counts also, it is dangerous to regard the information on plant counts as being a concomitant variable and adjust the yields on the basis of the analysis of covariance. Even if a test of significance of the effect of treatments on plant count indicates non-significance, we cannot be sure that the concomitant variable is unaffected by the treatments. For this reason the analysis of covariance as a means of increasing precision of treatment comparisons should be confined to cases where the experimenter is sure that the variations in the concomitant variable are unrelated to treatments. If the concomitant variable is observed before the experiment commenced, this condition is certainly satisfied.

The same type of reasoning is involved in tests of significance of treatment effects when there are missing data.

In other cases even when there are treatment effects on the concomitant variate, we may be interested in the effect of treatments on yield keeping the concomitant variate constant: for example, the effect on yield keeping number of plants constant in an agronomic experiment. In making this type of inference, we are dependent on the assumption that the effect of treatments on the concomitant variable is given by a linear regression on that variate. The validity of inferences made by the analysis of covariance is discussed by Bartlett.[21]

8.8 A TEST FOR ADDITIVITY

We have found that additivity is very important in the interpretation of experimental data, for, in the absence of additivity, the model should be written

$$y_{ij} = \mu + b_i + t_j + (bt)_{ij} + e_{ij} \tag{29}$$

In this case the error mean square will contain terms in $(bt)_{ij}$ which may or may not be random variables, depending on the inference to be made. Even if they are assumed to be random variables, the error sum of squares may not be homogeneous, and the error mean square may not be applied to all treatment comparisons.

Tukey [22] has devised a test for non-additivity. The procedure is to obtain a sum of squares with one degree of freedom which will tend to be inflated if there is non-additivity. This test is obtained in terms of the infinite model.

The sum of squares for the one degree of freedom is

$$\frac{\left[\sum_{ij} y_{ij}(y_{i\cdot} - y_{\cdot\cdot})(y_{\cdot j} - y_{\cdot\cdot}) \right]^2}{\left[\sum_i (y_{i\cdot} - y_{\cdot\cdot})^2 \right]\left[\sum_j (y_{\cdot j} - y_{\cdot\cdot})^2 \right]} \tag{30}$$

This sum of squares may be tested against the residual mean square after it is deducted from the error sum of squares. The example given by Tukey is as follows:

$$j$$

	1	2	3	4
$i = 1$	14	2	1	2
2	2	0	2	2
3	2	1	5	0

and the analysis of variance is found in Table 8.6.

TABLE 8.6

Due to	df	Sum of Squares	Mean Square
Rows	2	24.5	12.2
Columns	3	46.9	15.6
Non-additivity	1	50.9	50.9
Balance	5	33.9	6.8
Total	11	156.2	

The one degree of freedom has a sum of squares which is significant by the F test at the 5 percent level. The reader is referred to Tukey's paper for a detailed discussion of the test.

REFERENCES

1. WELCH, B. L. On the z-test in randomized blocks and Latin squares. *Biometrika*, **29**, 21–52, 1937.
2. PITMAN, E. J. G. Significance tests which can be applied to samples from any populations. III. The analysis of variance test. *Biometrika*, **29**, 322–335, 1937.
3. NEYMAN, J., IWASZKIEWICZ, K., and KOLODZIECZYK, ST. Statistical problems in agricultural experimentation. *Suppl. Jour. Roy. Stat. Soc.*, **2**, 107–154, 1935.
4. McCARTHY, M. D. On the application of the z-test to randomised blocks. *Ann. Math. Stat.*, **10**, 337–359, 1937.
5. ANSCOMBE, F. J. On the validity of comparative experiments. *Jour. Roy. Stat. Soc. A*, **111**, 181–211, 1948.
6. FISHER, R. A. *The design of experiments.* Oliver and Boyd, Edinburgh. 4th ed. 1947.
7. BARBACKI, S., and FISHER, R. A. A test of the supposed precision of systematic arrangements. *Ann. Eng.*, **7**, 189–193, 1936.
8. YATES, F. The comparative advantages of systematic and randomised arrangements in the design of agricultural and biological experiments. *Biometrika*, **30**, 440–464, 1939.
9. "STUDENT." Cooperation in large scale experiments. *Suppl. Jour. Roy. Stat. Soc.*, **3**, 115–136, 1936.

9a. "Student." Comparison between balanced and random arrangements of field plots. *Biometrika*, **29**, 363–379, 1937.

10. Bartlett, M. S. The use of transformations. *Biometrics*, **3**, 39–52, 1947.

11. Bartlett, M. S. The square-root transformation in the analysis of variance. *Suppl. Jour. Roy. Stat. Soc.*, **3**, 38–78, 1936.

12. Bartlett, M. S., and Kendall, D. G. The statistical analysis of variance-heterogeneity and the logarithmic transformation. *Suppl. Jour. Roy. Stat. Soc.*, **8**, 128–138, 1946.

13. Bartlett, M. S. Some examples of statistical methods of research in agriculture and applied biology. *Suppl. Jour. Roy. Stat. Soc.*, **4**, 137–183, 1937.

14. Fisher, R. A. *Statistical methods for research workers.* Chapter 5. Oliver and Boyd, Edinburgh, 11th ed., 1950.

15. Beall, G. The transformation from entomological field experiments so that the analysis of variance becomes applicable. *Biometrika*, **32**, 243–262, 1942.

16. Finney, D. J. *Probit analysis.* Cambridge University Press, Cambridge, England. 1947.

17. Berkson, J. Application of the logistic function to bioassay. *Jour. Amer. Stat. Assoc.*, **39**, 357–365, 1944.

18. Fisher, R. A., and Yates, F. *Statistical tables.* Oliver and Boyd, Edinburgh. 3rd ed., 1948.

19. Fisher, R. A. *Statistical methods for research workers.* Section 49.2. Oliver and Boyd, Edinburgh. 11th ed., 1950.

20. Yates, F. The formation of Latin squares for use in field experiments. *Emp. Jour. Exp. Agr.*, **1**, 235–244, 1933.

21. Bartlett, M. S. A note on the analysis of covariance. *Jour. Agr. Sci.*, **26**, 488–491, 1936.

22. Tukey, J. W. One degree of freedom for non-additivity. *Biometrics*, **5**, 232–242, 1949.

FURTHER READING

23. Fisher, R. A. The arrangement of field experiments. *Jour. Min. Agr. Engl.*, **33**, 503–513, 1926.

24. Eisenhart, C. The assumptions underlying the analysis of variance. *Biometrics*, **3**, 1–21, 1947.

25. Cochran, W. G. Some consequences when the assumptions for the analysis of variance are not satisfied. *Biometrics*, **3**, 22–38, 1947.

26. Yates, F. Complex experiments (with discussion). *Suppl. Jour. Roy. Stat. Soc.*, **2**, 181–247, 1935.

27. Pearson, E. S. Some aspects of the problem of randomization. *Biometrika*, **29**, 53–64, 1937.

28. Curtiss, J. H. On transformations used in the analysis of variance. *Ann. Math. Stat.*, **14**, 107–122, 1940.

29. Scheffé, H. Statistical inference in the non-parametric case. *Ann. Math. Stat.*, **14**, 305–332, 1943.

30. Anscombe, F. J. The statistical analysis of insect counts based on the negative binomial distribution. *Biometrics*, **5**, 165–173, 1949.

CHAPTER 9

Randomized Blocks

9.1 INTRODUCTION

In presenting the various experimental patterns, it is convenient to consider first the basic designs, and then to examine the problems of choice of experimental unit. The latter will be discussed in Chapter 11, together with details of experimental technique for particular types of experiments, such as field experiments and animal experiments. The basic designs are randomized blocks and Latin squares. We have already discussed in some detail the nature of the inference in randomized blocks. In this chapter we shall give an account of the uses of the randomized block design and its analysis.

Throughout this book we shall use the term "experimental unit" to denote the unit that is allocated a treatment independently of the other units. The experimental unit can contain several observational units; for instance, a class of students that receive a certain method of teaching in common can be an experimental unit, while the individual students are observational units. The distinction is, as we shall see, very important, because, from the point of view of inference on the effects of treatments, the experimental unit must be considered as a whole, and the variation between the observational units within an experimental unit is usually of little value in assessing the errors of estimates of treatment effects.

We shall suppose then that we have determined our experimental unit and wish to compare t treatments. Suppose also that we decide to subject r experimental units to each of the t treatments. One possibility is to allocate the t treatments at random to the total of rt experimental units, with the restriction that each treatment is applied to r of the units. This we may refer to as complete randomization, or randomization with no restrictions. Another possibility is to divide the rt experimental units into r sets of t units, in such a way that the sets are as homogeneous as possible and that differences among the experimental units are accounted for as much as possible by differences between the

163

sets. This is an ideal requirement which can be achieved only to a limited extent in any particular case.

For example, suppose the experimental unit is a cow and that we wish to compare 5 treatments and decide to test each treatment on 4 cows. Suppose, furthermore, that we are interested in the effect of the treatments on yield of milk. This particular example is chosen because quite a lot is known about the factors influencing milk production. We therefore require 20 cows in order to perform the experiment. The experiment with complete randomization would consist of the division at random of the 20 cows into 5 sets of 4 cows and the allocation of the treatments to the sets at random. To visualize how good such a procedure is, we have to consider the sort of data we shall obtain and the model of variation we may suppose the observations to follow.

We saw in the previous chapters that we could represent the model by

$$y_{ij} = \mu + t_i + e_{ij}, \qquad i = 1, \cdots, 5$$
$$j = 1, \cdots, 4$$

where the e_{ij}'s have the same variance and are uncorrelated. Any contrast among the treatment constants, i.e., a treatment comparison, say,

$$\Sigma\lambda_i t_i = \lambda_1 t_1 + \lambda_2 t_2 + \lambda_3 t_3 + \lambda_4 t_4 + \lambda_5 t_5$$

where $\Sigma\lambda_i = 0$, is best estimated by

$$\lambda_1 y_1. + \lambda_2 y_2. + \lambda_3 y_3. + \lambda_4 y_4. + \lambda_5 y_5.$$

where $y_i. = \frac{1}{4} \sum_{j=1}^{4} y_{ij}$.

Furthermore, the variance of this estimate with this design is

$$\sum_i \lambda^2{}_i \frac{\sigma^2}{4}$$

where σ^2 may be regarded as the variance of each yield.

The variance σ^2 is estimated by the variance between cows having the same treatment and is a measure of the extent to which animals subjected to the same treatment give different yields. The information provided by the experiment on any treatment comparison (which is the reciprocal of the variance) is inversely proportional to the variance σ^2. If we know anything at all about cows and their ability to produce milk, we shall know relationships between attributes of the cow and her yielding ability. For instance we know definitely that yield depends on the following attributes to an appreciable extent:

1. *Breed of cow.*
2. *Age of cow:* the relation between lactation number and age is usually quite close.
3. *Stage within lactation:* milk yield is known to be related to time from parturition, and the relationship is known to a greater or less degree of accuracy.

We could continue for some time to list factors affecting milk production, but the above are quite sufficient for purposes of illustration. Now suppose we have available for the experiment 10 Guernsey cows and 10 Holsteins, 2 breeds that we know to differ considerably in their yield, and suppose that in all other respects the cows are more or less similar. With complete randomization we allow of the possibility of unequal numbers of the 2 breeds being subjected to the 5 treatments. The measure σ^2 of the extent to which cows receiving the same treatment give different yields will then include a component due to the breed difference. We can in any particular instance, assuming a certain definite difference between the breeds, obtain the contribution to σ^2 which arises from our allowing the following possibilities to happen: (a) all 4 cows receiving a treatment are of the same breed, (b) 3 are of one breed, (c) 2 are of one breed and 2 of the other. There is little point in stating this more precisely or evaluating the contribution: It is sufficient to know that the contribution may be large, relative to the variance between cows of the same breed. The experimenter would then be ignoring valuable *a priori* information by using complete randomization. Furthermore, he would allow the possibility arising of particular treatment comparisons he wishes to make being affected by breed differences which he does not know precisely. A general term for such a situation is confounding: A treatment comparison will be subject by chance to a greater or lesser degree of confounding with breed differences. If, for example, the experimenter wished to compare treatment 1 with treatment 2, i.e., estimate the difference of the yields under treatment 1 and treatment 2, it would happen with a particular frequency, if complete randomization is used, that all the cows receiving treatment 1 were Holsteins and all receiving treatment 2 were Guernseys. In this case we would say that the comparison of treatments 1 and 2 was confounded completely with the breed difference. At the other extreme, it could happen that, for both treatments 1 and 2, two of the cows are of each breed, and then the treatment difference would be unconfounded with breed difference.

In passing it should be noted that there is no bias in the complete randomization plan. Bias is defined in terms of what would happen with a large number of repetitions of the experiment, and it is easily seen that, on the average of all possible randomizations, the treatment difference will not be affected by the breed difference.

As a first modification on the plan of complete randomization then, we would divide the cows into 2 groups of 10 according to breed and within each group of 10 apply the 5 treatments each to 2 cows at random. Any treatment comparisons will then be comparisons between cows of the same breed, and the variance σ^2 will measure the extent to which cows of the same breed give different yields under the same treatment. The variance σ^2 under this plan will be no larger than under complete randomization and, if the breed difference is large, will be considerably less. To continue further with this example, we will suppose that all the cows are at approximately the same stage of the lactation period, for differences in stage of lactation have such a large effect on yield that, if this factor is not controlled, the experimental results are likely to be of little value.

Finally to bring in the other factor mentioned, age or lactation number, we will suppose that 5 of the cows of each breed are in their second lactation and 5 in their third lactation. We can prevent the lactation number from introducing variability into treatment comparisons by further dividing each group of 10 cows into 2 groups of 5 cows according to lactation number, so that we finally have 4 groups of 5 cows: (1) Guernsey second lactation, (2) Guernsey third lactation, (3) Holstein second lactation, (4) Holstein third lactation. The experimental plan would then be to apply the 5 treatments at random within each of the 4 groups or replicates. This plan is known as *randomized blocks of 5 plots*. Each block of 5 plots is called a replicate.

In the previous chapter we discussed difficulties in the analysis of variance of the randomized block test, and these should be borne in mind in the setting up of the design. The two crucial points that we found were (a) that the treatments be additive in their effects and (b) that the units within the block be subject to the same variance. If we knew that a was satisfied for a particular experiment, we would know a lot about the experimental material, and there might not be the need for the experiment. It is usual, however, that we can obtain a good idea of whether additivity would hold on some scale, and we should work only within sets of experimental units for which this is likely to hold. Likewise, as far as b is concerned, we should attempt to use blocks or replicates that are likely to have much the same variability between plots within them.

Before the analysis of such an experiment is described, the general principles utilized in its construction will be emphasized. The characteristic that is to be observed is known to be affected by many factors, some of which have large effects, and, in addition, by many unknown factors. The factors that are known to have an effect fall with a particular situation of the experimenter into two groups: those he can control easily and those he cannot. The procedure is to decide which factors shall be actually controlled by making up groups or blocks homogeneous for these factors, and to control all other factors by the device of randomization. Of course, in actually controlling a factor, we do not achieve perfection, and the extent to which factors are not actually controlled is measured exactly by the variance between units treated alike. It would be entirely reasonable to make up the groups on the basis of a regression function of yield on the factors that are known to affect the yield. Experimental units would be sorted into groups, or what we usually call blocks, on the basis of their values for the regression function.

This procedure should be carefully differentiated from a procedure that is superficially valid which has some vogue in the social sciences. In the social sciences it is difficult if not impossible to perform experiments, and the following procedure is resorted to. Suppose that it were, in fact, very difficult to perform our experiment on the cows, but that, of the large number of cows in the United States, some have received treatment 1, some treatment 2, and so on. We know that it is useless merely to compare those receiving the different treatments, because they will differ in many respects other than the treatment. We, therefore, find, among our population of cows, some cows that receive each of the treatments but are "identical" with respect to the factors we listed above, namely, breed, lactation number, and stage in lactation, and we compare the cows receiving the various treatments. Any differences we observe we shall attribute to the effect of the treatments. In drawing such an inference with such data, we have to assume that the cows are identical in all respects except that they received different treatments. In fact, we cannot make the cows identical in the factors on the basis of which we select our "experimental" animals, because 2 of the 3 variables are continuous variables. By the term breed we merely mean that the cows have many superficial characteristics in common, say, certain genes controlling, to a greater or lesser degree, color, size and conformation, and a certain amount of common ancestry. The stage in lactation is a continuous variable ranging from zero to some number of months after parturition, and it is most unlikely that we could find 2 cows that gave birth to calves at the same time. It is for these reasons that we put the word identical above in quotes.

We have the further difficulty that the "treatments" appear to be the ones we wish to compare, but it may and will generally be the case that the "treatments" were associated with other husbandry practices, and we would not be measuring the effect of the "treatments" only. For example, suppose the treatments consisted of different levels of nutrition during lactation. Dairymen who feed their cows at a high level of nutrition while they are in production feed them at a high level of nutrition throughout their lives. We would then be measuring the effect of the treatment plus the effect of some treatment applied before the period of observation. In some instances inferences made in this way are valuable; and most of our knowledge in a field such as psychology is based on this type of inference. Frequently, however, we may obtain an entirely erroneous conclusion. In determining treatment effects in a true experiment, we, in fact, estimate the effect of the treatment and any factors associated with it. But in all cases we are concerned with the possible happenings in an indefinitely large set of repeated experiments. As long as the treatments are kept constant, including the factors associated with the treatments, we draw the correct inference. This point serves to emphasize the necessity of exact reporting of treatments and experimental procedures.

The randomized block design for the testing of t treatments with r replications consists then of the division of the total of rt experimental units into blocks of t units, within each of which the treatments are applied at random.

9.2   THE ANALYSIS OF RANDOMIZED BLOCKS

The yields of the experiment may be arranged in an $r \times t$ table (Table 9.1).

TABLE 9.1

Treatment

Block	1	2	3	$\cdots$	t	
1	y_{11}	y_{12}	etc.			$Y_1.$
2						$Y_2.$
3						$Y_3.$
.						.
.						.
.						.
r						$Y_r.$
	$Y._1$	$Y._2$	$Y._3$		$Y._t$	$Y..$

The marginal totals are then obtained, and the analysis of variance is calculated as in Chapter 6 (Table 9.2).

TABLE 9.2

Due to	df	Sum of Squares	Mean Squares
Blocks	$r - 1$	$\sum_i \dfrac{Y^2_{i.}}{t} - \dfrac{Y^2_{..}}{rt}$	B
Treatments	$t - 1$	$\sum_j \dfrac{Y^2_{.j}}{r} - \dfrac{Y^2_{..}}{rt}$	T
Error	$(r - 1)(t - 1)$	By subtraction	E
Total	$rt - 1$	$\Sigma y^2_{ij} - \dfrac{Y^2_{..}}{rt}$	

The mean squares are obtained by dividing the sum of squares by the corresponding degrees of freedom. The test of the null hypothesis that the treatments have no effect, i.e., that the treatment constants are equal, is to compare the observed variance ratio T/E with the tabulated values of the F distribution with $(t - 1)$ and $(r - 1)(t - 1)$ degrees of freedom.

The results of such an experiment are simply presentable in the form:

$$
\begin{array}{cc}
Treatment & Mean \\
1 & \dfrac{Y_{.1}}{r} \\
2 & \dfrac{Y_{.2}}{r} \\
\vdots & \vdots \\
t & \dfrac{Y_{.t}}{r}
\end{array} \right\} \pm \sqrt{\dfrac{E}{r}}
$$

The estimated standard error of each mean is $\sqrt{E/r}$ for the comparison of means, and any treatment comparison

$$\Sigma\lambda_j t_j \quad \text{with} \quad \Sigma\lambda_j = 0$$

is estimated by

$$\Sigma\lambda_j \frac{Y_{.j}}{r}$$

with an estimated standard error of $\sqrt{\Sigma\lambda^2_j}\sqrt{E/r}$. In order to test whether this comparison takes on a particular prechosen value, say, c, we evaluate Student's t equal to

$$\frac{\Sigma \lambda_j Y._j / r - c}{\sqrt{\Sigma \lambda^2_j} \sqrt{E/r}} \tag{1}$$

and compare this observed value with tabulated values of the t distribution with $(r-1)(t-1)$ degrees of freedom, the number of degrees of freedom on which the estimate E of the error variance is based.

Confidence limits on the value of the comparison are given by

$$\Sigma \lambda_j \frac{Y._j}{r} \pm t_{p,(r-1)(t-1)} \sqrt{\Sigma \lambda^2_j} \sqrt{\frac{E}{r}} \tag{2}$$

where $t_{p,(r-1)(t-1)}$ is the value of t for the probability p with degrees of freedom $(r-1)(t-1)$.

We note that, from the point of view of restricted sampling, the variance of a treatment mean for comparison with outside data is $\sigma^2(t-1)/rt$ which is estimated by $E(t-1)/rt$.

9.3 BREAKDOWN OF THE TREATMENT SUM OF SQUARES

The experimenter may wish to test various hypotheses about the treatments. Any comparison that he had a prior basis for testing may be tested in the above way. Frequently a partitioning of the treatment sum of squares is desirable. In the extreme case, it may be desirable to obtain an orthogonal set of $(t-1)$ treatment comparisons. An orthogonal set may be denoted by

$$\sum_j \lambda_{kj} t_j, \qquad k = 1, 2, \cdots, t-1$$

where, for each k, $\sum_j \lambda_{kj} = 0$, and, for each k and l with $k \neq l$,

$$\sum_j \lambda_{kj} \lambda_{lj} = 0$$

For example, a set of orthogonal comparisons for 4 treatments is the following:

$$t_1 + t_2 - t_3 - t_4$$

$$t_1 - t_2 + t_3 - t_4$$

$$t_1 - t_2 - t_3 + t_4$$

The stated properties should be verified. The particular set of orthogonal treatment comparisons to be used depends entirely on the hypothesis the experimenter wishes to test; i.e., they can be specified only by the experimenter or by someone with knowledge of the experimental material and treatments.

The estimate with the randomized block design and no missing data of any comparison

$$\sum_j \lambda_{kj} t_j \tag{3}$$

is

$$\sum_j \lambda_{kj} \frac{Y_{\cdot j}}{r} \tag{4}$$

and the corresponding sum of squares with one degree of freedom is

$$\left(\sum_j \lambda_{kj} \frac{Y_{\cdot j}}{r} \right)^2 \bigg/ \left(\sum_j \frac{\lambda^2_{kj}}{r} \right) \tag{5}$$

A partitioning of the sum of squares which is frequently desirable is the following: Suppose the treatments form k groups $(1, \cdots, p)$, $(p + 1, \cdots, p + q)$, etc. The total sum of squares for treatments would then be broken down into

Between groups	$(k - 1)$
Within group 1	$(p - 1)$
Within group 2	$(q - 1)$
etc.	

The sum of squares between groups will be obtained in the usual way, namely, that, if pr plots make up the first group, qr make up the second, and so on, it is equal to

$$\frac{(\text{Total of group 1})^2}{pr} + \frac{(\text{total of group 2})^2}{qr} + \text{etc.} - \frac{Y^2_{\cdot \cdot}}{rt}$$

The sum of squares within a group, say, the first, will be

$$\frac{Y^2_{\cdot 1}}{r} + \frac{Y^2_{\cdot 2}}{r} + \cdots + \frac{Y^2_{\cdot p}}{r} - \frac{(Y_{\cdot 1} + Y_{\cdot 2} + \cdots + Y_{\cdot p})^2}{pr}$$

and so on.

In testing several components of a treatment sum of squares by comparing each with the same error mean square by F tests, it should be remembered that the F tests are not independent, because the same denominator is used in all the tests. The degree of correlation decreases as the number of degrees of freedom on which the error mean square is based increases. (See Finney [1] for further discussion on the normal theory or infinite model.)

9.4 RANDOMIZATION TEST

We are basing our conclusions on randomization tests, as discussed in the previous two chapters. Perhaps, however, we should emphasize that, although the approach we adopt appears to be that of an infinite model, we have justified this method by reference to randomization tests. The relation of the randomization test to the corresponding F test was indicated in Chapter 8, by obtaining moments of the criterion (treatment mean square/error mean square) over the population of randomizations. These moments were found to be close to those of the theoretical F distribution. This is not, of course, a perfect proof of the correspondence, for we are not particularly interested in the correspondence over the bulk of the distribution, but in the upper tail; also we know little of the rate of approach of the randomization distribution to the F distribution with increasing size of experiment.

9.5 THE TREATMENT OF RANDOMIZED BLOCK EXPERIMENTS WITH MISSING DATA

Let us suppose, for purposes of illustration, that the observation for treatment 1 in block 1 is missing. The procedure is to substitute a symbol x, say, for the missing observation and perform the analysis of variance. This will be as in Table 9.3, where

$Y'_1.$ = now the total for the $(t - 1)$ plots in block 1 for which yields were obtained

$Y'._1$ = the total of the $(r - 1)$ plots of treatment 1 for which yields were obtained

and

$Y'..$ = the total of the observed yields

TABLE 9.3   ALGEBRAIC ANALYSIS OF VARIANCE

Due to	Sum of Squares
Blocks	$\dfrac{(Y'_1. + x)^2}{t} + \dfrac{Y^2_2.}{t} + \cdots + \dfrac{Y^2_r.}{t} - \dfrac{(Y'.. + x)^2}{rt}$
Treatments	$\dfrac{(Y'._1 + x)^2}{r} + \dfrac{Y^2._2}{r} + \cdots + \dfrac{Y^2._t}{r} - \dfrac{(Y'.. + x)^2}{rt}$
Error	By subtraction
Total	$\Sigma y^2_{ij} + x^2 - \dfrac{(Y'.. + x)^2}{rt}$

The error sum of squares is then

$$x^2 + \frac{(Y'_{..} + x)^2}{rt} - \frac{(Y'_{1.} + x)^2}{t} - \frac{(Y'_{.1} + x)^2}{r} + \text{terms not involving } x.$$

This sum of squares is now to be minimized for variation in x, and this is simply done by equating the differential with regard to x to zero and solving for x: i.e.,

$$2x + \frac{2(Y'_{..} + x)}{rt} - \frac{2(Y'_{1.} + x)}{t} - \frac{2(Y'_{.1} + x)}{r} = 0$$

giving

$$x\left(1 + \frac{1}{rt} - \frac{1}{t} - \frac{1}{r}\right) = \frac{Y'_{1.}}{t} + \frac{Y'_{.1}}{r} - \frac{Y'_{..}}{rt}$$

or

$$x = \frac{rY'_{1.} + tY'_{.1} - Y'_{..}}{(r-1)(t-1)} \tag{6}$$

The quantity x is the best estimate of the yield of the missing plot under the model. This value for x may then be inserted in the original table of yields, the marginal means of the augmented table give the block and treatment means, and comparisons of treatments are obtainable directly by taking the same comparison of the treatment means from the augmented table.

An approximate test of significance of the null hypothesis that the treatments have no differential effects may be obtained by analyzing the augmented table in the usual way, with the modification that the degrees of freedom for the error sum of squares is diminished by the number of plots for which observations are missing (in this case, 1). This test can be shown to be biased in that the expectation of the treatment mean square is greater than the expectation of the error mean square under the null hypothesis. If the approximate test of significance indicates that there are no significant treatment differences, there is no need to perform the accurate test of significance.

The accurate test of significance in the above case is made by the analysis of variance given in Table 9.4. (This test is accurate on the

TABLE 9.4 ANALYSIS OF VARIANCE FOR EXACT TEST OF SIGNIFICANCE

Due to	df	Sum of Squares	Mean Square
Blocks	$r-1$	$\dfrac{Y'^2_{1.}}{t-1} + \dfrac{Y^2_{2.}}{t} + \cdots + \dfrac{Y^2_{r.}}{t} - \dfrac{Y'^2_{..}}{rt-1}$	
Treatments	$t-1$	By subtraction	
Error	$(r-1)(t-1)-1$	As in the analysis of variance of the augmented table	
Total	$rt-2$	$\Sigma y^2_{ij} - \dfrac{Y'^2_{..}}{rt-1}$	

basis of normal law theory.)   Mean squares are then compared by the F distribution in the usual way.

The extensions of this procedure to cases where more than 1 plot is missing will not be given.   The reader may find it instructive to work through a simple case with more than one missing observation.   A somewhat involved case is described by Yates.[2]

A simple method when there are several missing observations is to replace each missing observation by the mean of the block in which it lies, as a first approximation.   The formula for 1 missing plot is then used to estimate a second approximation for the missing observations in order, utilizing either the block mean or the new approximation, if it has been obtained for all missing plots except the one being estimated. Such a procedure converges rapidly, in general.

Either of these procedures is valid as long as each block and treatment is represented at least once in the table of observed yields.   If the whole of a block or of a treatment is missing, the·experiment is regarded and treated as an experiment of correspondingly reduced size.   If only 1 treatment is represented in a block, the block is omitted as the 1 plot gives no information on treatment differences.

In some situations, when the number of missing plots is large, it is computationally simpler to follow the standard methods for the 2-way classification outlined in Chapter 6.

9.6 THE VARIANCE OF TREATMENT COMPARISONS WITH MISSING PLOTS

In a randomized block experiment with t treatments and r blocks, where no plots are missing, the variance of a treatment mean for comparisons with other treatment means has been shown to be σ^2/r, where σ^2 is estimated by the mean square for error in the analysis of variance.

When a single plot is missing, the treatment mean containing an estimated yield is a simple linear function of known yields; i.e., if the plot corresponding to the kth treatment and the lth block (y_{kl}) is missing, then it has been shown that the best estimate of the yield for that plot is

$$x = \frac{tT'_k + rB'_l - T'}{(r-1)(t-1)}$$

where T'_k is the sum of all *known* yields for plots receiving treatment k, B'_l is the sum of all the known yields from plots in block l, and T' is the sum of *all known* yields. The estimate of the kth treatment mean is then

$$\hat{t}_k = \frac{1}{r}(T'_k + x) = \frac{1}{r}\left[T'_k + \frac{tT'_k + rB'_l - T'}{(r-1)(t-1)}\right]$$

Using the fact that the y_{ij} are distributed with common variance σ^2 and that the variance of

$$\Sigma\lambda_{ij}y_{ij}$$

is $\sigma^2\Sigma\lambda^2_{ij}$ (apart from covariance terms which vanish in any comparison orthogonal to blocks as discussed in Chapter 8), we find that

$$\text{var}\,(\hat{t}_k) = \frac{\sigma^2}{r-1}\left[1 + \frac{1}{r(t-1)}\right]$$

$$= \frac{\sigma^2}{r}\left[1 + \frac{t}{(r-1)(t-1)}\right]$$

The variance of any other treatment mean is, as above, σ^2/r, and the treatment means are (in a sense) uncorrelated. For any contrast among the treatment means,

$$\sum_{i=1}^{t} \lambda_i\hat{t}_i \quad \text{with} \quad \Sigma\lambda_i = 0$$

the variance of the contrast is

$$\frac{\sigma^2}{r}\sum_{i\neq k} \lambda^2_i + \lambda^2_k\frac{\sigma^2}{r}\left[1 + \frac{t}{(r-1)(t-1)}\right] \tag{7}$$

If 2 plot yields are missing, the variance of any contrast among treatment means may be found by expressing the contrast as a linear function of all the known plots, the variance of which is easily evaluated. As the number of missing plots increases beyond 2, the algebra involved in such calculations becomes extremely tedious and not worth while, and it is probably best if accurate variances and covariances are needed to have recourse to the methods of Chapter 6 for the 2-way classification with unequal numbers.

Yates [2] sets upper and lower limits on the variance of the difference of 2 treatment means by ignoring the block classification altogether to get a lower limit and by rejecting all those blocks that do not contain both treatments to set the upper limit. He also proposed the approximate rule of giving ½ weight to each plot of a treatment that has no corresponding plot in the same block belonging to the other treatment.

For example, suppose we had treatments a, b, c, d, e in 6 blocks as shown in Figure 7, where the shaded plots are missing.

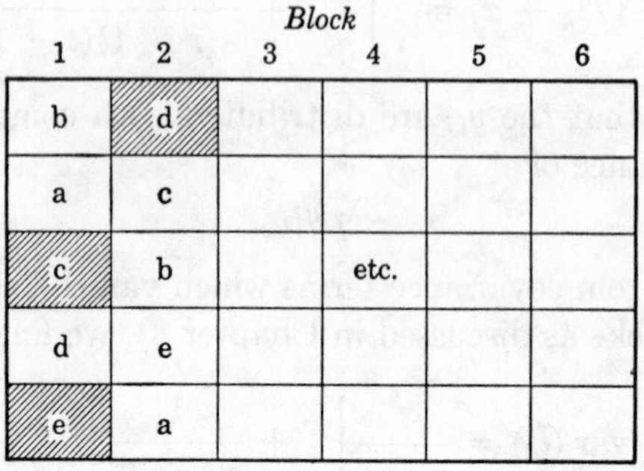

FIGURE 7.

The rule in comparing 2 treatments a and b is:

If a and b both occur in a block, give each a weight of 1.
If a occurs without b in a block, give a weight of $\frac{1}{2}$.
If b occurs without a in a block, give b weight of $\frac{1}{2}$.
If both a and b do not occur in a block, give each a weight of 0.

Thus,

$$\text{var}\,(\hat{t}_a - \hat{t}_b) = (\tfrac{1}{6} + \tfrac{1}{6})\sigma^2$$

$$\text{var}\,(\hat{t}_a - \hat{t}_c) = \left(\frac{1}{5\frac{1}{2}} + \frac{1}{6}\right)\sigma^2$$

$$\text{var}\,(\hat{t}_c - \hat{t}_e) = (\tfrac{1}{5} + \tfrac{1}{5})\sigma^2$$

When data are missing, an easy partitioning of the treatment sum of squares is no longer possible, since the effects due to each factor are no longer independent of the order in which they are estimated. This is a consequence of the non-orthogonality of the data, and reference should be made to Chapter 6 for the treatment of such a situation.

9.7 DIFFICULTIES OF RANDOMIZED BLOCKS

We may summarize the relevant discussion of the previous chapter in stating that the following difficulties of randomized block experiments are fairly common:

1. *Missing data:* procedures for this problem are given above.
2. *Heterogeneity of Errors:* this may be of two types:

(a) That the variance of the experimental errors is related to the expected yields because of non-additivity, or differential variability from block to block. In this case the appropriate procedure is to use a transformation, which results in error variance being independent of expected yield, and to apply Tukey's test for non-additivity.

(b) That the error variance of some treatment comparisons is greater than that for other comparisons because of non-additivity, or sampling errors within the plot, if sampling is used. It is an advantage of randomized blocks that an error variance may be obtained for each treatment comparison. This is done by evaluating the comparison in each block and estimating the variance of the mean comparison by the sum of squares between the values for each block divided by the number of blocks minus one, and by the number of blocks.

9.8 THE PURPOSES OF REPLICATION

In any randomized block experiment it is necessary to have at least two replications in order that an estimate of the experimental error variance may be obtained. With increasing replication the error variance will be estimated with increasing accuracy, the estimated error variance being subject to a standard deviation of approximately

$$\sigma^2 \sqrt{\frac{2}{n_e}}$$

where σ^2 is the true value and n_e is the number of degrees of freedom on which the estimate of the error variance is based, according to the infinite model. In general, it will be expected, and it is assumed in the analysis, that the true value of the error variance does not depend on the number of replicates, since it measures the variation within replicates if the treatments are identical.

The important purpose of replication is, however, to decrease the error of treatment comparisons. The true variance of any treatment comparison was shown earlier to be proportional to σ^2/r, where σ^2 is the variance per plot and r is the number of replicates. This variance decreases directly with increasing r, and the information on the comparison which is proportional to r/σ^2 increases proportionally with r.

It is intuitively obvious that increasing replication results in increasing sensitivity of the experiment. We shall devote a chapter later to this subject. For the moment we shall consider a simple aspect of the problem, originally discussed by Neyman et al.[3] We suppose that we are comparing 2 treatments, A and B, and wish to test the hypothesis that B gives greater yields than A. We suppose that the infinite model can be used so that we obtain an estimate d of the difference $B - A$, with an estimate of error s^2 based on n degrees of freedom, the estimate

d being normally distributed around the true value Δ with variance σ^2_d, and the estimate of variance s^2 being distributed independently of d as

$$\frac{\sigma^2_d}{n} \chi^2_{(n)}$$

With this formulation the test of the hypothesis $\Delta > 0$ will be the t test with n degrees of freedom and level of significance equal to twice the corresponding tabular level. The probability of concluding on the basis of this test that Δ is not greater than zero is easily obtained by integration of the joint probability density of d and s^2. From tables given by Neyman we have constructed the relations given in Table 9.5 between number of replicates r and probability of rejecting the null hypothesis for various values of Δ/σ, σ being the standard deviation, with randomized blocks of 2 plots.

TABLE 9.5 SENSITIVITY OF EXPERIMENTS IN RANDOMIZED BLOCKS OF 2 PLOTS

	Δ/σ		
r	1	2	3
Probability of Rejecting Null Hypothesis with a 1% Test (Approximate)			
2	0.03	0.05	0.08
3	0.05	0.13	0.25
4	0.09	0.27	0.53
5	0.13	0.42	0.77
6	0.16	0.57	0.92
7	0.20	0.74	0.96
8	0.24	0.81	0.99
9	0.29	0.86	
10	0.36	0.91	
16	0.60	0.99	
32	0.81		
44	0.99		
Probability of Rejecting Null Hypothesis with a 5% Test (Approximate)			
2	0.14	0.25	0.36
3	0.22	0.49	0.74
4	0.30	0.69	0.92
5	0.38	0.82	0.99
6	0.45	0.88	
7	0.51	0.94	
8	0.56	0.97	
9	0.61		
10	0.65		
16	0.84		
32	0.99		

This table emphasizes the importance of replication, for the experimenter should have in mind the magnitude of true differences which will be shown with high probability by the experiment to be significant. Thus, the experimenter should be in the position of being able to state that, if the true difference is x units, he wants a probability of 95 percent that the experiment he will do will indicate that there is a difference. If, for example, $\Delta/\sigma = 1$ and a 5 percent test is to be used, then about 23 replicates are necessary for the probability to be 95 percent of deciding on the basis of the test that there is a difference. The above discussion indicates the importance of making the quantity Δ/σ as large as possible. This may be done either by reducing σ or by increasing Δ or by both. The increasing of Δ is much a matter of experimental technique and may not be possible without some redefinition of the problem. An example in which this has been used is in biological assay where the problem is to estimate the effects of different proteins on growth of rats, and the technique is to reduce the animals to a very low plane of nutrition with consequent magnification of Δ over what would have been obtained with ordinary animals. The reduction of σ^2 is one of the prime problems of experimental design, and we shall see the development of various experimental patterns devised to remove variation between experimental units treated differently.

9.9 THE USE OF CONCOMITANT INFORMATION

After the experiment has been conducted, information additional to yield may be obtained, or there may have been obvious simple positional effects in the experiment. It may then be desirable to take account of this concomitant variation. For example, in a plant experiment, it may happen that, for no reason related to the treatment, there resulted variation in number of plants per plot. If the experimenter is sure that this variation is not related to treatments, the effect of the concomitant variation may be removed by the analysis of covariance. Again, in a greenhouse experiment, it may be thought that variation in light due to differing distances of the experimental units from the side of the greenhouse may have produced some variation in the yield and that such variation is in no way related to treatment. The experimenter is then at liberty to treat the distance of the unit from the side of the greenhouse as a concomitant variable and to use the analysis of covariance. The only purpose of using such information is to increase the accuracy of treatment comparisons, and whether this result is achieved may be determined by testing the error regression of the yield on the concomitant variable for significance. If it is not significant, it will not be worth while to make the adjustments.

In accordance with the discussion of the previous chapter, the inference on the unadjusted yields is based on randomization considerations, while the inference on the adjusted yields is based on the assumption of the model

$$y_{ij} = \mu + b_i + t_j + \beta x_{ij} + e_{ij} \tag{8}$$

where x_{ij} is the concomitant variable, and the e_{ij}'s are normally and independently distributed. The additional information which the covariance analysis gives is, therefore, obtained at the cost of this assumption, and it is necessary to be sure that the variation in the concomitant variable has not arisen as a result of the treatments. In the case of positional effects, the experimenter is fairly safe in using the procedure. In the case of a concomitant variable like number of plants, however, such an assumption may not be acceptable.

In such instances we may wish to determine the effect of treatment on yields, supposing plant number were kept constant, and, for this type of inference, the analysis of covariance is satisfactory, providing again that the model is reasonably satisfied. In some cases, for example, one should use as the concomitant variable some function of the plant numbers.

9.10 THE EFFICIENCY OF RANDOMIZED BLOCKS

In a field experiment, there is generally no difficulty in arranging the testing of the t treatments in r blocks of t plots. In other experimental situations, there may be some difficulty in arranging the experimental units in groups of t units, each group forming a block. It is desirable, therefore, to investigate the efficiency of the arrangement in randomized blocks relative to the complete randomization arrangement. The word "efficiency" as used here and elsewhere refers to the efficiency of estimates.

The best method by which this may be done is to have available so-called uniformity trial data: that is, data obtained on a large number of experimental units with a common treatment. These are then divided into sets of rt units, each set simulating the actual experiment to be done, and each set being divided into r blocks of t units, according to some known information about the experimental units. For example, if the experimental unit is a cow, the cows may be arranged in blocks on the basis of breed, age, stage in lactation, and so on. An analysis of the consequent observations is then made with the result shown in Table 9.6, supposing there are k sets of rt units.

TABLE 9.6

Due to	df	Mean Square
Sets	$k - 1$	
Blocks within sets	$k(r - 1)$	B
Within blocks	$kr(t - 1)$	E
Total	$krt - 1$	

The mean square E is then an estimate of the experimental error σ^2 with randomized blocks of t plots, and B is an estimate of the variance between blocks within the experiment.

We can then say that the analysis for a single experiment with dummy treatments will be as shown in Table 9.7.

TABLE 9.7

Due to	df	Sum of Squares
Blocks	$r - 1$	$(r - 1)B$
Within blocks	$r(t - 1)$	$r(t - 1)E$
Total	$rt - 1$	$(r - 1)B + r(t - 1)E$

If the blocks were not used, the variances of treatment comparisons would be proportional to the total mean square, i.e., to

$$\frac{(r - 1)B + r(t - 1)E}{rt - 1}$$

whereas with the blocks they are proportional to E. The relative efficiency of randomized blocks to complete randomization is then

$$\frac{(r - 1)B + r(t - 1)E}{(rt - 1)E} \tag{9}$$

In general, B will be greater than E unless the blocks are entirely ineffective in removing heterogeneity, so that the relative efficiency of randomized blocks is greater than or equal to 100 percent.

The field experimenter will almost invariably use blocks, so that the question is for him somewhat academic. When confounding, which will be discussed in a later chapter, is used, however, it is of interest even for field experiments. With confounding the size of the block will be less than the number of treatments, and this results in a loss of information on confounded comparisons. It is important to estimate whether the gain in information on the unconfounded comparisons, which results from the smaller size of block, outweighs the loss in information on the confounded comparisons.

In the general type of experiment, the above method may be used to determine how much information or efficiency is gained by controlling on particular extraneous factors: that is, holding these constant to a particular degree. For example, how important is it that observations on industrial articles produced under different treatments be made under environmental conditions held constant in a particular respect? It was stated earlier that the essence of experimentation is the controlling of extraneous factors easy to control, and randomization over all other factors. This process is put on an economic basis by considerations of efficiency of arrangements in blocks made up in particular ways; i.e., we wish to maximize efficiency by variation in size and shape of blocks and number of characteristics controlled for a fixed or minimum cost.

It is possible with any experiment laid out with certain restrictions on the location of treatments to estimate how much information would have been lost by using a smaller number of restrictions. For example, with an experiment of r blocks of t plots testing t treatments, it is possible to estimate what the relative efficiency of an arrangement with no blocks would be. It will, in fact, be

$$\frac{(rt - 1)E}{(r - 1)B + r(t - 1)E}$$

where E is the error mean square and B is the block mean square.

The reader should note that the argument used in obtaining the relative efficiency of randomized blocks is exactly the same as that used in Chapter 8 and is based on the finite model. Instead of being within blocks, the randomization is within the total set of rt plots. To verify the formula for the relative efficiency, we note that, with complete randomization,

$$\delta_{ij}^k = 1 \text{ with probability } \frac{1}{t}$$

and, if $\delta_{ij}^k = 1$, then $\delta_{i'j'}^k = 1$, with probability $\frac{r - 1}{rt - 1}$, $(i', j') \neq (i, j)$. The plot yields y_{ij} are given by

$$y_{ij} = y.. + (y_{ij} - y..)$$
$$= y.. + d_{ij} \tag{10}$$

and it is readily found that the error mean square has an expectation of

$$\frac{1}{(rt-1)} \sum_{ij} d^2_{ij}$$

Now,

$$d_{ij} = b_i + e_{ij} \tag{11}$$

where b_i and e_{ij} are defined as in Section 8.2, and so the expectation of the error mean square is

$$\sigma'^2 = \frac{1}{(rt-1)} \left(t \sum_i b^2_i + \sum_{ij} e^2_{ij} \right) \tag{12}$$

We found in section 8.2 that the expectation of the block mean square B is $t\Sigma b^2_i/(r-1)$, and of the error mean square E is $\sum_{ij} e^2_{ij}/r(t-1)$, so that the expectation of $\dfrac{(r-1)B + r(t-1)E}{rt-1}$ is σ^2, in accordance with the result stated above. This method is not then empirical, but is in strict accordance with randomization theory. The assumption behind the calculation is that *exactly* the same experimental units will be used in either design. In applying the formula to field plot experiments, it should be noted that the size and shape of plots are considered to be exactly identical for the two designs, and this may vitiate the calculation to some extent, in that a different division of the total experimental material into plots may be desirable for the two designs.

The above discussion is concerned with efficiency of estimation and not relative sensitivity. The latter depends not only on the error variance but also on the number of degrees of freedom for error, and will be be discussed in Chapter 12.

REFERENCES

1. FINNEY, D. J. The joint distribution of variance ratios based on a common error mean square. *Ann. Eug.*, **11**, 136–140, 1941.
2. YATES, F. The analysis of replicated experiments when the field results are incomplete. *Emp. Jour. Exp. Agr.*, **1**, 129–142, 1933.
3. NEYMAN, J., IWASZKIEWICZ, K., and KOLODZIECZYK, ST. Statistical problems in agricultural experimentation. *Suppl. Jour. Roy. Stat. Soc.*, **2**, 107–154, 1935.

CHAPTER 10

Latin Squares

10.1 INTRODUCTION

The randomized block type of experiment may be regarded as an arrangement in which treatments are randomized under one restriction: namely, that each treatment must occur in each block. If, for instance, the experimental unit is a cow, blocks may be made up of cows of the same lactation number. Now it is fairly obvious that this may be extended so that the cows are divided into groups by lactation number and also into groups by, say, yield in previous lactation, so that each animal falls into one of the lactation number groups and one of the previous yield groups. If the numbers of groups on each of the 2 factors are equal to, say, 4, the cows may be regarded as forming a 4 × 4 arrangement as shown in Figure 8.

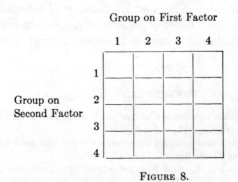

FIGURE 8.

It is then possible to superimpose 4 treatments on this arrangement so that each treatment occurs once and only once in each row of the plan and in each column. Such an arrangement is called a Latin square. These arrangements were first used in experimental agriculture in which the above arrangement is merely a division of the experimental area

184

into k^2 plots. Such arrangements have fairly obvious properties, the important one being that any comparison of treatments is unaffected by average differences which exist between the rows or between columns. Such differences will not affect the errors of treatment comparisons so that such arrangements are likely to lead to greatly increased precision. The order in which Latin squares will be discussed is to present the combinatorial properties of these arrangements first and then to discuss the uses of these arrangements for experimental purposes. Some detailed discussion of the combinatorial properties is necessary, as these properties lead to an understanding of the randomization test and also to designs other than the simple Latin square.

10.2 COMBINATORIAL PROPERTIES

A reduced Latin square (or a Latin square in standard form) is one in which the first row and the first column are arranged in alphabetical order: e.g.,

$$A \quad B \quad C \quad D$$

$$B \quad C \quad D \quad A$$

$$C \quad D \quad A \quad B$$

$$D \quad A \quad B \quad C$$

The number of squares that can be generated from a reduced Latin square by permutation of the rows, columns, and letters is $(k!)^3$. These are not necessarily all different. If all rows but the first and all columns are permuted, we generate $k!(k-1)!$ squares.

We proceed to give an enumeration of the smaller squares.

10.2.1 3 × 3 Square

There is only one reduced Latin square, namely:

$$A \quad B \quad C$$

$$B \quad C \quad A$$

$$C \quad A \quad B$$

From this we can generate 12 squares by permuting all rows except the first and all columns.

10.2.2 4 × 4 Squares

There are 4 reduced Latin squares which fall into two sets as in Table 10.1.

TABLE 10.1 THE REDUCED 4 × 4 LATIN SQUARES

First Transformation Set			Second Transformation Set
A B C D	A B C D	A B C D	A B C D
B A D C	B C D A	B D A C	B A D C
C D B A	C D A B	C A D B	C D A B
D C A B	D A B C	D C B A	D C B A
(1)	(2)	(3)	(4)

One square of the transformation set may be obtained from the other by permutation of letters and subsequent rearrangement into reduced or standard form. This is the definition of a transformation set. For example, any interchange of letters and rearrangement into standard form of the member of the second transformation set result in its reproduction. Thus, by interchanging A and C, we have

$$
\begin{array}{ccc}
\begin{array}{cccc} C & B & A & D \\ B & C & D & A \\ A & D & C & B \\ D & A & B & C \end{array}
&
\begin{array}{cccc} A & B & C & D \\ D & C & B & A \\ C & D & A & B \\ B & A & D & C \end{array}
&
\begin{array}{cccc} A & B & C & D \\ B & A & D & C \\ C & D & A & B \\ D & C & B & A \end{array}
\end{array}
$$

In the first transformation set, square 2 can be obtained from square 1, for example, by interchanging A and D in 1 and rearranging, thus:

$$
\begin{array}{ccc}
\begin{array}{cccc} D & B & C & A \\ B & D & A & C \\ C & A & B & D \\ A & C & D & B \end{array}
&
\begin{array}{cccc} A & B & C & D \\ C & D & A & B \\ D & A & B & C \\ B & C & D & A \end{array}
&
\begin{array}{cccc} A & B & C & D \\ B & C & D & A \\ C & D & A & B \\ D & A & B & C \end{array}
\end{array}
$$

10.2.3 5 × 5 Squares

There exist 2 transformation sets, one containing 50 reduced Latin squares and the other containing 6 reduced Latin squares. An example for each set is listed by Fisher and Yates.[1]

10.2.4 6 × 6 Squares

Fisher and Yates [1,2] list a square from each of the 22 transformation sets, which contain a total of 9408 reduced Latin squares.

10.2.5 Larger Squares

An exhaustive enumeration of 7×7 squares was made by Norton.[3] Fisher and Yates [1] give examples of squares of sides 7, 8, 9, 10, 11, 12. A square of any side may be obtained by writing down the corresponding number of letters to make the first row, making the second row by moving the first row along one step, and putting the last letter of row 1 in the first position in row 2, and so on.

10.2.6 Selection of a Random Square

The procedure for obtaining a random square is given by Fisher and Yates.[1] This consists of first selecting a reduced square at random. For squares of side 3, 4, or 5, permute all rows except the first and all columns, or all rows and all columns except the first, and assign treatments at random to the letters A, B, C, $\cdots$. For 6×6 squares, select a reduced square at random, and permute all rows and columns, and then assign the letters to treatments at random. For larger squares, it is satisfactory to take any square and permute rows, columns, and treatments.

10.3 GRAECO-LATIN SQUARES

The Graeco-Latin square properties are exemplified simply by the square of side 3, the only one apart from permutation of rows, columns, Greek letters.

$$
\begin{array}{ccc}
A_\alpha & B_\beta & C_\gamma \\
B_\gamma & C_\alpha & A_\beta \\
C_\beta & A_\gamma & B_\alpha
\end{array}
$$

In this arrangement every Latin letter occurs once in each row and once in each column, each Greek letter occurs once in each row and once in each column, and each Greek letter occurs once with each Latin letter.

Graeco-Latin squares of side k exist when k is a prime number or a power of a prime. They also exist for all other odd numbers. In fact, it has been shown that Graeco-Latin squares of side k exist for all k except 2 and 6.

10.4 THE COMPLETELY ORTHOGONALIZED SQUARE

As an example the square of side 4 is given in Table 10.2.

TABLE 10.2 THE 4×4 COMPLETELY ORTHOGONALIZED SQUARE

$$
\begin{array}{cccc}
A_{1\alpha} & B_{2\beta} & C_{3\gamma} & D_{4\delta} \\
B_{4\gamma} & A_{3\delta} & D_{2\alpha} & C_{1\beta} \\
C_{2\delta} & D_{1\gamma} & A_{4\beta} & B_{3\alpha} \\
D_{3\beta} & C_{4\alpha} & B_{1\delta} & A_{2\gamma}
\end{array}
$$

Note that the Latin letters, the Greek letters, and the numerals have the Latin square property, and also that the Latin and Greek letters form a Graeco-Latin square, as do the Latin letters and numerals, and that the Greek letters and numerals have the Graeco-Latin square property.

The extensions of this are given by the following theorem, due to Stevens [4] and Bose: [5] When k is a prime or a power of a prime, there exists a $k \times k$ square with each cell containing a letter of each of $(k - 1)$ languages, such that the letters of any two languages form a square with the Graeco-Latin square property.

The proof of this theorem follows from the existence of Galois fields of p^n elements where p is a prime and n is an integer. When n is unity, the Galois field may be represented by the numbers $0, 1, 2, \cdots, (p - 1)$, where the operations of ordinary arithmetic are performed, except that any resulting number is replaced by the remainder when it is divided by p (i.e., is reduced modulo p). Let the coordinates of any cell be given by x and y, where x and y each run from 0 to $(p - 1)$. Then a square in each language is given by inserting in the (x, y) cell the number $x + \lambda y$, reduced modulo p. By using values of $1, 2, \cdots, p - 1$, for λ, $(p - 1)$ different squares will be obtained, and, when superimposed, the squares form, as is easily proved, the completely orthogonalized square.

Corresponding to the existence of a completely orthogonalized square of side p there exists a very useful partitioning of p^2 objects. Note that, with the 4×4 completely orthogonalized square, the 16 cells may be divided into groups of 4 in 5 ways, namely:

> By rows
> By columns
> By Latin letters
> By Greek letters
> By numerals

These groupings are orthogonal in the sense that any grouping gives 4 groups, each of 4 cells, and the 4 cells that occur in 1 group of any grouping lie 1 each in the 4 groups of any other grouping. It follows that, if the cells are occupied by p^2 uncorrelated random variables, any contrast among the groups of one grouping will be orthogonal to any contrast among the groups of another grouping. For example, a group of 4 cells according to Latin letters in the 4×4 example above consists of the cells with A which are

$$1, 6, 11, 16$$

where the cells are numbered serially from left to right.   The groups by numerals are:

$$(1) \quad 1, 8, 10, 15$$

$$(2) \quad 2, 7, \ \ 9, 16$$

$$(3) \quad 3, 6, 12, 13$$

$$(4) \quad 4, 5, 11, 14$$

and we see that the cells containing A are distributed one each in the groups of numerals.

Among 16 objects there will be 15 degrees of freedom with the usual analysis of variance.   These 15 degrees of freedom may be broken down into 5 sets of 3 degrees of freedom, any set of 3 degrees of freedom being given by the contrast among the 4 groups according to one of the methods of classification.

In general, the $(p^{2n} - 1)$ degrees of freedom among p^{2n} objects may be divided into $(p^n + 1)$ sets of $(p^n - 1)$ degrees of freedom.   This property is the basis for lattice square designs and is of frequent value in other connections.

10.5   THE ANALYSIS OF THE LATIN SQUARE DESIGN

We shall examine the Latin square design from the same point of view as that which we used for randomized blocks.   We suppose then that the subscripts (i, j, k) denote the row, column, and treatment of a particular plot.   In all there are t^3 possible yields, for each treatment can conceptually be applied to each plot, and from this population of true yields we draw a sample which is based on a random $t \times t$ Latin square.   Such a sample has obvious properties of balance, particularly when we are concerned with the comparison of treatments.

The following relation is identically true:

$$y_{ijk} = y_{\cdots} + (y_{i\cdots} - y_{\cdots}) + (y_{\cdot j\cdot} - y_{\cdots})$$

$$+ (y_{ij\cdot} - y_{i\cdots} - y_{\cdot j\cdot} + y_{\cdots}) + (y_{\cdot\cdot k} - y_{\cdots})$$

$$+ (y_{i\cdot k} - y_{i\cdots} - y_{\cdot\cdot k} + y_{\cdots}) + (y_{\cdot jk} - y_{\cdot j\cdot} - y_{\cdot\cdot k} + y_{\cdots})$$

$$+ (y_{ijk} - y_{ij\cdot} - y_{\cdot jk} - y_{i\cdot k} + y_{i\cdots} + y_{\cdot j\cdot} + y_{\cdot\cdot k} - y_{\cdots}) \quad (1)$$

$$i, j, k = 1, 2, \cdots, t$$

Now suppose that

$$y_{ijk} = x_{ij} + \tau_k$$

where x_{ij} is the yield under a uniform treatment of plot (ij): that is, that treatments are additive in their effects. The relation then reduces to

$$y_{ijk} = (x.. + \tau.) + (x_i. - x..) + (x._j - x..) + (\tau_k - \tau.)$$
$$+ (x_{ij} - x_i. - x._j + x..) \quad (2)$$

which we may write as

$$y_{ijk} = \mu + \rho_i + \gamma_j + \tau_k + e_{ij} \quad (3)$$

The last term is a random variable since we have chosen a random $t \times t$ Latin square, and the particular $(x_{ij} - x_i. - x._j + x..)$ associated with τ_k is therefore chosen at random. Let δ_{ij}^k be the random variable which takes the value unity if treatment k is on the plot (i, j) and is zero otherwise. The joint distribution of the δ_{ij}^k's is determined by the particular family of Latin squares from which the one actually used is chosen at random.

Now we examine the expected value of treatment totals, of the error of treatment totals, of the treatment sum of squares, and so on. By definition ρ_i, γ_j, and τ_k have zero means.

A treatment total T_k is equal to

$$t\mu + t\tau_k + \sum_{ij} \delta_{ij}^k e_{ij} \quad (4)$$

Now if we choose a particular $t \times t$ Latin square and randomize rows, columns, and treatments, δ_{ij}^k is equal to unity with probability $1/t$ and equal to zero with probability $\left(\dfrac{t-1}{t}\right)$. So the expected value of T_k is

$$E(T_k) = t\mu + t\tau_k + \frac{1}{t}\sum_{ij} e_{ij}$$
$$= t(\mu + \tau_k) \quad (5)$$

The variance of a treatment total is equal to

$$E[T_k - E(T_k)]^2 = E\left(\sum_{ij} \delta_{ij}^k e_{ij}\right)^2$$
$$= E\left[\sum_{ij}(\delta_{ij}^k)^2 e^2_{ij} + \sum_{i' \neq i}\sum_j \delta_{ij}^k \delta_{i'j}^k e_{ij}e_{i'j}\right.$$
$$\left. + \sum_i\sum_{j' \neq j} \delta_{ij}^k\delta_{ij'}^k e_{ij}e_{ij'} + \sum_{i' \neq i}\sum_{j' \neq j} \delta_{ij}^k\delta_{i'j'}^k e_{ij}e_{i'j'}\right] \quad (6)$$

From the structure of Latin squares, we have:

If

$$\delta_{ij}^k = 1 \quad \text{then} \quad \delta_{i'j}^k = 0 \quad \text{and} \quad \delta_{ij'}^k = 0$$

and if

$$\delta_{ij}^k = 1 \quad \text{then} \quad \delta_{i'j'}^k = 1 \text{ with probability } \frac{1}{t-1}$$

The variance of a treatment total is then

$$\frac{1}{t} \sum_{ij} e^2_{ij} + \frac{1}{t(t-1)} \sum_{i' \neq i} \sum_{j' \neq j} e_{ij}e_{i'j'} = \frac{1}{t} \sum_{ij} e^2_{ij}$$

$$+ \frac{1}{t(t-1)} \left[\left(\sum_{ij} e_{ij} \right)^2 - \sum_{ij} e^2_{ij} - \sum_{i' \neq i} \sum_j e_{ij}e_{i'j} - \sum_i \sum_{j' \neq j} e_{ij}e_{ij'} \right]$$

But

$$\sum_{i' \neq i} \sum_j e_{ij}e_{i'j} = \sum_j e_{ij} \sum_{i'} e_{i'j} - \sum_{ij} e^2_{ij}$$

$$= - \sum_{ij} e^2_{ij}$$

and

$$\sum_i \sum_{j' \neq j} e_{ij}e_{ij'} = - \sum_{ij} e^2_{ij}$$

since

$$\sum_i e_{ij} = \sum_j e_{ij} = 0$$

The variance is therefore

$$\left(\sum_{ij} e^2_{ij} \right) \left[\frac{1}{t} + \frac{1}{t(t-1)}(-1+1+1) \right] = \left(\sum_{ij} e^2_{ij} \right) \left[\frac{1}{t} + \frac{1}{t(t-1)} \right]$$

$$= \frac{1}{t-1} \sum_{ij} e^2_{ij} \tag{7}$$

The covariance of any 2 treatment totals

$$E \left[\left(\sum_{ij} \delta_{ij}^k e_{ij} \right) \left(\sum_{ij} \delta_{ij}^{k'} e_{ij} \right) \right]$$

is found to be

$$- \frac{1}{(t-1)^2} \sum_{ij} e^2_{ij} \tag{8}$$

The variance of any linear contrast of the treatment totals

$$\Sigma \lambda_i T_i \quad \text{with} \quad \Sigma \lambda_i = 0$$

is then

$$(\Sigma \lambda^2_i) \frac{1}{t-1} \sum_{ij} e^2_{ij} - \frac{1}{(t-1)^2} \left(\sum_{i' \neq i} \lambda_i \lambda_{i'} \right) \sum_{ij} e^2_{ij}$$

$$= (\Sigma \lambda^2_i) \frac{t}{(t-1)^2} \sum_{ij} e^2_{ij} \tag{9}$$

Infinite model theory leads us to the partitioning for the analysis of variance given in Table 10.3, and we proceed to obtain the expectations

TABLE 10.3

	df
Rows	$t - 1$
Columns	$t - 1$
Treatments	$t - 1$
Error	$(t - 1)(t - 2)$
Total	$t^2 - 1$

of the mean square under the model we are using. It is found that

$$E \text{ (row mean square)} = \frac{t}{t - 1} \sum_i \rho^2{}_i$$

$$E \text{ (column mean square)} = \frac{t}{t - 1} \sum_j \gamma^2{}_j$$

$$E \text{ (treatment mean square)} = \frac{1}{(t - 1)^2} \sum_{ij} e^2{}_{ij} + \frac{t}{t - 1} \sum_k \tau^2{}_k \tag{10}$$

$$E \text{ (error mean square)} = \frac{1}{(t - 1)^2} \sum_{ij} e^2{}_{ij}$$

The Latin square is, therefore, unbiased in the sense of the expectation of the mean square for treatments equaling the expectation of the mean square for error under the null hypothesis that the treatments have identical effects on every plot or experimental unit.

It may be further noted that, if the expectation of the mean square for error is denoted by σ^2, the variance of any contrast of treatment means

$$\Sigma \lambda_i \overline{T}_i \quad \text{with} \quad \Sigma \lambda_i = 0$$

is $(\Sigma \lambda^2{}_i) \sigma^2 / t$, and that the covariance of two contrasts given by λ_i and λ'_i is $(\Sigma \lambda_i \lambda'_i) \sigma^2 / t$.

We are now in a position to understand the rule stated by Fisher [6] that the random Latin square should be chosen out of a number of Latin squares, in which every pair of plots that do not occur in the same row or column belongs to the same treatment with equal frequency. In our derivation of the analysis of the Latin square, we used the result that, if δ_{ij}^k equals unity, then $\delta_{i'j'}^k$, with $i \neq i'$ and $j \neq j'$, equals unity with probability $1/(t - 1)$. The probability of plots (ij) and $(i'j')$ being occupied by the same treatment is therefore $1/t(t-1)$, the same for all treatments. It may be noted in the derivation that we obtained the results using only the properties of any individual Latin square, such as that the probability that δ_{ij}^k equals unity is $1/t$, together with the statement that the probability that $\delta_{ij}^k \delta_{i'j'}^k$ equals unity is equal to $1/t(t-1)$. If we had not chosen these rules, the expression in equation 6 would not be the same for all treatments. Furthermore there would be no possibility of estimating the variances and covariances such as $E[T_k - E(T_k)]^2$ or $E\{[T_k - E(T_k)][T_{k'} - E(T_{k'})]\}$.

The testing of the hypothesis that there are no treatment effects is made by the randomization test. In view of the expectations given above, a criterion which is intuitively reasonable is that of (treatment mean square/error mean square). This will be evaluated for the square actually used and for all other squares that we could have obtained by the randomization procedure. If the value for the square actually used is equaled or exceeded by that of 5 percent or less of the possible arrangements, we shall say that we have significance at the 5 percent level. The evaluation of the significance level in a particular experiment would be a very laborious task, and we rely on the fact that the distribution of the criterion will be closely approximated by the F distribution with $(t-1)$ and $(t-1)(t-2)$ degrees of freedom. This distribution would hold exactly if the error terms in the model were normally and independently distributed with mean zero and variance σ^2. The extent to which the distribution of the criterion over the possible randomizations may be represented by the F distribution has been examined by Welch.[7] We have seen above that the quantity (treatment sum of squares/treatment plus error sum of squares), U, say, has a mean value of $1/(t-1)$, and this is the mean value of the beta distribution which is the transform of the F distribution. This was obtained, moreover, with only the specification that the probability that $\delta_{ij}^k \delta_{i'j'}^k$ equals unity is $1/t(t-1)$ and therefore holds for any transformation set.

Welch[7] found that the variance of U depended on the transformation set, and also on the quantities:

$$D = \sum_{ij} e^4{}_{ij}, \qquad\qquad F = \left(\sum_{ij} e^2{}_{ij}\right)^2$$

$$G = \sum_i \left(\sum_j e^2{}_{ij}\right)^2 + \sum_j \left(\sum_i e^2{}_{ij}\right)^2, \qquad H = \sum_{im} \left(\sum_j e_{ij}e_{mj}\right)^2$$

Welch examined the variance of U for some constructed data and for some sets of uniformity data and found that the proportion of times the 5 percent value of U from the beta distribution was exceeded ranged from 2.7 to 6.2 percent. The approximation by the F distribution is therefore not entirely satisfactory, but the evidence is not conclusive, in that the approximation depends on the quantities D, F, G, H above, and, in a particular case, we do not know these values, nor do we know the values we shall meet in practice. The rules given above for the choice of a random Latin square are designed to give equal probability to all possible Latin squares of size less than 7×7, and in the present state of knowledge this appears to be a desirable procedure. To conclude this aspect of the Latin square, we shall assume that normal theory gives satisfactory approximations to corresponding randomization tests.

Finally we should note some properties of the smaller Latin squares and the impact of these properties on randomization tests. We consider first the 2×2 Latin square, for which there are only 2 different ones: namely,

$$
\begin{array}{cc}
A \ B & B \ A \\
& \text{and} \\
B \ A & A \ B
\end{array}
$$

This square has no degrees of freedom for error, as is obvious from the fact that, if we use one square and obtain the treatment difference, then the treatment difference given by the other square is the negative of the difference with the former square. If then we wish to compare 2 treatments with 2×2 Latin squares, we must use many squares, and to make any test we must assume that the difference is constant from square to square. The randomization test is so simply performed in this case, that with a small number of squares, say, 6 or less, it would probably be advisable to rely on the randomization test procedures rather than the usual F distribution approximation (unless, of course, one can assume the infinite model).

In the case of the 3×3 Latin square, it is important to note that there are, in fact, only 2 different partitions of the 9 cells into 3 sets of 3, in such a way that each set is represented in each row and in each column. There are 12 different 3×3 Latin squares, but these give the same partitioning in sets of 3. If we wish to test the null hypothesis that there are no differences among the 3 treatments, we shall use the ratio of treatment mean square to error mean square as the test criterion. If this takes the value R with the randomization we in fact used, it will take the same value for 5 of the other 11 randomizations, and the value $1/R$ for the remaining 6. This happens because the sum of the treatment sum of squares with 2 degrees of freedom and the error sum of squares with 2 degrees of freedom is constant for all randomizations, and a randomization that gives a partitioning different from the one actually used will have the treatment and error sum of squares interchanged. We are, therefore, in the position of not being able to make a significance test for which the chance of rejecting the hypothesis when true is less than 50 percent (or, in other words, of size less than 0.50). This fact is important because, if we use the infinite model in which the errors in the model are assumed to be normally and independently distributed with mean zero and constant variance σ^2, we shall use the F test with 2 and 2 degrees of freedom and can make a test at any significance level we please. The distinction we make throughout this book between the finite and infinite model is therefore extremely relevant. If we consider a particular treatment contrast, and evaluate it for the 12 possible 3×3 Latin squares, we shall find that there are 6 possible values which the criterion (mean square due to treatment comparison/error mean square) can take. We therefore only make a test of significance with level 1-in-6, of the hypothesis that the true comparison is zero, if we use a 2-tailed test. For these reasons, a single 3×3 Latin square experiment is virtually valueless, and, if we use a small number of repetitions, we should, as with the 2×2 square, probably use the randomization test procedures, although it is often found that the usual F test gives a remarkably similar answer.

There are in all 4(4!3!) or 576 different 4×4 Latin squares, but these lead to only 24 different partitions of the 16 cells into 4 sets of 4, in such a way that each set is represented in each row and in each column. It is therefore desirable to make the test strictly according to the randomization test procedure.

Squares of side 5 and 6 were examined by Welch in the afore-mentioned work. For squares of side 7 or more it seems reasonable to assume that the F distribution is satisfactory.

We shall not give a lengthy discussion of the analysis of variance when the additive model does not hold. It is clear that, if there are row-treatment or column-treatment interactions, these will enter into the error mean square but not into the treatment mean square. The situation is entirely analogous to that of randomized blocks in that block-treatment interactions enter the error mean square but not the treatment mean square. Using a scale of measurement on which effects are additive is, therefore, very important. For tests of hypothesis we rely on the validity of F tests and t tests in finite populations.

We may, therefore, use the model

$$y_{ijk} = \mu + \rho_i + \gamma_j + \tau_k + e_{ijk}$$

the quantities μ, ρ_i, γ_j, and τ_k being fixed unknown constants and the

e_{ijk}'s being normally and independently distributed around zero with constant variance as an easy *substitute* for the laborious restricted sampling approach. Alternatively one may prefer to use the infinite model from the start. There is only one difference, other than those we have already mentioned in connection with tests of hypotheses, between the two approaches: namely, that the variance of a treatment mean for comparison with results of other experiments is σ^2/t with the infinite model but $\sigma^2/(t-1)$ with the finite model. When we make a statement about the variance of a treatment mean, we shall mean the variance appropriate for comparisons within the experiment, which is, in this case, σ^2/t. In this way we may ignore algebraically the correlation of treatment means.

10.6 ANALYSIS OF THE LATIN SQUARE WITH THE INFINITE MODEL

The basis of the usual analysis of the Latin square is the assumption of a model

$$y_{ijk} = m + \rho_i + \gamma_j + \tau_k + e_{ijk}, \qquad i = 1, \cdots, t$$

where $\qquad\qquad\qquad\qquad\qquad\qquad\qquad j = 1, \cdots, t$

m = the contribution common to all plots
ρ_i = the contribution common to all plots of the ith row
γ_j = the contribution common to all plots of the jth column
τ_k = the contribution common to all plots of the kth treatment

and the e_{ijk}'s are random errors, normally distributed about a mean of zero with constant variance σ^2.

This model leads to the analysis of variance (Table 10.4), where R_i, C_j, T_k, and G are row, column, treatment, and grand totals, respectively.

TABLE 10.4 ANALYSIS OF VARIANCE FOR A $t \times t$ LATIN SQUARE EXPERIMENT

Due to	df	Sum of Squares	Mean Square
Rows	$t-1$	$\sum \dfrac{R^2_i}{t} - \dfrac{G^2}{t^2}$	R
Columns	$t-1$	$\sum \dfrac{C^2_j}{t} - \dfrac{G^2}{t^2}$	C
Treatments	$t-1$	$\sum \dfrac{T^2_k}{t} - \dfrac{G^2}{t^2}$	T
Error	$(t-1)(t-2)$	By subtraction	E
Total	$t^2 - 1$	$\sum y^2_{ijk} - \dfrac{G^2}{t^2}$	

The mean square E is an estimate of σ^2, and, if there are no differential treatment effects, i.e., the τ_k's are equal, the mean square T is an estimate of σ^2, both sums of squares being distributed independently according to $\chi^2\sigma^2$, with the appropriate number of degrees of freedom for χ^2, by virtue of Cochran's theorem (cf. Chapter 5).

The estimated standard error of each treatment mean will be $\sqrt{E/t}$, which is appropriate for any treatment comparison. The results may be presented simply as in the case of randomized blocks: namely, a statement of treatment means with this standard error. Errors of particular comparisons, confidence limits, and so on are obtained as in that case, and the treatment sum of squares may be partitioned similarly.

10.7 MISSING DATA

The solution for 1 missing plot is fairly easily obtained and will be given. Suppose the yield on the plot in row 1, column 1, is missing and that this plot received treatment 1.

Let R_i $(i = 2, \cdots, t)$ be the total for the ith row, C_j $(j = 2, \cdots, t)$ be the total for the jth column, and T_k $(k = 2, \cdots, t)$ be the total for treatment k. Let R'_1 be the total of the *known* yields in row 1, and define C'_1 and T'_1 in the same manner. G' is the total of all known yields.

The procedure, as in the case of randomized blocks, will be to minimize the error variance with respect to the missing plot. In the analysis of variance given above we have the modification shown in Table 10.5.

TABLE 10.5

Due to	Sum of Squares
Rows	$\dfrac{1}{t}(R'_1 + x)^2 + \dfrac{1}{t}\sum_{i=2}^{t} R^2{}_i - \dfrac{(G' + x)^2}{t^2}$
Columns	$\dfrac{1}{t}(C'_1 + x)^2 + \dfrac{1}{t}\sum_{j=2}^{t} C^2{}_j - \dfrac{(G' + x)^2}{t^2}$
Treatments	$\dfrac{1}{t}(T'_1 + x)^2 + \dfrac{1}{t}\sum_{k=2}^{t} T^2{}_k - \dfrac{(G' + x)^2}{t^2}$
Error	Difference
Total	$x^2 + \sum_{ijk} y^2{}_{ijk} - \dfrac{(G' + x)^2}{t^2}$

We differentiate the error sum of squares with respect to x and, setting the derivative equal to zero solve for x. We need consider only those terms involving x, say, Q, where

$$Q = x^2 - \frac{(G' + x)^2}{t^2} - \frac{1}{t}(R'_1 + x)^2 + \frac{(G' + x)^2}{t^2} - \frac{1}{t}(C'_1 + x)^2$$

$$+ \frac{(G' + x)^2}{t^2} - \frac{1}{t}(T'_1 + x)^2 + \frac{(G' + x)^2}{t^2}$$

$$= x^2 + \frac{2(G' + x)^2}{t^2} - \frac{1}{t}[(R'_1 + x)^2 + (C'_1 + x)^2 + (T'_1 + x)^2]$$

$$\frac{\partial Q}{\partial x} = 2x + \frac{4(G' + x)}{t^2} - \frac{2}{t}[(R'_1 + x) + (C'_1 + x) + (T'_1 + x)]$$

It can be easily verified that setting this equal to zero and solving for x yields

$$x = \frac{tR'_1 + tC'_1 + tT'_1 - 2G'}{(t - 1)(t - 2)} \tag{11}$$

In general, if the yield corresponding to the uth row, vth column, wth treatment is missing, then the estimate of that yield is

$$x = \frac{tR'_u + tC'_v + tT'_w - 2G'}{(t - 1)(t - 2)}$$

where the quantities R'_u, C'_v, T'_w, and G' are defined as above. As before, we may replace the missing yield with this quantity and perform the analysis of variance exactly as above with this modification: The degrees of freedom for error will be $(t - 1)(t - 2) - 1 = t^2 - 3t + 1$, and for the total we will have $t^2 - 2$ degrees of freedom. The usual tests of significance may be performed, but the F will have an upward bias. Thus, if non-significance is found, we can stop. If F is significant, however, we cannot be sure that it is due to treatments and not to this bias.

Exact tests of significance in terms of infinite model theory, although easy to describe in terms of general theory, are somewhat difficult to obtain. It is necessary to evaluate the sum of squares attributable to rows and columns ignoring treatments, and to rows, columns, and treatments. The difference of these 2 sums of squares may then be tested against the error with the reduced sum of squares. To compute the necessary quantities, the experiment is first regarded as an experiment in rows and columns with one observation missing and the minimum sum of squares for error obtained. This sum of squares, W, say, will have $(t^2 - 2t)$ degrees of freedom. The minimum sum of squares for error, when treatments are taken into account, is obtained by analyzing the augmented table. E, say, with $(t^2 - 3t + 1)$ degrees of freedom.

The quantity $(W - E)/(t - 1)$ is the mean square for treatments, which is tested against $E/(t^2 - 3t + 1)$ by the F test with $(t - 1)$ and $(t^2 - 3t + 1)$ degrees of freedom.

If more than 1 plot, say, n, are missing, we can denote them by x_1, x_2, $\cdots$, x_n and proceed exactly as above. Partial derivatives with respect to the x_i's set equal to zero will give n equations in the n variables, which can be solved for exact solutions. However, if n is greater than 2 or 3, the algebra becomes very involved and tedious. Yates [8] has given an iterative method for solving for these unknown yields. For the plots x_2, x_3, $\cdots$, x_n we substitute the general mean of all known yields, $G'/(t^2 - n)$ and solve for x_1 as above in the case of 1 missing plot. Using this value for x_1 we can solve for x_2, etc. For the first approximation the quantity G' can be left equal to

$$G' + \frac{nG'}{(t^2 - n)}$$

until all n x_i's are calculated. These values, say, x'_i, are then put into the place of the missing plots, the new marginal and treatment totals are calculated, and a second approximation is calculated in the same manner. Yates [8] states that two approximations usually give sufficiently accurate values. More approximations are necessary if greater accuracy is desired.

The analysis of variance is then performed as with 1 missing plot, with the same restrictions. The degree of freedom for "error" and "total" are reduced by n from what they would be with no missing plots. The method for accurate F tests is unchanged.

10.7.1 The Case of a Missing Row, Column, or Treatment

The analysis of a Latin square experiment with a missing row (say, row 1) may be made in terms of the model

$$y_{ijk} = \mu + \rho_i + \gamma_j + \tau_k + e_{ijk}$$

where

$$i = 2, 3, \cdots, t$$

$$j = 1, 2, 3, \cdots, t$$

$$k = 1, 2, 3, \cdots, t$$

Least squares leads to simple equations for estimating the constants.

A similar setup is used for the case of a missing treatment. Suppose the rows and columns are named so that the missing treatment, say, treatment 1, lies along the leading diagonal. Then the normal equations are, utilizing the conditions, $\Sigma\hat{\rho}_i = \Sigma\hat{\gamma}_j = \Sigma\hat{\tau}_k = 0$:

$$t(t-1)\hat{\mu} = G$$

$$(t-1)\hat{\mu} + (t-1)\hat{\rho}_1 - \hat{\gamma}_1 = R_1$$

$$(t-1)\hat{\mu} + (t-1)\hat{\rho}_2 - \hat{\gamma}_2 = R_2$$

$$\cdots\cdots\cdots\cdots\cdots\cdots$$

$$(t-1)\hat{\mu} - \hat{\rho}_1 + (t-1)\hat{\gamma}_1 = C_1 \qquad (12)$$

$$(t-1)\hat{\mu} - \hat{\rho}_2 + (t-1)\hat{\gamma}_2 = C_2$$

$$\cdots\cdots\cdots\cdots\cdots\cdots$$

$$t\hat{\mu} + t\hat{\tau}_2 = T_2$$

$$t\hat{\mu} + t\hat{\tau}_3 = T_3$$

$$\cdots\cdots\cdots$$

where G, R_1, R_2, $\cdots$, C_1, C_2, $\cdots$, T_2, T_3, $\cdots$, are, respectively, the grand total, row totals, column totals, and treatment totals. The estimates of treatment differences are given by differences of the observed treatment means. The only further question is the analysis of variance. The estimates of the row and column parameters are given by the equations,

$$t(t-1)\hat{\mu} + t(t-2)\hat{\rho}_i = (t-1)R_i + C_i$$

$$t(t-1)\hat{\mu} + t(t-2)\hat{\gamma}_i = (t-1)C_i + R_i \qquad (13)$$

The sum of squares due to fitting the ρ's and γ's may be split into two portions:

1. *Sum of Squares for Columns Ignoring Rows:*

$$\frac{1}{t-1}\Sigma C^2_i - \frac{G^2}{t(t-1)} \qquad (14)$$

2. *Sum of Squares for Rows Eliminating Columns:*

$$\frac{1}{t(t-1)(t-2)}\Sigma[(t-1)R_i + C_i]^2 - \frac{G^2}{(t-1)(t-2)} \qquad (15)$$

The error sum of squares is obtained by subtraction. The variance of treatment means for comparison of means is, of course, σ^2/t.

The reader may refer to Yates [8] for a discussion of the above and of the case when both one row and column are missing and to Yates and Hale [9] when 2 or more rows, columns, or treatments are missing.

An important fact about the Latin square with 1 row, column, or treatment missing is that the design is unbiased in the sense that the expectation over possible randomizations of the error mean square is equal to the expectation of the treatment mean square. The same holds for the case of 1 row and 1 column, 1 row and 1 treatment, or 1 column and 1 treatment. The reader is referred to Yates [8] for proofs. By virtue of these facts, such patterns give valid experimental designs and can be used directly when the occasion arises. No examination of these patterns from the point of view of randomization tests except in regard to the mean value of the test criterion appears to have been made.

10.8 EFFICIENCY OF LATIN SQUARES

It may be desirable to test whether the row classification or the column classification or both have led to increased precision in the experiment. To obtain relative efficiencies suppose the mean squares in the analysis of variance of the Latin square are labeled as in Table 10.6.

TABLE 10.6

Due to	df	Mean Square
Rows	$r - 1$	R
Columns	$r - 1$	C
Treatments	$r - 1$	T
Errors	$(r - 1)(r - 2)$	E
Total	$r^2 - 1$	

With rows as blocks, and no treatment effects so that T will on the average equal E, the analysis of variance would be as shown in Table 10.7.

TABLE 10.7

Due to	df	Sum of Squares
Blocks (rows)	$r - 1$	$(r - 1)R$
Error	$r(r - 1)$	$(r - 1)C + (r - 1)^2 E$

If then the column classification had not been made, the error mean square would have been

$$\frac{(r - 1)C + (r - 1)^2 E}{r(r - 1)} = \frac{C + (r - 1)E}{r}$$

and the efficiency of the Latin square relative to randomized blocks made up by rows is estimated by

$$\frac{(r-1)C + (r-1)^2E}{r(r-1)E} = \frac{C + (r-1)E}{rE} \tag{16}$$

Similarly, the relative efficiency of the Latin square to randomized blocks made up of columns is estimated by

$$\frac{(r-1)R + (r-1)^2E}{r(r-1)E} = \frac{R + (r-1)E}{rE} \tag{17}$$

The efficiency of the Latin square relative to complete or unrestricted randomization is estimated by

$$\frac{(r-1)R + (r-1)C + (r-1)^2E}{(r^2-1)E} = \frac{R + C + (r-1)E}{(r+1)E} \tag{18}$$

In the above we have assumed that exactly the same plots would have been used in either of the other designs considered. The argument given is an intuitive one. It may be verified by the reader that an approach by the finite model gives the same result.

It may be noted that it is possible to estimate the efficiency of a particular design, relative to other designs obtained by dropping any of the restrictions in the particular design, from the results of actual experiments. This procedure is entirely valid, but it must be remembered that, if, to take an example, randomized blocks of size r were to be used instead of a Latin square, the best shape of block from the point of view of experimental procedure might have been of shape other than that given by rows or columns. This tends to vitiate many comparisons that are made in this way. The argument here is entirely one from the point of view of estimation.

10.8.1 Some Results on Efficiencies

Yates in his paper, "Complex Experiments," [10] gives some results on the efficiencies of complete randomization relative to randomized blocks and Latin squares for the case of field experiments:

	1932	1933
Randomized blocks	72% (22)	75% (22)
Latin square	54% (38)	57% (37)

The figures in brackets denote the number of experiments on which the means efficiencies are based.

It may be deduced that with this type of experiment and experimental unit randomized blocks necessitate about $\frac{3}{4}$ (72–75%) the number of plots that the completely randomized experiment requires to achieve a particular accuracy. A Latin square requires about $\frac{1}{2}$ the number of plots.

On another set of experiments he found that the efficiency of randomized blocks relative to Latin squares was about 60 percent. In a comparison of 5×5 Latin squares and randomized blocks of 5 plots, he found that about $2\frac{1}{2}$ times as many plots were necessary with the randomized blocks as with the Latin squares to achieve a particular accuracy. These results should be regarded only as an indication of the sort of results that may be obtained with different experimental material.

10.9 DESIGNS BASED ON GRAECO-LATIN SQUARES

A Graeco-Latin square pattern may be utilized to compare t (not equal to 6) treatments if the experimental units can be classified in 3 mutually orthogonal ways, corresponding, say, to rows, columns, and Latin letters. The treatments will be assigned to the Greek letters. These designs may, however, be unsatisfactory from the point of view of randomization tests. To take the case of t equal to 7, the treatment sum of squares is a random $\frac{1}{5}$ of the treatment plus error sum of squares (see Chapter 17). A test of significance can, therefore, work only at the level of rejecting the hypothesis that there are no treatment effects in $\frac{1}{5}$ of cases when it is true. For this reason, these designs are not to be recommended for any purposes other than exploratory. Their range of utility is restricted very much also by the necessity of having an orthogonal 3-way classification of the experimental units.

10.10 THE USE OF SYSTEMATIC LATIN SQUARES

In accordance with the basis of inference on which we rely throughout, we shall not consider the use of systematic Latin squares such as the Knut Vik square. The reader should refer to Fisher [11] for a discussion of this matter. The conclusion reached was that systematic squares prevented an estimation of the error of each treatment comparison and should not, therefore, be used. We shall examine the Knut Vik square in Chapter 17 when we have developed a notation that is particularly convenient for the purpose. Any of the designs that we consider apart from those using complete randomization are in a sense systematic, but we attempt to ensure that we always have a reasonable randomization test. Without such a test, we are completely at the mercy of whatever pattern of heterogeneity Nature chooses to impose on the experiment.

10.11 FURTHER REMARKS ON LATIN SQUARES

The following remarks may be made about Latin squares:

1. The need for transformations may arise as with randomized blocks.

2. A disadvantage of Latin squares is that the analysis becomes rather arduous if whole rows, columns, or treatments are missing.

3. It is not possible to partition the error sum of squares into components for particular treatment comparisons. If then the yields under 1 treatment are subject to a variance different from that with other treatments, the analysis becomes difficult if not impossible: This does not, fortunately, happen very often, and, if the experimenter has any inkling that such a possibility may occur, which cannot be corrected by a transformation, he should avoid Latin squares.

4. In general, the Latin square will be more efficient than the randomized block experiment, if only because a second classification added to a block classification can never lower the *true* efficiency.

5. The number of replicates must equal the number of treatments, and for this reason Latin squares are not popular with 8 or more treatments.

6. Squares of size 4 × 4 or less are unsatisfactory from the point of view of randomization tests and should be repeated; the same holds with the infinite model because of the low number of degrees of freedom for error.

7. The large Latin squares suffer from another defect that column effects, for example, could vary considerably over the experiment, and also row and column interaction with treatments become more likely.

REFERENCES

1. FISHER, R. A., and YATES, F. *Statistical tables.* Oliver and Boyd, Edinburgh. 3rd ed., 1948.
2. FISHER, R. A., and YATES, F. The 6 × 6 Latin squares. *Proc. Camb. Phil. Soc.*, **30**, 492–507, 1934.
3. NORTON, H. W. The 7 × 7 squares. *Ann. Eug.*, **9**, 269–307, 1939.
4. STEVENS, W. L. The completely orthogonalised square. *Ann. Eug.*, **9**, 82–93, 1938.
5. BOSE, R. C. On the application of Galois fields to the problem of the construction of Hyper-Graeco-Latin squares. *Sankhyā*, **3**, 323–338, 1938.
6. FISHER, R. A. The arrangement of field experiments. *Jour. Min. Agr. Engl.*, **33**, 503–513. 1926.

7. WELCH, B. L. On the z-test in randomised blocks and Latin squares. *Biometrika*, **29**, 21-52, 1937.

8. YATES, F. Incomplete Latin squares. *Jour. Agr. Sci.*, **26**, 301-315, 1936.

9. YATES, F., and HALE, R. W. The analysis of Latin squares when two or more rows, columns, or treatments are missing. *Suppl. Jour. Roy. Stat. Soc.*, **6**, 67-79, 1939.

10. YATES, F. Complex experiments. *Suppl. Jour. Roy. Stat. Soc.*, **2**, 181-247, 1935.

11. FISHER, R. A. *The design of experiments.* Oliver and Boyd, Edinburgh. 4th ed., 1947.

CHAPTER 11

Plot Technique

11.1 INTRODUCTION

Under this general heading will be considered matters relating to the choice of experimental unit for various types of experiments.   There are very few general considerations, but a large body of information has been accumulated over the past twenty or so years on field plot technique, that is, technique for field experiments.   Most of the difficulties are illustrated by this case, which will be described, and the reader should have no difficulty in translating notions like size and shape of plot and block into the language of another subject-matter field.   The uses of sampling in experimentation will also be discussed.

11.2 FIELD EXPERIMENTS

The following matters are of importance:

1. Size and shape of plot.
2. Size and shape of block.

The considerations that influence the choice on these matters are of two types: statistical and other.   Under statistical considerations we include topics such as the effect of size and shape of plot on error variance and accuracy of estimation.   The non-statistical considerations include such matters as the feasibility of particular sizes and shapes of plot from the point of view of experimentation.

11.2.1 Size and Shape of Plots

The most extensive investigation on size and shape of plot and size of block is that of Fairfield Smith.[1]   By harvesting a crop in very small units, he found that the variance *per unit area* for plots of area x units was given approximately by

$$V_x = \frac{V_1}{x^b} \tag{1}$$

where b is a characteristic of the soil, and a measure of the correlation among contiguous units. For example, if $b = 1$, $V_x = V_1/x$, and the units making up the plot of x units are not correlated at all. If, on the other hand, the x units are perfectly correlated, $b = 0$ and $V_x = V_1$, so that there is no gain due to the use of the larger size of plot. In general, b will be between zero and unity, so that the larger plots give more information with the same number of plots. This is to be expected in that a larger experimental area is being used. This formula can be interpreted in the other direction: Suppose we are to use a fixed area, so that we have the choice of r plots of size x units, $2r$ plots of size $x/2$ units, $3r$ plots of size $x/3$ units, etc., for each treatment. The variances of treatment means will then be as shown in Table 11.1.

TABLE 11.1

Size of Unit	No. of Replicates	Variance of Treatment Means per Unit Area
x	r	$\dfrac{V_x}{r}$
$\dfrac{x}{2}$	$2r$	$\dfrac{V_{x/2}}{2r}$
$\dfrac{x}{3}$	$3r$	$\dfrac{V_{x/3}}{3r}$
.	.	.
.	.	.
.	.	.
$\dfrac{x}{k}$	kr	$\dfrac{V_{x/k}}{kr}$

Using the above empirical relationship the variance of treatment means per unit area with kr replicates is

$$\frac{1}{kr}\frac{V_1}{\left(\dfrac{x}{k}\right)^b} = \frac{V_1}{rx^b}\frac{1}{k^{(1-b)}} \tag{2}$$

and this decreases as k increases since b must be between zero and unity.

This argument would lead us then to the use of as small a plot as possible (as large k as possible), and this is what is generally done. There is, however, a definite lower limit in a particular experimental situation on the size of plot. First, regardless of size of plot a certain amount on the border of the plot has to be rejected because there may be some carryover of treatment effects from plots to neighboring plots.

Second, it is necessary to use certain agricultural equipment for the cultivation and other agricultural operations on each plot; the gain from small plots may be more than offset by the increased cost of these experimental details with the small plots. Third, the argument assumes that the amount of work involved in the experiment is proportional to the area, whereas it is more reasonable to assume that the total cost is a function of the area and the number of plots.

As the size of plot decreases, the proportion of the experimental area that has to be devoted to guard rows or areas becomes very large, and this, together with the cost of agricultural operations, tends to produce a medium-sized plot. For example, with experiments on agronomic treatments on potatoes, a row crop, or small grains a plot of $\frac{1}{80}$th to $\frac{1}{20}$th of an acre has been found to be more or less optimum. The exact details of this problem are a topic for the subject-matter field under consideration and will not be discussed here. An easily examined instance of difficulties arising from border effects occurs in tree experiments, say, on apple trees. If the experimental unit is 1 tree and it is necessary to have each experimental unit guarded from each other by 1 tree, the experimental setup will be of the type shown in Figure 9, e denoting an experimental tree and g a guard tree.

$$\begin{array}{cccc} \cdot & \cdot & \cdot & \cdot \\ \cdot & \cdot & \cdot & \cdot \\ \cdots \ \ e & g & e & g \ \cdots \\ \cdots \ \ g & e & g & e \ \cdots \\ \cdots \ \ e & g & e & g \ \cdots \\ \cdot & \cdot & \cdot & \cdot \\ \cdot & \cdot & \cdot & \cdot \end{array}$$

FIGURE 9.

With this arrangement somewhat less than one half of the trees in an experiment will be non-experimental. It is easily verified that, as the size of experimental unit increases, the proportion of non-experimental trees decreases.

In agricultural crops and particularly tree crops the question of size of plot must be considered in relation to the amount of competition and the effect of treatments on adjacent plots that may be expected. In some instances one might expect the effect of competition will be to lower treatment differences for a tree experiment. In some cases taking account of the difficulty of using guard trees, plots of individual trees may be recommended. It is, of course, necessary to consider the actual treatments being investigated, and no general rules can be stated. A design that was found to be very successful recently in the determination of a small effect on corn utilized plots of a single kernel of corn. With this size of plot the amount of replication possible was, by ordinary standards, tremendous.

Fairfield Smith found little effect of shape in the sets of uniformity data he examined, but this is somewhat contrary to our general expectation. If there are no fertility trends in the experimental area, we would expect long narrow plots to be more efficient, as the correlation between small areas within the plot will be less than in a square plot of the same area, if it is assumed, as appears reasonable, that the correlation between two points is a function of their distance apart. If, however, the experimenter uses long narrow plots which run perpendicular to the direction of fertility changes, he may expect to obtain lower accuracy than with square plots and *a fortiori* with the same-shaped plots running parallel to the direction of fertility changes. In the absence of any knowledge of fertility trends, it is probably better to use square plots, though again experimental details, such as ease of cultivation, sowing, and harvesting, may lead the experimenter to rectangular plots with one dimension different from the other. There is, of course, no necessity of insisting on rectangular plots except for reasons of convenience. Sometimes in experiments on terraced land it may be necessary to use plots that are not rectangular.

An original type of experimental unit was devised at the Connecticut Agricultural Experimental Station for the testing of fungicides on plants. The difficulty arose that the plants have to be watered every day. The experimental area was a continuous row of plants somewhat in the form of an equiangular spiral (Figure 10).

FIGURE 10.

The water was brought to the plants by means of an underground pipe to the center of the spiral, a vertical pipe, and a horizontally swinging arm, at the end of which was a rubber hose. It was then a simple matter to turn on the water, walk around the spiral, and water the continuous row. The experimental unit was, in this case, a particular length of row. This example is mentioned to indicate that there is scope for ingenuity in the choice of a suitable experimental unit.

If Latin squares are to be used, the more nearly square the plot is, the more efficient the Latin square may be expected to be, from general considerations. For example, with 9 treatments on corn, a 9 × 9 Latin square with 2 by 10 hill plots will be of dimensions 18 by 90 hills (disregarding borders). Such a design has considerable defects. It may not be easy to find a reasonably homogeneous area of these dimensions, and also column effects at one end of the experiment may be very different from column effects at the other end. Such an effect would increase both treatment and error mean squares. It would not introduce any bias in the estimation of average effects but would render an analysis very difficult and would result in lower efficiency.

11.2.2 Size and Shape of Blocks

The size of block in an ordinary randomized block experiment is determined by the number of treatments, the size and shape of plots, and the way they are aggregated into blocks. In general the division of the experimental material into blocks is made in such a way that plots within blocks are as homogeneous as possible. Blocks should remove as much of trends in the material as possible; for example, if there is a fertility trend from north to south on the experimental land, the blocks should lie in that same direction relative to each other. Each plot should be as representative as possible of conditions in the block so that one reaches an arrangement like that shown in Figure 11.

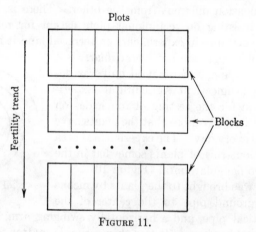

FIGURE 11.

In the absence of any knowledge of trends in the experimental material with regard to the characteristic observed, it is better to use plots that are more nearly square and to make the blocks as compact as possible.

Fairfield Smith [1] deduced the following relationship for the variance per unit area between plots of size x units in blocks of m plots,

$$(V_x)_m = \frac{m(1 - m^{-b})}{m - 1} (V_x)_\infty \tag{3}$$

where $(V_x)_\infty$ is the variance in an infinite field, and hence he obtained the relative efficiency of blocks of m plots relative to blocks of n plots to be the same, regardless of size of plot and equal to

$$\frac{(V_x)_n}{(V_x)_m} = \frac{n(m-1)(1-n^{-b})}{m(n-1)(1-m^{-b})} \tag{4}$$

The value of this formula is limited, because the value of b is erratic over different areas, and one cannot predict the value that one will meet. Fairfield Smith found it to lie generally between 0.2 and 0.7. The results in Table 11.2 are calculated from the above formula.

TABLE 11.2 EFFICIENCY OF BLOCKS OF x PLOTS

x	5	10	20	40
$b = 0.2$	1.56	1.30	1.13	1
$b = 0.7$	1.12	1.06	1.03	1

In general, it is best to make the blocks as small as possible, and this is the reason for the use of incomplete block designs to be discussed in later chapters. These are designs for comparing a number t of treatments in blocks of less than t plots. In some cases the gain in information from using the smaller blocks will be small, but generally it will be considerable, as evidenced by the fact that most trials involving a large number of varieties are arranged in some incomplete block arrangements.

11.3 ANIMAL EXPERIMENTS

In this group we include experiments on cows, for example, and experiments whose purpose is to perform a biological assay, for example, with rats or mice. Very little is known, but some pointers and warnings of pitfalls may be given.

We remember that the experimental unit is defined as the unit for which a treatment is chosen at random. For example, with a hog-feeding experiment it may be convenient to apply the treatment to groups of, say, 6 hogs, the hogs having a common feeding arrangement. It would be a mistake to regard the individual hog as the experimental unit, because there will be competition between animals within a lot. In field experiments the purpose of guard rows is to prevent plots from being influenced by the treatments on neighboring plots and to some extent to prevent competition between plots. How important the competition effect will be depends on many factors: the duration of the experiment, the extent to which the animals in a lot are of the same size and vigor, and so on. If the experiment is of long duration, there are large treatment effects, and the animals were initially of different vigors, the treatments may enhance these differences and result in their becoming larger. Under most circumstances the variance within lots may have little meaning, and it is extremely risky, for example, to draw inferences for one size of lot from what was observed with another size of lot by the use of components of variance.

To give another example of the difficulties that may arise in animal experiments, consider a grazing experiment, where it is necessary to graze experimental areas with animals, say, cows or sheep. Such a problem arises often on its own, and very frequently in rotation experiments, when one or more crops of the rotation are to be grazed. If a very small plot is used, it is not possible to graze with more than one animal, and animals do not like being segregated to this extent. The animal will spend most of its time walking around the boundary of the plot looking for a way of escape, and the whole purpose of the experiment will be vitiated. If a large plot is used, this problem is avoided, but very low statistical efficiency results. For sheep it has been found that plots of $\frac{1}{40}$ of an acre are reasonably satisfactory, though rather on the small side, but for large animals such as cows the best size of plot appears to be between 1 and 5 acres. Another point is that, with very few animals, the yield of a plot, say, by live weight increases, is subject to considerable errors of measurement.

11.4 THE USE OF SAMPLING IN EXPERIMENTS

We have seen that the optimum size of experimental unit is governed by many considerations. Frequently it is not possible or not desirable to measure the characteristic, say, yield, on the whole of each experimental unit, or it may be desirable to estimate some characteristics on the whole of the unit and other characteristics on a random sample only of the unit. To examine these questions, it is necessary to choose a sampling unit and, this having been done, to obtain data that can give the necessary information.

Suppose then that we have an experiment in r randomized blocks of t plots and that the characteristic has been observed on a random sample of s sampling units from each plot. The observations may be denoted by y_{ijk} where i denotes the block ($i = 1, 2, \cdots, r$), j the treatment ($j = 1, 2, \cdots, t$), and k the sampling unit ($k = 1, 2, \cdots, s$), and we assume the following model:

$$y_{ijk} = m + r_i + t_j + e_{ij} + \eta_{ijk}$$

where

m = the general mean
r_i = the replicate effect
t_j = the treatment effect
e_{ij} = the experimental error of plot (ij)

and

η_{ijk} = the sampling error of the kth observation on the (ij)th plot

The expectation of η_{ijk} will be zero, and we suppose that the expectation of e_{ij} is zero. We suppose for the present purpose that the η_{ijk}'s are normally and independently distributed with the same variance σ^2_s and the e_{ij}'s normally and independently distributed with variance σ^2_e. The η_{ijk}'s will, of course, be independent of the e_{ij}'s if the sampling is random.

This model leads to the analysis of variance on a sample basis given in Table 11.3, where

TABLE 11.3

Due to	df	Sum of Squares	Mean Square	Expectation of Mean Square
Replicates	$r - 1$	$\dfrac{1}{ts} \sum_i Y^2_{i\cdot\cdot} - C$		
Treatments	$t - 1$	$\dfrac{1}{rs} \sum_j Y^2_{\cdot j\cdot} - C$	T	$\sigma^2_s + s\sigma^2_e + \dfrac{rs}{t-1}\Sigma(t_j - t_\cdot)^2$
Replicates by treatments	$(r-1)(t-1)$	$\dfrac{1}{s}\sum_{ij} Y^2_{ij\cdot} - \dfrac{1}{ts}\sum_i Y^2_{i\cdot\cdot}$ $- \dfrac{1}{rs}\sum_j Y^2_{\cdot j\cdot} + C$	E	$\sigma^2_s + s\sigma^2_e$
Samples within plots	$rt(s-1)$	$\sum_{ijk}\left(y_{ijk} - \dfrac{Y_{ij\cdot}}{s}\right)^2$	S	σ^2_s
Total	$rts - 1$	$\sum_{ijk} y^2_{ijk} - C$		

$$Y_{ij\cdot} = \sum_k y_{ijk}$$

$$Y_{i\cdot\cdot} = \sum_{jk} y_{ijk}$$

$$Y_{\cdot j\cdot} = \sum_{ik} y_{ijk}$$

$$Y_{\cdots} = \sum_{ijk} y_{ijk}$$

$$C = \frac{Y^2_{\cdots}}{rts}$$

The test of significance for treatment effects is, of course, the F test of T/E with $(t-1)$ and $(r-1)(t-1)$ degrees of freedom.

The components of variance σ^2_s and σ^2_e may be estimated by

$$\hat{\sigma}^2_s = S$$

$$\hat{\sigma}^2_e = \frac{E-S}{s}$$

(5)

The estimated variance of treatment comparisons on a per sample basis will be proportional to E/rs.

We may estimate the variance of treatment comparisons with, say, r' replicates and s' samples per plot to be proportional to

$$\frac{\hat{\sigma}^2_s}{r's'} + \frac{\hat{\sigma}^2_e}{r'} = \frac{S}{r's'} + \frac{E-S}{r's}$$

$$= \frac{E}{r's} + \frac{S}{r'}\left(\frac{1}{s'} - \frac{1}{s}\right)$$

(6)

Note that, when $r' = r$, $s' = s$, this equals E/rs as before. The relative information with varying values of r' and s' may then be estimated, that for r' replicates and s' samples per plot, relative to the use of r replicates and s samples per plot, being

$$\frac{r's'E}{r[s'E + (s-s')S]}$$

(7)

With infinite sampling of each plot ($s' = \infty$), the efficiency becomes

$$\frac{r'E}{r(E-S)}$$

(8)

and this is the maximum that can be achieved. This will often be uneconomical, and it is necessary to consider the costs of the various operations.

A simple cost structure is to let

$$C = \text{cost per plot excluding harvesting}$$

$$C_s = \text{cost per sample of harvesting}$$

With r replicates and s samples per plot the cost of the experiment per treatment is

$$rC + rsC_s$$

The information on each treatment mean, assuming the variance components to be known, is

$$\frac{rs}{\sigma^2{}_s + s\sigma^2{}_e}$$

We shall wish to choose r and s, so that we maximize the information for a given cost C_0 per treatment, say.

We then have

$$r(C + sC_s) = C_0$$

so that the information is

$$\frac{sC_0}{(C + sC_s)(\sigma^2{}_s + s\sigma^2{}_e)}$$

It is simpler to minimize the reciprocal of this, namely,

$$\frac{1}{C_0}\left(\frac{C\sigma^2{}_s}{s} + C_s\sigma^2{}_s + C\sigma^2{}_e + sC_s\sigma^2{}_e\right)$$

and, by differentiating and equating to zero, we get

$$-\frac{C\sigma^2{}_s}{s^2} + C_s\sigma^2{}_e = 0$$

so that

$$s = \sqrt{\frac{C\sigma^2{}_s}{C_s\sigma^2{}_e}} \tag{9}$$

is the optimum number of samples per plot. This leads to the optimum value of r: namely,

$$r = \frac{C_0}{C + \sqrt{CC_s\dfrac{\sigma^2{}_s}{\sigma^2{}_e}}}$$

In some cases the experimenter may have no choice but to sample the experimental unit for the observation of the characteristic: for example, if the unit is an apple tree and the characteristic is volume of apple (say, number per bushel, or some such measure). In other cases the choice may be between the optimum amount of sampling and complete harvesting.

Suppose then that the cost of complete harvesting each plot is C_h. Then, with complete harvesting, the cost is

$$r'(C + C_h)$$

and the information is

$$\frac{r'}{\sigma^2{}_e}$$

(Note that the component for sampling variation within a plot no longer appears in the formula.) The number of replicates possible with total cost C_0 is then

$$r = \frac{C_0}{C + C_h}$$

and the information per treatment mean is

$$\frac{C_0}{(C + C_h)\,\sigma^2_e}$$

To compare this with the information with optimum sampling we need a conversion factor to convert information on a sample basis to information on a plot basis, and we suppose that a plot is equivalent to λ samples. To simplify the formula, we denote

$$\frac{\sigma^2_s}{\sigma^2_e}$$

by V^2. Then the relative efficiency of optimum sampling to complete harvesting is

$$\lambda^2 \frac{\sqrt{\dfrac{C}{C_s}}\,V}{(C + \sqrt{CC_s}V)\left(V + \sqrt{\dfrac{C}{C_s}}\,V\right)} \frac{(C + C_h)}{} \tag{10}$$

This is a somewhat unmanageable formula, and it is probably better to derive the result directly in any particular instance.

The following notes may be added to the above. It is usually desirable to tabulate the efficiencies of various choices of r and s relative to some base, as the cost situation may be more complex than the above. In the above derivation it was assumed that the population within a plot was effectively infinite, so that any finite sampling corrections could be ignored. The reader should refer to Yates and Zacopanay[2] for further discussion of the problem of sampling replicated experiments and to Cochran.[3]

REFERENCES

1. FAIRFIELD SMITH, H. An empirical law describing heterogeneity in the yields of agricultural crops. *Jour. Agr. Sci.*, 28, 1–29, 1938.
2. YATES, F., and ZACOPANAY, I. The estimation of the efficiency of sampling with special reference to sampling for yields in cereal experiments, *Jour. Agr. Sci.*, 25, 545–577, 1935.
3. COCHRAN, W. G. The estimation of the yields of cereal experiments by sampling for the ratio of grain to total produce. *Jour. Agr. Sci.*, 30, 262–275, 1940.

CHAPTER 12

The Sensitivity of Randomized Block and Latin Square Experiments

12.1 INTRODUCTION

In performing an experiment, the experimenter has two primary objects: to test hypotheses, and to estimate parameters. As long as the experimenter's interest is in the estimation of parameters, we have provided him with the necessary tools for the planning of his experiment: namely, the errors of estimation of the parameters, say, treatment differences, in terms of the number of experimental units, the design, and the error variance. We have examined the dependence of the error variance on the design and on the type of experimental unit, insofar as any general knowledge exists. If any one experiment that we use is one of a series of similar experiments, this may satisfy us except for the problems of the interpretation of groups of similar experiments, which will be taken up in later chapters. In the individual experiment the experimenter is likely to be interested not only in the accuracy of his estimates but also in the probability or chance he has of proving the existence of treatment differences if they are of a certain size. It is of little use to the individual experimenter to reach a "nearly significant" conclusion, say, that the effect of a treatment is to produce a response of 5 units with a standard error of 3 units. It may be that another worker in the field has found a response of, say, 3 units with a standard error of 2 units, so that the two investigations appear to indicate a real effect. The combination of pieces of knowledge of this sort is, in part, a statistical problem to which an answer exists under certain assumptions. But also involved in such a combination is the evaluation of the two studies, whether in fact they are concerned with the same problem and whether the two results may legitimately be pooled.

As a simplification of the needs of the experimenter, we may suggest the curve in Figure 12 for the case of a treatment and a control, in which we plot the true difference on the abscissa and the probability of a difference being shown to exist on the ordinate.

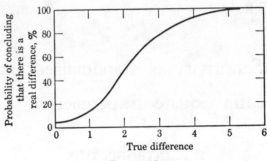

FIGURE 12.

The experimenter's rule of action is that he will use a certain test of significance, e.g., the 5 percent F test, and, if he obtains a significant difference, he will conclude that there is a real treatment difference. If the true difference is sufficiently small, the experimenter is not interested in concluding that it exists, but, if it is very large, he wishes to have a high probability of concluding that a difference exists. Many practical experimenters do not think in these terms because to do so requires some acquaintance with statistical notions: e.g., the probability of reaching various decisions. One of the important contributions of statistics to experimentation is in fact the ability to evaluate a particular scientific procedure in the above way.

We have already considered the question of the sensitivity of an experiment in Chapter 7. We noted that, if the triangular taste trial is used and the experimenter wishes to conclude with probability 0.95 that there is a difference, when, in fact, the odd one is picked out correctly 50 percent of times, a total of 92 repetitions must be used. In passing, we may note that a simple problem of this type can be tackled experimentally by means of sequential analysis, and the sequential method would result in a considerable saving of time (see references 1 and 2). If, on the other hand, the same reliability of conclusion is necessary when the true proportion picked out correctly is 75 percent, only 13 repetitions are necessary. Thus, the size of the experiment depends markedly on the sensitivity we desire.

In this chapter we are concerned with the sensitivity of randomized block and Latin square experiments. We have based our tests of hypotheses with these designs on randomization tests, and we should approach the question of the sensitivity of these experiments in the same way. Operationally we should take a set of data occupying the same experimental layout as the design we are to use and similar to the data we would get with a uniformity trial. We should then superimpose all the possible, N, say, randomization patterns on the design and adjust the data according to a set of preassigned treatment effects. For each of the N randomizations of treatments, and, therefore, for each of the N possible patterns of experimental results we could get, with a set of treatment effects, we should determine whether treatments have significant effects by the randomization test. The proportion of the N randomizations of treatments that gave significant effects could then be obtained, and this proportion could be called the power of the randomization test used against the alternative hypothesis with the preassigned effects. We can use a randomization test with any significance level we choose, and for each chosen significance level, we could, therefore, obtain the power of the test against the chosen alternative. We should then examine, theoretically at least, the possible alternatives which we are interested in discovering, and, supposing the alternatives can be mapped in a line (plane, etc.), we would have a power curve (surface, etc.). This procedure for obtaining the sensitivity of the randomization test is tedious and somewhat intractable, and so we shall first consider the infinite model modification.

12.2 THE POWER OF THE ANALYSIS OF VARIANCE TEST

We have seen that the randomization test is approximately represented by the analysis of variance test, and so we shall discuss the sensitivity of the randomization test by supposing that not only the null hypothesis test but also the distributions under alternative hypotheses can be specified by the general linear hypothesis.

In Chapter 9 we described Neyman's approach to the sensitivity of the randomized block test for 2 treatments, and we shall now review the work of Tang [3] for the more general case. It is assumed that the observations y are expressible as known linear functions of unknown parameters plus residuals which are normally and independently distributed with mean zero and the same variance σ^2. This case includes the randomized block experiment in which the yields y_{ij}, $i(= 1, 2, \cdots, r)$ being the block number, and $j(= 1, 2, \cdots, t)$ the treatment number, are given by

$$y_{ij} = \mu + b_i + t_j + e_{ij} \tag{1}$$

μ, b_i, and t_j being unknown parameters and the e_{ij}'s being normally and independently distributed with mean zero and the same unknown variance σ^2. In such a case the results are analyzed by the analysis of variance (Table 12.1).

TABLE 12.1

Due to	df	Mean Square
Blocks	$r - 1$	
Treatments	$t - 1$	T
Error	$(r - 1)(t - 1)$	E
Total	$rt - 1$	

The experimenter decides on the level of significance he wishes to use and compares T/E with the corresponding F value. If the observed ratio exceeds the tabulated value he concludes that there are treatment differences.

Under the assumptions of the model, the error sum of squares is distributed as $\chi^2\sigma^2$, where χ^2 has $(r - 1)(t - 1)$ degrees of freedom. The treatment sum of squares is equal to $r\Sigma(y_{\cdot j} - y_{\cdot\cdot})^2$, and this may be expressed in the form

$$\frac{r}{2}(y_{\cdot 1} - y_{\cdot 2})^2 + \frac{r}{6}(y_{\cdot 1} + y_{\cdot 2} - 2y_{\cdot 3})^2 + \cdots$$

$$+ \frac{r}{t(t - 1)}[y_{\cdot 1} + y_{\cdot 2} + \cdots + y_{\cdot(t-1)} - (t - 1)y_{\cdot t}]^2 \quad (2)$$

which we may write as

$$z^2_1 + z^2_2 + \cdots + z^2_{t-1} \quad (3)$$

Each of the quantities z_i is normally distributed with variance σ^2 around a mean α_i, say, and, furthermore, the z_i's are uncorrelated and therefore independent. The distribution of Σz^2_i may be obtained by one of several methods, the easiest being the use of characteristic functions (see Cramer,[4] for example). The method used by Tang was to make a transformation of variables. It is found that the distribution of

$$\frac{\Sigma z^2_i}{\sigma^2} = \chi'^2$$

depends on the number of degrees of freedom, $t - 1$ in this case, which is denoted by f_1 generally, and on

$$\frac{\Sigma \alpha^2_i}{2\sigma^2} = \lambda$$

say, being

$$f(\chi'^2) = e^{-\lambda} \sum_{m=0}^{\infty} \frac{\lambda^m}{m!} f_{2m+f_1}(\chi'^2) \tag{4}$$

where $f_{2m+f_1}(\chi'^2)$ is the density for the ordinary χ^2 distribution with $2m + f_1$ degrees of freedom. This distribution is known as the non-central χ^2 distribution, and is a weighted mean of an infinite number of ordinary χ^2 distributions, as equation 4 indicates. Explicitly, the form of the distribution is

$$f(\chi'^2) = e^{-\lambda} \sum_{m=0}^{\infty} \frac{\lambda^m}{m!} \frac{e^{-\frac{1}{2}\chi'^2}(\chi'^2)^{m+\frac{1}{2}f_1-1}}{2^{m+\frac{1}{2}f_1}\Gamma(m + \frac{1}{2}f_1)} \tag{5}$$

This distribution has some interesting properties, and, in particular, is reproductive in that the sum of 2 quantities distributed independently according to the non-central χ^2 distribution with parameters λ_1, f_1 and λ_2, f_2, respectively, is distributed according to the non-central χ^2 distribution with parameters $\lambda_1 + \lambda_2$, $f_1 + f_2$. The distribution of the ratio u of 2 independent non-central χ'^2 with parameters λ_1, f_1 and λ_2, f_2 for numerator and denominator, respectively, is found to be (cf. Tang)

$$f(u) = \sum_{j=0}^{\infty} \sum_{i=0}^{\infty} \frac{\lambda_1^i \lambda_2^j e^{-(\lambda_1+\lambda_2)} u^{i+\frac{1}{2}f_1-1}}{i!j!B(\frac{1}{2}f_1 + i, \frac{1}{2}f_2 + j)(1 + u)^{i+j+\frac{1}{2}(f_1+f_2)}} \tag{6}$$

where $B(\frac{1}{2}f_1 + i, \frac{1}{2}f_2 + j)$ is the beta function. We may note that, if λ_1 and $\lambda_2 = 0$, we have the ordinary F distribution expressed in terms of sums of squares rather than mean squares. We are concerned here with the case when λ_2 is equal to zero, for the error sum of squares divided by σ^2 is distributed as χ^2: i.e., a non-central χ^2 with $\lambda = 0$. The distribution of the ratio of the sum of squares for treatments with f_1 degrees of freedom over the sum of squares for error with f_2 degrees of freedom is then

$$f(u) = \sum_{i=0}^{\infty} \frac{\lambda^i}{i!} \frac{e^{-\lambda} u^{i+\frac{1}{2}f_1-1}}{B(\frac{1}{2}f_1 + i, \frac{1}{2}f_2)(1 + u)^{i+\frac{1}{2}(f_1+f_2)}} \tag{7}$$

Under the null hypothesis that the treatments have no effect, the distribution of u is $f_0(u)$, say, where

$$f_0(u) = \frac{u^{\frac{1}{2}f_1-1}}{B(\frac{1}{2}f_1, \frac{1}{2}f_2)(1 + u)^{\frac{1}{2}(f_1+f_2)}} \tag{8}$$

The position may be represented by Figure 13.

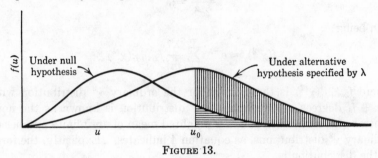

FIGURE 13.

Suppose we have decided to use a 5 percent significance test, then we shall reject the null hypothesis if the observed value of u is greater than u_0, given by $P(u \geq u_0) = 0.05$: i.e., lies in the portion of the distribution under the null hypothesis which is shaded horizontally. We now wish to obtain the probability that u is greater than u_0 under the hypothesis specified by λ: i.e., to find the area in the distribution under the alternative hypothesis which is shaded vertically or horizontally.

The only tables existing are those of Tang [3] which are given in the Appendix. He chose to work in terms of the quantity $E^2 = u/(1 + u)$, and the tables contain the value of E^2 which is exceeded by chance in 5 percent of times, $E^2_{0.05}$, and the value which is exceeded by chance in 1 percent of times, $E^2_{0.01}$, under the null hypothesis. These are, of course, simple transformations of the corresponding variance ratios F, since $F = \dfrac{f_2}{f_1} u$, so that

$$E^2 = \frac{f_1 F}{f_2 + f_1 F}$$

Furthermore, instead of obtaining the probability of concluding that there is in fact a difference, Tang's tables give the probability of failing to conclude that there is a difference, P_{II}: namely, the error of the second kind. Also, instead of obtaining P_{II} as it is related to λ, he obtained P_{II} for chosen values of

$$\phi = \sqrt{\frac{2\lambda}{f_1 + 1}}$$

We shall now give some examples of the use of these tables.

12.3   RANDOMIZED BLOCKS

In the case of randomized blocks, f_1 equals $(t - 1)$ and $f_2 = (r - 1) \times (t - 1)$. The quantity λ is equal to $r\Sigma(t_j - \bar{t})^2/2\sigma^2$, as is easily seen by taking expectation of the z_i's in equation 3, squaring, and adding. We find, therefore, that the sensitivity of the randomized block experiment is a function of the number of replicates, the true error variance σ^2, and the sum of squares about their mean of the *true* treatment means. We now give some examples.

12.3.1 Randomized Blocks for 2 Treatments

The case of randomized blocks comparing 2 treatments is simple to understand. The following is concerned with testing for a difference, and not with the situation discussed in Chapter 9 where one is testing whether a chosen one of the treatments is better than the other. In this case

$$\lambda = \frac{r[(t_1 - \bar{t})^2 + (t_2 - \bar{t})^2]}{2\sigma^2} = \frac{r(t_1 - t_2)^2}{4\sigma^2} = \frac{r\Delta^2}{4\sigma^2}$$

where

$$\Delta = t_1 - t_2$$

Also

$$f_1 = 1 \quad \text{so} \quad \phi = \sqrt{\lambda} = \sqrt{r}\,\frac{\Delta}{2\sigma} \quad \text{and} \quad f_2 = r - 1$$

where r is the number of replicates. The probability of concluding that there is no difference is, therefore, given by reading Tang's tables with $\phi = \sqrt{r}\Delta/2\sigma$: i.e.,

$$\sqrt{r} \times \frac{\text{true treatment difference}}{2 \text{ true standard deviation per plot}}$$

Let us suppose that the experimenter is interested in detecting a treatment difference equal to twice the standard deviation per plot, so that $\Delta/2\sigma = 1$ and $\phi = \sqrt{r}$, and that he will use a 5 percent significance test. For various values of r we find the data in Table 12.2.

TABLE 12.2

r	f_2	ϕ	P_{II} (Approximate)
3	2	1.73	0.71
5	4	2.24	0.34
7	6	2.65	0.13
9	8	3.00	0.04
11	10	3.32	0.03
16	15	4.00	0.001
31	30	5.57	0.001

So, if the experimenter wishes to have a 90 percent chance of concluding by a 5 percent test that there is a difference, when the true difference is twice the standard deviation per plot, he should use about 8 replicates ($P_{II} = 0.08$).

We now consider the case when a 1 percent significance test is used (Table 12.3).

TABLE 12.3

r	f_2	ϕ	P_{II} (Approximate)
3	2	1.73	0.93
5	4	2.24	0.72
7	6	2.65	0.44
9	8	3.00	0.22
11	10	3.32	0.09
16	15	4.00	0.01
31	30	5.57	0.001

It should be noted that the use of a test that rejects the null hypothesis less frequently when it is true also results in the less frequent rejection of the null hypothesis when an alternative is true. In order that the probability of concluding by a 1 percent test that there is a treatment difference be 90 percent, about 11 replicates are necessary, as opposed to 8 for the 5 percent test.

The values of P_{II} for various values of Δ/σ and r have been obtained and are given in Table 12.4.

TABLE 12.4   SENSITIVITY OF RANDOMIZED BLOCK EXPERIMENT FOR 2 TREATMENTS

Approximate Δ/σ

	5% Test			1% Test		
r	½	1	2	½	1	2
3	0.93	0.85	0.71	0.98	0.96	0.93
5	0.90	0.76	0.34	0.98	0.93	0.72
7	0.86	0.64	0.13	0.97	0.87	0.44
9	0.83	0.54	0.04	0.95	0.81	0.22
11	0.80	0.43	0.03	0.93	0.72	0.09
16	0.74	0.25	0.001	0.90	0.52	0.01
31	0.52	0.03	0.001	0.75	0.13	0.001
64	0.01			0.43		
144				0.05		

It is clear from Table 12.4 that the use of a 5 percent or a 1 percent test, when the difference to be detected is of the order of half the standard deviation per plot, will lead to an acceptance of the null hypothesis in an inordinately high frequency of cases with the number of replicates usually considered, say, up to 20. If the experimenter cannot use more than this number of replicates, it would appear advisable to use perhaps a 10 percent significance test.

The most important conclusion from Table 12.4 is that the experimenter will have great difficulty with up to 20 replicates in showing the existence of a difference Δ which is less than or equal to the standard deviation per plot. This is the most potent reason for the reduction of σ^2, for a given Δ, if the plot variance σ^2 can be reduced by a factor of 4, say, by the choice of experimental unit, the experiment will have much more value to the individual experimenter than would be indicated merely by the relative information: namely, 4.

12.3.2 The General Case

For the general case of t treatments, the degrees of freedom f_1 for treatments is equal to $(t-1)$ and for error is $(r-1)(t-1)$. The quantity λ is given by

$$\lambda = \frac{r}{2\sigma^2} \Sigma(t_i - \bar{t})^2$$

where t_i is the true treatment mean. It is a simple matter to obtain the sensitivity of any experiment.

For an example, let us suppose that we have 5 treatments and that the true treatment means expressed about zero and in terms of the standard deviation are

$$-2, \quad -1, \quad 0, \quad 1, \quad 2$$

Then,

$$\lambda = \frac{r}{2}(10) = 5r$$

and

$$\phi = \sqrt{\frac{2\lambda}{f_1 + 1}} = \sqrt{\frac{2 \times 5r}{5}} = \sqrt{2r}$$

Using Tang's tables, we find the data in Table 12.5.

TABLE 12.5

P_{II} (*Approximate*)

r	5% Test	1% Test
2	0.47	0.82
3	0.08	0.34
4	0.01	0.08
5	0.001	0.018

Thus, in this situation, at least 3 (4) replicates are necessary if the experimenter is using a 5 percent (1 percent) significance test and desires a 90 percent chance of showing that there are treatment effects, when the true treatment effects are as specified above.

The true treatment effects we have considered are perhaps somewhat large for most experimental situations, for we have said that the best and worst treatments differ by 4 times the standard deviation per plot. If, instead, we take the case -1, -0.5, 0, 0.5, 1 as the true treatment deviations in terms of the standard deviation per plot, we have

$$\lambda = \frac{r}{2}\,(2.5), \qquad \phi = \sqrt{\frac{2}{5}\frac{r}{2}\,(2.5)} = \sqrt{\frac{r}{2}}$$

For this case, we find the data in Table 12.6.

TABLE 12.6

P_{II} (*Approximate*)

r	5% Test	1% Test
4	0.33	0.76
8	0.07	0.23
10	0.05	0.12
12	0.01	0.05

The experimenter will, therefore, need of the order of 8 or 10 replicates for adequate sensitivity. The general conclusion which might be drawn from this examination is that, with the smaller numbers of replicates, a 5 percent or 1 percent test, i.e., a test with a type-I error of 5 percent or 1 percent, is too strong in that it will very frequently result in the non-rejection of the null hypothesis when another hypothesis in fact holds: i.e., in a type-II error. It is rather difficult, however, to make a stronger statement, because the situation can only be represented in terms of type-I errors which may be fixed arbitrarily by choice of significance level and type-II errors which depend on the number of replicates and on the true treatment differences. In certain cases, the experimenter can possibly attach weights to the two types of error, though this will be difficult in any but a technological experiment. It is clear, however, that, if the experiment to be performed is not one of a series of similar experiments, Tang's tables should be used to enable a judgment as to whether it is worth while at all, in view of the experimenter's aims and resources for the experiment. If an experimenter is interested in discovering a certain magnitude of treatment effect and the resources he can use give him only, say, a 20 percent chance of concluding that there are treatment effects, when the true effects are of the chosen magnitude, there seems little point in the experimenter's doing the experiment. He would, under these circumstances, be well advised to choose a topic less expensive of his resources than the one under consideration.

12.3.3 Single Degree of Freedom Contrasts in Randomized Blocks

Usually in the randomized block experiment with several treatments, the experimenter has in mind certain single degree of freedom contrasts among the treatments that he believes to be important. For this situation the tables of Tang for $f_1 = 1$ and $f_2 =$ the number of degrees of freedom for error should be consulted. Actually, for given ϕ, the change of P_{II} with the number of degrees of freedom for error (if not less than 12, say) is not great although it is consistent. The value of ϕ will depend on the true contrast, and, if we suppose this is equal to Δ, then,

$$\lambda = \frac{r\Delta^2}{2\sigma^2}$$

and

$$\phi = \sqrt{\lambda} = \sqrt{\frac{r}{2}}\frac{\Delta}{\sigma}$$

so that we are back with the case of randomized blocks of 2 plots except that we have $(r-1)(t-1)$ degrees of freedom for error. For most purposes we may use the value for f_2 of 60 and suppose that a 5 percent test will be used. If, then, the size of the experiment is to be such that the experimenter is to have a 95 percent chance of discovering an effect, when it is of size Δ, we must have approximately

$$r > 2(2.6)^2\frac{\sigma^2}{\Delta^2}$$

or

$$r > 14\frac{\sigma^2}{\Delta^2}$$

To have a chance of 80 percent or more of discovering an effect when it is of size Δ, we must have

$$\sqrt{\frac{r}{2}}\frac{\Delta}{\sigma} > 2.0$$

i.e.,

$$r > \frac{8\sigma^2}{\Delta^2}$$

For a 50 percent chance of discovering an effect in the same situation, we must have approximately

$$r > \frac{5\sigma^2}{\Delta^2}$$

These 3 rules on the number of replicates necessary will be satisfactory for most purposes.

As a variation on the above, consider the testing of 5 rates of a stimulus, say, 0, 1, 2, 3, 4 units, and suppose that the experimenter wishes to conclude by a 5 percent test that there is a linear regression of yield on dose when the true regression is β. Then,

$$\lambda = \frac{r}{2} \cdot \frac{10\beta^2}{\sigma^2}$$

We have, therefore, that, if a 50 percent, 80 percent, and 95 percent probability is required of deciding that there is a linear regression of dose on stimulus, r must be greater than

$$\frac{5\sigma^2}{10\beta^2}, \quad \frac{8\sigma^2}{10\beta^2}, \quad \text{and} \quad \frac{14\sigma^2}{10\beta^2}$$

respectively. If the required number of replicates cannot be performed, the experimenter should consider the possibility of the linear regression holding over a greater range of rates. If this could be assumed, and if, instead of the above, rates of 0, 2, 4, 6, 8 units are used, the number of replicates would be ¼ of those stated.

12.4 LATIN SQUARES

For the Latin square for t treatments we have $f_1 = t - 1$, $f_2 = (t-1)(t-2)$, $\lambda = \dfrac{t}{2} \dfrac{\Sigma(t_i - \bar{t})^2}{\sigma^2}$, and $\phi = \sqrt{\dfrac{2\lambda}{f_1 + 1}} = \sqrt{\dfrac{\Sigma(t - \bar{t})^2}{\sigma^2}}$.

It is a routine matter to consult Tang's tables, and, as an example, we consider the case of 5 treatments with means $-2, -1, 0, 1, 2$ in units of standard deviation σ. The quantity ϕ is then $\sqrt{10} = 3.16$ and $f_2 = 12$ so that, with a 5 percent test, P_{II} is less than 0.001, and, with a 1 percent test, P_{II} is about 0.035.

12.5 COMPARISON OF RANDOMIZED BLOCKS WITH LATIN SQUARES

As we saw in earlier chapters, the Latin square tends to give more information than the randomized block layout, because the error variance will usually be less and cannot be greater than in the latter case. In this statement we have used information in the technical sense of reciprocal of variance, and were, therefore, thinking primarily of estimation. It is not true that Latin squares are always better than randomized blocks from the point of view of sensitivity. The example we discussed for both randomized blocks and Latin squares is a case in which the reduction of degrees of freedom for error concomitant with the Latin square design results in a lowering of sensitivity unless accompanied by a decrease in σ^2 and, therefore, an increase in λ. Given a large set of uniformity data on the material under experiment, we could estimate the values of σ^2 for the designs and, hence, obtain λ for a given set of treatment effects. It would then be possible to make a true comparison of the sensitivity of the two designs.

In general, however, such a comparison seems somewhat academic in that, even from the point of view of estimation, we take account in an intuitive way of the number of degrees of freedom for error and would not use the Latin square unless we have, say, 12 or more degrees of freedom for error. The circumstances under which we would consider the 4×4 Latin square with only 4 (not a multiple of 4) replicates, and, hence, 6 degrees of freedom for error, for the comparison of 4 treatments would only be for answering questions about a large population. In this case the experimental material would be arranged in strata and 2 or more experiments would be conducted in each stratum. From the point of view of answering questions about the population, there are 2 variances: namely, the error variance and the variance of true treatment differences from experiment to experiment within a stratum. One is not primarily concerned with the sensitivity of the individual experiment, and the gain in accuracy of the estimate for the whole population from the use of individual Latin squares may be worth while.

There seems little doubt that Latin square designs of side 5 or more are better than randomized blocks of the same size, if the model for the Latin square can be assumed to hold, for the change in P_{II} with change in error degrees of freedom will not be large enough to compensate for the change in the error variance σ^2. As we have seen already, the larger Latin squares, say, with side greater than 8, tend to be of little value for field experiments and probably for most other types of experiment also. If the number of replicates contemplated for the tests involving 4 treatments is such that 2 or more Latin squares may be used, again there seems little doubt that the Latin square is to be preferred, though it is necessary to consider the extent to which the Latin square will result in a reduction of σ^2. If the reduction will be only slight for the type of experimental material under investigation, randomized blocks would be preferred.

12.6 THE VALIDITY OF THE INFINITE MODEL APPROACH

We noted in Chapter 7 that the F distribution may be expected to represent quite closely the distribution over possible randomizations of the criterion

$$\frac{\text{Treatment mean square}}{\text{Error mean square}}$$

regardless of the yield figures subjected to the analysis. This distribution will be approximately the same for all additions to the basic yields of treatment effects, according to any randomization pattern. It may, therefore, strike the reader as a little odd that we introduce the non-central F distribution to indicate the sensitivity of the experiment.

To examine the sensitivity of an experiment according to randomization tests, we may suppose that we are dealing with a randomized experiment on t treatments in r randomized blocks and that we have available the yield for each plot which we would obtain in the absence of treatment effects. We may choose a set of treatment effects, and, for each of the $(t!)^r$ possible randomizations, we may superimpose the treatment effects, giving $(t!)^r$ sets of yield data, say, $Y_1, Y_2, \cdots, Y_N, N = (t!)^r$. Each set of yield data is then examined by the randomization test for significance of treatment effects at a chosen significance level. If a p percent significance test is used, the treatment effects will be stated to exist, if a proportion p or less of the randomizations gives a value for the criterion greater than or equal to that given by the particular randomization according to which the treatments were applied. The proportion of treatment patterns that show the treatment effects to exist is the relevant measure of the sensitivity of the experiment. To carry out an examination in this way, we need to take a set of uniformity data and for each set of treatment effects prepare an $N \times N$ table (Table 12.7).

TABLE 12.7

Treatments Applied according to Randomization No.	Value of Criterion for Randomizations of Yields				
	1	2	3	$\cdots$	N
1	.	.	.		.
2	.	.	.		.
3	.	.	.		.
. . .					
N					

Such a procedure is impossible, in view of the amount of computation that would be necessary, nor, so far as we know, has a mathematical solution to the problem been obtained.

It seems intuitively that the following statements are true:

1. The treatment sum of squares is distributed over the randomizations for a given set of yields, approximately as $\chi^2 \sigma^2$, where χ^2 is distributed according to the central χ^2 distribution.

2. The error sum of squares is distributed approximately as $\chi^2 \sigma^2$ (though we have evidence that this is not quite the case).

3. The treatment sum of squares for the randomization pattern according to which treatments are applied is distributed over randomizations approximately as $\chi'^2 \sigma^2$, where χ'^2 is distributed according to the non-central χ^2 distribution: and, to support this statement, we may point out that the treatment sum of squares is equal to the sum of squares among a set of t variables, each variable being made up of a random variable, which is subject to constant variance, plus a fixed variable: namely, the treatment effect.

Under these circumstances and with independence, we would get the non-central F distribution which we used earlier in the chapter. It also seems fairly certain that the non-central F distribution can be used for experiments with large blocks, for the correlation between plot errors within a block is $-1/(k-1)$, where k is the size of block. It is, however, difficult to say more about the matter.

To shed some light on the problem, an example has been worked through as outlined above. The case considered was the comparison of 2 treatments on 8 plots whose yields with a uniform treatment (around an arbitrary base) were 6, 4, 7, 2, 1, 8, 3, 5. There are 70 possible randomization patterns for applying each treatment to 4 plots, and all 70 possible yield patterns with true treatment differences Δ equal to 0, 2, 4, 6, 8, and 10 units were considered. Each yield pattern was examined by the randomization test,

$$\frac{\text{Treatment mean square}}{\text{Error mean square}}$$

being used as the criterion. The proportion of the 70 possible randomizations for treatments that gave a significant treatment effect at a significance level of $\frac{2}{35}$ ($= 5.72\%$) was obtained. This proportion is compared in Table 12.8 with the proportion significant using a 5 percent F test and the proportion expected to be significant from Tang's tables.

TABLE 12.8 THE VALIDITY OF THE F TEST AND THE SENSITIVITY OF THE EXPERIMENT

Percentage Significant

True Treatment Difference	By Randomization Test: Significance Level: 5.72%	By F Test: Significance Level: 5%	Expected from Tang's Tables (Approximate) with a 5% Test
0	5.7	5.7	5
2	7.1	10.0	18
4	34.3	34.3	53
6	81.4	82.9	86
8	100.0	100.0	97
10	100.0	100.0	100

As a by-product of this examination, we may note how closely the proportions significant by the randomization test and by the use of the F distribution agree even with as small an experiment as the one considered. The example, however, indicates that Tang's tables may give some inflation of the proportion significant over what was actually obtained. This inflation occurs in a range that may be important to experimenters. From some points of view, this might be expected in that, according to general linear hypothesis theory, new random variables for the base yields are chosen with each repetition, but there appears to be no simple reason for a deviation in one direction rather than another.

We may conclude then by stating that Tang's tables may be used to give an indication of the sensitivity of experiments with respect to the randomization test, but, in the case of small experiments, we cannot claim, in the present state of knowledge, that the indication is other than an approximate one.

REFERENCES

1. WALD, A. *Sequential analysis.* John Wiley & Sons, New York. 1947.
2. FREEMAN, H. A., FRIEDMAN, M., MOSTELLER, F., and WALLIS, W. A. *Sampling inspection.* McGraw-Hill, New York. 1948.
3. TANG, P. C. The power function of the analysis of variance tests with tables and illustrations of their use. *Stat. Res. Mem.,* **2**, 126–149, 1938.
4. CRAMÉR, H. *Mathematical methods of statistics.* Princeton University Press, Princeton. 1946.

CHAPTER 13

Experiments Involving Several Factors

13.1 INTRODUCTION

So far we have considered the testing of a number of treatments, not necessarily related to each other, in randomized blocks or Latin squares: for example, varieties or fertilizer treatments. Frequently we know that several factors may affect the characteristic in which we are interested, and we wish to estimate the effects of each of the factors and how the effect of one factor varies over the levels of other factors. For example, the yields of most agricultural crops are affected by three plant nutrients, nitrogen n, phosphate p, and potash k. Given a population of experimental units, we may ask what is the effect of imposing nitrogen, what is the effect of adding nitrogen after the addition of phosphate, and so on. One experimental procedure would be to estimate the effect of nitrogen keeping all the other factors at a constant level in one experiment; the effect of nitrogen after phosphate is added, keeping the remaining factors constant; and so on. This procedure would generally be used when the purpose is to establish a fundamental law, for we have no reason to expect the law to be of a simple form nor the other factors to have simple effects. If we allowed all the factors to vary at will or according to some chosen scheme, it would probably be impossible to establish the law because of the various possible interactions of the factors. The experimenter would be advised, once he has decided which factors are important, to apply them one at a time, at least until he has formulated a law for the effects of any one of the factors.

Another experimental procedure would be to vary each of the factors and to estimate the characteristic for each combination of the factors. This procedure has much to recommend it at the beginning of an investigation to suggest possible response relations and to solve many technological problems, for in these situations the experimenter does not know which factors are important or whether each factor exerts its effect independently of the other factors. The previous procedure would lead to detailed knowledge of the effect of one factor when the others were held constant but would give no information at all on the dependence of the effect of the factor on the levels at which the other factors were held constant. It, therefore, provides, on its own, information of little general value.

The choice between the two procedures is largely a question of the nature and stage of the research. If the research is of the technological type, that we wish to determine the effect of particular amounts of nitrogen, phosphates, and potash on the yield of corn in Iowa, for example, we should test all of the treatment combinations. If the research is of the fundamental type, dealing with the formulation of laws and the prediction of effects, we should first determine which factors are important and the degree of the interdependence of their effects and then isolate some of the factors for detailed study and return to the general problem when laws have been formulated. The distinction made above is somewhat artificial but is of value in the formulation of a research program.

13.2 EFFECTS AND INTERACTIONS

13.2.1 The Case of 2 Factors

We test the 4 combinations of 2 factors each at 2 levels, say, nitrogen at levels n_0 and n_1 and phosphates at levels p_0 and p_1. The 4 treatment combinations may be represented as

$$n_0 p_0$$
$$n_1 p_0$$
$$n_0 p_1$$
$$n_1 p_1$$

We can estimate the effect of increasing nitrogen from n_0 to n_1 at each of the 2 levels of phosphate. If yields are represented by the treatment symbols we have

Effect of nitrogen at level $p_0 = n_1 p_0 - n_0 p_0$

Effect of nitrogen at level $p_1 = n_1 p_1 - n_0 p_1$

As an approximation to the effect of nitrogen, we may obtain an average effect which we denote by N,

$$N = \tfrac{1}{2}(n_1 p_1 - n_0 p_1 + n_1 p_0 - n_0 p_0) \tag{1}$$

or

$$N = \tfrac{1}{2}(n_1 - n_0)(p_1 + p_0)$$

where the expression is to be expanded algebraically and the yields substituted for the treatment symbols.

If the 2 factors were acting independently we would expect the 2 effects, at levels p_0 and p_1, to be equal, but, in general, they will be different, and their difference is a measure of the extent to which the factors interact. For convenience we take half the difference of the effect at level p_1 and the effect at level p_0 and denote it by NP, thus,

$$NP = \tfrac{1}{2}(n_1p_1 - n_0p_1 - n_1p_0 + n_0p_0) = \tfrac{1}{2}(n_1 - n_0)(p_1 - p_0) \quad (2)$$

In the same way we may obtain the effect of phosphate,

At level n_0 of nitrogen, $n_0p_1 - n_0p_0$

At level n_1 of nitrogen, $n_1p_1 - n_1p_0$

The average of these two is the average effect of phosphate denoted by P,

$$P = \tfrac{1}{2}(n_1p_1 - n_1p_0 + n_0p_1 - n_0p_0) = \tfrac{1}{2}(n_1 + n_0)(p_1 - p_0) \quad (3)$$

The interaction of phosphate with nitrogen we would obtain as before,

$\tfrac{1}{2}$(effect of p at level n_1 − effect of p at level n_0)

which equals

$$PN = \tfrac{1}{2}(n_1p_1 - n_1p_0 - n_0p_1 + n_0p_0)$$

and we see that this is the same as the interaction of nitrogen with phosphate NP, so that we need not bother about the order in which we write down the letters.

We note that the effects and interaction are 3 mutually orthogonal contrasts of the yields of the 4 treatment combinations:

	n_1p_1	n_1p_0	n_0p_1	n_0p_0
$2N$	+	+	−	−
$2P$	+	−	+	−
$2NP$	+	−	−	+

If we denote the mean yield of the 4 treatment combinations by M we have the transformation of the yields represented by

$$
\begin{bmatrix} 4M \\ 2N \\ 2P \\ 2NP \end{bmatrix}
=
\begin{bmatrix}
1 & 1 & 1 & 1 \\
1 & 1 & -1 & -1 \\
1 & -1 & 1 & -1 \\
1 & -1 & -1 & 1
\end{bmatrix}
\begin{bmatrix} n_1p_1 \\ n_1p_0 \\ n_0p_1 \\ n_0p_0 \end{bmatrix}
\quad (4)
$$

The matrix of the transformation is orthogonal except that it is not normalized.

This relationship may be inverted, giving

$$n_1 p_1 = M + \tfrac{1}{2}N + \tfrac{1}{2}P + \tfrac{1}{2}NP$$

$$n_1 p_0 = M + \tfrac{1}{2}N - \tfrac{1}{2}P - \tfrac{1}{2}NP$$

$$n_0 p_1 = M - \tfrac{1}{2}N + \tfrac{1}{2}P - \tfrac{1}{2}NP$$

$$n_0 p_0 = M - \tfrac{1}{2}N - \tfrac{1}{2}P + \tfrac{1}{2}NP$$

i.e.,

$$
\begin{bmatrix} n_1 p_1 \\ n_1 p_0 \\ n_0 p_1 \\ n_0 p_0 \end{bmatrix} = \frac{1}{2} \begin{bmatrix} 1 & 1 & 1 & 1 \\ 1 & 1 & -1 & -1 \\ 1 & -1 & 1 & -1 \\ 1 & -1 & -1 & 1 \end{bmatrix} \begin{bmatrix} 2M \\ N \\ P \\ NP \end{bmatrix}
\tag{5}
$$

It should be noted that we have used the convention that treatment combinations are represented by lower-case letters and effects and interactions by capitals. This convention is valuable in many ways and should be adhered to strictly to prevent confusion.

13.2.2 The Case of 3 Factors

Suppose that we wish to determine the increase in yield on corn brought about by increasing the dose of nitrogen from n_0 to n_1, of phosphates from p_0 to p_1, and of potash from k_0 to k_1. We test all the treatment combinations of which there will be 8 ($= 2 \times 2 \times 2$), namely:

$$n_0 p_0 k_0$$

$$n_1 p_0 k_0$$

$$n_0 p_1 k_0$$

$$n_1 p_1 k_0$$

$$n_0 p_0 k_1$$

$$n_1 p_0 k_1$$

$$n_0 p_1 k_1$$

$$n_1 p_1 k_1$$

The order in which these are written is a standard order which is valuable from many points of view.

Suppose we determine the yields of each of these combinations without error and denote the yield by the same symbol as the treatment.

The effect of increasing the nitrogen from n_0 to n_1 is given in Table

13.1, the yields of the treatment combinations again being denoted by their symbols.

TABLE 13.1

Level of p	Level of k	Effect of Nitrogen
p_0	k_0	$n_1 p_0 k_0 - n_0 p_0 k_0$
p_1	k_0	$n_1 p_1 k_0 - n_0 p_1 k_0$
p_0	k_1	$n_1 p_0 k_1 - n_0 p_0 k_1$
p_1	k_1	$n_1 p_1 k_1 - n_0 p_1 k_1$

Mean effect of n $\frac{1}{4}$ (Sum of above)

The effect of nitrogen will depend on the level of the other factors, and there are then the above 4 effects. If we take the mean of these 4 differences, we obtain what is termed the average effect of nitrogen, denoted by N. We can average the differences we obtained above over the levels of potash, for each level of phosphate, giving

Effect of nitrogen, at p_0, mean of k_0 and $k_1 = \frac{1}{2}(n_1 p_0 k_0 - n_0 p_0 k_0$

$$+ \, n_1 p_0 k_1 - n_0 p_0 k_1)$$

Effect of nitrogen, at p_1, mean of k_0 and $k_1 = \frac{1}{2}(n_1 p_1 k_0 - n_0 p_1 k_0$

$$+ \, n_1 p_1 k_1 - n_0 p_1 k_1)$$

These 2 effects will, in general, be different, and $\frac{1}{2}$ of the lower minus the upper one is called the interaction of nitrogen and phosphate and is denoted by NP. We can represent this formally by the expression

$$NP = \tfrac{1}{4}(n_1 - n_0)(p_1 - p_0)(k_1 + k_0) \qquad (6)$$

in which we expand the expression algebraically and substitute the yields.

We can also evaluate the interaction of nitrogen and phosphate at each level of potash, thus,

At level k_0 of potash $\frac{1}{2}(n_1 p_1 k_0 + n_0 p_0 k_0 - n_1 p_0 k_0 - n_0 p_1 k_0)$

At level k_1 of potash $\frac{1}{2}(n_1 p_1 k_1 + n_0 p_0 k_1 - n_1 p_0 k_1 - n_0 p_1 k_1)$

The average of these 2 quantities is the interaction NP above. The 2 interactions may be different, and, as a measure of the extent to which they are different, we form $\frac{1}{2}$ of the interaction of nitrogen and phosphate at the upper level of potash minus that at the lower level, giving the 3-factor interaction,

$$NPK = \tfrac{1}{4}(n_1 p_1 k_1 + n_0 p_0 k_1 - n_1 p_0 k_1 - n_0 p_1 k_1$$

$$- \, n_1 p_1 k_0 - n_0 p_0 k_0 + n_1 p_0 k_0 + n_0 p_1 k_0 \qquad (7)$$

This may be represented formally by the expression

$$NPK = \tfrac{1}{4}(n_1 - n_0)(p_1 - p_0)(k_1 - k_0)$$

and this symbolism shows that it is also the interaction of the interaction NK with phosphate, and so on.

As in the 2-factor case, we denote the mean yield of the 8 treatment combinations by M.

Corresponding to this definition of mean and effects and interactions, we have the following expression for the yield of a treatment combination,

$$2n_r p_s k_t = 2M + (-1)^{r-1}N + (-1)^{s-1}P$$
$$+ (-1)^{[(r-1)+(s-1)]}NP + (-1)^{t-1}K + (-1)^{[(r-1)+(t-1)]}NK$$
$$+ (-1)^{[(s-1)+(t-1)]}PK + (-1)^{[(r-1)+(s-1)+(t-1)]}NPK \quad (8)$$

where the possible values for each subscript r, s, and t are zero and unity.

We may condense the symbols for the treatment combinations by replacing n_0, p_0, k_0 by unity and n_1, p_1, k_1 by n, p, k, respectively. In this way the symbol pk, for example, represents nitrogen at the lower level, and phosphate and potash at the upper levels. We denote by (1) the treatment combination for which all the factors are at the lower level. We have then definitions of effects and interactions exemplified by

$$N = \tfrac{1}{4}(n - 1)(p + 1)(k + 1)$$
$$NP = \tfrac{1}{4}(n - 1)(p - 1)(k + 1)$$
$$NPK = \tfrac{1}{4}(n - 1)(p - 1)(k - 1)$$

a minus sign appearing in any factor on the right if the letter is present on the left. Note the importance of the convention of using small letters for treatment combinations and large letters for effects and interactions. Without it there would be hopeless confusion for most people. The effects and interactions are a transformation of the yields shown in Table 13.2.

TABLE 13.2

	(1)	n	p	np	k	nk	pk	npk
$8M$	1	1	1	1	1	1	1	1
$4N$	−1	1	−1	1	−1	1	−1	1
$4P$	−1	−1	1	1	−1	−1	1	1
$4NP$	1	−1	−1	1	1	−1	−1	1
$4K$	−1	−1	−1	−1	1	1	1	1
$4NK$	1	−1	1	−1	−1	1	−1	1
$4PK$	1	1	−1	−1	−1	−1	1	1
$4NPK$	−1	1	1	−1	1	−1	−1	1

This matrix of numbers is simply constructed: we have adopted the standard order for the treatment symbols and the effect symbols, and the numbers for N, P, and K are easily written down, being $+1$ if the corresponding small letter is present and -1 if absent. The numbers for any combination of letters, say, NP, are the product of the corresponding numbers for N and P and so on.

13.2.3 The General Case

With n factors a, b, c, d, e, etc., the effects and interactions may be represented by

$$X = \frac{1}{2^{n-1}}(a \pm 1)(b \pm 1)(c \pm 1)(d \pm 1)(e \pm 1) \cdots, \qquad (9)$$

where the sign in each bracket is positive if the corresponding capital letter is not contained in X and negative if it is contained in X, and the whole expression on the right-hand side is to be expanded algebraically and yields are to be substituted in place of the corresponding treatment combination.

The yield of a treatment combination is best written down by writing the treatment combination as $a_i b_j c_k \cdots$ etc., where absence is denoted by the subscript taking the value zero, and presence by the subscript taking the value unity. Then

$$2a_i b_j c_k = 2M \pm A \pm B \pm AB \pm C \pm AC, \text{ etc.} \qquad (10)$$

where the sign

On A is -1 if $i = 0$, $+1$ if $i = 1$

On B is -1 if $j = 0$, $+1$ if $j = 1$

and so on

and the sign on a term involving several letters is the product of the signs on the individual letters.

13.3 THE INTERPRETATION OF EFFECTS AND INTERACTIONS

The interpretation of effects and interactions follows closely from the definitions. The main effect N is the effect of increasing nitrogen from amount n_0 to amount n_1 (or from the basic amount to amount n), averaging over all the possible combinations of p and k, phosphate and potash.

Now suppose we wish to obtain the effect of nitrogen, averaging over presence and absence of phosphate, but in the absence of potash (i.e.,

at the basal level k_0).   In terms of treatment combinations this is equal
to
$$\tfrac{1}{2}[np - p + n - (1)]$$
the divisor of 2 being used because we wish the effects to be on the basis
of differences on a single plot.   This is equal to
$$N - NK$$
for
$$N = \tfrac{1}{4}(n - 1)(p + 1)(k + 1)$$
and
$$NK = \tfrac{1}{4}(n - 1)(p + 1)(k - 1)$$
so that
$$N - NK = \tfrac{1}{4}(n - 1)(p + 1)[k + 1 - (k - 1)]$$
$$= \tfrac{1}{2}(n - 1)(p + 1)$$
which equals, on expansion,
$$\tfrac{1}{2}[np - p + n - (1)]$$

In a similar way we obtain the following:

Effect of n, averaging over levels of p, k present $= N + NK$

Effect of n, p absent, averaging over levels of $k = N - NP$

Effect of n, p present, averaging over levels of $k = N + NP$

Effect of n, p present, k present $= N + NP + NK + NPK$

Effect of n, p present, k absent $= N + NP - NK - NPK$

These expressions may be written down formally as
$$N(1 + K)$$
$$N(1 - P)$$
$$N(1 + P)$$
$$N(1 + P)(1 + K)$$
$$N(1 + P)(1 - K)$$
and this gives an easy way of remembering them and of writing down
the effect of any one factor for any situation with regard to the other
factors.

13.4 A SIMPLE EXAMPLE OF A FACTORIAL EXPERIMENT

So far we have considered only the breakdown of the treatments into
a set of orthogonal contrasts which have practical utility.   Thus with 4

treatments, (1), n, p, and np, say, we have the 3 mutually orthogonal contrasts (Table 13.3).

TABLE 13.3

Contrast	(1)	n	p	np
N	−	+	−	+
P	−	−	+	+
NP	+	−	−	+

These contrasts have been defined for the true yields under a particular set of circumstances. When we test the treatment combinations, we shall obtain estimates of the true yields, rather than the true yields themselves. In order to obtain estimates of the true effects and interactions, we utilize the fact that, under additivity, the observed yields will be given by a general linear hypothesis model as, for example,

$$y_{ij} = \mu + b_i + t_j + e_{ij} \qquad \text{(Randomized blocks)}$$

or

$$y_{ijk} = \mu + r_i + c_j + t_k + e_{ijk} \qquad \text{(Latin squares)}$$

that is, in which the observed yield is made up additively of components for positional effects plus a treatment effect plus an error effect. Under the finite model we use for randomized blocks, the true yield of treatment j in block i is $\mu + b_i + t_j$, and only the t_j's enter into the effects and interactions. We know also that the best estimate of a linear contrast among the treatments is the same linear contrast of the estimates of the treatment effects. For randomized blocks or Latin squares, for which no observations are missing, the best estimate of any treatment contrast is given by the same contrast of the treatment means. So far then, we use the factorial scheme as giving us a valuable breakdown of the treatment effects and sum of squares.

A simple factorial experiment is given in Table 13.4.

TABLE 13.4   POTATOES: EFFECT OF INORGANIC AND ORGANIC FERTILIZERS [1]

I	4	3	2	1
II	1	2	3	4
III	3	4	1	2
IV	2	1	4	3

Variety: King Edward
System of replication: Latin square
Area of each plot: $\frac{1}{50}$ acre
Treatments:
   1 = blood, superphosphate
   2 = sulphate of ammonia, superphosphate
   3 = sulphate of ammonia, steamed bone flour
   4 = blood, steamed bone flour
Rates: 0.5 cwt N and 0.6 cwt P_2O_5 per acre. All plots received sulphate of potash at the rate of 1.25 cwt K_2O per acre

Table 13.4 Potatoes: Effect of Inorganic and Organic Fertilizers [1]
(*Continued*)

Actual Weights in Pounds

Row	Column			
	1	2	3	4
I	645	667	670	787
II	752	637	655	576
III	642	627	686	575
IV	621	762	596	660

The treatments have a factorial structure:

n, say: Blood (n_0) or sulphate of ammonia (n_1)

p, say: Superphosphate (p_0) or steamed bone flour (p_1)

The designations n_0, n_1, p_0, and p_1 are arbitrary: i.e., n_0 is not necessarily the lower level of n, etc.

The analysis of variance is given in Table 13.5.

Table 13.5 Analysis of Variance for Experiment of Table 13.4

Due to	df	Sum of Squares	Mean Square
Rows	3	7,285.2	
Columns	3	1,515.2	
Treatments	3	44,462.2	14,820.7
Error	6	4,649.1	774.8
Total	15	57,911.7	

The treatment totals are:

$n_0 p_0 : 2987$

$n_1 p_0 : 2503$

$n_0 p_1 : 2444$

$n_1 p_1 : 2624$

The effects are then estimated by

$$N = -2987 + 2503 - 2444 + 2624 = -304$$
$$P = -2987 - 2503 + 2444 + 2624 = -422$$
$$NP = 2987 - 2503 - 2444 + 2624 = +664$$

To convert these totals to estimates of effects on the basis of a single plot, it is necessary to divide by 8 [= 4 (= no. of reps) × 2] giving

$$N = -38.00$$
$$P = -52.75$$
$$NP = 83.00$$

We have estimated the error variance per plot to be 774.8, and the variance of each effect and interaction is estimated by $\frac{1}{4} \times 774.8 = 193.7 = (13.9)^2$, so that to each estimate we may attach a standard error of 13.9 and test each with the t test with 6 degrees of freedom, the number of degrees of freedom on which the error is based.

The divisor of 4 in $\frac{1}{4}s^2$, s^2 being the estimated error variance, is obtained by noting that the estimate of each effect and interaction is equal to

$$\tfrac{1}{8}(\text{sum of 8 plots} - \text{sum of 8 plots})$$

so that the true variance is equal to

$$\frac{1}{8^2}(8 + 8)\sigma^2 = \frac{1}{4}\sigma^2$$

and we substitute s^2 for σ^2.

Alternatively, we may obtain a sum of squares for each effect and interaction by squaring the total effect and dividing by 16 (the sum of squares of the coefficients of plot yields in the estimating expression), thus:

Sum of squares for N = $(-304)^2/16 = 5{,}776.00$

Sum of squares for $\overset{}{P}$ = $(-422)^2/16 = 11{,}130.25$

Sum of squares for NP = $(664)^2/16 = 27{,}556.00$

The sum of these 3 sums of squares is, of course, equal to the total sum of squares for treatments, and we may test each sum of squares against the error mean square using the F test with 1 and 6 degrees of freedom. The test of significance for each effect and interaction in this way is the same as the t test given above, because F with 1 degree of freedom and n_1 degrees of freedom is equal to the square of t with n_1 degrees of freedom, at the same level of significance. The statistical interpretation of the experiment is simple, that there is some evidence of an average n effect or difference between blood and sulphate of ammonia; there is an average effect of p, or difference between superphosphate and steamed bone flour, which is significant at about the 1 in 100 level; and there is an interaction which is significant at a somewhat higher level (about 0.001).* We ignore the correlation between these tests of significance; its effect in as small an experiment as this is possibly appreciable, but it decreases with increasing number of degrees of freedom on which the error is based. It should be noted that, if the experiment is arranged in randomized blocks, it is possible to estimate the error independently for each effect and interaction when each treatment combination is represented at least twice in the experiment. If this were done, the correlation between tests would be removed, but, in general, the assumption that the errors are homogeneous will be a valid one, and there would result a loss in sensitivity for each test from the reduced number of degrees of freedom on which each error estimate would be based. This is not possible with the Latin square, as has been mentioned previously.

Finally we have the following condensation of the results:

Difference (blood − sulphate of ammonia) on

the average $\hspace{5.5cm} = N \hspace{1.3cm} = \;\; -38.00$

Difference (blood − sulphate of ammonia) with

superphosphate $\hspace{4cm} = N - NP = -121.00$

Difference (blood − sulphate of ammonia) with

steamed bone flour $\hspace{3.5cm} = N + NP = \hspace{0.8cm} 45.00$

Difference (sbf − superphosphate) on the aver-

age $\hspace{6cm} = P \hspace{1.3cm} = \;\; -52.75$

Difference (sbf − superphosphate) with blood $\;\; = P - NP = -135.75$

Difference (sbf − superphosphate) with sul-

phate of ammonia $\hspace{3.7cm} = P + NP = \hspace{0.8cm} 30.25$

13.5 THE GENERAL CASE OF SEVERAL FACTORS EACH AT 2 LEVELS

We suppose we have factors $a, b, c, d, e, \cdots$, each with 2 levels, and in designating any treatment combination we include each letter if the cor-

---

* We have used the conventional F test, though this is perhaps not desirable (cf. Chapter 10).

responding factor is at the upper level. The treatment combinations may then be written out in order, as shown in Table 13.6.

TABLE 13.6

(1)	d	e	de
a	ad	ae	ade
b	bd	be	bde
ab	abd	abe	abde	etc.
c	cd	ce	cde
ac	acd	ace	acde
bc	bcd	bce	bcde
abc	abcd	abce	abcde

We may enumerate the effects and interactions in the same way (Table 13.7).

TABLE 13.7

	Number
Main effects	n
2-factor interactions	$\dfrac{n(n-1)}{2}$
3-factor interactions	$\dfrac{n(n-1)(n-2)}{6}$
4-factor interactions	$\dfrac{n(n-1)(n-2)(n-3)}{24}$
	....
Total	$2^n - 1$

The effects and interactions are exemplified by

$$A = \frac{1}{2^{n-1}} (a-1)(b+1)(c+1)(d+1)(e+1) \cdots \text{etc.}$$

$$AB = \frac{1}{2^{n-1}} (a-1)(b-1)(c+1)(d+1)(e+1) \cdots$$

$$ABC = \frac{1}{2^{n-1}} (a-1)(b-1)(c-1)(d+1)(e+1) \cdots$$

$$ABCD = \frac{1}{2^{n-1}} (a-1)(b-1)(c-1)(d-1)(e+1) \cdots$$

etc.

If the interaction $XYZ \cdots$, where $X, Y, Z \cdots$ are each one of the letters $A, B, C, D \cdots$, contains an odd (even) number of letters, it is given by the mean of the treatment combinations with an odd (even) number of letters in common with $XYZ \cdots$, minus the mean of the combinations with an even (odd) number of letters in common with $XYZ \cdots$ (zero being regarded as an even number).

For example, in a 2^4 factorial experiment we may write down immediately the expressions given in Table 13.8. The 2-factor interactions

TABLE 13.8

Yields of Treatment Combinations

Effects and Interactions	(1)	a	b	ab	c	ac	bc	abc	d	ad	bd	abd	cd	acd	bcd	abcd
8BCD	−	−	+	+	+	+	−	−	+	+	−	−	−	−	+	+
8AB	+	−	−	+	+	−	−	+	+	−	−	+	+	−	−	+
8ABCD	+	−	−	+	−	+	+	−	−	+	+	−	+	−	−	+
8B	−	−	+	+	−	−	+	+	−	−	+	+	−	−	+	+
8A	−	+	−	+	−	+	−	+	−	+	−	+	−	+	−	+

are regarded as the interaction of 2 main effects in the following way. The plots are divided into 4 groups on the basis of the table:

For A

	−	+
For B −	1	2
+	3	4

the plots in cell 1 being (1), c, d, and cd in the case of a 2^4 factorial experiment. Then the interaction AB is equal to

$$\frac{1}{2^{n-1}} \text{(sum of plots in cells 1 and 4 − sum of plots in cells 2 and 3)}$$

Corresponding to any 2 effects *or* interactions, say, X and Y, where

X and Y contain different selections of the letters A, B, C, D, etc., we may divide the treatment combinations as follows:

For X

		−	+
	−	1	2
For Y	+	3	4

The contrast, treatments in cells 1 and 4 versus treatments in cells 2 and 3, is known as the generalized interaction of the effects or interactions X and Y. It is easily verified that this is, in fact, the effect or interaction obtained by multiplying the symbols X and Y together and equating the square of any letter to unity. Thus we have, for example, the results given in Table 13.9.

TABLE 13.9

X	Y	Generalized Interaction
A	BC	ABC
AB	BC	$AB^2C = AC$
$ABCD$	$ABEF$	$A^2B^2CDEF = CDEF$

13.5.1 The Analysis of 2^n Factorial Experiments

If a 2^n experiment is replicated r times in randomized blocks of 2^n plots, the analysis follows directly from the definitions. A computational procedure is illustrated by an example in Chapter 14. Each effect or interaction is estimated by the mean of $r2^{n-1}$ yields minus the mean of $r2^{n-1}$ yields and therefore has a variance of

$$\left(\frac{1}{r2^{n-1}} + \frac{1}{r2^{n-1}}\right)\sigma^2$$

which equals

$$\frac{1}{r2^{n-2}}\sigma^2 \tag{11}$$

Furthermore the estimates of effects and interactions are uncorrelated, so that we can obtain the variance of any linear function of them by the standard rules.

13.6 THE INFORMATION GIVEN BY FACTORIAL EXPERIMENTS

We may sum up the value of the factorial experiment by stating that we obtain

$$\frac{r2^{n-2}}{\sigma^2}$$

units of information on every effect and interaction. This may be compared to the experiment in which we vary one factor at a time. In this case, if the error variance σ^2 were the same, we would need exactly the same number of experimental units to obtain this amount of information on each main effect. In addition to giving equal information on main effects, the factorial experiment gives information on the interactions of the factors. It must be only rarely in experimentation that interactions do not exist. A case in which they may be safely assumed not to exist is in the weighing of objects, where the weight of 2 objects is equal to the sum of their weights individually. For such a case there is a class of designs which have come to be known as weighing designs, and these will be discussed in a later chapter.

If we wish to determine the difference between the yields of 2 treatment combinations from a factorial experiment, we are in no better position than with an experiment designed for estimating this difference. In a 2^n factorial experiment the difference between 2 treatment combinations is estimated with a variance of $2\sigma^2/r$, and this is the same as if $2r$ experimental units had been used to estimate this difference, if it is assumed that σ^2 is the same in the two cases. The factorial experiment then does not give exactly the same type of information as the experiment with one factor varied at a time unless there are no interactions of the factors. If, however, there are interactions between the factors, the factorial experiment will bring them to the attention of the experimenter, whereas with the other type of experiment the experimenter can obtain no knowledge of them. In most fields of research, particularly any branch of biology, interactions have been found to exist. The success of experiments varying one factor at a time can only be attributed to the fact that, in general, interactions are of lower magnitude than main effects. These experiments have, however, certainly led to much confusion in biology and probably in other fields also.

Fisher [2] has summed up the advantages of factorial experiments in that they result in (1) greater efficiency, as we have seen above, and (2) greater comprehensiveness in that (a) effects and interactions are estimated, and (b) conclusions drawn from factorial experiments have a wider inductive basis. The exact standardization of experimental conditions results in information only for the chosen conditions, and the experimenter is frequently unable to specify the set of conditions that will suit his aims. This is particularly so if the aim of the experimenter is to establish best treatments for a wide range of conditions, as occurs, for example, in agricultural research or in medical research where the aim is to find the treatment that cures a particular illness. The standardization that is discussed here should not be confused with the standardization of technique and conditions that is designed to reduce the error variance. Factorial experimentation does not remove the necessity for controlling heterogeneity of conditions, but it will result in sets of conditions, chosen with respect to some attributes, being represented with particular frequencies.

There are situations in which factorial experiments will be difficult to interpret: namely, when high-order interactions are of a magnitude appreciable relative to the main effects. This fact is, however, not at all an argument for experiments in which one factor is varied at a time, unless the experimenter does not have the facilities to perform a large factorial experiment. For, with one factor varied at a time and the presence of interactions, the results will possibly lead to incorrect action, and it will often happen that 2 experimenters, using the one-factor experiment approach, will fail to agree on their conclusions.

A difficulty that will be encountered with factorial experiments is that treatments may not act additively on any one scale of measurement. We may expect such to be the case when some of the factors in the experiment have effects that are large, say, 40 percent of the mean or more. It may be possible, under these circumstances, to find a scale for which the treatments are additive in their effects, though we encounter the difficulty that tests of additivity may have rather low power in detecting non-additivity. Alternatively, the experiment may be divided into parts, for example, by the levels of one factor, for which additivity is better satisfied, and, in general, there will be no objections to this procedure, for, if effects and interactions are large, the estimation of their relative magnitude depends very much on the scale of measurement used. Once such a situation has been shown to exist, the procedure of the experimenter is clear, namely, to establish response laws for the factors, and for this purpose several levels of the factors will be required.

13.7 THE SENSITIVITY OF FACTORIAL EXPERIMENTS

We may use the results of Chapter 12 to obtain an indication of the sensitivity of factorial experiments. For the case in which one effect (or interaction) of the 2^n system with r replicates is tested against a true error mean square (i.e., not an error mean square made up of high-order interactions), we have

$$E \text{ (sum of squares for effect)} = \sigma^2 + r2^{n-2}\Delta^2$$

where Δ is the true effect (or interaction) on a per plot basis. So we have

$$\lambda = \frac{r2^{n-2}\Delta^2}{2\sigma^2} = r2^{n-3}\frac{\Delta^2}{\sigma^2}$$

and

$$\phi = \sqrt{r2^{n-3}}\,\frac{\Delta}{\sigma}$$

Under the circumstances we are considering, we may regard the error as being based on, say, 30 degrees of freedom, and, therefore, using Tang's tables we find that, if a 5 percent test of significance is used and Δ/σ equals unity, the quantity $\sqrt{r2^{n-3}}$ must be, at a minimum, 2.73, in order that the experimenter may have a 95 percent chance of concluding that the effect exists. Therefore, with varying n, we should have at least the following numbers of replicate:

n	No. of Replicates Necessary, r
3	8
4	4
5	2

Corresponding results may be obtained for different values of Δ/σ.

REFERENCES

1. Annual Report. Rothamsted Experimental Station, Harpenden, England. 1931.
2. FISHER, R. A. *The design of experiments.* Oliver and Boyd, Edinburgh. 4th ed., 1947.
3. YATES, F. *The design and analysis of factorial experiments.* Imp. Bur. Soil Sci., Harpenden, England, 1937.

CHAPTER 14

Confounding in 2^n Factorial Experiments

14.1 INTRODUCTION

In the earlier chapter on "Plot Technique," we found that the experimental error variance was related to the size of block, increasing to a greater or lesser degree as the size of block increased. If we were testing 5 factors each with 2 levels, we would have 32 treatment combinations and would require randomized blocks of 32 plots in order to compare them. In field experiments it is generally acknowledged that, if at all possible, the size of block should not be greater than 16 and if possible 8, though, of course, there are no hard and fast rules, and one experiment with blocks of 16 may well give a lower experimental error than another on similar material with blocks of 8 plots. In other situations, it may be impossible to have blocks as large as this without randomizing over factors that cause considerable variation. It is desirable to have some means of reducing the size of block, and for this purpose the device of confounding has been found very useful.

To take the very simple situation of 3 factors each at 2 levels, say, a, b and c, we have the effects and interactions defined as in Table 14.1 (apart from the standard numerical divisor).

TABLE 14.1

	(1)	a	b	ab	c	ac	bc	abc
A	-1	$+1$	-1	$+1$	-1	$+1$	-1	$+1$
B	-1	-1	$+1$	$+1$	-1	-1	$+1$	$+1$
AB	$+1$	-1	-1	$+1$	$+1$	-1	-1	$+1$
C	-1	-1	-1	-1	$+1$	$+1$	$+1$	$+1$
AC	$+1$	-1	$+1$	-1	-1	$+1$	-1	$+1$
BC	$+1$	$+1$	-1	-1	-1	-1	$+1$	$+1$
ABC	-1	$+1$	$+1$	-1	$+1$	-1	-1	$+1$

252

Suppose that the 8 treatment combinations are arranged in 2 blocks, according to their sign in the ABC interaction (Figure 14).

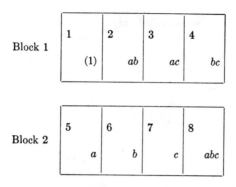

FIGURE 14.

The quantity we use to estimate A is orthogonal to blocks in that it is given by $\frac{1}{4}(-1 + 2 + 3 - 4 + 5 - 6 - 7 + 8)$ (the numerals denoting the yields of plots of that number), and of the 4 plots entering the estimate positively 2 are in each block, and likewise for the 4 plots entering negatively. The estimate will then contain none of the additive block effects.

The same is true of the other main effects and 2-factor interactions. The 3-factor interaction is, of course, $\frac{1}{4}(-1 - 2 - 3 - 4 + 5 + 6 + 7 + 8)$, and this estimate measures not only the true ABC interaction but also the block difference (block 2 minus block 1). It is not possible to separate the true interaction from the block difference, or, in other words, the interaction and block difference are inextricably mixed up or completely *confounded* with each other.

The main value of the use of the factorial structure lies in the observed fact that in many situations the high-order interactions are of inappreciable magnitude. If they were not, we would be merely replacing the 32 yields of treatment combinations in a 2^5 experiment by the mean yield and 31 effects and interactions. It may be noted that the words used are "of inappreciable magnitude." It would be a highly unlikely event that they were actually zero, because the characteristic y may be expected to be a function, say, $f(a, b, c, \text{etc.})$ of the levels of factors a, b, c, etc., and, if all interactions involving more than 2 factors were actually zero, the function would have to be of the form

$$f(a, b, c, \text{etc.}) = \mu + \alpha_1 a + \beta_1 b + \gamma_1 c + \cdots$$

$$+ \text{ (a quadratic form in } a, b, c, \text{ etc.)}$$

and such a situation is very unlikely. It is likely, however, that over a particular range of the levels of the factors, the function $f(a, b, c, \cdots)$ may be expanded in a Taylor-Maclaurin series of the above form a remainder that is inappreciable compared to the actual value of the function. In passing it should be noted that, even when interactions are not negligible, the factorial structure and expression of effects and interactions is a very useful and logical way of describing the experimental results.

Suppose then that the 3-factor interaction may be assumed to be trivial and we perform the experiment in the 2 blocks given above: i.e., with ABC confounded with blocks. As before, we use the reciprocal of the true variance of each estimate as a measure of the information on each effect or interaction. The results may be condensed as in Table 14.2.

TABLE 14.2

Effect or Interaction	Information with Blocks of 8 Plots	Information with ABC Confounded
A		
B		
AB		
C	$\dfrac{2r}{\sigma^2{}_8}$	$\dfrac{2r}{\sigma^2{}_4}$
AC		
BC		
ABC		Zero

We have supposed there to be r replicates of the whole experiment in each case and that the true error variance with blocks of 8 plots and of 4 plots is $\sigma^2{}_8$ and $\sigma^2{}_4$, respectively. We know that $\sigma^2{}_4$ will generally be less than $\sigma^2{}_8$, so that we have increased our information on main effects and 2-factor interactions in the ratio

$$\frac{\sigma^2{}_8}{\sigma^2{}_4}\left(= \frac{2r}{\sigma^2{}_4} \div \frac{2r}{\sigma^2{}_8}\right)$$

by using blocks of 4 plots, at the expense of obtaining zero information on the 3-factor interaction instead of $2r/\sigma^2{}_8$ units.

14.2 AN EXAMPLE

The following experiment conducted to compare the effect of poultry manure m with that of equivalent sulphate of ammonia n and super-phosphate p on the yield of Brussels sprouts is included to give an illustration of the use of complete confounding. In the statistical analysis of factorial experiments a simple arithmetical procedure is available to obtain the estimates of the effects and interactions, and this procedure is also illustrated.

TABLE 14.3 DESIGN AND DATA OF EXPERIMENT ON BRUSSELS SPROUTS [1]

Plan and Yields in Pounds of Salable Sprouts (Total All Pickings)

I		II		III	
np 48.81	nm 58.88	nm 50.43	(1) 40.26	n 47.37	p 37.25
pm 46.11	(1) 38.62	pm 52.31	np 49.62	npm 46.87	m 46.94
m 40.49	npm 61.55	p 32.36	npm 48.49	pm 39.30	nm 49.93
p 32.75	n 55.07	m 51.94	n 53.86	(1) 39.23	np 51.43
IV		V		VI	

Block Totals

I	192.42
II	192.62
III	178.43
IV	189.86
V	186.65
VI	179.89
Total	1119.87

System of replication: 3 replicates of 2 randomized blocks of 4 plots each, 6 blocks in all. *NPM* confounded with block differences.

Area of each plot: 0.01033 acres (5 yd × 10 yd).

Treatments: All combinations of:

(a) No poultry manure, and poultry manure at the rate of 0.6 cwt N per acre with addition of superphosphate at the rate of 0.116 cwt P_2O_5 per acre, to give a total of 0.6 cwt P_2O_5 per acre (m).

(b) No sulphate of ammonia, and sulphate of ammonia at the rate of 0.6 cwt N per acre (n).

(c) No superphosphate, and superphosphate at the rate of 0.6 cwt P_2O_5 per acre (p).

Basal manuring: Muriate of potash at the rate of 1.0 cwt K_2O per acre.

TABLE 14.4   COMPUTATION OF EXAMPLE

Treatment		Yield (0)	1	2	3 Effects * (Totals)	Name of Contrast
(1)		118.11	274.41	526.63	1119.87	Mean
n	w	156.30	252.22	593.24	124.75	N
p		102.36	298.61	85.69	−26.17	P
np	x	149.86	294.63	39.06	8.63	NP
m		139.37	38.19	−22.19	66.61	M
nm	y	159.24	47.50	−3.98	−46.63	NM
pm		137.72	19.87	9.31	18.21	PM
npm	z	156.91	19.19	−0.68	−9.99	NPM (confounded)

Totals for Checks

Upper half	Odds	$220.47 = a_0$	$573.02 = a_1$	$612.32 = a_2$	$1093.70 = a_3$
	Evens	$306.16 = b_0$	$546.85 = b_1$	$632.30 = b_2$	$133.38 = b_3$
Lower half	Odds	$277.09 = c_0$	$58.06 = c_1$	$-12.88 = c_2$	$84.82 = c_3$
	Evens	$316.15 = d_0$	$66.69 = d_1$	$-4.66 = d_2$	$-56.62 = d_3$

* To convert the effect totals to conform to our definition of effects and interactions divide by ($2^{n-1} \times$ no. of reps = 4×3).

To compute the estimates of the effects and interactions the total yields for each combination must first be arranged in a standard order such as that shown in the column "yield" of Table 14.4, this giving column 0. Column 1 is then formed in the following way. The first 4 numbers are the sums of the pairs of yields labeled w, x, y, and z, respectively. The last 4 numbers are obtained by subtracting the upper number in each pair from the lower. Thus, 274.41 is the sum of 118.11 and 156.30 and 38.19 = 156.30 − 118.11. Column 2 is then formed in the same manner from column 1, and the process is completed by forming column 3 from column 2 similarly. In a 2^n experiment, the process would be continued through n such stages. The totals for checks given at the bottom of Table 14.4 are used in the following way: In any column after the first, i.e., columns 1, 2, and 3, the totals must satisfy the conditions,

$$a_i + b_i = a_{i-1} + b_{i-1} + c_{i-1} + d_{i-1}$$
$$i = 1, 2, 3$$
$$c_i + d_i = -a_{i-1} + b_{i-1} - c_{i-1} + d_{i-1}$$

Thus, in column 2, for instance,

$$a_2 + b_2 = a_1 + b_1 + c_1 + d_1$$

$$1244.62 = 573.02 + 546.85 + 58.06 + 66.69, \text{ the sum of the four}$$

totals in the preceding column 1

Similarly,

$$c_3 + d_3 = -a_2 + b_2 - c_2 + d_2$$

or

$$28.20 = [-(612.32) + (632.30) - (-12.88) + (-4.66)]$$

This gives a check of all entries in the table other than the yields. The analysis of variance is given in Table 14.5.

TABLE 14.5 ANALYSIS OF VARIANCE OF EXPERIMENT

Source of Variation	df	Sum of Squares	Mean Square
Blocks			
Reps	2 ⎫	⎧ 42.59	
NPM	1 ⎬ 5	⎨ 4.16	
Reps × NPM	2 ⎭	⎩ 1.38	
Treatments			
N	1 ⎫		
P	1		
NP	1		
M	1 ⎬ 6	969.37	
NM	1		
PM	1 ⎭		
Error	12	340.81	28.40
Total	23	1,358.31	

The detailed computations are as follows:

Correction factor: $\dfrac{(1119.87)^2}{24} = 52{,}254.53$

Total sum of squares: $(48.81)^2 + \cdots + (51.43)^2 - CF = 1358.31$

Block sum of squares: $\frac{1}{4}[(192.42)^2 + \cdots + (179.89)^2] - CF = 48.12$

Replicate sum of squares:

$$\tfrac{1}{8}[(382.28)^2 + (379.27)^2 + (358.32)^2] - CF = 42.59$$

Sum of squares for NPM: $\dfrac{(-9.99)^2}{24} = 4.16$

Sum of squares for replicates × NPM: block ss − (rep ss + ss for NPM)=1.38

Treatment sum of squares: $\frac{1}{24}[(124.75)^2 + \cdots + (18.21)^2] = 969.37$

Error sum of squares (by subtraction): 340.81

As explained previously, it is immaterial whether an F test, with 1 and 12 degrees of freedom, or a t test with 12 degrees of freedom is used for testing the main effects and unconfounded interactions. The results may be presented thus:

Total Effects

N	124.75	
P	−26.17	SE $= \sqrt{24(28.40)} = 26.1$
NP	8.63	
M	66.61	5% sig. level $= 56.90 = (26.1)t_{0.05}$, 12 df
NM	−46.63	
PM	18.21	1% sig. level $= 79.7 = (26.1)t_{0.01}$, 12 df

It may be worth while to note that the sum of squares for reps $\times$ NPM may be obtained in the following way:

	Rep 1	Rep 2	Rep 3	Total
NPM (−)	192.42	192.62	179.89	
NPM (+)	189.86	186.65	178.43	
	−2.56	−5.97	−1.46	−9.99

$$\text{SS for } NPM \times \text{reps} = \frac{1}{8}[(-2.56)^2 + (-5.97)^2 + (-1.46)^2] - \frac{(-9.99)^2}{24} = 1.38.$$

We may also note that formally we have a test of NPM by comparing the mean square for NPM with the mean square for $NPM \times$ reps. This test has, however, very low sensitivity and in the present case is very unreliable.

In presenting the results of the yields of treatment combinations and the estimates of the effects and interaction, results should be converted to the customary units: in agriculture, for instance, bushels, tons or hundredweights per acre. In the present case the yields per plot can be converted to cwt ($= 100$ lb) per acre by multiplying by the factor $1/0.01033 \times \frac{1}{100} = 0.968$. To obtain the mean yields for treatment combinations and what we have defined as the main effects and interactions in terms of hundredweights per acre, the entries in the column "yields" and column 3 of Table 14.4 are multiplied by $0.968/3$ and $0.968/12$, respectively. The standard error for the main effects and interactions (excluding NPM), when converted, is then

$$0.968 \sqrt{\frac{E}{r2^{n-2}}} = 0.968 \sqrt{\frac{28.40}{6}} = 2.11$$

Finally, a convenient way to summarize the results of the experiment in a concise form is given in Table 14.6.

TABLE 14.6 PRESENTATION OF RESULTS

Mean Yield = 45.1 cwt per Acre

	Avg. Effects	n		p		m	
		Absence	Presence	Absence	Presence	Absence	Presence
n	N 10.06	......	......	N − NP 9.36	N + NP 10.76	N − NM 13.82	N + NM 6.30
p	P −2.11	P − NP −2.81	P + NP −1.41	....	.....	P − PM −3.58	P + PM −0.64
m	M 5.37	M − NM 9.13	M + NM 1.61	M − PM 3.90	M + PM 6.84	......	......
SE	2.11	$2.11\sqrt{2} = 2.98$					

It may be desirable from some points of view to present also a table of the yield of each treatment combination. In the case of the experiment under discussion, we have no information on the 3-factor interaction, so that it is impossible to estimate the block effects and, hence, remove them from a table of yields. The yield of each treatment combination, if it is assumed that the 3-factor interaction is negligible, is easily computed.

The plus and minus process of Yates,[2] given here for obtaining effects and interactions from the yields of the treatment combinations, can be used inversely to obtain the yields of the treatment combinations from the mean, effects, and interactions. The modification is to arrange the interactions, effects, and twice the mean in backward order in a column and to go through the same addition and subtraction process. This leads to twice the yields of the treatment combinations in reverse standard order.

14.3 SYSTEMS OF CONFOUNDING FOR 2^n EXPERIMENTS

Suppose we have 5 factors, a, b, c, d, e, giving 32 treatment combinations in all and we wish to use blocks of 8 experimental units. The experiment will consist of 4 blocks of 8 units, and there will be 3 effects or interactions confounded with blocks.

If we confound the interaction ABC, the treatment combinations fall into 2 groups, each group consisting of 2 of the blocks, namely:

(α) : (1), ab, ac, bc, d, abd, acd, bcd, e, abe, ace, bce, de, abde, acde, bcde

(β) : a, b, c, abc, ad, bd, cd, abcd, ae, be, ce, abce, ade, bde, cde, abcde

If we also confound, say, ADE, we divide the treatment combinations again into 2 groups:

(γ) : (1), ad, ae, de, b, abd, abe, bde, c, acd, ace, cde, bc, abcd, abce, bcde

(δ) : a, d, e, ade, ab, bd, be, abde, ac, cd, ce, acde, abc, bcd, bce, abcde

If each of the comparisons (α) versus (β), and (γ) versus (δ) is to be a block comparison, the blocks must consist of the following:

(1) treatments in (α) and (γ)
(2) treatments in (α) and (δ)
(3) treatments in (β) and (γ)
(4) treatments in (β) and (δ)

The blocks are then as shown in Table 14.7.

TABLE 14.7 BLOCKS

(1)	(2)	(3)	(4)
(1)	d	b	a
bc	bcd	c	abc
de	e	bde	ade
bcde	bce	cde	abcde
abd	ab	ad	bd
acd	ac	abcd	cd
abe	abde	ae	be
ace	acde	abce	ce

The interaction ABC is equal to blocks 1 and 2 versus blocks 3 and 4, and the interaction ADE is equal to blocks 1 and 3 versus blocks 2 and 4. These are 2 orthogonal contrasts among the 4 blocks, and there is a third contrast orthogonal to each of these: namely, blocks 1 and 4 versus blocks 2 and 3. It is easily verified that this is, in fact, the interaction $BCDE$.

The general rule exemplified by this case is that, if any 2 effects or interactions are completely confounded with blocks, then so is their generalized interaction, as defined in the previous chapter. This enables an easy enumeration of systems of confounding. We give in Table 14.8 typical examples of the systems of confounding for up to 8

TABLE 14.8   TYPES OF CONFOUNDING FOR 2^n FACTORIAL SYSTEMS

The same confounding is possible for a 2^r experiment in blocks of 2^s as for a 2^{r+p} experiment in blocks of 2^{s+p}. These are therefore not included.

(1) 2 factors

Blocks of 2	Any one effect or interaction

(2) 3 factors

Blocks of 4	Any one effect or interaction
Blocks of 2	AB, AC, BC
	A, BC, ABC

(3) 4 factors

Blocks of 8	Any one effect or interaction
Blocks of 4	$A, BCD, ABCD$
	$AB, CD, ABCD$
	AB, ACD, BCD
Blocks of 2	A, B, AB, C, AC, BC, ABC
	$A, B, AB, CD, ACD, BCD, ABCD$
	$A, BC, ABC, BD, ABD, CD, ACD$
	$AB, AC, BC, AD, BD, CD, ABCD$

(4) 5 factors

Blocks of 16	Any one effect or interaction
Blocks of 8	$A, BCDE, ABCDE$
	$AB, CDE, ABCDE$
	$ABC, CDE, ABDE$
Blocks of 4	$A, B, AB, CDE, ACDE, BCDE, ABCDE$
	$A, BC, ABC, DE, ADE, BCDE, ABCDE$
	$A, BC, ABC, CDE, ACDE, BDE, ABDE$
	$AB, AC, BC, DE, ABDE, ACDE, BCDE$
	$AB, CD, ABCD, BDE, ADE, BCE, ACE$
Blocks of 2	AB, AC, AD, AE, and all generalized interactions
	A, BC, BD, BE and all generalized interactions

For the case of 6 factors or more, we shall list only systems of confounding which are more frequently useful ones, and some others of interest.

(5) 6 factors

Blocks of 16	$ABCD, CDEF, ABEF$
Blocks of 8	$ACE, BDE, ABCD, BCF, ABEF, CDEF, ADF$
Blocks of 4	$AB, CD, ABCD, EF, ABEF, CDEF, ABCDEF$
	$ACE, BCE, ADE, BDE, ACF, BCF, ADF, BDF$
Blocks of 2	AB, AC, AD, AE, AF, and all generalized interactions [not particularly useful except with partial confounding (Chapter 15)]
	A, BC, BD, BE, BF, and all generalized interactions

(6) 7 factors

Blocks of 16	$ACEG, BDE, ABCDG, BCF, ABEFG, CDEF, ADFG$
Blocks of 8	$ABC, ADE, BCDE, BDF, ACDF, ABEF, CEF, ABCDEFG$
	$DEFG, BCFG, AFG, ACEG, BEG, CDG, ABDG$
Blocks of 4	AB, AC, AD, AE, AF, AG, and all generalized interactions (again not particularly useful)
	A, BC, BD, BE, BF, BG, and all generalized interactions

(7) 8 factors

Blocks of 16	As for 7 factors in blocks of 8
Blocks of 8	ABC, ADE, AFG, BDG, and CH and all their generalized interactions; CH is the only 2-factor interaction confounded.

factors. Only those systems are given that result in a block size of 16 or less. The allocation of letters to factors is a matter for the experimenter, and the type exemplified by ABC, ABD, CD for 4 factors in blocks of 4 plots includes 5 additional systems: namely, AB, ACD, BCD; AC, ABD, BCD; AD, ABC, BCD; BC, ABD, ACD; BD, ABC, ACD. If the experimenter wishes to use this type of confounding, he should decide which of the six 2-factor interactions is least important and choose the system involving that one.

There is a remarkable theorem obtained by Fisher [3] that, so long as the number of units in the block exceeds the number of factors, we can find arrangements in which no confounded interaction involves less than 3 factors.

14.4 THE COMPOSITION OF BLOCKS FOR A PARTICULAR SYSTEM OF CONFOUNDING

The composition of the blocks may be simply obtained by first constructing the so-called intrablock subgroup. This group is based on the following properties. First, when an effect or interaction is confounded, all the treatment combinations in a block have *either* an even number of letters in common with the effect or interaction *or* an odd number. No 2 treatment combinations in the same block can have one an odd number of letters and the other an even number of letters in common with any effect or interaction that is confounded. Second, the treatment combinations in any one block may be obtained from those in another block by multiplying the symbols of the treatment combinations in the one block by the symbol of one treatment combination of the whole set in another block, replacing the square of any letter by unity. Third, the treatment combinations in the block containing the control form a group if the symbol (1) is treated as unity, and the rule of multiplication is the ordinary algebraic rule with the square of any letter replaced by unity. These treatment combinations form an Abelian group. The treatment combinations in the block containing the control is called the intrablock subgroup.

14.4.1 Example 1. 2^3 Experiment Confounding AB, AC, and BC

Each block will contain 2 treatment combinations, and we first obtain the intrablock subgroup. This contains treatment combinations with an even number of letters in common with the symbols AB, AC, and BC. Clearly there are only 2: namely, the control (1) which has no letters in common, and abc with 2 letters in common with each of AB, AC, and BC. The intrablock subgroup is then (1) and abc.

Intrablock subgroup	(1), abc	Block I
Multiply by a	$a, a^2bc = bc$	Block II
Multiply by b	$b, ab^2c = ac$	Block III
Multiply by c	$c, abc^2 = ab$	Block IV

Note that the second rule holds in that, for example, block II is obtained from block I by multiplying the elements of block I by a, but could have been obtained by multiplying these elements by bc. The third rule is exemplified by the following relations:

$$(1) \times (1) = (1)$$
$$(1) \times abc = abc$$
$$abc \times abc = a^2b^2c^2 = (1)$$

14.4.2   Example 2. 2^7 Experiment in Blocks of 16 Plots

Suppose we confound ABC, DEF, $ABCDEF$, BDG, $ACDG$, $BEFG$, $ACEFG$. To obtain the intrablock subgroup, we ascertain which treatment combinations have an even number of letters in common with each of the 7 interactions. To do this we run through the treatment combinations systematically in the order: a, b, c, d, e, f, g, ab, ac, ad, ae, af, ag, bc, bd, be, bf, bg, cd, ce, cf, cg, de, df, dg, ef, eg, fg, abc, abd, abe, abf, abg, acd, ace, acf, and so on. The first treatment combinations with the desired property are ac, ef, and with these we get the 4 treatment combinations:

(1)

ac

ef

$acef \ (= ac \times ef)$

Next, we find abg, and this, combined with the 4 above, gives

(1)

ac

ef

$acef$

abg

$bcg \ (= abg \times ac)$

$abefg \ (= abg \times ef)$

$bcefg \ (= abg \times acef)$

Finally we find deg, and this, with the above elements and their products with deg, gives column I of Table 14.9.

TABLE 14.9   BLOCK STRUCTURE FOR 2^7 EXPERIMENT

I	II	III	IV	V	VI	VII	VIII
(1)	a	b	d	e	g	ad	ae
ac	c	abc	acd	ace	acg	cd	ce
ef	aef	bef	def	f	efg	$adef$	af
$acef$	cef	$abcef$	$acdef$	acf	$acefg$	$cdef$	cf
abg	bg	ag	$abdg$	$abeg$	ab	bdg	beg
bcg	$abcg$	cg	$bcdg$	$bceg$	bc	$abcdg$	$abceg$
$abefg$	$befg$	$aefg$	$abdefg$	$abfg$	$abef$	$bdefg$	bfg
$bcefg$	$abcefg$	$cefg$	$bcdefg$	$bcfg$	$bcef$	$abcdefg$	$abcfg$
deg	$adeg$	$bdeg$	eg	dg	de	aeg	adg
$acdeg$	$cdeg$	$abcdeg$	$aceg$	$acdg$	$acde$	ceg	cdg
dfg	$adfg$	$bdfg$	fg	$defg$	df	afg	$adefg$
$acdfg$	$cdfg$	$abcdfg$	$acfg$	$acdefg$	$acdf$	cfg	$cdefg$
$abde$	bde	ade	abe	abd	$abdeg$	be	bd
$bcde$	$abcde$	cde	bce	bcd	$bcdeg$	$abce$	$abcd$
$abdf$	bdf	adf	abf	$abdef$	$abdfg$	bf	$bdef$
$bcdf$	$abcdf$	cdf	bcf	$bcdef$	$bcdfg$	$abcf$	$abcdef$

The elements in the other columns are obtained by multiplying the first column by a (giving II), b (giving III), by d, e, g, ad, ae, in order. Note that block II would be generated again by multiplying block I by the element c.   As a final check one should:

(a) Check that all treatment combinations are present.

(b) Check that one block other than I has the property of having either an odd or an even number of letters in common with each of the confounded interactions.

(c) Obtain each block other than that in b by multiplication by an appropriate symbol.

The statistician is frequently presented with the job of analyzing an experiment that he has not designed.   It is then necessary for him to discover the system of confounding on which the plan is based.   This may be done by reversing the above procedure.   Take, for example, the block given above consisting of ad, cd, $adef$, $cdef$, bdg, $abcdg$, $bdefg$, $abcdefg$, aeg, ceg, afg, cfg, be, $abce$, bf, and $abcf$.   No 2-factor interactions are confounded because no 2-factor interaction has a number of letters in common with each of the treatment symbols which is always even or always odd; e.g., AB has 1 letter in common with ad and none in common with cd. We note that ABC has either 3 or 1 letters in common with each of the treatment symbols; also BDG. The product of these, $ACDG$, has either 4, 2, or no letters in common with the treatment symbols. Also DEF has 3 or 1 letters in common. The confounded interactions are then

$$ABC, BDG, ACDG \ (= ABC \times BDG), DEF$$

$$ABCDEF \ (= ABC \times DEF), BEFG \ (= BDG \times DEF), \text{ and}$$

$$ACEFG \ (= ACDG \times DEF)$$

14.5 THE EFFECTS OF DIFFERENTIAL TREATMENT EFFECTS IN BLOCKS

There is one aspect of confounding that merits attention, namely, that, depending on the nature of the blocks and how they were constructed, and on the nature of the treatments, the true treatment effects may vary from block to block. A brief discussion of this problem is given in references 4 and 5.

The general effect of such interactions may be illustrated simply in the 2^3 experiment on factors a, b, c with ABC confounded. The plan will be (apart from randomization) as shown in Figure 15.

Suppose a produces an effect in block I and no effect in block II and the effects of factors b and c are additive with no interactions. Then, in addition to showing effects of a, b, and c, the experiment analyzed in the usual way will show an interaction of b and c. This is almost obvious but may be verified by constructing the yields of the treatment combinations in accordance with previously given rules, allowing for an effect B, an effect C, no interactions, and an effect of, say, A in the first block and of zero in the second block.

I	II
(1)	a
ab	b
ac	c
bc	abc

FIGURE 15.

Similarly, in an experiment in which, say, $ABCD$ is confounded, a significant BCD interaction could have arisen from the existence of differential responses to a in the various blocks.

The importance of these effects should not be overemphasized but, on the other hand, should not be ignored. The experimenter should be aware of the possibility of such effects confusing his interpretation of an experiment and guard against it. A similar argument applies, as we found, to the ordinary randomized blocks experiment in that differential effects of treatments from block to block can produce heterogeneity of error, with inaccurate estimation of the error of treatment comparisons.

14.6 THE USE OF ONLY ONE REPLICATE

The effects and interactions with the 2^n factorial scheme may be enumerated thus:

Main effects	n
2-factor interactions	$\dfrac{n(n-1)}{2!}$
3-factor interactions	$\dfrac{n(n-1)(n-2)}{3!}$
	....
Total	$2^n - 1$

We have already considered the case when some of the interactions involving several factors can be regarded as trivial. It is a simple extension of this principle, to suppose that interactions involving several factors may be used to estimate the experimental error. Take a 2^6 experiment, for example. The 63 effects and interactions consist of:

Main effects	6
2-factor interactions	15
3-factor interactions	20
4-factor interactions	15
5-factor interactions	6
6-factor interactions	1

If we may regard interactions involving 4 or more factors as trivial, we may estimate the error variance by the mean square due to these interactions, this being based on 22 degrees of freedom.

The effect of including, in the sum of squares by which the error is estimated, some non-zero high-order interactions will be to inflate this estimate of error variance. The actual effect may be expressed in terms of the true interactions. This inflation will be negligible for most types of factorial experiments, though, in some instances, it can be appreciable. For example, if main effects or 2-factor interactions are very large compared with the mean, it may be expected that a function involving, say, only terms of up to the second degree in the amounts of the factors may give an inadequate representation of the yields.

If the true value of an interaction term in a 2^n experiment is I, the expectation of the sum of squares for the corresponding degree of freedom is $\sigma^2 + 2^{n-2}I^2$. The bias in the estimation of σ^2 will then be 2^{n-2} (average value of I^2), the average being taken over the interaction terms included in the error sum of squares. The process more or less followed is to use higher-order interactions for the larger experiments, so that, as n increases, the average value of I^2 will generally decrease, and it is not easy to visualize the over-all effect of this procedure. The error sum of squares will not be distributed approximately according to $\chi^2\sigma^2$, with the appropriate degrees of freedom (if the infinite model holds), but according to the non-central χ^2 distribution (Chapter 12). The general result will be an underestimation of the significance of effects, with an overestimation of the errors of estimated effects. It appears that this bias could, under some circumstances, be quite appreciable, particularly if the error variance is small relative to effects and interactions. Under some circumstances, particularly in determining broad technological procedures, this bias is probably not important, but, in more accurate scientific research, a single replicate cannot be regarded in any way as adequate with less than, say, 6 factors.

14.7 AN EXAMPLE

The illustration of these principles is a report of an experiment conducted at Rothamsted to determine the effect of certain fertilizers on the yield of mangolds (Table 14.10).

Since the confounded interactions are not indicated, we proceed to determine them. We note first that the intrablock subgroup is (1), kd,

TABLE 14.10 PLAN AND YIELDS IN POUNDS OF MANGOLD ROOTS [6]

I				II			
pkd	nd	sk	spknd	d	pknd	k	snd
844	1104	1156	1508	1248	1100	784	1376
spn	kn	sd	p	spkd	skn	sp	pn
1312	1000	1176	888	1356	1376	1008	964
kd	spd	pnd	pkn	skd	spkn	knd	spnd
896	1284	996	860	1328	1292	1008	1324
sn	spk	(1)	sknd	pd	pk	n	s
1184	984	740	1468	1008	692	780	1108
III				IV			

Block Totals

I	8,988
II	9,212
III	8,412
IV	8,540
Total	35,152

TABLE 14.10   PLAN AND YIELDS IN POUNDS OF MANGOLD ROOTS [6] (*Continued*)

System of replication: 4 randomized blocks of 8 plots each. Certain high order interactions are confounded with blocks.

Area of each plot: (After rejecting edge rows) 0.02322 acre. Plots actually $\frac{1}{45}$ acre.

Treatments: 2^5 factorial design

Sulphate of ammonia:	None, or 0.6 cwt N per acre (s)
Superphosphate:	None, or 0.5 cwt P_2O_5 per acre (p)
Muriate of potash:	None, or 1.0 cwt K_2O per acre (k)
Agricultural salt:	None, or 5 cwt per acre (n)
Dung:	None, or 10 tons per acre (d)

Basal manuring: Nil

spd, pnd, pkn, sn, spk, sknd. Since all the 3-factor treatment combinations in this subgroup contain p, which is not included in *sknd*, and, since the remaining elements of the subgroup are check and 2-factor treatment combinations not including p, we know that *SKND* is confounded. After further inspection we note that *PKD* is confounded, and hence the remaining confounded interaction is *SPN*. ($SPN \times PKD = SP^2KND = SKND.$)

	No. of Letters in Common							
Interactions	(1)	kd	spd	pnd	pkn	sn	spk	sknd
SKND	0	2	2	2	2	2	2	4
PKD	0	2	2	2	2	0	2	2
SPN	0	0	2	2	2	2	2	2

First compute Table 14.11.

If we assume that the error is estimated from the unconfounded 3-, 4-, and 5-factor interactions, the analysis of variance table is constructed in the following way.

Correction factor: $\dfrac{(35,152)^2}{32} = 38,614,470$

Total sum of squares: $(844)^2 + (1104)^2 + \cdots + (1108)^2 - CF = 40,176,128 - CF$

$= 1,561,658$

Error sum of squares: $\frac{1}{32}$ (sum of squares of unconfounded 3-, 4-, and 5-factor interaction totals) $= 88,286$

Treatment sum of squares: $\frac{1}{32}$ (sum of squares of total main effect and 2-factor interactions) = 1,420,538

Block sum of squares: $\frac{1}{32}$ (sum of squares of total PKD, SPN, and $SKND$) = 52,832

Note that the sums of squares for treatment, blocks, and error, except for a multiplicative factor, are obtained immediately by squaring and

TABLE 14.11 COMPUTATION OF EXAMPLE

Treatments	Yields	1	2	3	4	5	Total Effects
(1)	740	1848	3744	7360	16128	35152	Mean
s	1108	1896	3616	8768	19024	5328	S
p	888	1940	4240	9140	2712	−312	P
sp	1008	1676	4528	9884	2616	104	SP
k	784	1964	4716	1152	−128	152	K
sk	1156	2276	4424	1560	−184	1240	SK
pk	692	2376	4800	1148	−328	−448	PK
spk	984	2152	5084	1468	432	−96	SPK
n	780	2424	488	−216	160	2152	N
sn	1184	2292	664	88	−8	728	SN
pn	864	2224	752	−156	232	432	PN
spn	1312	2200	808	−28	1008	−96	SPN (confounded)
kn	1000	2480	204	−328	−848	992	KN
skn	1376	2320	944	0	400	−592	SKN
pkn	860	2476	600	428	280	−40	PKN
spkn	1292	2608	868	4	−376	104	SPKN
d	1248	368	48	−128	1408	2896	D
sd	1176	120	−264	288	744	−96	SD
pd	1008	372	312	−292	408	−56	PD
spd	1284	292	−224	284	320	760	SPD
kd	896	404	−132	176	304	−168	KD
skd	1328	348	−24	56	128	776	SKD
pkd	844	376	−160	740	328	1248	PKD (confounded)
spkd	1356	432	132	268	−424	−656	SPKD
nd	1104	−72	−248	−312	416	−664	ND
snd	1376	276	−80	−536	576	−88	SND
pnd	996	432	−56	108	−120	−176	PND
spnd	1324	512	56	292	−472	−752	SPND
knd	1008	272	348	168	−224	160	KND
sknd	1468	328	80	112	184	−352	SKND (confounded)
pknd	1100	460	56	−268	−56	408	PKND
spknd	1508	408	−52	−108	160	216	SPKND

Totals for check:

Upper { Odd	6708	17732	19544	18528	18208	38080	
half { Even	9420	17420	20936	21744	22912	6720	
Lower { Odd	8204	2612	168	192	2464	3648	
half { Even	10820	2716	−376	656	1216	−192	

summing the relevant entries in column 5, Table 14.11. In addition to the usual check for the entries in Table 14.11, a further check of the calculations is thus available in this case: The total sum of squares calculated directly from the yields of the treatment combinations must be the total of the sums of squares for blocks, treatments and error as calculated above.

TABLE 14.12 ANALYSIS OF VARIANCE

Source of Variation	df	Sum of Squares	Mean Square
Blocks	3	52,832	
Treatments	15	1,420,538	
Error	13	88,286	6,791.23
Total	31	1,561,656	

Mean yield: 1,098.50 lb per plot
Standard error: 82.4 lb per plot or 7.5 percent of the mean

Finally the effects and interactions should be converted to tons per acre and the results summarized in the usual form (indicated in the previous illustrative example).

REFERENCES

1. Annual Report. Rothamsted Experimental Station, Harpenden, England. 1933.
2. YATES, F. *The design and analysis of factorial experiments.* Imp. Bur. Soil Sci., Harpenden, England. 1937.
3. FISHER, R. A. The theory of confounding in factorial experiments in relation to the theory of groups. *Ann. Eug.*, **11**, 341–353, 1942.
4. YATES, F. Complex experiments. *Suppl. Jour. Roy. Stat. Soc.*, **2**, 181–247, 1935.
5. KEMPTHORNE, O. A note on differential responses in blocks. *Jour. Agr. Sci.*, **37**, 245–248, 1947.
6. Annual Report. Rothamsted Experimental Station, Harpenden, England. 1936.

CHAPTER 15

Partial Confounding
in 2^n Factorial Experiments

15.1 A SIMPLE CASE

Consider the simplest possible factorial scheme, that involving 2 factors a, b, each at 2 levels, and suppose that it is necessary to use blocks of 2 experimental units. The necessity of blocks of this size might arise, for example, in an experiment on young cattle, because it is easy to obtain a number of identical twins: that is, twins of the same genetic constitution and each pair of twins being a block. The advisability of using such material follows from the fact that error variance may be reduced to as little as 10 percent of the value with a randomly chosen pair. Again it may be that the experimenter can handle only 2 experimental units at the same time and that, if units were treated in random order, the experimental errors introduced by randomizing over "times" would be considerable. Another possible use of blocks of 2 plots would be in plant pathological work, the block being a leaf and the plots the 2 halves. Suppose also that the experimenter wishes to obtain information on both main effects and the 2-factor interaction.

The basic pattern of the experiment would then consist of 3 replicates arranged as in Figure 16.

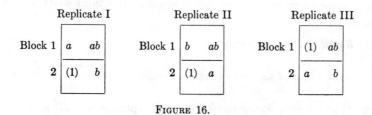

FIGURE 16.

Such a design arises if we decide that each treatment combination shall occur with every other treatment once in a block and is, therefore,

271

one of the general class of designs called "balanced incomplete block designs." We do not consider this class of designs until later chapters but examine the pattern in Figure 16 from the factorial point of view.

It is obvious that in replicate I we have confounded with blocks the effect A, in replicate II the effect B, and in replicate III the 2-factor interaction AB. Each effect and interaction is then "partially confounded" with blocks. In view of this, we shall estimate the effects and interaction from the replicates in which they are unconfounded with blocks: namely,

	Estimated from Replicates
Effect A	II, III
Effect B	I, III
Interaction AB	I, II

These estimates will be subject to an error based on the variance of units within blocks of 2 units treated alike, and, in order to obtain a reasonably precise estimate of this error variance, we shall need several repetitions of the basic pattern. Supposing we have r repetitions of the basic pattern (i.e., $3r$ replicates in all), the analysis of variance will have the structure shown in Table 15.1.

TABLE 15.1 STRUCTURE OF ANALYSIS OF VARIANCE

	df
Replicates	$3r - 1$
Blocks within replicates	$3r$
A	1
B	1
AB	1
Experimental error	$6r - 3$
Total	$12r - 1$

It is somewhat difficult to devise a notation that will allow all the mean squares to be written down algebraically, and so they will be described.

1. Replicate Sum of Squares

$$\frac{1}{4}(\text{sum of squares of replicate sums}) - \frac{(\text{grand total})^2}{12r}$$

2. Blocks within Replicates. For each replicate we will have

$$\frac{1}{2}(\text{sum of squares of block totals}) - \frac{(\text{total of replicate})^2}{4}$$

each of these sums of squares having one degree of freedom, and there being $3r$ in all.

3. Sum of Squares for A. The estimate of A will be

$$\hat{A} = \frac{1}{4r}[(\text{sum of plots with } a - \text{sum of plots without } a) \text{ for replicates of}$$

types II and III]

$$= \frac{1}{4r}[A] \quad \text{say.}$$

The sum of squares will be $[A]^2/8r$.

4. Sum of Squares for B. The estimate of B will be

$$\frac{1}{4r}[(\text{sum of plots with } b - \text{sum of plots without } b) \text{ for replicates of types I}$$

and III] $= \frac{1}{4r}[B]$ say,

and the sum of squares will be $[B]^2/8r$.

5. Sum of Squares for AB. The estimate of AB will be

$$\frac{1}{4r}[(\text{sum of plots with neither or both of } a \text{ and } b - \text{sum of plots with one}$$

of a and b) for replicates of types I and II] $= \frac{1}{4r}[AB]$ say,

and the sum of squares for AB will be $[AB]^2/8r$.

6. Sum of Squares for Experimental Error. This may be obtained by subtraction.

It is of value in the analysis of most experiments, where possible, to examine the structure of the sum of squares for experimental error. We note that this is obtained in the following way. The effect A is estimated from $2r$ replicates in all, and we could number these replicates $1, 2, \cdots, 2r$ and the estimate in each replicate $\frac{1}{2}[A_i]$, where i runs from 1 to $2r$. The differences between these estimates are attributable entirely to experimental error, each estimate being a comparison within blocks of the replicate. It follows that

$$\sum_{i=1}^{2r} \frac{1}{4}[A_i]^2 - \frac{1}{8r}[A]^2$$

is an estimate of $(2r-1)\sigma^2$, where σ^2 is the experimental error. Similarly, B and AB each contribute $(2r-1)$ degrees of freedom, making up the total of $(6r - 3)$ degrees of freedom for experimental error. The tests of significance are made in the usual way.

With the usual procedure for obtaining the variance of a linear function of random normal variables, the true variance of the estimate of A is

$$\frac{1}{(4r)^2} (4r + 4r)\sigma^2 = \frac{\sigma^2}{2r}$$

and likewise for B and AB.

15.2 EFFICIENCY OF PARTIAL CONFOUNDING

In many cases the experimenter testing 2 factors may have the choice of using blocks of 2 units with partial confounding or blocks of 4 units with no confounding. If blocks of 4 units were used, each effect and interaction would be estimated from all of the replicates and would be subject to an error variance of $\sigma^2_4/3r$, where σ^2_4 is the error variance with blocks of 4 units.

	Information	
	No Confounding	Above Partial Confounding
A		
B	$\dfrac{3r}{\sigma^2_4}$	$\dfrac{2r}{\sigma^2_2}$
AB		

The information of the partially confounded scheme, relative to that of the scheme with no confounding, is

$$\frac{2r}{\sigma^2_2} \bigg/ \frac{3r}{\sigma^2_4} = \frac{2}{3}\frac{\sigma^2_4}{\sigma^2_2}$$

where the subscript on σ^2 denotes the number of units per block. If σ^2_4 is greater than $\frac{3}{2}\sigma^2_2$ (or σ^2_2 is less than $\frac{2}{3}\sigma^2_4$), the information is greater with the partially confounded design. In general, σ^2_4 will be greater than σ^2_2, but whether it will be sufficiently greater to give the advantage to the partially confounded design depends on the experimental material. We have considered a scheme of partial confounding which results in equal information on main effects and the 2-factor interaction, but it may be more appropriate to obtain greater information on main effects. This would entail smaller representation of replicates of types I and II than of replicates of type III, to an extent depending on the relative amounts of information required.

15.3 PARTIAL CONFOUNDING OF 2^3 EXPERIMENTS

The arrangements utilizing partial confounding that are best for any situation depend on the information the experimenter wishes to obtain. Suppose, for example, with an experiment on 3 factors, a, b, c, each at 2 levels, the experimenter desires the maximum possible accuracy on main effects and equal information on the 2-factor and 3-factor interactions. He will then use a number of repetitions of the pattern shown in Figure 17.

I		II		III		IV	
(1)	a	(1)	a	(1)	b	(1)	a
ab	b	ac	c	bc	c	ab	b
c	ac	b	ab	a	ab	ac	c
abc	bc	abc	bc	abc	ac	bc	abc

Confounding AB AC BC ABC

FIGURE 17.

Suppose he uses r repetitions, the position of replicates, blocks within replicates, and plots within blocks being randomized. The information on each effect and interaction with no confounding and with the above system is given in Table 15.2, and the estimates will be made in the stated replicates.

TABLE 15.2 INFORMATION GIVEN BY DESIGN FOR 2^3 SYSTEM IN BLOCKS OF 4

	No Confounding		Above Pattern	
	Information	Estimate from	Information	, Estimate from
A			$8r/\sigma^2_4$	All replicates
B			$8r/\sigma^2_4$	All replicates
AB			$6r/\sigma^2_4$	Replicates of types II, III, IV
C	$\dfrac{8r}{\sigma^2_8}$	All replicates	$8r/\sigma^2_4$	All replicates
AC			$6r/\sigma^2_4$	Replicates of types I, III, IV
BC			$6r/\sigma^2_4$	Replicates of types I, II, IV
ABC			$6r/\sigma^2_4$	Replicates of types I, II, III

The units of information on each effect and interaction are obtained by noting that, for example, the effect A is estimated from all replicates and, on a single plot basis, will be $\dfrac{1}{16r}$ (sum of $16r$ plots − sum of $16r$ plots) with a variance of $\dfrac{1}{16^2r^2}(16r + 16r)\sigma^2_4 = \dfrac{\sigma^2_4}{8r}$. Interaction AB, for example, will be estimated from replicates of types II, III, and IV, because the replicates of type I give no information on AB, which may be separated from block differences. It is, therefore, equal to $\dfrac{1}{12r}$ (sum of $12r$ plots − sum of $12r$ plots) and has a variance of $\dfrac{1}{12^2r^2}(12r + 12r)\sigma^2_4$ $= \dfrac{1}{6r}\sigma^2_4$. Note that the information on interactions relative to main effects is $\tfrac{3}{4}$, which is easily seen since the interactions are based on $\tfrac{3}{4}$ of the replicates. The variance of main effects is $\sigma^2_4/8r$, and that of interactions will be

$$\frac{\sigma^2_4}{8r} \times \frac{4}{3} = \frac{\sigma^2_4}{6r}$$

If σ^2_4 is less than $\tfrac{3}{4}\sigma^2_8$, the partially confounded design will yield more information on interactions than the unconfounded design and substantially more information on main effects.

The partition of degrees of freedom in the analysis of variance will be as in Table 15.3. The calculation of the sums of squares is made ex-

TABLE 15.3 STRUCTURE OF ANALYSIS OF VARIANCE

	df
Replicates	$4r - 1$
Blocks within replicates	$4r$
A	1
B	1
AB	1
C	1
AC	1
BC	1
ABC	1
Error	$24r - 7$
Total	$32r - 1$

actly analogously to the previous case.

It is instructive to examine the constitution of the block sum of squares and of the error sum of squares. First, the degrees of freedom for error are shown in Table 15.4.

TABLE 15.4

A	by replicates	(All)	$4r - 1$
B	by replicates	(All)	$4r - 1$
C	by replicates	(All)	$4r - 1$
AB	by replicates	(II, III, IV)	$3r - 1$
AC	by replicates	(I, III, IV)	$3r - 1$
BC	by replicates	(I, II, IV)	$3r - 1$
ABC	by replicates	(I, II, III)	$3r - 1$
	Total		$24r - 7$

The interaction AB, for example, is estimated from $3r$ replicates, and the sum of squares between the estimates for each replicate will have $(3r - 1)$ degrees of freedom.

The composition of the block sum of squares is obtained from the fact that each of the interactions AB, AC, BC, and ABC is confounded in r of the replicates, so that the sum of squares could be broken down according to the partition given in Table 15.5.

TABLE 15.5

	df
AB	1
AC	1
BC	1
ABC	1
Block error	$4r - 4$
Total	$4r$

This is mentioned here as a simple illustration of the fact that information on confounded interactions can be obtained from block comparisons. It is usual with small experiments to ignore this information, relying completely on intrablock (i.e., within block) comparisons. When we deal with quasifactorial designs, we shall find the utilization of this information to be important.

15.4 CONFOUNDING WITH 4 FACTORS IN BLOCKS OF 4 PLOTS

As a more complicated example of partial confounding the following is of some interest for 4 factors in blocks of 4 plots. The basic pattern is of 4 replicates, the confounding being

Replicate	Confounding
I	AB, CD, ABCD
II	AC, BD, ABCD
III	AD, ABC, BCD
IV	BC, ABD, ACD

In this case there is full information on main effects, $\frac{3}{4}$ information on 2- and 3-factor interactions and $\frac{1}{2}$ information on the 4-factor interaction.

A second example on the 2^4 system in blocks of 4 plots is based on the completely orthogonalized 4×4 square. Consider the square shown in Table 15.6.

TABLE 15.6

	(1)	a	b	ab
(1)	$A\alpha_1$	$B\beta_2$	$C\gamma_3$	$D\delta_4$
c	$B\gamma_4$	$A\delta_3$	$D\alpha_2$	$C\beta_1$
d	$C\delta_2$	$D\gamma_1$	$A\beta_4$	$B\alpha_3$
cd	$D\beta_3$	$C\alpha_4$	$B\delta_1$	$A\gamma_2$

If we insert a completely orthogonalized square, it will be found that making up blocks according to columns, rows, Latin letters, Greek letters, and numerals (say) corresponds to the confounding of

$$A, \quad B, \quad AB$$
$$C, \quad D, \quad CD$$
$$AC, \quad BD, \quad ABCD$$
$$AD, \quad ABC, \quad BCD$$
$$BC, \quad ABD, \quad ACD$$

The analysis of such an experiment is left to the reader.

15.5   PARTIAL CONFOUNDING OF A 2^4 EXPERIMENT IN BLOCKS OF 2

As a final example of partial confounding of a 2^n experiment in a design with one restriction, we may consider the case of a 2^4 experiment in blocks of 2 plots. With r replicates we shall have $7r$ degrees of freedom for blocks within replicates, up to 15 for treatments and, therefore, about $(8r-15)$ degrees of freedom for error. In order to have an error based on a reasonable number of degrees of freedom, we need at least 4 replicates. With 4 replicates, the best confounding appears to be (cf. Table 14.8):

I $A, BC, ABC, BD, ABD, CD, ACD$
II $B, AC, ABC, AD, ABD, CD, BCD$
III $C, AB, ABC, AD, ACD, BD, BCD$
IV $D, AB, ABD, AC, ACD, BC, BCD$

These 4 replicates give ¾ relative information on main effects, ½ relative information on 2-factor interactions, ¼ relative information on 3-factor interactions, and full relative information on the 4-factor interaction. The design specified by these systems of confounding appears satisfactory for a situation in which an experimenter wishes to test 4 factors each at 2 levels in blocks of 2 plots. The analysis is left as an exercise for the reader, since it presents no new difficulties.

15.6 CONFOUNDING IN LATIN SQUARES

It is sometimes possible to arrange the treatment combinations in the form of a square such that interactions of no interest to the experimenter are confounded with rows and columns of the square. It must be remembered that, in order to obtain an unbiased estimate of error from a square, all rows and all columns must be rearranged in a random order. Thus, we cannot arrange the experiment so that rows (or columns) forming each complete replication necessarily fall together in the field. In this section we shall consider the various types applicable to sets of factors at 2 levels only.

15.6.1 The 2^3 Design in Two 4 × 4 Latin Squares

As we have seen, we can arrange a 2^3 design in blocks of 4 plots in such a way as to confound any 1 degree of freedom for treatments. So, in a 4 × 4 square we may, considering rows as blocks, confound 1 degree of freedom with rows, and then, considering columns as blocks, confound 1 degree of freedom with columns. Since 2 replicates are necessary to get an adequate estimate of error, we may completely confound these 2 degrees of freedom, or we may partially confound 4 degrees of freedom, or we may partially confound 2 degrees of freedom (say, two 2-factor interactions) and completely confound 1 degree of freedom, say, the 3-factor interaction. Examples of each follow.

Suppose we are testing all combinations of the 3 common fertilizers n, p, and k. The 8 treatments are:

$$(1),\ n,\ p,\ np,\ k,\ nk,\ pk,\ npk$$

1. If NPK is confounded with columns, PK with rows, both replicates will be randomizations of 1 of the 2 squares:

(1)	n	pk	npk		(1)	n	pk	npk
np	p	nk	k		np	k	nk	p
nk	k	np	p	or	nk	p	np	k
pk	npk	(1)	n		pk	npk	(1)	n

The reader may verify that the effects given are actually confounded. The analysis of variance appears in Table 15.7.

TABLE 15.7

Due to		df
Squares		1
Rows within squares		6
Columns within squares		6
Treatments		5
N	1	
P	1	
K	1	
NP	1	
NK	1	
Error		13
Total		31

It will perhaps be instructive to the reader to sketch the analysis of this design from the point of view of least squares. We shall take, for this purpose, the case of 2 replicates like the first square. The model we shall use is

$$y_{ijk} = \mu + s_i + \rho_{ij} + \gamma_{ik} + \tau_l + e_{ijkl}$$

where i denotes the square, j the row, k the column, l the treatment combination on plot (ijk), the other symbols having the obvious meaning. We may suppose that the rows and columns in each square are numbered in order as the rows and columns of the first square listed above. Then we may write, for example:

$$y_{111} = \mu + s_1 + \rho_{11} + \gamma_{11} - \tfrac{1}{2}N - \tfrac{1}{2}P + \tfrac{1}{2}NP - \tfrac{1}{2}K + \tfrac{1}{2}NK$$
$$+ \tfrac{1}{2}PK - \tfrac{1}{2}NPK + e_{111}$$

$$y_{112} = \mu + s_1 + \rho_{11} + \gamma_{12} + \tfrac{1}{2}N - \tfrac{1}{2}P - \tfrac{1}{2}NP - \tfrac{1}{2}K - \tfrac{1}{2}NK$$
$$+ \tfrac{1}{2}PK + \tfrac{1}{2}NPK + e_{112}$$

$$y_{113} = \mu + s_1 + \rho_{11} + \gamma_{13} - \tfrac{1}{2}N + \tfrac{1}{2}P - \tfrac{1}{2}NP + \tfrac{1}{2}K - \tfrac{1}{2}NK$$
$$+ \tfrac{1}{2}PK - \tfrac{1}{2}NPK + e_{113}$$

$$y_{114} = \mu + s_1 + \rho_{11} + \gamma_{14} + \tfrac{1}{2}N + \tfrac{1}{2}P + \tfrac{1}{2}NP + \tfrac{1}{2}K + \tfrac{1}{2}NK$$
$$+ \tfrac{1}{2}PK + \tfrac{1}{2}NPK + e_{114}$$

and so on. It will be found that γ_{11}, γ_{21}, γ_{13}, and γ_{23} always are associated with $-\tfrac{1}{2}NPK$, and the other column constants with $+\tfrac{1}{2}NPK$. The least squares procedure may now be applied, and it will lead to the usual estimates of N, P, NP, K, and NK, which are orthogonal to squares, row and column estimates, and, hence, to the analysis of variance given.

2. If NPK, NP, NK, and PK are partially confounded, we get the results shown in Table 15.8.

TABLE 15.8 DESIGN FOR 2^3 IN TWO 4×4 LATIN SQUARES

Square I					Square II			
(1)	n	pk	npk		(1)	p	npk	nk
np	p	nk	k		np	n	k	pk
nk	k	np	p		npk	nk	(1)	p
pk	npk	(1)	n		k	pk	np	n

In this case, we have confounded NPK with columns and PK with rows in replicate I, and NK with rows and NP with columns in replicate II, so that NPK and NP are estimated from II only and NK and NP from I only. We obtain full information on main effects and $\tfrac{1}{2}$ relative information on all the interactions, and the analysis of variance given in Table 15.9, in which the terms are computed in the ordinary fashion. The reader would be well advised to examine this design also, from the point of view of least squares.

TABLE 15.9 ANALYSIS OF DESIGN OF TABLE 15.8

Due to		df
Reps		1
Rows within reps		6
Columns within reps		6
Treatments		7
	N	1
	P	1
	K	1
	NP	1
	NK	1
	PK	1
	NPK	1
Error		11
Total		31

3. An example, completely confounding 1 degree of freedom and partially confounding 2 degrees of freedom is given in Table 15.10.

TABLE 15.10 DESIGN FOR 2^3 IN TWO 4 × 4 LATIN SQUARES

Square I					Square II			
(1)	n	pk	npk		(1)	k	np	npk
np	p	nk	k		nk	n	pk	p
nk	k	np	p		np	npk	(1)	k
pk	npk	(1)	n		pk	p	nk	n

Here we have confounded NPK with columns in both squares and PK with rows in square I, NP with rows in square II. Thus we

TABLE 15.11 ANALYSIS OF VARIANCE FOR DESIGN OF TABLE 15.10

Due to		df
Reps		1
Rows within reps		6
Columns within reps		6
Treatments		6
	N	1
	P	1
	K	1
	NP	1
	NK	1
	PK	1
Error		12
Total		31

have full information on N, P, K, NK; $\frac{1}{2}$ relative information on NP and PK, and no information on NPK, NP being estimated from I and PK from II.

15.6.2 The 2^3 Design in Three 4×4 Latin Squares

With 3 squares the 3-factor interaction may be confounded with columns in all 3 squares and each 2-factor interaction confounded with rows in 1 square. Then we have $\frac{2}{3}$ the relative information on the 2-factor interactions. Alternatively, if 2-factor interactions are of the same interest as main effects, we may confound each in $\frac{1}{2}$ of a square, giving $\frac{5}{6}$ the relative information on each effect except the 3-factor interaction which is confounded in all 3 replicates, as shown in Table 15.12.

TABLE 15.12 DESIGN FOR 2^3 IN THREE 4×4 LATIN SQUARES

	Square I					*Square II*					*Square III*			
N	(1)	p	pk	k	P	(1)	n	nk	k	K	(1)	n	np	p
	np	n	nk	npk		np	p	pk	npk		nk	k	pk	npk
NK	pk	k	np	n	PK	nk	k	np	p	NP	pk	p	nk	n
	nk	npk	(1)	p		pk	npk	(1)	n		np	npk	(1)	k

Here NPK is confounded with columns in each replicate, while the effect confounded in each row pair is indicated. N and NK are estimated from replicates II and III, P and PK from I and III, and K and NP from I and II, and from respective row pairs where unconfounded.

TABLE 15.13 ANALYSIS OF VARIANCE OF DESIGN OF TABLE 15.12

Due to		df
Reps		2
Rows within reps		9
Columns within reps		9
Treatments		6
N	1	
P	1	
K	1	
NP	1	
NK	1	
PK	1	
Error		21
Total		47

15.6.3 2^4 Design in 8×8 Latin Squares

Insofar as we are considering only complete confounding of interactions with rows or columns, the only other square layout to be considered is the 8 × 8 square. Any 1 degree of freedom for a main effect or interaction may be confounded with rows, and, at the same time, another degree of freedom for a main effect or interaction may be confounded with columns. Alternatively, partial confounding may be adopted, each of 4 degrees of freedom for 3-factor interactions being confounded in one of the 4 row pairs, and the 4-factor interaction being completely confounded in the 4 column pairs. Three quarters of the relative information will then be available on the 3-factor interactions.

In Table 15.14, ABC, ABD, ACD, BCD are confounded with row

TABLE 15.14 DESIGN FOR 4 FACTORS IN AN 8 × 8 SQUARE

I	(1)	d	ab	abd	ac	acd	bc	bcd
	ad	a	bd	b	cd	abc	abcd	c
II	ab	c	(1)	abc	ad	bcd	bd	acd
	ac	b	bc	a	abcd	abd	cd	d
III	cd	abc	ac	bcd	(1)	b	ad	abd
	bc	acd	abcd	c	bd	d	ab	a
IV	bd	abd	cd	acd	bc	a	(1)	abc
	abcd	bcd	ad	d	ab	c	ac	b

pairs I, II, III, IV, respectively, and each may be estimated from those rows in which it is not confounded. $ABCD$ is completely confounded with columns. Further partial confounding may be done as with 2^3 experiments. The structure of the analysis of variance for this example is given in Table 15.15.

TABLE 15.15 ANALYSIS OF VARIANCE FOR DESIGN OF TABLE 15.14

Due to	df
Rows	7
Columns	7
Treatments	14
(One each for A, B, AB, C, AC, BC, ABC, D, AD, BD, ABD, CD, ACD, BCD)	
Error	35
	—
Total	63

15.6.4 Arrangements for 5 and 6 Factors in an 8 × 8 Square

Yates [1] gives a balanced group of sets for confounding in a 2^5 design in blocks of 8 plots:

ABC	*ADE*	*BCDE*
ABD	*BCE*	*ACDE*
ACE	*BCD*	*ABDE*
ACD	*BDE*	*ABCE*
ABE	*CDE*	*ABCD*

If only a single 8 × 8 square is available, 4 out of the 5 sets may be confounded, 2 with rows and 2 with columns. In the square in Table 15.16 the first group is confounded in rows 1–4, the second in rows 5–8, the third in columns 1–4, the fourth in columns 5–8, and the fifth group is unconfounded.

TABLE 15.16

(1)	*abe*	*bc*	*ace*	*abd*	*bcde*	*de*	*acd*
bce	*ac*	*e*	*ab*	*bcd*	*abde*	*acde*	*d*
cde	*abcd*	*bde*	*ad*	*abce*	*b*	*c*	*ae*
bd	*ade*	*cd*	*abcde*	*be*	*abc*	*a*	*ce*
abc	*ce*	*acde*	*bcd*	(1)	*ad*	*abe*	*bde*
acd	*bcde*	*abce*	*c*	*ade*	*e*	*bd*	*ab*
abde	*d*	*a*	*be*	*cde*	*ace*	*abcd*	*bc*
ae	*b*	*abd*	*de*	*ac*	*cd*	*bce*	*abcde*

The analysis is performed in the usual way, partially confounded interactions being estimated from the rows or columns in which they are unconfounded. As with all these designs in Latin squares, rows and columns must be completely randomized among themselves in order for an unbiased estimate of the error to be obtained. In the case of 6 factors, the system of confounding will be of the type:

Rows *ACE, ADF, BDE, BCF, ABCD, ABEF, CDEF*

Columns *ABF, ADE, BCD, CEF, ABCE, ACDF, BDEF*

The square in Table 15.17 confounds these interactions. If 128 plots are available, a second square confounding a different set of 3-factor interactions may be obtained from the above square by transforming *a* to *c*, *c* to *f*, *f* to *e*, and *e* to *a*. Two 4-factor interactions will be confounded in both squares (completely confounded).

TABLE 15.17

(1)	ade	bdf	abef	cdef	acf	bce	abcd
aef	df	abde	b	acd	ce	abcf	bcdef
bdef	abf	e	ad	bc	abcde	cdf	acef
abd	be	af	def	abcef	bcdf	acde	c
cde	ac	bcef	abcdf	f	adef	bd	abe
acdf	cef	abc	bcde	ae	d	abdef	bf
bcf	abcdef	cd	ace	bde	ab	ef	adf
abce	bcd	acdef	cf	abdf	bef	a	de

Yates has pointed out [2] that there are some difficulties with this design. It is possible, with certain arrangements of the rows and columns, for the contrast representing one of the main effects to consist of the contrast between the diagonally opposite pairs of quarters of the whole square. This will occur with considerable frequency if rows and columns are randomized, as they should be. Yates makes tentative suggestions for overcoming this defect, but it is probably better in the present state of knowledge to avoid the design, or to replicate it.[*]

15.7 DOUBLE CONFOUNDING

This term is used to denote the arrangement of a set of factorial combinations in a rectangular array, say, rows by columns, in such a way that interactions of little interest are confounded either with rows or with columns. With a 2^n experiment, we shall have 2^r rows and 2^{n-r} columns. For 5 factors each at 2 levels we could use the arrangement given in Table 15.18 before randomization.

TABLE 15.18 2^5 EXPERIMENT IN 4×8 PATTERN

(1)	ab	de	abde	ace	bce	acd	bcd
abe	e	abd	d	bc	ac	bcde	acde
cde	abcde	c	abc	ad	bd	ae	be
abcd	cd	abce	ce	bde	ade	b	a

In the arrangement, ABC, CDE, $ABDE$ are confounded with rows, and AB, CD, $ABCD$, BDE, ADE, BCE, and ACE are confounded with

[*] See in this connection "Restricted randomization and quasi-Latin squares." P. M. Grundy and M. J. R. Healy. *J. Roy. Stat. Soc.* (B), **12**, 286–291, 1950.

columns. The design is simply obtained by writing down the intra-block subgroup corresponding to the row confounding in a row and the intrablock subgroup corresponding to the column confounding in the first column and taking products according to the usual rules. This particular design is of little value unless repeated, for the only means of estimating the error variance is to use unconfounded interactions involving 3 or more factors, so that only 8 degrees of freedom are available. In repetitions it would be well to use different schemes of confounding so that some within-row-and-column information could be obtained on all effects and interactions. The general value of such designs is limited because it is necessary to assume that row effects are constant over all columns, and the minimum number of columns is 8. If long rectangular plots are used, the design could, however, be valuable for field experiments. The designs in Latin squares are, of course, a particular case of the general class discussed in this section.

15.8 MISSING VALUES IN FACTORIAL EXPERIMENTS

Unconfounded factorial experiments present no new problem. Factorial experiments in which only complete confounding is used may be "filled in" in a simple way. Considering the case of 1 missing plot in 1 block of 1 replicate, we may obtain the difference between the mean of the other treatments of this block and the missing treatment in the other replicates and apply this to the mean of the treatments represented in the block to give an estimated value for the missing observation. Thus, suppose we had 2 replicates, and the 2 relevant blocks are as

(1)	8
npk	9
ks	10
nps	Missing

nps	13
(1)	12
ks	15
npk	14

FIGURE 18.

shown in Figure 18, then the estimated value is

$$\frac{8 + 9 + 10}{3} + \left(13 - \frac{12 + 15 + 14}{3}\right) = 9 + (13 - 13\tfrac{2}{3}) = 8\tfrac{1}{3}$$

This value may be inserted for purposes of estimation. For tests of significance and estimation of the error of estimates, the position is more complex, and it will, for most purposes and with large experiments (say, involving 4 or more factors), be sufficient for us to reduce the error degrees of freedom by the number of missing plots before the error mean square is obtained and, thenceforth, to disregard the fact that any observations were missing.

In partially confounded experiments the situation is more complex. We can certainly follow the usual procedure of inserting algebraic values for the missing values and then minimizing the error sum of squares with respect to these algebraic values. This procedure could be very tedious, and a simpler approximate device would be to find other blocks containing the missing combination and some of the other combinations of the block with the missing observation, and perform a calculation like the above for the complete confounding case.

REFERENCES

1. YATES, F. *The design and analysis of factorial experiments.* Imp. Bur. Soil Sci., Harpenden, England. 1937.
2. YATES, F. Discussion of paper by Anscombe. *Jour. Roy. Stat. Soc. A,* **61,** 204–205, 1948.

CHAPTER 16

Experiments Involving
Factors with 3 Levels

16.1 INTRODUCTION

In the case of factors each at 2 levels, we have seen that the differences between yields of treatment combinations may be expressed simply in terms of main effects and interactions. This simplicity arises because each factor has 2 levels, and the effect of any 1 factor may be expressed by 1 figure, the yield with the factor at the higher level minus the yield with the factor at the lower level. With factors at 3 levels, we can express the effect of a factor in 2 ways. First, we can express the yield at each level as a deviation from the mean yield at the 3 levels, giving, say, A_0, A_1, and A_2, where $A_0 + A_1 + A_2 = 0$. This method is useful mathematically, as will be seen later in that symmetry properties are retained.

The experimenter is however more likely to be interested in the other method. We suppose that the 3 levels of a factor, say, 0, 1, 2, correspond to amounts of a factor (e.g., fertilizer 0, 1, and 2 cwt per acre). Suppose these yields are plotted on a graph as in Figure 19.

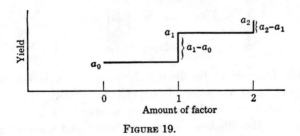

FIGURE 19.

There are 2 responses to a unit amount of the factor, $a_1 - a_0$ at the level 0, and $a_2 - a_1$ at the level 1. We may take the sum of these as the average effect of the factor, i.e., $[(a_2 - a_1) + (a_1 - a_0)]$ which equals $(a_2 - a_0)$. As a measure of the extent to which the response is falling off as the level increases, we may take $(a_2 - a_1) - (a_1 - a_0)$ which equals $a_2 - 2a_1 + a_0$. We therefore define the linear effect of the factor a by

$$A' = (a_2 - a_0)$$

and the quadratic effect by

$$A'' = \tfrac{1}{2}(a_2 - 2a_1 + a_0)$$

These may be derived apart from constant divisors by regression theory if one wishes. The linear regression coefficient of yield on amount of factor is equal to $(a_2 - a_0)/2$ corresponding to $\Sigma(x - \bar{x})(y - \bar{y})/\Sigma(x - x)^2$ for the linear regression of y on x. The quadratic effect is the linear contrast among a_0, a_1, a_2, which is orthogonal to the linear effect $(a_2 - a_0)$. In passing it may be noted that, if the a levels do not correspond to equal spacing, it may be preferable to define the linear effect differently (according to the regression approach) and the quadratic effect correspondingly.

Now consider 2 factors, a, b, each at 3 levels, which we denote by subscripts 0, 1, and 2. The interaction of these 2 factors will be the interaction of a 3×3 table and will have 4 degrees of freedom. These 4 degrees of freedom may be separated into contrasts each with a single degree of freedom in many ways. The most useful in the interpretation of experiments is the following:

$$A'B' = \tfrac{1}{2}(a_2 - a_0)(b_2 - b_0)$$

$$A''B' = \tfrac{1}{4}(a_2 - 2a_1 + a_0)(b_2 - b_0)$$

$$A'B'' = \tfrac{1}{4}(a_2 - a_0)(b_2 - 2b_1 + b_0)$$

$$A''B'' = \tfrac{1}{8}(a_2 - 2a_1 + a_0)(b_2 - 2b_1 + b_0)$$

each having 1 degree of freedom. The choice of a divisor in each of these expressions is a matter of convention entirely. Throughout we have used the convention that any effect or interaction is to be expressed on the basis of the difference between 2 plots, and we shall adhere to this rule.

This system for expressing the results may be extended indefinitely. Thus, for 3 factors, a, b, and c, we shall have 26 degrees of freedom of the following types:

3 linear effects: e.g., $\frac{1}{9}(a_2 - a_0)(b_0 + b_1 + b_2)(c_0 + c_1 + c_2) = A'$

3 quadratic effects: e.g., $\frac{1}{18}(a_2 - 2a_1 + a_0)(b_0 + b_1 + b_2)(c_0 + c_1 + c_2) = A''$

3 linear $\times$ linear interactions: e.g., $\frac{1}{6}(a_2 - a_0)(b_2 - b_0)(c_0 + c_1 + c_2) = A'B'$

6 linear $\times$ quadratic interactions: e.g., $\frac{1}{12}(a_2 - a_0)(b_2 - 2b_1 + b_0) \times (c_0 + c_1 + c_2) = A'B''$

3 quadratic $\times$ quadratic interactions: e.g., $\frac{1}{24}(a_2 - 2a_1 + a_0)(b_2 - 2b_1 + b_0)(c_0 + c_1 + c_2) = A''B''$

1 linear $\times$ linear $\times$ linear interaction: $\frac{1}{4}(a_2 - a_0)(b_2 - b_0)(c_2 - c_0) = A'B'C'$

3 linear $\times$ linear $\times$ quadratic interactions: e.g., $\frac{1}{8}(a_2 - a_0)(b_2 - b_0) \times (c_0 - 2c_1 + c_2) = A'B'C''$

3 linear $\times$ quadratic $\times$ quadratic interactions: e.g., $\frac{1}{16}(a_2 - a_0)(b_2 - 2b_1 + b_0) \times (c_2 - 2c_1 + c_0) = A'B''C''$

1 quadratic $\times$ quadratic $\times$ quadratic interaction: $\frac{1}{32}(a_2 - 2a_1 + a_0) \times (b_2 - 2b_1 + b_0)(c_2 - 2c_1 + c_0) = A''B''C''$

The value of this system depends entirely on the presupposition that the factors will be largely linear in their effects and that interactions involving quadratic effects will be less important. This is frequently the case, though the above procedure must be regarded as an easily understood approximation to the facts, just as the use of effects and low-order interactions for factors at 2 levels is an approximation, as was noted in Chapter 13.

16.2 THE FORMAL METHOD OF DEFINING EFFECTS AND INTERACTIONS

We shall introduce this method by an intuitive argument. Consider first the case of 2 factors, a, b, each at 2 levels, 0 and 1. The 4 treatment combinations may be represented by the points (0, 0), (1, 0),

(0, 1), and (1, 1) on the Euclidean plane with axes x_1, x_2, the first co-ordinate referring to the level of a and the second to the level of b. The effects and interactions defined in previous chapters have a simple algebraic interpretation. The effect of A is, for example, the comparison of treatment combinations for which $x_1 = 0$ against those for which $x_1 = 1$. Likewise, the B effect is the comparison of those treatment combinations for which $x_2 = 0$ versus those for which $x_2 = 1$. The interaction is in the former notation, the comparison among treatment combinations.

$$(1) + ab - a - b$$

i.e., of the points (0, 0) and (1, 1) versus the points (1, 0) and (0, 1). For the first point (0, 0),

$$x_1 + x_2 = 0$$

and, for the second (1, 1),

$$x_1 + x_2 = 2$$

and, for the other 2 points,

$$x_1 + x_2 = 1$$

If we work with numbers reduced modulo 2, that is, we replace any number by the remainder when it is divided by 2, the interaction is the comparison of those treatment combinations for which

$$x_1 + x_2 = 0 \bmod 2$$

versus those for which

$$x_1 + x_2 = 1 \bmod 2$$

With 3 factors, a, b, c, each at 2 levels, we represent the treatment combinations by a point in 3-dimensional space (x_1, x_2, x_3). Thus:

$$(1) = (0, 0, 0); \quad a = (1, 0, 0); \quad b = (0, 1, 0); \quad ab = (1, 1, 0)$$

$$c = (0, 0, 1); \quad ac = (1, 0, 1); \quad bc = (0, 1, 1); \quad abc = (1, 1, 1)$$

It is easily verified (and follows from the relations of evenness of number of letters in common between treatment symbols and symbols for effect and interaction) that the effects and interactions are based on a comparison of 2 groups of the treatment combinations given by the equations in Table 16.1.

TABLE 16.1

Effect or Interaction	Left-Hand Side of Equation
A	x_1
B	x_2
AB	$x_1 + x_2$
C	x_3
AC	$x_1 + x_3$
BC	$x_2 + x_3$
ABC	$x_1 + x_2 + x_3$

For example, the treatment combinations entering the ABC negatively are (1), ab, ac, and bc, and for these $x_1 + x_2 + x_3$ equals 0, 2, 2, and 2, respectively: in other words it equals 0 modulo 2. The treatment combinations entering positively are a, b, c, and abc, and for these $x_1 + x_2 + x_3$ equals 1, 1, 1, and 3, respectively, or equals 1 modulo 2 for each treatment combination. It is a simple matter to derive the rule of the generalized interaction with this notation.

The above approach for the 2^n system suggests the appropriate approach for the 3^n system. Consider the arrangement of the 9 treatment combinations with 2 factors.

Level of a

	.(0, 0)	.(1, 0)	.(2, 0)	x_1
Level of b	.(0, 1)	.(1, 1)	.(2, 1)	
x_2	.(0, 2)	.(1, 2)	.(2, 2)	

The main effect of a will be represented by the comparisons among 3 means: those for which $x_1 = 0$, for which $x_1 = 1$, and for which $x_1 = 2$. The representation of these effects as 2 linearly independent numbers may be obtained by considering each mean as a deviation from the over-all mean. Likewise, the main effect of b will be represented by the comparison among the 3 means, those for which $x_2 = 0$, $x_2 = 1$, and $x_2 = 2$. The interaction of the factors a and b we know to have 4 degrees of freedom. We can consider these 4 degrees of freedom from the point of view of the completely orthogonalized 3×3 square. If we insert Latin and Greek letters so as to get a completely orthogonalized square, we have the square:

$$A\alpha \quad B\beta \quad C\gamma$$
$$B\gamma \quad C\alpha \quad A\beta$$
$$C\beta \quad A\gamma \quad B\alpha$$

The comparison among columns gives the effect of a, among rows the effect of b. Those among Latin letters and those among Greek letters each with 2 degrees of freedom represent the 4 degrees of freedom for the interaction of the 2 factors. Consider the grouping given by Latin letters, namely:

$$(0, 0), (2, 1), \text{ and } (1, 2)$$

$$\text{versus} \quad (1, 0), (0, 1), \text{ and } (2, 2)$$

$$\text{versus} \quad (2, 0), (0, 2), \text{ and } (1, 1)$$

For the first set of 3 treatment combinations, $x_1 + x_2$ takes on the value 0, 3, and 3, i.e., 0 modulo 3; for the second set, $x_1 + x_2$ takes on the values 1, 1, and 4, i.e., 1 modulo 3; and, for the third set, $x_1 + x_2$ equals 2, 2, and 2. So 2 degrees of freedom are given by the comparisons among plots for which $x_1 + x_2 = 0, = 1, = 2$ mod 3.

Similarly, the Greek letters give the grouping:

$$(0, 0), (1, 1), \text{ and } (2, 2)$$

$$\text{versus} \quad (1, 0), (2, 1), \text{ and } (0, 2)$$

$$\text{versus} \quad (2, 0), (0, 1), \text{ and } (1, 2)$$

The function $x_1 + 2x_2$ modulo 3 takes on the value 0 for the first group, 1 for the second, and 2 for the third ($1 + 2 \times 2 = 5 = 2$ mod 3).

In summary then, the effects and interactions for 3^2 design are given in pairs of degrees of freedom by the comparisons among 3 sets of treatment combinations, as follows:

$$\left. \begin{array}{l} A: \quad x_1 = 0, = 1, = 2, \\ B: \quad x_2 = 0, = 1, = 2, \\ \text{Interaction} \begin{cases} x_1 + x_2 = 0, = 1, = 2, \\ x_1 + 2x_2 = 0, = 1, = 2. \end{cases} \end{array} \right\} \text{mod } 3$$

It is convenient to denote the pair of degrees of freedom corresponding to the equations $x_1 + x_2 = 0, = 1, = 2$ by the symbol AB and the pair corresponding to $x_1 + 2x_2 = 0, = 1, = 2$ by AB^2. The interaction degrees of freedom may also be represented by BA and BA^2, respectively. The pair of degrees of freedom corresponding to BA are given by the contrasts among the 3 groups of treatment combinations for which

$$\left. \begin{array}{l} x_2 + x_1 = 0 \\ x_2 + x_1 = 1 \\ x_2 + x_1 = 2 \end{array} \right\} \text{mod } 3$$

and

and these equations are identical with those specifying the groups that give the interaction degrees of freedom denoted above by AB. The interaction degrees of freedom corresponding to BA^2 are given by the contrasts among the 3 sets of treatment combinations specified by the equations:

$$\left.\begin{array}{l} x_2 + 2x_1 = 0 \\ x_2 + 2x_1 = 1 \\ x_2 + 2x_1 = 2 \end{array}\right\} \bmod 3$$

But the solutions of the equation

$$x_2 + 2x_1 = 0 \bmod 3$$

are the same as the solutions of the equation:

$$2(x_2 + 2x_1) = 0 \bmod 3$$

i.e.,

$$2x_2 + 4x_1 = 0 \bmod 3$$

i.e.,

$$x_1 + 2x_2 = 0 \bmod 3$$

Similarly, the solutions of the equation

$$x_2 + 2x_1 = 1 \bmod 3$$

are the same as the solutions of the equation

$$2x_2 + x_1 = 2 \bmod 3$$

and the solutions of the equation

$$x_2 + 2x_1 = 2 \bmod 3$$

are the same as those of

$$2x_2 + x_1 = 1 \bmod 3$$

The groups given by the symbols AB^2 and BA^2 are the same, and the sum of squares will be the same, being that ascribable to differences among the 3 groups. It is convenient, in order to obtain a complete and unique enumeration of the pairs of degrees of freedom, to adopt the rule that an order of the letters is to be chosen in advance and that the power of the first letter in a symbol must be unity. This latter is obtained by taking the square of the symbol with the rule that the cube of any letter is to be replaced by unity, if the initial letter of the symbol occurs raised to the power of 2.

We may extend this process indefinitely. For 3 factors we have the results shown in Table 16.2, where only the left-hand side of the equation is written down in each case.

TABLE 16.2

Effect or Interaction	Equation
A	x_1
B	x_2
AB	$x_1 + x_2$
AB^2	$x_1 + 2x_2$
C	x_3
AC	$x_1 + x_3$
AC^2	$x_1 + 2x_3$
BC	$x_2 + x_3$
BC^2	$x_2 + 2x_3$
ABC	$x_1 + x_2 + x_3$
ABC^2	$x_1 + x_2 + 2x_3$
AB^2C	$x_1 + 2x_2 + x_3$
AB^2C^2	$x_1 + 2x_2 + 2x_3$

Note that the 8 degrees of freedom for the 3-factor interaction break down into 4 sets of 2 degrees of freedom. This may be shown (cf. Fisher [1]) by considering the 3×3 Latin square.

The 4-factor interactions of 4 factors each at 3 levels correspondingly breaks down into 8 sets of 2 degrees of freedom, which may be denoted as in Table 16.3.

TABLE 16.3

Symbol	Equation (LHS only)
$ABCD$	$x_1 + x_2 + x_3 + x_4$
$ABCD^2$	$x_1 + x_2 + x_3 + 2x_4$
ABC^2D	$x_1 + x_2 + 2x_3 + x_4$
ABC^2D^2	$x_1 + x_2 + 2x_3 + 2x_4$
AB^2CD	$x_1 + 2x_2 + x_3 + x_4$
AB^2CD^2	$x_1 + 2x_2 + x_3 + 2x_4$
AB^2C^2D	$x_1 + 2x_2 + 2x_3 + x_4$
$AB^2C^2D^2$	$x_1 + 2x_2 + 2x_3 + 2x_4$

The extensions are quite straightforward and will not be enumerated. For the 3^n system we shall have $(3^n - 1)/2$ symbols, each representing 2 degrees of freedom.

In presenting the above we have relied on intuitional generalization. The properties indicated are easily proved and will be presented for the general p^n system in the next chapter.

16.2.1 Yields of Treatment Combinations in Terms of Effects and Interactions

The symbols used above to denote pairs of degrees of freedom will also be used to denote the magnitudes of effects and interactions in the following way. Each symbol represents a division of the 3^n treatment combinations into 3 groups of 3^{n-1} treatment combinations. The symbol, with a subscript which is at the right-hand side of the equation determining the particular one of the 3 groups in which treatment combinations lie, will denote the mean yield of that group as a deviation from the mean. Thus, e.g.:

A_0 = (mean of treatment combinations containing a_0) − (mean

of all treatment combinations)

AB_0 = (mean of treatment combinations for which $x_1 + x_2$

= 0 mod 3) − (mean of all treatment combinations)

AB_1 = (mean of treatment combinations for which $x_1 + x_2$

= 1 mod 3) − (mean of all treatment combinations)

AB^2C_1 = (mean of treatment combinations for which $x_1 + 2x_2 + x_3 =$

1 mod 3) − (mean of all treatment combinations)

With these definitions the yield of a treatment combination $a_ib_jc_k$ in terms of effects and interactions is

$$a_ib_jc_k = \mu + A_i + B_j + AB_{i+j} + AB^2_{i+2j} + C_k$$
$$+ AC_{i+k} + AC^2_{i+2k} + BC_{j+k} + BC^2_{j+2k} + ABC_{i+j+k}$$
$$+ ABC^2_{i+j+2k} + AB^2C_{i+2j+k} + AB^2C^2_{i+2j+2k}$$

where all subscripts are reduced modulo 3, and μ is the mean of all combinations. For example, the yield of the treatment combination $a_1b_1c_2$ is given by

$$a_1b_1c_2 = \mu + A_1 + B_1 + AB_2 + AB^2_0 + C_2 + AC_0 + AC^2_2$$
$$+ BC_0 + BC^2_2 + ABC_1 + ABC^2_0 + AB^2C_2 + AB^2C^2_1$$

Given this rule it is possible to express any linear contrast of the yields of the treatment combinations in terms of the effects and interactions. The process appears somewhat complex but is in fact very simple to operate, once one acquires the rules of reduction modulo 3: i.e., that every subscript is to be divided by 3 and the remainder substituted. It may be noted that this reparametrization of the general linear hypothesis model is not of full rank, in that $A_0 + A_1 + A_2 = 0$, for example (see Chapter 6). If a reparametrization of full rank were used, the symmetry in the equation for $a_i b_j c_k$ could not be retained.

Now suppose that the treatment combinations are tested the same number of times in a randomized block trial. Then the yield of a treatment combination will, under additivity, be equal to the true yield plus an error. The errors may be regarded as uncorrelated, and the best estimate of any contrast of the true yields is the same contrast of observed means. It is easily verified that the estimates of quantities $\alpha_i - \alpha_j$ and $\beta_k - \beta_l$, where α, β are different ones of the set of symbols A, B, AB, AB^2, ABC, etc., and the i, j, k, l have values equal to 0, 1, or 2, are uncorrelated.

16.3 CONFOUNDING

We came across the notion of generalized interaction for 2^n experiments, namely, that, if effects or interactions represented by X and Y are confounded, so is XY, obtained by multiplying the symbols together, eliminating common letters (or what amounts to the same thing) equating the square of any letter to unity. This notion enabled an easy enumeration of systems of confounding.

In the 3^n system we have noted that the $3^n - 1$ degrees of freedom may be broken down into $(3^n - 1)/2$ sets of 2 degrees of freedom, to each set of which we have attached a symbol. We note also that the interaction of 2 effects consists of 2 pairs of degrees of freedom; the interaction of A and B being AB and AB^2. The rule of the generalized interaction for the 3^n system is that, if pairs of degrees of freedom corresponding to X and Y are completely confounded, then so are the pairs of degrees of freedom corresponding to XY and XY^2, where the rule of multiplication is the ordinary commutative one with the condition that the cube of any letter is to be equated to unity. The ambiguity which could apparently arise if a different order were taken is nonexistent, because the effect or interaction given by, say, the comparison of treatment combinations for which $\lambda_1 x_1 + \lambda_2 x_2 + \lambda_3 x_3 + \cdots = 0$, $= 1$, $= 2$ is the same as that given by the comparison of treatment combinations for which $2\lambda_1 x_1 + 2\lambda_2 x_2 + 2\lambda_3 x_3 + \cdots = 0$, $= 2$, $= 1$. We have adopted the rule that, in any symbol, the power of the first letter should be unity. If a multiplication results then in $A^2 BCD$, say, we replace this by $(A^2 BCD)^2 = A^4 B^2 C^2 D^2 = AB^2 C^2 D^2$. In this way we achieve a complete and unique specification of all the effects and interactions.

An example of the use of this symbolism is the following. Suppose we wish to arrange a 3^3 experiment in blocks of 3. A complete list of the 13 systems of confounding is given in Table 16.4, in each system 4 pairs of degrees of freedom being confounded. For example, if AB and AC^2 are confounded, so is

$$AB \times AC^2 = A^2BC^2 = A^4B^2C^4 = AB^2C$$

and also

$$AB \times AC^2AC^2 = A^3BC^4 = BC$$

TABLE 16.4 SYSTEMS OF CONFOUNDING FOR 3^3 EXPERIMENT IN BLOCKS OF 3

A	B	AB	AB^2	C	AC	AC^2	BC	BC^2	ABC	AB^2C	ABC^2	AB^2C^2
x	x	x	x									
x				x	x	x						
x							x		x			x
x								x		x	x	
	x			x			x	x				
	x				x				x	x		
	x					x					x	x
		x		x					x		x	
		x			x			x				x
		x				x	x			x		
			x	x						x		x
			x		x		x				x	
			x			x		x	x			

The composition of the blocks is easily obtained from the definition of the effects and interactions. We take for illustration the case when AB, AC^2, AB^2C, and BC are confounded. There are 9 blocks given by the solutions of the equations,

$$x_1 + x_2 = i \bmod 3$$

$$x_1 + 2x_3 = j \bmod 3$$

where i, j each take on the values 0, 1, and 2. There are then 9 pairs of equations, each pair giving 1 block. The block containing the control $(a_0b_0c_0)$ is that for which the equations,

$$x_1 + x_2 = 0 \bmod 3$$

and

$$x_1 + 2x_3 = 0 \bmod 3$$

are satisfied, because these equations are obviously satisfied when $x_1 = x_2 = x_3 = 0$. The set of treatment combinations satisfying these equations is the intrablock subgroup. When $x_1 = 1$, x_2 must equal 2, because $1 + 2 = 3 = 0 \bmod 3$, and x_3 must equal 1, because $1 + 2 \times 1 = 3 = 0 \bmod 3$. One of the other treatment combinations in the block is therefore $a_1b_2c_1$. When $x_1 = 2$, x_2 must equal $1 (2 + 1 = 3 = 0 \bmod 3)$, and x_3 must equal $2 (2 + 2 \times 2 = 6 = 0 \bmod 3)$. The third treatment combination is then $a_2b_1c_2$ so that the block containing the control consists of the 3 combinations, $a_0b_0c_0$, $a_1b_2c_1$, and $a_2b_1c_2$.

Another block is given by the equations,

$$x_1 + x_2 = 0 \bmod 3$$

$$x_1 + 2x_3 = 1 \bmod 3$$

and we may get this block by adding (modulo 3) 2 to the level of x_3 in the control block, because, if $x_1 + 2x_3 = 0 \bmod 3$, then $x_1 + 2(x_3 + 2) = 1 \bmod 3$. In a similar way, we generate the 9 blocks, where we represent the treatment combinations by the subscripts only:

I	II	III	IV	V	VI	VII	VIII	IX
000	002	001	010	012	011	020	022	021
121	120	122	101	100	102	111	110	112
212	211	210	222	221	220	202	201	200

16.4 USEFUL SYSTEMS OF CONFOUNDING FOR 3^n EXPERIMENTS

We now proceed to list the more useful designs utilizing confounding involving factors at 3 levels.

16.4.1 2 Factors

We can confound any pair of effect or interaction degrees of freedom. If we were equally interested in main effects and interactions, we would use a basic pattern of 4 replicates with the following confounding:

I	A	Blocks—00, 01, 02; 10, 11, 12; 20, 21, 22
II	B	Blocks—00, 10, 20; 01, 11, 21; 02, 12, 22
III	AB	Blocks—00, 12, 21; 01, 10, 22; 02, 11, 20
IV	AB^2	Blocks—00, 11, 22; 02, 10, 21; 01, 12, 20

With r repetitions of this basic pattern, that is, $4r$ replicates in all, we would have the partition of the degrees of freedom shown in Table 16.5, the sums of squares being obtained in the usual way.

TABLE 16.5

	df
Replicates	$4r - 1$
Blocks within replicates	$8r$
A	2
B	2
AB	2
AB^2	2
Error	$24r - 8$
	$36r - 1$

The error sum of squares will be made up of the following:

A by replicates of types II, III, and IV with $2(3r - 1)$ df.

B by replicates of types I, III, and IV with $2(3r - 1)$ df.

AB by replicates of types I, II, and IV with $2(3r - 1)$ df.

AB^2 by replicates of types I, II, and III with $2(3r - 1)$ df.

We are always interested in the magnitude of the effects and interactions, or of particular treatment contrasts, and it is found that these are expressible in terms of differences of the type

$$\lambda X_0 + \mu X_1 + \nu X_2$$

where $\lambda + \mu + \nu = 0$, and X is one of the effect or interaction symbols. The variance of any such quantity will be $(\lambda^2 + \mu^2 + \nu^2|) \times$ (variance of the mean of the plots which fall into any one group defined by a linear relation of the form $\Sigma \alpha_i x_i = j$ mod 3). The reciprocal of the variance of the mean of such plots will therefore be used as a measure of the information on the effect or interaction. Thus, if ABC is confounded in 1 of 4 replicates, the quantity ABC_i, $i = 0, 1, 2$ is (the mean of 27 plots − mean of 81 plots). The mean of the 27 plots will have variance $\dfrac{\sigma^2}{27}$

$= \dfrac{\sigma^2}{36} \times \dfrac{1}{3/4}$, and the information is $\dfrac{27}{\sigma^2} = \dfrac{9}{\sigma^2} \times 4 \times \dfrac{3}{4}$.

The comparison of the above confounded design with a design using blocks of 9 and, hence, no confounding is given in Table 16.6, where $\sigma^2{}_3$ and $\sigma^2{}_9$ are the experimental error variance with blocks of 3 plots and blocks of 9 plots, respectively.

TABLE 16.6 INFORMATION

	Above Design	No Confounding	Relative Information Assuming $\sigma^2{}_3 = \sigma^2{}_9$
A B AB AB^2	$\dfrac{9r}{\sigma^2{}_3}$	$\dfrac{12r}{\sigma^2{}_9}$	$\dfrac{3}{4}$

Now suppose we wished to obtain the maximum information possible on main effects. We would then use a basic pattern of 2 replicates: namely, types III and IV. The analysis of variance for such an experiment presents no difficulties, and the relative information on main effects will be unity and on each of the interactions $\frac{1}{2}$. This results in information on A and B of $12r/\sigma^2{}_3$ units, and on AB and AB^2 of $6r/\sigma^2{}_3$ units.

16.4.2 3 Factors

1. Blocks of 9 Plots. With blocks of 9 plots the most useful experiment consists of one or more repetitions of a basic pattern of 4 replicates confounding ABC, ABC^2, AB^2C, and AB^2C^2, respectively. This will result in full information on all main effects and 2-factor interactions with $\frac{3}{4}$ information on the 3-factor interaction. If the experiment is to use 2 replicates, any 2 of the 4 pairs of interaction degrees of freedom may be chosen for confounding. The blocks for each of the 4 confoundings are given in Table 16.7, the level of c being in the body of the table, each column giving a block and each set of 3 columns a replicate.

TABLE 16.7 DESIGNS FOR 3^3 EXPERIMENT IN BLOCKS OF 9 CONFOUNDED DEGREES OF FREEDOM

Level of a	b	ABC			ABC^2			AB^2C			AB^2C^2		
0	0	0	1	2	0	2	1	0	1	2	0	2	1
1	0	2	0	1	1	0	2	2	0	1	1	0	2
2	0	1	2	0	2	1	0	1	2	0	2	1	0
0	1	2	0	1	1	0	2	1	2	0	2	1	0
1	1	1	2	0	2	1	0	0	1	2	0	2	1
2	1	0	1	2	0	2	1	2	0	1	1	0	2
0	2	1	2	0	2	1	0	2	0	1	1	0	2
1	2	0	1	2	0	2	1	1	2	0	2	1	0
2	2	2	0	1	1	0	2	0	1	2	0	2	1

The effect of changing the order of the letters in the definitions is easily found. One reason for preferring the notation we use over that of Yates [2] is this, the other being the ease of representation of all facets of the situation. Thus:

$$ABC = BCA = CAB$$

$$ABC^2 = BC^2A = CA^2B^2 = CB^2A^2$$

$$AB^2C = BA^2C^2 = BC^2A^2 = CAB^2 = CB^2A$$

The definition of these interactions by the equations in the treatment combinations suggests the appropriate computational procedure. For example, the treatment combinations for which $x_1 + x_2 + x_3 = 0 \mod 3$ are those for which

$$x_1 + x_2 = 0, \qquad x_3 = 0$$

or

$$x_1 + x_2 = 1, \qquad x_3 = 2$$

or

$$x_1 + x_2 = 2, \qquad x_3 = 1$$

In order to obtain the 3-factor interactions, we therefore obtain the two 2-factor interaction contrasts at each level of the third factor and then form the interaction of these with the third factor. Numerical examples will be given later.

In the same way that we evaluate the relative information on effects and interactions which a confounded design gives, we may obtain the information given by the confounded design relative to that of the unconfounded design on any treatment comparison. As an example we take the comparison $(a_0b_0c_0 - a_0b_0c_1)$. Now the estimated yield in terms of estimated effects and interactions of the combination $a_0b_0c_0$ is

$$a_0b_0c_0 = \text{mean} + A_0 + B_0 + AB_0 + AB^2_0 + C_0 + AC_0 + AC^2_0$$
$$+ BC_0 + BC^2_0 + ABC_0 + ABC^2_0 + AB^2C_0 + AB^2C^2_0$$

and of $a_0b_0c_1$ is

$$a_0b_0c_1 = \text{mean} + A_0 + B_0 + AB_0 + AB^2_0 + C_1 + AC_1 + AC^2_2$$
$$+ BC_1 + BC^2_2 + ABC_1 + ABC^2_2 + AB^2C_1 + AB^2C^2_2$$

so that the estimate of $(a_0b_0c_0 - a_0b_0c_1)$ is

$$(a_0b_0c_0 - a_0b_0c_1) = (C_0 - C_1) + (AC_0 - AC_1) + (AC^2_0 - AC^2_2)$$
$$+ (BC_0 - BC_1) + (BC^2_0 - BC^2_2) + (ABC_0 - ABC_1)$$
$$+ (ABC^2_0 - ABC^2_2) + (AB^2C_0 - AB^2C_1) + (AB^2C^2_0 - AB^2C^2_2)$$

Each quantity in parentheses is estimated independently of the others, with a variance depending on the system of confounding used. If a multiple r of 2 replicates were used, confounding ABC in r replicates and ABC^2 in r replicates, the relative information and variance for each effect and interaction would be as given in Table 16.8.

TABLE 16.8

	Relative Information	Variance
Main effects 2-factor interactions AB^2C, AB^2C^2	1	$\sigma^2/18r$
ABC, ABC^2	½	$\sigma^2/9r$

The variance of $(C_0 - C_1)$ is then $2\sigma^2/18r$ and so on, so that the variance of $(a_0b_0c_0 - a_0b_0c_1)$ is

$$\frac{2\sigma^2}{18r}(7 + 2 \times 2) = \frac{11}{9}\left(\frac{\sigma^2}{r}\right)$$

With no confounding and the same error variance, the variance of the comparison would have been σ^2/r, so that the relative information on this comparison is $\frac{9}{11}$.

2. Blocks of 3 Plots. The number of different systems of confounding in blocks of 3 plots is $13 \cdot 12/4 \cdot 3 = 13$. The complete list of these was given in Table 16.4. Suitable confounding for a 3^3 experiment in blocks of 3 would be the following:

$$
\begin{array}{ll}
\text{I} & AB,\ AC,\ BC^2,\ AB^2C^2 \\
\text{II} & AB^2,\ AC,\ BC,\ ABC^2 \\
\text{III} & AB,\ AC^2,\ BC,\ AB^2C \\
\text{IV} & AB^2,\ AC^2,\ BC^2,\ ABC
\end{array}
$$

With r repetitions of these 4 replicates, the partition of the degrees of freedom in the analysis of variance would be as shown in Table 16.9.

TABLE 16.9

Source	df
Replicates	$4r - 1$
Blocks within replicates	$32r$
A, B, C $\quad$ $AB, AB^2, AC, AC^2, BC, BC^2$ $\quad$ $ABC, AB^2C, ABC^2, AB^2C^2$	26
Error	$72r - 26$
Total	$108r - 1$

The relative information and variances are as given in Table 16.10.

TABLE 16.10

	Relative Information	Variance with Blocks of 27	Variance with Above Design
Main effects	1		$\sigma^2_3/36r$
2-factor interactions	½	$\sigma^2_{27}/36r$	$\sigma^2_3/18r$
3-factor interactions	¾		$\sigma^2_3/27r$

In many cases it may be anticipated that the gain in information resulting from lower variance with blocks of 3 plots relative to blocks of 27 plots would outweigh the loss in relative information resulting from the confounding. It should be noted that, in all the cases discussed in this and the previous two chapters, we have not considered the utilization of the information on effects and/or interactions given by block comparisons. This problem will be discussed in a later chapter on quasifactorial designs. For most of the designs we have discussed, the information contained in block comparisons will be rather trivial.

16.4.3   4 Factors

1. Blocks of 27 Plots. In general, the experimenter will wish to avoid blocks of size as large as 27, though, in some fields of experimentation and with some types of experimental material, the effect on error variance of reducing block size from 27 to 9 may be so small as not to offset any loss in relative information which will result from confounding. With 4 factors each at 3 levels in blocks of 27 plots, any of the 8 pairs of degrees of freedom of the 4-factor interactions may be confounded. These are as given earlier represented by the symbols $ABCD$, $ABCD^2$, ABC^2D, ABC^2D^2, AB^2CD, AB^2CD^2, AB^2C^2D, and $AB^2C^2D^2$. The actual design may be simply constructed by reference to the linear equations which define the interactions. Thus, if we confound AB^2CD^2, the intrablock subgroup will consist of the treatment combinations $a_{x_1}b_{x_2}c_{x_3}d_{x_4}$, where x_1, x_2, x_3, x_4 satisfy the equation

$$x_1 + 2x_2 + x_3 + 2x_4 = 0 \bmod 3$$

The other 2 blocks are obtained by substituting 1 and 2, respectively, on the right-hand side of the equation. The solution of these equations is simple, but it is perhaps worth while to give an example. Taking the above equation then, we know that a solution exists for every value of x_1, x_2, and x_3, and so we choose particular values for these and solve the equation for x_4. When, for example, $x_1 = 0$, $x_2 = 0$, $x_3 = 0$, we have

$$0 + 2 \times 0 + 0 + 2x_4 = 0 \bmod 3$$

and so $x_4 = 0$. When

$$x_1 = 1, \qquad x_2 = 2, \qquad x_3 = 2$$

we have

$$1 + 4 + 2 + 2x_4 = 0 \bmod 3$$

i.e.,

$$7 + 2x_4 = 0 \bmod 3$$

i.e.,

$$1 + 2x_4 = 0 \bmod 3$$

i.e.,

$$x_4 = 1 \quad \text{because} \quad 1 + 2 = 3 = 0 \bmod 3$$

and so on.

2. Blocks of 9 Plots. The 130 systems of confounding are of the following types:

$$A, \qquad B, \qquad AB, \qquad AB^2$$

$$A, \qquad BC, \qquad ABC, \qquad AB^2C^2$$

$$A, \qquad BCD, \quad ABCD, \; AB^2C^2D^2$$

$$AB, \quad AC, \qquad BC^2, \qquad AB^2C^2$$

$$AB, \quad CD, \quad ABCD, \; ABC^2D^2$$

$$AB, \quad ACD, \; BC^2D^2, \; AB^2C^2D^2$$

$$ABD, \; ACD^2, \; AB^2C^2, \; BC^2D^2$$

The most useful type of confounding is obviously the last one and is the basis of the design given by Yates.[2] There are in all 8 such systems of the type

$$AB^iC^j, \; AC^{3-j}D^k, \text{ etc., etc.}$$

because i, j, k may each take the values 1 or 2. We give as an example the design in which ABD, ACD^2, AB^2C^2, and BC^2D^2 are confounded (Table 16.11). The others are obtained by simple operations on the superscripts.

TABLE 16.11 3^4 BLOCKS OF 9: CONFOUNDING ABD, ACD^2, AB^2C^2, AND BC^2D^2

I	II	III	IV	V	VI	VII	VIII	IX
0000	1000	0100	0010	0001	2000	0200	0020	0002
1101	2101	1201	1111	1102	0101	1001	1121	1100
2202	0202	2002	2212	2200	1202	2102	2222	2201
0122	1122	0222	0102	0120	2122	0022	0112	0121
0211	1211	0011	0221	0212	2211	0111	0201	0210
1012	2012	1112	1022	1010	0012	1212	1002	1011
1220	2220	1020	1200	1221	0220	1120	1210	1222
2110	0110	2210	2120	2111	1110	2010	2100	2112
2021	0021	2121	2001	2022	1021	2221	2011	2020

3. Blocks of 3 Plots. It would be somewhat tedious (though quite straightforward) to enumerate all the possible types of confounding for this case. It is impossible to avoid confounding a main effect, so that we might use the following set of 4 replicates confounding

I	A, BC, BD	and their interactions
II	B, AC, AD^2	and their interactions
III	C, AB, AD^2	and their interactions
IV	D, AB^2, AC^2	and their interactions

The complete set of effects and interactions confounded in I is as follows:

$$A, BC, ABC, AB^2C^2, BD, ABD, AB^2D^2$$

$$CD^2, BC^2D^2, AB^2CD, ACD^2, AC^2D, \text{ and } ABC^2D^2$$

This design will result in ¾ information on main effects and ¾ information on all the 2-factor interaction pairs of degrees of freedom.

16.4.4 5 Factors

For most purposes 243 plots in a block is entirely too many, so that it is of little value to consider unconfounded designs. Blocks of 81 plots are subject to the same objection, and we would not often use blocks of 27. In the latter case it may be shown that it is not possible to find a design confounding only 4- and 5-factor interactions. If a 5-factor interaction is confounded, at least two 3-factor interactions will be confounded, if no 1- or 2-factor interaction is to be confounded. It is possible, however, to confound one 3-factor interaction and three 4-factor interactions. An example of this is the design confounding ABC, AB^2DE, $AC^2D^2E^2$, and BC^2DE.

Likely, the most useful confounded 3^5 designs are those confounding in blocks of 9. These have the disadvantage that it is not possible to avoid confounding a main effect or 2-factor interaction. Designs could be based on the confounding of ACE^2, AD^2E, AB^2CE, ABD^2E^2, $BCDE^2$, ABC^2DE, AC^2D, CDE, ABC, BE, BC^2D^2, $AB^2C^2DE^2$, AB^2D^2, and permutations of this set.

16.5 AN EXAMPLE

The experiment [3] is concerned with the effect of sowing date, spacing of rows, and sulphate of ammonia on sugar beets. Blocks of 9 plots were used. Table 16.12 shows the plan and percent sugar, the third and sixth columns give coded values obtained by the equation $x =$

$100(y - 16)$, where y is the percent sugar. Treatments are as follows:

Sowing Dates	d	Spacing	s	Sulphate of Ammonia	n
March 15	0	10-inch	0	None	0
April 18	1	15-inch	1	0.3 cwt N	1
May 16	2	20-inch	2	0.6 cwt N	2

This example is described solely to present the computational procedure.

TABLE 16.12   PLAN AND PERCENT SUGAR

Treatment dsn	% Sugar	Code	Treatment dsn	% Sugar	Code
012	16.70	70	121	16.79	79
202	16.50	50	100	16.88	88
001	17.00	100	112	16.39	39
210	17.05	105	002	16.18	18
020	16.50	50	210	16.88	88
122	16.79	79	011	16.53	53
111	17.05	105	020	16.21	21
100	16.85	85	222	16.39	39
221	16.36	36	201	16.39	39
201	16.53	53	211	16.43	43
000	16.79	79	202	16.42	42
011	17.05	105	122	16.30	30
022	15.98	−2	012	16.10	10
102	16.79	79	220	17.08	108
220	16.56	56	021	16.36	36
212	16.59	59	000	16.47	47
110	16.62	62	101	16.33	33
121	16.44	44	110	16.44	44
222	16.21	21	102	16.44	44
200	16.59	59	212	16.42	42
101	16.47	47	200	16.27	27
211	16.96	96	111	16.04	4
010	16.30	30	022	16.56	56
112	16.13	13	010	16.33	33
120	16.65	65	120	17.05	105
002	16.85	85	221	16.68	68
021	16.70	70	001	16.27	27

Note that the interaction DS^2N is confounded in the left-hand replicate, and that DS^2N^2 is confounded in the right-hand replicate.

In computing the analysis of variance, first separate out the data to form Table 16.13, by summing over replicates.

TABLE 16.13 SUMS OVER REPLICATES

	n_0			n_1			n_2		
	s_0	s_1	s_2	s_0	s_1	s_2	s_0	s_1	s_2
d_0	126	63	71	127	158	106	103	80	54
d_1	173	106	170	80	109	123	123	52	109
d_2	86	193	164	92	139	104	92	101	60

The next step is to obtain the total sum of squares, the sum of squares for blocks, and the sum of squares for treatments, ignoring confounding. It is convenient to tabulate block totals at this time.

Block Totals

Rep 1	Rep 2
680	464
535	393
486	406
1701	1263
2964	

Correction factor: $\text{CF} = \dfrac{(2964)^2}{54} = 162{,}690.66$

Total sum of squares:

$$(70^2 + 50^2 + \cdots + 27^2) - \text{CF} = 205{,}916 - 162{,}690.66 = 43{,}225.34$$

Block (and replicate) sum of squares:

$$\frac{(680^2 + \cdots + 406^2)}{9} - \text{CF} = 168{,}822.44 - 162{,}690.66 = 6131.79$$

Treatment sum of squares, ignoring confounding:

$$\frac{(126^2 + 173^2 + \cdots + 60^2)}{2} - \text{CF} = 181{,}368 - 162{,}690.66 = 18{,}677.34$$

Next form the 2-way tables given in Table 16.14, which are easily obtained from Table 16.13.

TABLE 16.14   2-WAY TABLES

	s_0	s_1	s_2	
d_0	356	301	231	888
d_1	376	267	402	1045
d_2	270	433	328	1031
	n_0	n_1	n_2	
d_0	260	391	237	
d_1	449	312	284	
d_2	443	335	253	
s_0	385	299	318	1002
s_1	362	406	233	1001
s_2	405	333	223	961
	1152	1038	774	

These tables are used to compute sums of squares for main effects and 2-factor interactions. For example the sums of squares for the effects and interactions D, S, DS, and DS^2 are obtained from the upper table as

$$\frac{(356^2 + 376^2 + \cdots + 328^2)}{6} - \text{CF} = 168{,}823.33 - 162{,}690.66 = 6132.67$$

The first 3 entries in Table 16.15 are computed in this way.   Sums of

TABLE 16.15   TREATMENT SUMS OF SQUARES

D, S, DS, DS^2	6,132.67
D, N, DN, DN^2	8,765.00
S, N, SN, SN^2	6,236.34
D	838.78
S	60.78
N	4,177.34
DSN^2	446.34
DSN	552.34
DS^2N^2 partially confounded	231.45
DS^2N partially confounded	1,390.11
Treatment total	18,677.35

squares for main effects are obtained from the marginal totals, as

$$D : \frac{888^2 + 1045^2 + 1031^2}{18} - \text{CF} = 163{,}529.44 - 162{,}690.66 = 838.78$$

TABLE 16.16   COMPUTATION OF 3-FACTOR INTERACTIONS

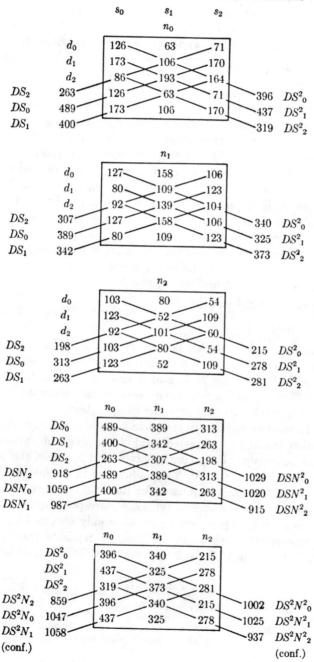

The calculation of sums of squares for the 3-factor interactions is more troublesome but proceeds in an orderly fashion. The 2-way tables of Table 16.16 are obtained from Table 16.12. Note that, in the first three of the tables, the first and second rows are written beneath the third, in order, and the diagonal terms are summed, as indicated. In this manner we obtain the sum of yields of plots for which $x_1 + 2x_2 = 0, 1, 2 \mod 3$, by summing downward toward the right, and successive tables yield this sum for $x_3 = 0, 1,$ and 2. Similarly, summing diagonally downward to the left yields sums corresponding to $x_1 + x_2 = 0, 1, 2 \mod 3$. The last two tables are formed from the above sums in a straightforward way, and the diagonal summation process is applied. The object of the process is now apparent. It was desired to obtain sums, for example, for which $x_1 + x_2 + 2x_3 = 0, 1, 2 \mod 3$. The solutions, for example, to the equation $x_1 + x_2 + 2x_3 = 1 \mod 3$ are those for which $x_1 + x_2 = 0, 2x_3 = 1 \mod 3$; $x_1 + x_2 = 1, 2x_3 = 0$; and $x_1 + x_2 = 2, 2x_3 = 2 \mod 3$.

With the results of the diagonal summation process applied to the last two tables, now compute sums of squares for the 3-factor interactions, still ignoring confounding. Thus,

$$DSN^2 : \frac{1029^2 + 1020^2 + 915^2}{18} - CF = 163{,}137 - 162{,}690.66 = 446.34$$

The sums of squares thus obtained are entered into Table 16.14. As a check on the work, compute the treatment sums of squares by subtracting the sums of square for D, S, and N from the sum of the remaining entries in Table 16.15 which have been so far computed. This, of course, must check with the previous computation.

If the interactions had been completely confounded, the preliminary computation would be completed, and the analysis of variance table could now be set up. However, in the present example, the contrasts are partially confounded. DS^2N is confounded in the first replicate, so that, to obtain the sums of squares for this interaction, we require the sums of yields from the second replicate corresponding to solution of $x_1 + 2x_2 + x_2 = i$. These sums may be readily obtained by subtraction of appropriate block totals for the first replicate from the sums obtained from the last of the 2-way tables of Table 16.16 (see Table 16.17).

TABLE 16.17

DS^2N_0	DS^2N_1	DS^2N_2	
1047	1058	859	Sum of reps 1 and 2
535	680	486	Sum of rep 1
512	378	373	

The sums of yields in the first replicate corresponding to the solution of the above equations are the block totals, for this was the way in which the confounding was accomplished. Care must be taken, however, to subtract the appropriate block totals. Our notation simplifies this, for, in the column headed by DS^2N_0, we need find the block containing solutions to $x_1 + 2x_2 + x_3 = 0$; that is, we need only pick out the block containing the control, which is seen to be the second. In the column headed by DS^2N_1, correspondingly we need only look for the block containing the treatment $d_1s_0n_0$, the upper block. The sum of squares for the interaction DS^2N is then computed in the usual way as

$$\frac{512^2 + 378^2 + 373^2}{9} - \frac{1263^2}{27} = 60,461.88 - 59,080.33 = 1381.55$$

In a similar manner, the sum of squares for DS^2N^2 is computed (Table 16.18).

TABLE 16.18

$DS^2N^2_0$	$DS^2N^2_1$	$DS^2N^2_2$
1002	1025	937
393	464	406
609	561	531

$$\frac{609^2 + 561^2 + 531^2}{9} - \frac{1701^2}{27} = 107,507 - 107,163 = 344.00$$

The analysis of variance table may now be set forth, as in Table 16.19, error sum of squares being obtained by subtraction.

TABLE 16.19 ANALYSIS OF VARIANCE

Due to		Sum of Squares	Mean Square	F
Blocks	5	6,131.78		
D	2	838.78	419.39	
S	2	60.78	30.39	
N	2	4,177.34	2,088.67	2.509
D × S	4	5,233.11	1,308.28	
D × N	4	3,748.88	937.22	
S × N	4	1,998.22	499.55	
D × S × N Unconf.	4	998.68	249.67	
Partial conf.	4	1,725.55	431.39	
Error	22	18,312.22	832.37	
Total	53	43,225.34		

16.5.1 Presentation of Results

For most purposes it is best to form the 3 × 3 tables, as in Table 16.20. These are directly computed from Table 16.14 in this case, because 3-factor interactions only are confounded. Standard errors are also included.

TABLE 16.20 PRESENTATION OF RESULTS

Mean	Spacing			Sulphate of Ammonia			Mean
	10 in.	15 in.	20 in.	None	0.3 cwt N	0.6 cwt N	
Mar. 15	16.59	16.50	16.38	16.43	16.65	16.40	16.49
Apr. 18	16.62	16.44	16.67	16.75	16.52	16.47	16.58
May 16	16.45	16.72	16.55	16.75	16.55	16.42	16.57
Means	16.56	16.56	16.53	16.64	16.58	16.43	

Spacing	Sulphate of Ammonia		
	None	0.3 cwt N	0.6 cwt N
10 in.	16.64	16.50	16.53
15 in.	16.60	16.68	16.39
20 in.	16.67	16.56	16.37

Standard error of means (means of 18 plots)   = 0.068   General mean = 16.55
Standard error of cell figures (means of 6 plots) = 0.118

One may also set out the results in a form such as Table 16.21, which is compiled on the basis of the definitions of effects and interactions.

It should be noted that, for the interactions that are confounded, the mean of plots for the replicates in which the interaction is not confounded is subtracted instead of the over-all mean.

Table 16.21 may be used to construct the estimated yield of any treatment combination or the estimate of any contrast among the treatment combinations by use of the formula given earlier.

TABLE 16.21   ESTIMATES OF EFFECTS AND INTERACTIONS

Effect or Interaction	Level			Linear	Quadratic
	0	1	2		
D	-0.056	0.032	0.024	0.079 ± 0.096	0.048 ± 0.083
S	0.008	0.007	-0.015	-0.023 ± 0.096	0.011 ± 0.083
N	0.091	0.028	-0.119	-0.210 ± 0.096	0.042 ± 0.083
DS	0.113	0.009	-0.122		
DS^2	-0.021	0.029	-0.008		
DN	-0.061	0.058	0.002		
DN^2	-0.091	0.018	0.072		
SN	-0.021	-0.058	0.078		
SN^2	0.014	0.014	-0.028		
DSN	0.039	-0.001	-0.039		
DSN^2	0.023	0.018	-0.041		
DS^2N^2	0.006	-0.143	-0.148		
DS^2N^2	0.047	-0.007	-0.041		

16.6   THE USE OF ONLY ONE REPLICATE

Frequently, it is desired to use only one replicate of a 3^3 experiment. For example, if inferences are to be drawn about effects over a certain geographical area, it may be better to use as many randomly sited locations as possible with only one replicate at each place. The best confounding would be to confound one pair of the 3-factor interaction degrees of freedom to give blocks of 9 plots. In this case the analysis of variance for each experiment could be based possibly on the assumption that interactions except linear $\times$ linear interactions between 2 factors are negligible. This gives the breakdown shown in Table 16.22.

TABLE 16.22

Source of Variation	df
Blocks	2
Main effects	6
Linear $\times$ linear interaction between two factors	3
Error (higher-order interaction)	15
	26

The computation proceeds in a straightforward fashion. There is no difficulty in obtaining the sums of squares for blocks or for the main effects. The linear $\times$ linear interactions of 2 factors may be obtained by considering the contrasts previously defined. Since the defined contrasts are orthogonal, we may compute a square for each of the 3 interactions. Thus the square for $A_L \times B_L = \frac{1}{12}[a_2 - a_0)(b_2 - b_0)(c_0 + c_1 + c_2)]^2$, in which the expression in the brackets is to be expanded algebraically and yields are to be substituted. The divisor is obtained in the usual manner; the expression to be squared is formed by (sum of yields of 6 plots − sum of yields of 6 plots), and so the divisor is 12. Squares for $A_L \times C_L$ and $B_L \times C_L$ may be similarly computed. The sum of squares for the remaining interactions may then be obtained by subtraction.

This type of experiment should, by and large, be confined to technological problems. The assumptions that must be made to obtain estimates of error are somewhat drastic and unrealistic for most situations. Of course, with prior information, one may be able to make the necessary assumptions on the smallness of some high-order interactions.

16.7 CONFOUNDING 3^n EXPERIMENTS IN LATIN SQUARES

Under some circumstances it may be desirable to impose a double restriction on the pattern of a 3^n experiment. Thus, there are arrangements for a 3^3 and 3^4 experiment in 9×9 squares such that only high-order interactions are confounded with rows and columns (Yates,[2] Cochran and Cox [4]). For the 3^3 experiment one may confound any one 3-factor interaction with rows and another with columns. For the 3^4 experiment, one may use 2 different systems of confounding that give 9 blocks of 9 plots for rows and columns: e.g., confound ABC, AC^2D, AB^2D^2, BC^2D^2 with rows and ABC^2, ACD^2, AB^2D, BCD with columns, as shown in Table 16.23.

TABLE 16.23

0000	0211	0122	1102	1110	1021	2101	2012	2220
2102	2010	2221	0011	0212	0120	1200	1111	1022
1201	1112	1020	2100	2011	2222	0002	0210	0121
0222	0100	0011	1121	1002	1210	2020	2201	2112
2021	2202	2110	0220	0101	0012	1122	1000	1211
1120	1001	1212	2022	2200	2111	0221	0102	0010
0111	0022	0200	1010	1221	1102	2212	2120	2001
2210	2121	2002	0112	0020	0201	1011	1222	1100
1012	1220	1101	2211	2122	2000	0110	0021	0202

The combinations of this table are easily obtained by termwise addition modulo 3: e.g., $(0000) + (0211) = 0211$, and $(2102) + (0211) = (2010)$.

Of a somewhat different nature are designs in 3×3 squares for 3^2 factorial systems. Thus, we may have available a number of experimental animals for 3 periods, which are the same for the animals in groups of 3. Under these circumstances, we may make up a design which has valuable properties:

Animal	Period			Animal	Period		
	1	2	3		1	2	3
1	00	01	02	4	00	11	22
2	10	11	12	5	21	02	10
3	20	21	22	6	12	20	01

Denoting the 2 factors by a and b, in the first square, we have A confounded with animals and B with period, while AB and AB^2 are unconfounded. In the second square, AB is confounded with periods, and AB^2 with animals. If, therefore, one can assume additivity, repetitions of the basic pattern of the above 2 squares give information on all effects and interactions, this information being obtained by comparisons within animals and within periods. As a field experiment, for animals we can read "rows" and for periods we can read "columns."

REFERENCES

1. FISHER, R. A. *The design of experiments.* Oliver and Boyd, Edinburgh. 4th ed., 1947.
2. YATES, F. *The design and analysis of factorial experiments.* Imp. Bur. Soil Sci., Harpenden, England. 1937.
3. Annual Report. Rothamsted Experiment Station, Harpenden, England. 1935.
4. COCHRAN, W. G., and COX, G. M. *Experimental designs.* John Wiley & Sons, New York. 1950.

CHAPTER 17

The General p^n Factorial System

17.1 THE REPRESENTATION OF EFFECTS AND INTERACTIONS

We shall use p to denote a prime number, and the following treatment is fairly easily seen to be the straightforward generalization of the case $p = 3$, and indeed also of $p = 2$. In the latter case, however, the general system is amenable to a modification which simplified the presentation. This is easily seen by noting that there are only 2 numbers modulo 2, namely, 0 and 1, and the correspondence of the attributes of even and odd to the numbers 0 and 1 is exact and simple to understand.

We can see the generalization from the 3^n system fairly easily, without introducing proofs. These proofs are based on the properties of Galois fields which will be given later. The non-mathematical reader can easily verify that the system works in particular cases. It should be noted that we specified that p is a prime number and the system is valid only for such numbers.

We represent the treatment combination by numbers $x_1 x_2 \cdots x_n$, x_i being the level of the ith factor in the particular combination. The number x_i will take on values from 0 to $(p - 1)$. All the numbers we deal with are reduced modulo p; i.e., if we obtain by calculation a number greater than $(p - 1)$ we replace it by the remainder after division by p. The $p^n - 1$ degrees of freedom between the p^n treatment combinations may be partitioned into $\left(\dfrac{p^n - 1}{p - 1}\right)$ sets of $(p - 1)$ degrees of freedom, each set of $(p - 1)$ degrees of freedom being given by the contrasts among the p sets of p^{n-1} treatment combinations specified by the following p equations:

$$\left.\begin{aligned}
\alpha_1 x_1 + \alpha_1 x_2 + \cdots + \alpha_n x_n &= 0 \\
\alpha_1 x_1 + \alpha_2 x_2 + \cdots + \alpha_n x_n &= 1 \\
\cdots\cdots\cdots\cdots\cdots\cdots\cdots\cdots \\
\alpha_1 x_1 + \alpha_2 x_2 + \cdots + \alpha_n x_n &= (p - 1)
\end{aligned}\right\} \bmod p \qquad (1)$$

318

The coefficients of these equations, the α_i's, must be positive whole numbers between 0 and $(p - 1)$, not all equal to zero, and, for uniqueness of enumeration, we restrict the coefficient of the first x_i that is not zero to be equal to unity.   The sets given by the equations $\lambda(\Sigma\alpha_i x_i) = j$ mod p where j takes on necessarily the values, 0, 1, $\cdots$, $(p - 1)$, and λ is any whole number from 1 to $(p - 1)$ will be the same sets, in different order, as those given by

$$\Sigma\alpha_i x_i = k \bmod p \tag{2}$$

for there is a unique solution k to the equation

$$\lambda k = j \bmod p \tag{3}$$

and it is one of the numbers 0 to $(p - 1)$.   Without the restriction we can choose each α_i in p ways, giving p^n possible linear functions $\Sigma\alpha_i x_i$, and, excluding the case when all the α_i's are zero, and dividing by $(p - 1)$, the possible number of values of λ, we find that the number of sets of $(p - 1)$ degrees of freedom is $(p^n - 1)/(p - 1)$.   Two sets of $(p - 1)$ degrees of freedom resulting from equations with left-hand sides $\Sigma\alpha_i x_i$ and $\Sigma\beta_i x_i$ will be orthogonal unless $\beta_i = k\alpha_i$ for each i.   For the two equations,

$$\left.\begin{array}{l}\Sigma\alpha_i x_i = k \\ \Sigma\beta_i x_i = l\end{array}\right\} \bmod p \tag{4}$$

will be satisfied by p^{n-2} treatment combinations, if β_i is not equal to a constant multiplier of α_i.   The sense in which these 2 sets of $(p - 1)$ degrees of freedom are orthogonal is that any comparison with, of course, 1 degree of freedom, from the 1 set will be orthogonal to any comparison from the other set.   This may be examined by classifying the treatment combinations according to the scheme shown in Table 17.1.

Let n_{kl} be the number of treatment combinations in the (k, l) cell, and let the yield of each treatment combination be determined with independent errors subject to the same variance.   If we let X_0, X_1, $\cdots$, X_{p-1} be the total yields of treatment combinations for which $\Sigma\alpha_i x_i = 0$, 1, 2, $\cdots$, $p - 1$ and, correspondingly, for Y_0, Y_1, Y_2, $\cdots$, Y_{p-1}, 2 comparisons of the type in question may be represented by

$$\Sigma a_i X_i \quad \text{with} \quad \Sigma a_i = 0$$

and

$$\Sigma b_i Y_i \quad \text{with} \quad \Sigma b_i = 0$$

TABLE 17.1

$$\Sigma \alpha_i x_i = k$$

$\Sigma \beta_i x_i = l$	l	k				
		0	1	2	$(p-1)$	
	0					Y_0
	1					Y_1
	2					Y_2
	$p-1$					Y_{p-1}
		X_0	X_1	X_2	X_{p-1}	

The condition for orthogonality is then

$$\sum_{ij} a_i b_j n_{ij} = 0 \qquad (5)$$

and, because n_{ij} is constant (equal to p^{n-2}), the condition is satisfied.

Corresponding to the equations whose left-hand side is

$$\alpha_1 x_1 + \alpha_2 x_2 + \cdots + \alpha_n x_n$$

we use the symbol $A^{\alpha_1} B^{\alpha_2} C^{\alpha_3} \cdots$ to denote the set of $(p-1)$ degrees of freedom restricting the power of the first letter occurring to unity. In this way, we may enumerate, for example, the $31 \left(= \dfrac{5^3 - 1}{5 - 1} \right)$ sets of $4 [= (p-1)]$ degrees of freedom for the 5^3 system with factors a, b, c. They are:

Main effects:

$$A, B, C,$$

2-factor interactions:

Of a and b: AB, AB^2, AB^3, AB^4

Of a and c: AC, AC^2, AC^3, AC^4

Of b and c: BC, BC^2, BC^3, BC^4

3-factor interactions:

$$ABC,\ ABC^2,\ ABC^3,\ ABC^4$$

$$AB^2C,\ AB^2C^2,\ AB^2C^3,\ AB^2C^4$$

$$AB^3C,\ AB^3C^2,\ AB^3C^3,\ AB^3C^4$$

$$AB^4C,\ AB^4C^2,\ AB^4C^3,\ AB^4C^4.$$

17.2 CONFOUNDING WITH THE p^n SYSTEM

A system of notation such as the above is necessary in order to represent all the degrees of freedom in an orderly way and to make possible an enumeration and choice of systems of confounding. The only divisors of p^n are powers less than n of p, so that we can have equal-sized blocks of any size p^s, where s is less than n. The desirability of using equal-sized blocks, although intuitively fairly obvious, may be explained in terms of error variance, because the error variance will generally be a function of the size of block in a particular experimental situation, and, since homogeneity of error is the basis of the analysis on which we rely for the most part, it is desirable to have blocks of equal size. If we knew exactly the relation between the errors with various sizes of blocks, we could, conceptually at least, cope with the analysis of an experiment with unequal-sized blocks.

In order to devise systems of confounding in blocks of p^s, we need a rule of the generalized interaction corresponding to the rules in the case of $p = 2$ and $p = 3$ which have already been given. The general rule of generalized interactions may be stated as follows: If effects or interactions denoted by X, Y are completely confounded with blocks, then so are the $(p - 1)$ sets of $(p - 1)$ degrees of freedom denoted by XY, XY^2, $\cdots$, XY^{p-1} where these symbols are to be written in terms of the letters ABC, etc., the pth power of any letter is to be replaced by unity, and the resultant symbol is to be raised to such power as makes the first letter in it have a power of unity. This may be proved as follows: Let X correspond to the equations,

$$\alpha_1 x_1 + \alpha_2 x_2 + \cdots + \alpha_n x_n = 0,\ = 1,\ \cdots\ = (p - 1)\ \text{mod}\ p \qquad (6)$$

and Y to the equations,

$$\beta_1 x_1 + \beta_2 x_2 + \cdots + \beta_n x_n = 0,\ = 1,\ \cdots\ = (p - 1)\ \text{mod}\ p \qquad (7)$$

Because X and Y are confounded completely with blocks, the plots of any one block all satisfy the equations,

$$\alpha_1 x_1 + \alpha_2 x_2 + \cdots + \alpha_n x_n = i \bmod p$$

and   (8)

$$\beta_1 x_1 + \beta_2 x_2 + \cdots + \beta_n x_n = j \bmod p$$

where i, j are each one of the numbers 0 to $(p - 1)$. For these plots, the equations may be combined to give

$$(\alpha_1 + \lambda\beta_1)x_1 + (\alpha_2 + \lambda\beta_2)x_2 + \cdots + (\alpha_n + \lambda\beta_n)x_n = i + \lambda j \bmod p \quad (9)$$

where λ can take on any value from 1 to $(p - 1)$. The coefficients on the left- and right-hand sides must be reduced modulo p, and they then correspond to the symbol XY^λ given above. Thus, the plots of any block take on a constant value for any one of the equations corresponding to XY^λ, where λ is any value from 1 to $(p - 1)$. The effect or interaction XY^λ is therefore confounded with blocks for these values of λ.

The enumeration of systems of confounding is thus rendered very simple. The total number of systems of confounding for a p^n experiment in blocks of p^s is equal to

$$\frac{(p^n - 1)(p^n - p) \cdots (p^n - p^{n-s-1})}{(p^{n-s} - 1)(p^{n-s} - p) \cdots (p^{n-s} - p^{n-s-1})} \quad (10)$$

as may be verified by noting that the confounded effects and interactions are generated from a suitable choice of $(n - s)$ effects and interactions. These $(n - s)$ effects must be independent, in the sense that no one of them results from taking the generalized interaction of any of the others. The first may be chosen in $\left(\dfrac{p^n - 1}{p - 1}\right)$ ways: the second in $\left(\dfrac{p^n - p}{p - 1}\right)$ ways, and so on, giving $\left(\dfrac{p^n - 1}{p - 1}\right)\left(\dfrac{p^n - p}{p - 1}\right) \cdots \left(\dfrac{p^n - p^{n-s-1}}{p - 1}\right)$ as the total number of systems of confounding generated in this way. Any one system will, however, have been enumerated in $\left(\dfrac{p^{n-s} - 1}{p - 1}\right) \times \left(\dfrac{p^{n-s} - p}{p - 1}\right) \cdots \left(\dfrac{p^{n-s} - p^{n-s-1}}{p - 1}\right)$ different ways, so that the number of distinct systems is stated.

We now give two examples. First, we consider the arrangement of a factorial experiment on 2 factors each with 5 levels in blocks of 5 plots. The number of systems of confounding is equal to

$$\frac{(5^2 - 1)}{(5 - 1)} = 6$$

and they are the confounding of A, B, AB, AB^2, AB^3, and AB^4, respectively. The division of the 16 degrees of freedom for the interaction of a and b into 4 sets of 4 degrees of freedom is entirely a formal one and, in some senses, purely a mathematical device. If the experimenter is at all interested in estimating or testing for interaction, information must be obtained on all components. A suitable experiment might then consist of 4 replicates, confounding each of AB, AB^2, AB^3, and AB^4 in one of the 4 replicates. This design would give full information on main effects and $\frac{3}{4}$ relative information on the interaction. Alternatively, if the experimenter were equally interested in main effects and 2-factor interactions and could afford the necessary resources, 6 replicates could be used confounding each of A, B, AB, AB^2, AB^3, and AB^4 in 1 replicate.

Second, we consider the confounding for 3 factors each at 5 levels into blocks of 5 plots. The number of systems is

$$\frac{(5^3 - 1)(5^3 - 5)}{(5^2 - 1)(5^2 - 5)} = \frac{124.120}{24.20} = 31$$

The systems of confounding are of the following types, the number of distinct systems of each type being given in [ ]:

I : A, B, AB, AB^2, AB^3, AB^4 [3]

II : A, BC^i, with products ($i = 1, 2, 3, 4$)   [3 × 4]

III : AB^i, BC^j with products ($i = 1, 2, 3, 4; j = 1, 2, 3, 4$)   [16]

e.g.:

$$A,\ BC^2,\ ABC^2,\ AB^2C^4,\ AB^3C,\ AB^4C^3$$

It is easy to see that we have a complete enumeration. The systems of type A, AB^iC^j with products are contained in type II; e.g., A, AB^2C^3, give as products:

$$AAB^2C^3 = A^2B^2C^3 = (A^2B^2C^3)^3 = ABC^4$$

$$A^2AB^2C^3 = A^3B^2C^3 = (A^3B^2C^3)^2 = AB^4C$$

$$A^3AB^2C^3 = A^4B^2C^3 = (A^4B^2C^3)^4 = AB^3C^2$$

$$A^4AB^2C^3 = A^5B^2C^3 = B^2C^3 = (B^2C^3)^3 = BC^4$$

Note that we equate a symbol in which the power of the first letter is not unity to the power of itself which reduces the power of the first letter modulo 5 to unity.

If we wished to obtain the maximum possible accuracy on main effects, and were prepared to lose information to some extent on 2-factor interactions, we could use 2 replicates with the following systems of confounding:

First replicate, confound AB^2, BC^3, AB^3C^3, AB^4C, AC^4, ABC^2

Second replicate, confound AB, BC^2, AB^2C^2, AB^3C^4, AB^4C, AC^3

This experimental design would give:

Full information on main effects.

Half information on AB, AB^2, AC^3, AC^4, BC^2, BC^3.

Full information on all other 2-factor interaction components.

Zero information on AB^4C.

Half information on AB^2C^2, AB^3C^3, ABC^2, AB^3C^4.

Full information on all other 3-factor interaction components.

The composition of the blocks in this design is left as an exercise to the reader.

The constituents of each block may be obtained by the use of the intrablock subgroup. Consider the block for which the following two equations are satisfied:

$$\sum_{1}^{n} \alpha_i x_i = 0 \bmod p$$

$$\sum_{1}^{n} \beta_i x_i = 0 \bmod p \tag{11}$$

The treatment combination $(0, 0, 0, \cdots, 0)$ satisfies these equations. If $(y_1, \cdots, y_n)$ and $(z_1, z_2, \cdots, z_n)$ satisfy the equations, then so do the treatment combinations,

$$(\lambda y_1 + \mu z_1, \lambda y_2 + \mu z_2, \cdots, \lambda y_n + \mu z_n) \tag{12}$$

where λ and μ may each independently take any value from 1 to $(p - 1)$, and each term $(\lambda y_i + \mu z_i)$ is reduced modulo p. The treatment combinations which are in this block therefore form a group, if $(0, 0, 0, 0, \cdots, 0)$ is regarded as the unit element and the law of combination is addition of coordinates with reduction modulo p. If the treatment combination $(x_1, x_2, \cdots, x_n)$ is written as $a^{x_1}b^{x_2} \cdots$, the rule of combination is then multiplication with the proviso that the pth power of any letter is to be replaced by unity. The elements of this block are known as the intrablock subgroup. If $(x_1, \cdots, x_n)$ is an element of the intrablock subgroup and $(y_1, \cdots, y_n)$ lies in the block given by the equations,

$$\Sigma \alpha_i x_i = k \bmod p$$

$$\Sigma \beta_i x_i = l \bmod p$$

etc.

then the treatment combination $(x_1 + y_1, \cdots, x_n + y_n)$ lies in this block, for its coordinates satisfy the same equations as $(y_1, \cdots, y_n)$, and so the other blocks may be generated by addition.

We may give as an example of confounding the use of blocks of 9 plots for the 3^4 system. Suppose the confounded interactions are ABC, AB^2D, AC^2D^2, and BC^2D. The intrablock subgroup consists of treatment combinations satisfying

$$x_1 + x_2 + x_3 = 0 \bmod 3$$

$$x_1 + 2x_2 + x_4 = 0 \bmod 3$$

i.e., the treatment combinations:

0000	1110
0121	1201
0212	2011
1022	2102
	2220

We may note that this group is generated by 0121 and 1022. For calling these x and y, we have in order 0000, x, $2x$, y, $x + y$, $2x + y$, $2y$, $x + 2y$, $2x + 2y$. The whole set of 9 blocks is then as shown in Table 17.2.

TABLE 17.2

I	II	III	IV	V	VI	VII	VIII	IX
0000	1000	2000	0100	0200	0010	0020	0001	0002
0121	1121	2121	0221	0021	0101	0111	0122	0120
0212	1212	2212	0012	0112	0222	0202	0210	0211
1022	2022	0022	1122	1222	1002	1012	1020	1021
1110	2110	0110	1210	1010	1120	1100	1111	1112
1201	2201	0201	1001	1101	1211	1221	1202	1200
2011	0011	1011	2101	2211	2021	2001	2012	2010
2102	0102	1102	2202	2002	2112	2122	2100	2101
2220	0220	1220	2020	2120	2200	2210	2221	2222

17.3   YIELDS OF TREATMENT COMBINATIONS IN TERMS OF EFFECTS AND INTERACTIONS

It is convenient to define the main effect of factor a at level i as the mean yield of treatment combinations for which $x_1 = i$ minus the mean yield of all treatment combinations, μ, say, and to denote this effect by the symbol A_i. In the same way we denote by $A^{\alpha_1}B^{\alpha_2}C^{\alpha_3}\cdots_r$, the mean yield of the p^{n-1} treatment combinations for which $\sum_1^n \alpha_i x_i = r$ mod p minus μ.

In all, we shall have $\left(\dfrac{p^n - 1}{p - 1}\right)$ symbols $A^{\alpha_1}B^{\alpha_2}C^{\alpha_3}\cdots$, and we consider the quantity

$$\Sigma A^{\alpha_1}B^{\alpha_2}C^{\alpha_3}\cdots_{\alpha_1 i + \alpha_2 j + \alpha_3 k + \cdots} \tag{13}$$

where summation takes place over the $\left(\dfrac{p^n - 1}{p - 1}\right)$ possible choices of $(\alpha_1, \alpha_2, \cdots)$ and $i, j, k, \cdots$ are fixed and the suffix $\alpha_1 i + \alpha_2 j + \alpha_3 k + \cdots$ is reduced modulo p. The sum will contain

$$-\left(\frac{p^n - 1}{p - 1}\right)\mu$$

and we proceed to collect the other terms. The treatment combination $(i, j, k, \cdots)$ occurs in each symbol with a divisor p^{n-1}, because we consider the mean of the combinations satisfying an equation, so that the sum contains

$$\frac{1}{p^{n-1}}\left(\frac{p^n - 1}{p - 1}\right)t_{ijk}\cdots$$

where $t_{ijk}\cdots$ is the yield of the combination $(i, j, k, \cdots)$. Now consider any other treatment combination $(i', j', k', \cdots)$. If it occurs in the symbol $A^{\alpha_1}B^{\alpha_2}\cdots_{\alpha_1 i + \alpha_2 j + \cdots}$, then,

$$\alpha_1 i + \alpha_2 j + \cdots = \alpha_1 i' + \alpha_2 j' + \cdots \bmod p$$

or

$$\alpha_1(i - i') + \alpha_2(j - j') + \cdots = 0 \bmod p$$

If we regard this as an equation in $(\alpha_1, \alpha_2, \cdots)$, there are p^{n-1} solutions and $(p^{n-1} - 1)$ solutions apart from $(0, 0, 0, \cdots, 0)$. There are

$\left(\dfrac{p^{n-1} - 1}{p - 1}\right)$ distinct solutions, because, if $(\alpha_1, \cdots, \alpha_n)$ is a solution, $(k\alpha_1, \cdots, k\alpha_n)$ is the same solution, where $k = 2, 3, \cdots, (p - 1)$. The sum consists then of

$$\frac{1}{p^{n-1}}\left(\frac{p^n - 1}{p - 1}\right) t_{ijk\cdots} + \frac{(p^{n-1} - 1)}{p^{n-1}(p - 1)} \text{ (all other } t_{ijk\cdots}) - \left(\frac{p^n - 1}{p - 1}\right)\mu$$

and this equals

$$\frac{1}{p^{n-1}}\left(\frac{p^n - 1}{p - 1}\right) t_{ijk\cdots} + \frac{(p^{n-1} - 1)}{p^{n-1}(p - 1)} (p^n \mu - t_{ijk\cdots}) - \left(\frac{p^n - 1}{p - 1}\right)\mu$$

which equals $t_{ijk\cdots} - \mu$.

We have, therefore, the following expression for the true yield of the combination $(ijk\cdots)$ in terms of the effects and interactions: namely,

$$t_{ijk\cdots} = \mu + \sum_{(\alpha_1, \alpha_2, \cdots)} A^{\alpha_1} B^{\alpha_2} \cdots_{\alpha_1 i + \alpha_2 j + \cdots} \tag{14}$$

where summation is over the $\left(\dfrac{p^n - 1}{p - 1}\right)$ possible choices of $(\alpha_1, \alpha_2, \cdots, \alpha_n)$. For example with $p = 3$, $n = 3$, we have

$$t_{012} = \mu + A_0 + B_1 + AB_1 + AB^2{}_2 + C_2 + AC_2 + AC^2{}_1$$
$$+ BC_0 + BC^2{}_2 + ABC_0 + ABC^2{}_2 + AB^2 C_1 + AB^2 C^2{}_0$$

17.4 ANALYSIS OF p^n FACTORIAL SYSTEMS

The linear model for the p^n experiment may be written as

$$y_{ijk\cdots nm} = \mu + r_n + b_{nm} + t_{ijk\cdots} + \epsilon_{ijk\cdots n}$$

where the subscript n denotes the replicate number, r_n the contribution of the nth replicate, m the block within the replicate, and b_{nm} the contribution of the mth block within replicate n.

If confounding according to any of the systems discussed in this chapter is used in making up the blocks, when t_{ijk} is replaced by its expression in terms of effects and interactions, we shall find that any one block component will have the same coefficient as an effect or interaction component throughout a replicate in which that effect or interaction is confounded. For example, suppose we have a 2^2 experiment on factors a

and b in blocks of 2, confounding A in the first replicate and B in the second replicate. Then the 8 observations may be expressed as follows:

$$y_{0011} = \mu + A_0 + B_0 + AB_0 + r_1 + b_{11}$$

$$y_{0111} = \mu + A_0 + B_1 + AB_1 + r_1 + b_{11}$$

$$y_{1012} = \mu + A_1 + B_0 + AB_1 + r_1 + b_{12}$$

$$y_{1112} = \mu + A_1 + B_1 + AB_0 + r_1 + b_{12}$$

$$y_{0021} = \mu + A_0 + B_0 + AB_0 + r_2 + b_{21}$$

$$y_{1021} = \mu + A_1 + B_0 + AB_1 + r_2 + b_{21}$$

$$y_{0122} = \mu + A_0 + B_1 + AB_1 + r_2 + b_{22}$$

$$y_{1122} = \mu + A_1 + B_1 + AB_0 + r_2 + b_{22}$$

We note that the coefficients of b_{11} are the same as the coefficient of A_0, and those of b_{12} are the same as the coefficient of A_1 in the first replicate, and so on.

All coefficients in the model are either zero or unity, so that the normal equations are obtained by equating, for each parameter, the total of yields containing that parameter to its expectation in terms of all the parameters. If all the treatment combinations are represented equally frequently in the experiment, the normal equations reduce to simple equations: (1) that any unconfounded effect or interaction is estimated by the corresponding comparison of the actual yields over the whole experiment, and (2) that any confounded effect or interaction is estimated, likewise, from the replicates in which it is unconfounded.

17.5 THE INTERPRETATION OF EFFECTS AND INTERACTIONS

The usual regression approach may be adopted for the interpretation of main effects. With p equally spaced levels of the factor, we may calculate the linear effect of A, for example, as

$$A_L = \frac{\left[-\left(\dfrac{p-1}{2}\right)A_0 - \left(\dfrac{p-3}{2}\right)A_1 - \text{etc.} + \left(\dfrac{p-3}{2}\right)A_{p-2} + \left(\dfrac{p-1}{2}\right)A_{p-1} \right]}{\dfrac{p(p^2-1)}{12}} \tag{15}$$

and, with r replicates and A unconfounded, the corresponding sum of squares is

$$A^2{}_L \times \frac{p(p^2 - 1)}{12rp^{n-1}}$$

The quadratic effect is expressible as the following linear contrast among the yields at each level:

$$A_Q = \frac{\Sigma A_i \left[\left(i - \frac{p-1}{2} \right)^2 - \left(\frac{p^2 - 1}{12} \right) \right]}{\dfrac{p(p^2 - 1)(p^2 - 4)}{180}} \tag{16}$$

and, with r replicates and A unconfounded, the corresponding sum of squares is

$$A^2{}_Q \times \frac{p(p^2 - 1)(p^2 - 4)}{180rp^{n-1}}$$

Corresponding to these linear, quadratic, etc., effects, we may form the linear-by-linear interaction of 2 effects, and so on, as in the case of the 3^3 experiment described in Chapter 16.

If the levels are not equally spaced and occur at, say, $l_0, l_1, \cdots, l_{p-1}$, the linear effect of A may be obtained by finding the regression of A_i on l_i: i.e.,

$$A_L = \frac{\sum\limits_i (l_i - \bar{l}) A_i}{\sum\limits_i (l_i - \bar{l})^2} \tag{17}$$

The quadratic term must be orthogonal to this and is given by

$$A_Q = \sum_i c_i A_i \tag{18}$$

where c_i is equal to $(\alpha + \beta l_i + \gamma l^2{}_i)$, the coefficients α, β, and γ being chosen such that the A_Q is a contrast which is orthogonal to the A_L contrast. For these conditions to hold, we must have

$$\sum_i c_i = 0$$

$$\sum_i c_i(l_i - \bar{l}) = 0 \tag{19}$$

This process may be extended indefinitely.

17.6 THE KNUT VIK SQUARE

The Knut Vik square is a Latin square which results in an even distribution of treatments over the experimental area, thus:

$$
\begin{array}{ccccc}
A & B & C & D & E \\
D & E & A & B & C \\
B & C & D & E & A \\
E & A & B & C & D \\
C & D & E & A & B
\end{array}
$$

We have seen that, if we have 2 factors, x and y, each at 5 levels, the total of 24 degrees of freedom can be partitioned into 6 sets representable by X, Y, XY, XY^2, XY^3, XY^4. If rows and columns are regarded as the 2 factors with levels 0, 1, 2, $\cdots$, 4 in order, then, in the above square, treatments are arranged according to the partition denoted by XY^2. The partitions XY^4 and XY represent another systematic arrangement in which treatments tend to lie in diagonals. The other partition XY^3 gives the following square:

$$
\begin{array}{ccccc}
A & D & B & E & C \\
B & E & C & A & D \\
C & A & D & B & E \\
D & B & E & C & A \\
E & C & A & D & B
\end{array}
$$

which is identical with the Knut Vik square, except for inversion about the diagonal. The fact that there are two possible Knut Vik squares should not, however, lead us to suppose that a useful design may be obtained by taking one of these at random. If we remove the sum of squares represented by X, Y, XY, and XY^4 for positional effects, we shall have a treatment sum of squares whose expectation is the same as that of the error mean square. With a randomization test, we would be able to make a significance test only with a level of significance of 50 percent. Furthermore, there is no possibility of estimating the variance of plot errors to which treatment comparisons are subject.

17.7 THE ARRANGEMENT OF n FACTORS EACH WITH p^m LEVELS IN BLOCKS OF $(p^m)^s$

The general theory on which the previous parts of this chapter are based is a special case of Galois field theory. A treatment of group theory is essential because there are $(p^m)^n$ different treatment combinations which are to be arranged in equal-sized blocks in several ways. The $(p^m)^n$ treatment combinations may be regarded as the points of a finite geometry: that is, as the individual points of a set of points. Furthermore, it will be convenient if we can have a representation such that the points lie, in a particular sense, on lines, planes, and so on, so that we may take the lines (or planes, etc.) as blocks. The reader will, after having studied Chapter 16, see the value of such a representation. For, in the case of a 3^n experiment, we could represent the treatment combinations by the points of an n-dimensional lattice, such that each line on the lattice contained 3 points, each plane contained 9 points, and so on. The lines, planes, or hyperplanes would then be used to give blocks, because they occur in sets, each one of a set containing the same number of points. We proceed to give the elementary notions of fields and Galois fields, and the reader should have no difficulty in seeing the value of their introduction into the discussion.

A set of s elements $u_0, u_1, \cdots, u_{s-1}$ is said to be a finite field of order s, if

1. The elements may be combined by addition with the laws,

$$u_i + u_j = u_j + u_i; \qquad u_i + (u_j + u_k) = (u_i + u_j) + u_k$$

given u_i and u_k there is a unique u_j such that $u_i + u_j = u_k$, and the element having the additive property of zero is u_0 so that

$$u_0 + u_j = u_j \quad \text{for any } j$$

2. The elements may be combined by multiplication with the laws,

$$u_i u_j = u_j u_i; \qquad u_i(u_j u_k) = (u_i u_j)u_k; \qquad u_i(u_j + u_k) = u_i u_j + u_i u_k$$

and given any u_i ($\neq u_0$) and any u_k there is a unique u_j such that $u_i u_j = u_k$. It is verifiable that u_0 has the multiplicative properties of zero: i.e., that $u_0 u_i = u_0$. The element having the multiplicative property of unity is chosen to be u_1.

The finite field of p elements, where p is a prime number, may be represented by $u_0 = 0, u_1 = 1, u_2 = 2, \cdots, u_{p-1} = p - 1$, in which addition and multiplication are the ordinary arithmetic operations, except that the resulting number is reduced modulo p. That is to say, the resulting number is replaced by the remainder obtained after dividing by p. For example, with $p = 5$, $u_0 = 0$, $u_1 = 1$, $u_2 = 2$, $u_3 = 3$, $u_4 = 4$: $u_3 + u_4 = 3 + 4 = 2 = u_2$, and $u_2 u_4 = 2 \times 4 = 3 = u_3$, etc.

In general, a Galois field of p^m elements, which is a special representation of a finite field, is obtained as follows. Let $P(x)$ be a given polynomial in x of degree m with integral coefficients; and let $F(x)$ be any polynomial in x with integral coefficients. Then $F(x)$ may be expressed as

$$F(x) = f(x) + p \cdot q(x) + P(x)Q(x)$$

where

$$f(x) = a_0 + a_1 x + a_2 x^2 + \cdots + a_{m-1} x^{m-1}$$

and the coefficients $a_0, a_1, \cdots, a_{m-1}$ belong to the set $0, 1, 2, \cdots, p - 1$. This relationship may be written

$$F(x) = f(x) \ \text{mod} \ p, \ P(x) \tag{20}$$

and we say $f(x)$ is the residue of $F(x)$ modulis p and $P(x)$. The functions $F(x)$, which satisfy this relation when $f(x)$, p, and $P(x)$ are kept fixed, form a class. If p and $P(x)$ are kept fixed, but $f(x)$ is varied, p^m classes may be formed, since each coefficient in $f(x)$ may take the values $0, 1, 2, \cdots, p - 1$. It may be readily verified that the classes defined by the $f(x)$'s make up a field; for example, if $F_i(x)$ belongs to the class corresponding to $f_i(x)$, and $F_j(x)$ to the class corresponding to $f_j(x)$, then $F_i(x) + F_j(x)$ belongs to the class corresponding to $f_i(x) + f_j(x)$. The other operations defined for a field are, likewise, satisfied, any function obtained by ordinary algebraic operations being replaced by its residue modulis p and $P(x)$. In order that division be unique, it is also necessary that p be a prime number and that $P(x)$ cannot be expressed in the form

$$P(x) = P_1(x)P_2(x) + pP_3(x)$$

in other words, that $P(x)$ be irreducible modulo p, where $P_1(x)$ and $P_2(x)$ are polynomials with integral coefficients of degree positive and less than the degree of $P(x)$.

The finite field formed by the p^m classes of residues is called a Galois field of order p^m and is denoted by $\text{GF}(p^m)$. It is proved, in Carmichael,[1] for example, that the classes are the same, regardless of the choice of $P(x)$ subject to the restrictions imposed above, and that the field $\text{GF}(p^m)$ exists if p is a prime and m a positive integer. The classes of residues can be represented by the different possible functions $f_i(x)$, and may also be denoted by u_0, u_1, $\cdots$, u_{s-1}, where $s = p^m$.

To give an instance, we shall obtain the Galois field of 3^2 elements. We have then $p = 3$, $m = 2$, so that the possible polynomials of degree 2 $(= m)$ are $a_0 + a_1 x + a_2 x^2$, where a_0, a_1, a_2 may take the values 0, 1, 2. The function $P(x)$ must be irreducible modulo 3 so that we may exclude cases in which $a_0 = 0$. Take then $a_0 = 1$; we have as possible functions $P(x)$, $1 + a_1 x + a_2 x^2$. If $a_1 = 0$, then we have $(1 + a_2 x^2)$, and, with $a_2 = 2$, we have $(1 + 2x^2)$, which takes the value 0 modulo 3, when $x = 1$; and can be written as $(1 + x)(1 + 2x) - 3x$ so this case is impossible, leaving $1 + x^2$. When $x = 0, 1, 2$, this function takes the values 1, 2, 2 modulo 3, so that it is irreducible modulo 3. We take $P(x)$, therefore, to be $1 + x^2$. Now consider the possible $f(x)$'s. These are of the form $b_0 + b_1 x$, so that we have, as the elements of the field, $u_0 = 0$, $u_1 = 1$, $u_2 = 2$, $u_3 = x$, $u_4 = 2x$, $u_5 = 1 + x$, $u_6 = 2 + x$, $u_7 = 1 + 2x$, $u_8 = 2 + 2x$. There is a further theorem that all the elements or marks of the field except the zero element u_0 can be represented as the powers of an element which is of special type, known as a primitive mark. It is readily verified that $y = 1 + x$ is a primitive root. For

$$y = 1 + x$$

$$y^2 = 1 + 2x + x^2 = 2x$$

$$y^3 = 2x + 2x^2 = 2x + 1 + 2(1 + x^2) = 1 + 2x$$

$$y^4 = 4x^2 = x^2 = 2 + 1 + x^2 = 2$$

$$y^5 = 2 + 2x$$

$$y^6 = 4x = x$$

$$y^7 = 2 + 4x = 2 + x$$

$$y^8 = 4 = 1$$

The elements of the field are representable, therefore, by 0, 1, $1 + x$ $(= y)$, $2x$ $(= y^2)$, $1 + 2x$ $(= y^3)$, 2 $(= y^4)$, $2 + 2x$ $(= y^5)$, $(= y^6)$, $2 + x$ $(= y^7)$. Both representations are valuable, in that the representation in terms of x may be used for addition, and the representation in terms of y for multiplication, utilizing the fact that y^{p^m-1} $= 1$, thus, $y^5 = y^2 \times y^3 = 2x \times (1 + 2x) = 2x + 4x^2 = 2x + 2 = y^5$.

Table 17.3 contains a suitable $P(x)$ and a primitive mark for the Galois fields likely to occur in experimental design.

TABLE 17.3 GALOIS FIELDS: $P(x)$ AND PRIMITIVE MARKS

p^m	$P(x)$	Primitive Mark
2^2	$x^2 + x + 1$	x
2^3	$x^3 + x^2 + 1$	x
2^4	$x^4 + x + 1$	$x + 1$
3^2	$x^2 + 1$	$x + 1$
3^3	$x^3 + 2x + 1$	x
5^2	$x^2 + x + 1$	$x + 2$

The use of these fields in examining the $(p^m)^n$ $(= s^n)$ factorial system is exactly analogous to the use of $0, 1, 2, \cdots, p - 1$ for the p^n factorial system considered in the earlier part of this chapter. The treatment combinations may be denoted by $(x_1, x_2, \cdots, x_n)$ where each x_i can take one of the values from 0 to $s - 1$. The main effect of factor 1 will be given by the comparison of s sets of s^{n-1} plots, these sets being given by the equations:

$$
\begin{aligned}
x_1 &= 0, \\
&= 1, \\
&= 2, \\
&\ \vdots \\
&= s - 1
\end{aligned}
\left.\begin{aligned}
\right\}
\end{aligned}
\begin{aligned}
u_{x_1} &= u_0 \\
&= u_1 \\
&= u_2 \\
&\ \vdots \\
&= u_{s-1}
\end{aligned}
$$

Main effects for the other factors are similarly defined. The interaction of, say, factor 1 and factor 2 has $(s - 1)^2$ degrees of freedom, and these may be partitioned into $(s - 1)$ sets of $(s - 1)$ degrees of freedom. A set of $(s - 1)$ degrees of freedom is given by the comparison of s sets of s^{n-1} plots, these sets being given by the s equations:

$$
\begin{aligned}
u_{x_1} + \lambda u_{x_2} &= u_0 \\
u_{x_1} + \lambda u_{x_2} &= u_1 \\
u_{x_1} + \lambda u_{x_2} &= u_2 \\
\vdots \quad \vdots \quad \vdots \\
u_{x_1} + \lambda u_{x_2} &= u_{s-1}
\end{aligned}
\tag{21}
$$

in which λ is fixed for a set of s equations to be one of $u_1, u_2, \cdots, u_{s-1}$. The $(s-1)^3$ degrees of freedom for the 3-factor interaction may be partitioned into $(s-1)^2$ sets of $(s-1)$ degrees of freedom, each set being given by the equations:

$$u_{x_1} + \lambda u_{x_2} + \mu u_{x_3} = u_0$$

$$u_{x_1} + \lambda u_{x_2} + \mu u_{x_3} = u_1$$

$$u_{x_1} + \lambda u_{x_2} + \mu u_{x_3} = u_2 \qquad (22)$$

$$\cdot \qquad \cdot \qquad \cdot \qquad \cdot$$

$$\cdot \qquad \cdot \qquad \cdot \qquad \cdot$$

$$\cdot \qquad \cdot \qquad \cdot \qquad \cdot$$

$$u_{x_1} + \lambda u_{x_2} + \mu u_{x_3} = u_{s-1}$$

in which λ and μ are fixed for a set of s equations each to be one of $u_1, u_2, \cdots, u_{s-1}$, there being $(s-1)^2$ possible choices of λ and μ.

There is no point in continuing this description, in that it is entirely analogous to the case when $s = p$ given earlier. The formulas for number of systems of confounding can be written out by substituting s for p and so on. The $\left(\dfrac{s^n - 1}{s - 1}\right)$ sets of $(s-1)$ degrees of freedom are orthogonal, and the yields may be expressed in terms of the mean, effects, and interactions. The only complication is that we are working with the marks of the Galois field, which are not quite so easy to manipulate as the numbers $0, 1, 2, \cdots, p - 1$.

The essential fact, that we have used in the development herein, is that s^{n-1} treatment combinations $(x_1, \cdots, x_n)$ satisfy a relationship

$$\lambda_1 u_{x_1} + \lambda_2 u_{x_2} + \cdots + \lambda_n u_{x_n} = u$$

where $\lambda_1, \lambda_2, \cdots, \lambda_n$ are marks of the field not all zero and u is a mark of the field. This is simply verified by noting that, if r of the coefficients λ_i are equal to u_0, then all we need to do is to solve the equation in $(n - r)$ of the x_i, say,

$$\lambda_1 u_{x_1} + \cdots + \lambda_{n-r} u_{x_{n-r}} = u$$

where $\lambda_1, \cdots, \lambda_{n-r}$ are the λ's not equal to u_0. For each solution of this equation we will have s^r solutions to the original equation by combining with the solution any choice of u's for the other x's. This equation has, however, s^{n-r-1} solutions, for we may choose $x_1, \cdots, x_{n-r-1}$ arbitrarily, and we are left with an equation $\lambda_{n-r} u_{x_{n-r}} =$ some u, and there is a solution to this equation because of the definition of a field. The properties of orthogonality are easily verified.

As a short example we may consider the $(2^2)^2$ system: i.e., 2 factors each at 4 levels. For the Galois field of 4 elements a suitable $P(x)$ is $x^2 + x + 1$, and we have $u_0 = 0, u_1 = 1, u_2 = x$, and $u_3 = x^2 = x + 1$. It is necessary to form the addition and multiplication tables of this field. They are as shown in Table 17.4.

TABLE 17.4

	Addition					Multiplication			
	u_0	u_1	u_2	u_3		u_0	u_1	u_2	u_3
u_0	u_0	u_1	u_2	u_3	u_0	u_0	u_0	u_0	u_0
u_1		u_0	u_3	u_2	u_1		u_1	u_2	u_3
u_2			u_0	u_1	u_2			u_3	u_1
u_3				u_0	u_3				u_2

These are obtained as follows:

1. Addition: e.g.,

$$u_0 + u_1 = 0 + 1 = 1 = u_1$$

$$u_2 + u_2 = 2x = 0 \bmod 2, P(x) = u_0$$

$$u_2 + u_3 = 1 + 2x = 1 \bmod 2, P(x) = u_1$$

2. Multiplication:

$$u_0 \times u_i = 0 = u_0, u_1 \times u_i = u_i$$

$$u_2 \times u_2 = x^2 = [(x^2 + x + 1) + x + 1] \bmod [2, P(x)]$$

$$= x + 1 \bmod [2, P(x)]$$

$$= u_3$$

$$u_3 \times u_3 = 1 + 2x + x^2 = (1 + x + x^2) + x$$

$$= x \bmod [2, P(x)]$$

$$= u_2$$

We now obtain the sets of $(s - 1)$ $(= 3)$ degrees of freedom by making up the partitions of the 16 combinations into 4 sets of 4 combinations (Table 17.5).

TABLE 17.5   CALCULATION OF PARTITIONING FOR EFFECTS AND INTERACTIONS WITH 4^2 SYSTEM

x_1	x_2	Effect of Factor 1 u_{x_1}	Effect of Factor 2 u_{x_2}	Interaction $u_{x_1} + u_1 u_{x_2}$	$u_{x_1} + u_2 u_{x_2}$	$u_{x_1} + u_3 u_{x_2}$
0	0	u_0	u_0	u_0	u_0	u_0
0	1	u_0	u_1	u_1	u_2	u_3
0	2	u_0	u_2	u_2	u_3	u_1
0	3	u_0	u_3	u_3	u_1	u_2
1	0	u_1	u_0	u_1	u_1	u_1
1	1	u_1	u_1	u_0	u_3	u_2
1	2	u_1	u_2	u_3	u_2	u_0
1	3	u_1	u_3	u_2	u_0	u_3
2	0	u_2	u_0	u_2	u_2	u_2
2	1	u_2	u_1	u_3	u_0	u_1
2	2	u_2	u_2	u_0	u_1	u_3
2	3	u_2	u_3	u_1	u_3	u_0
3	0	u_3	u_0	u_3	u_3	u_3
3	1	u_3	u_1	u_2	u_1	u_0
3	2	u_3	u_2	u_1	u_0	u_2
3	3	u_3	u_3	u_0	u_2	u_1

For example, with $x_1 = 3$, $x_2 = 2$, we find, from the addition and multiplication tables:

$$u_{x_1} + u_1 u_{x_2} = u_3 + u_1 u_2 = u_3 + u_2 = u_1$$

$$u_{x_1} + u_2 u_{x_2} = u_3 + u_2 u_2 = u_3 + u_3 = u_0$$

$$u_{x_1} + u_3 u_{x_2} = u_3 + u_3 u_2 = u_3 + u_1 = u_2$$

Table 17.5 gives the partitioning of the 15 degrees of freedom for the 4^2 system into 2 main effects, each with 3 degrees of freedom, and 3 sets of 3 interaction degrees of freedom. In passing, it may be pointed out that the above gives the completely orthogonalized 4×4 Latin square: for let us make the following transpositions:

in the first column:

$$u_0 = \text{row 1}, \quad u_1 = \text{row 2}, \quad u_2 = \text{row 3}, \quad u_3 = \text{row 4}$$

in the second column:

$$u_0 = \text{col. 1}, \quad u_1 = \text{col. 2}, \quad u_2 = \text{col. 3}, \quad u_3 = \text{col. 4}$$

in the third column: $u_0 = A, \quad u_1 = B, \quad u_2 = C, \quad u_3 = D$

in the fourth column: $u_0 = \alpha, \quad u_1 = \beta, \quad u_2 = \gamma, \quad u_3 = \delta$

in the fifth column: $u_0 = 1, \quad u_1 = 2, \quad u_2 = 3, \quad u_3 = 4$

then the square is

$$
\begin{array}{cccc}
A\alpha_1 & B\gamma_4 & C\delta_2 & D\beta_3 \\
B\beta_2 & A\delta_3 & D\gamma_1 & C\alpha_4 \\
C\gamma_3 & D\alpha_2 & A\beta_4 & B\delta_1 \\
D\delta_4 & C\beta_1 & B\alpha_3 & A\gamma_2
\end{array}
$$

For a detailed discussion, the reader should refer to Bose [2] and to Mann.[3]

This exemplifies the general procedure for constructing a completely orthogonalized square of side p^n. The letter in the (ij)th cell, where $i, j = 0, 1, 2, \cdots, p^n - 1$, of the sth language is $u_i + u_s u_j$, s taking on the values $1, 2, \cdots, p^n - 1$. It is easily proved that the square constructed in this way has all the required properties (see Stevens [4]).

The use of this system in confounding will be exemplified by the 4^3 system on factors a, b, and c. The 63 degrees of freedom may be represented by the symbols:

Main effects: A, B, C

2-factor interactions: AB, AB^2, AB^3, AC, AC^2, AC^3, BC, BC^2, BC^3

3-factor interactions: ABC, ABC^2, ABC^3, AB^2C, AB^2C^2, AB^2C^3, AB^3C,

   AB^3C^2, AB^3C^3

Each symbol represents 3 degrees of freedom, those for AB^2C^2 being given by the 4 sets of equations:

$$
u_{x_1} + u_2 u_{x_2} + u_2 u_{x_3} = u_0
$$
$$
u_{x_1} + u_2 u_{x_2} + u_2 u_{x_3} = u_1
$$
$$
u_{x_1} + u_2 u_{x_2} + u_2 u_{x_3} = u_2
$$
$$
u_{x_1} + u_2 u_{x_2} + u_2 u_{x_3} = u_3
$$

The rule of the generalized interaction may be obtained by noting that, if effects or interactions corresponding to equations with left-hand sides,

$$
u_i u_{x_1} + u_j u_{x_2} + u_k u_{x_3}
$$

and

$$
u'_i u_{x_1} + u'_j u_{x_2} + u'_k u_{x_3}
$$

are completely confounded with blocks, then so are the effects or interactions given by the equations with right-hand sides,

$$
(u_i + \lambda u'_i) u_{x_1} + (u_j + \lambda u'_j) u_{x_2} + \text{etc.}
$$

where λ is a mark of the field. Thus, it may be verified that, if ABC^2 and AB^3C are confounded, then so are A, BC^2, and AB^2C^3.

The Galois field of p^n elements is principally of value in constructing completely orthogonalized squares, and most of the useful designs which involve Galois fields can be obtained directly from these squares.

17.8 FINITE GEOMETRIES

There is a close relationship of the material of this chapter to the subject of finite geometries. The reader who is interested in these per se is referred to Carmichael.[1] We shall give only material on finite geometries which is strictly relevant to the design of experiments.

A finite projective geometry is a finite set of elements or points which are subject to a number of postulates which are geometrical in nature: for example, that one and only one line contains 2 distinct points.

The finite projective k-dimensional geometry PG(k, p^n) consists of the points

$$(x_0, x_1, \cdots, x_k)$$

where $x_0, x_1, \cdots, x_k$ are elements of GF(p^n), at least one being different from zero, and where it is understood that the point $(y_0, y_1, \cdots, y_k)$ is the same point as the point $(x_0, x_1, \cdots, x_k)$ if for some element of the GF(p^n), say, α, the relations,

$$y_i = \alpha x_i, \qquad i = 0, 1, \cdots, k$$

hold.

This finite projective geometry is such that its points are a representation of the possible orthogonal sets of $(p^n - 1)$ degrees of freedom in the $(p^n)^{k+1}$ factorial system. For example, with $k = 2$, $p = 3$, and $n = 1$, we have denoted the effects and interactions by A, B, AB, AB^2, C, AC, AC^2, BC, BC^2, ABC, ABC^2, AB^2C, and AB^2C^2. These may be represented as the points of PG$(2, 3)$, namely $(1, 0, 0)$, $(0, 1, 0)$, $(1, 1, 0)$, $(1, 2, 0)$, $(0, 0, 1)$, $(1, 0, 1)$, $(1, 0, 2)$, $(0, 1, 1)$, $(0, 1, 2)$, $(1, 1, 1)$, $(1, 1, 2)$, $(1, 2, 1)$ and $(1, 2, 2)$. It will be remembered that we excluded symbols like A^2B, which would be represented by $(2, 1, 0)$, because $(2, 1, 0) = 2(1, 2, 0)$. In enumerating the effect and interaction symbols, we made the rule that the first non-zero exponent should be unity, and this is the same rule essentially as that given above for the exclusion of points in the finite projective geometry.

The k-dimensional finite Euclidean geometry EG(k, p^n) consists of the points $(x_1, x_2, \cdots, x_k)$, such that each x_i is an element of the Galois field GF(p^n). This geometry is the representation of treatment combinations that we used for the case of k factors each at p^n levels.

We now define lines, planes, and so on in these finite geometries. For the finite projective geometry PG(k, p^n) an m flat (or m space) is defined to be the points that satisfy $(k - m)$ independent homogeneous linear equations, a point being a 0 flat, a line a 1 flat, and so on. A point denotes a particular set of $p^n - 1$ degrees of freedom, a 1 flat contains the points for 2 sets of degrees of freedom and their generalized interaction. For example, the points corresponding to the confounding of AB, AC, BC^2, and AB^2C^2 in the 3^3 system, i.e., PG(2, 3), are (1, 1, 0), (1, 0, 1), (0, 1, 2) and (1, 2, 2) and the coordinates, denoted by x_1, x_2, x_3, satisfy the one equation

$$x_1 + 2x_2 + 2x_3 = 0 \bmod 3$$

Thus, systems of confounding for the $(p^n)^{k+1}$ factorial system in blocks of $(p^n)^r$ are given by the $(k - r)$ flats of PG(k, p^n). An enumeration of systems of confounding is then merely a matter of enumeration of m flats of the finite projective geometry.

The number of m flats in PG(k, p^n) is equal to

$$\phi(k, m, s) = \frac{(s^{k+1} - 1)(s^k - 1) \cdots (s^{k+1-m} - 1)}{(s^{m+1} - 1)(s^m - 1) \cdots (s - 1)} \tag{24}$$

where $s = p^n$.

Similarly, an m flat in EG(k, p^n) is the set of points that satisfy $(k - m)$ consistent and independent linear equations. The constituent treatment combinations of a block in the $(p^n)^k$ factorial experiment in blocks of $(p^n)^{k-m}$ plots with any of the systems of confounding discussed in this chapter form a flat. The number of m flats in EG(k, p^n) is

$$\phi(k, m, s) - \phi(k - 1, m, s)$$

since EG(k, p^n) is the set of points in PG(k, p^n) minus the points in the PG($k - 1$, p^n) for which $x_1 = 0$.

Our reason for describing these finite geometries is that we shall find them to be of use in deriving other designs, notably incomplete block designs.

REFERENCES

1. CARMICHAEL, R. D. *Introduction to the theory of groups of finite order.* Ginn, Boston. 1937.
2. BOSE, R. C. On the application of Galois fields to the problem of the construction of Hyper-Graeco Latin squares. *Sankhyā*, **3**, 323–338, 1939.
3. MANN, H. B. On the construction of sets of orthogonal Latin squares. *Ann. Math. Stat.*, **14**, 401–414, 1943.
4. STEVENS, W. L. The completely orthogonalised Latin square. *Ann. Eug.*, **9**, 82–93, 1938.
5. BOSE, R. C., and KISHEN, K. On the problem of confounding in general symmetrical factorial designs. *Sankhyā*, **5**, 21–26, 1940.

6. FISHER, R. A.   The theory of confounding in factorial experiments in relation to the theory of groups.   *Ann. Eug.*, **11**, 341–353, 1942.
7. KEMPTHORNE, O.   A simple approach to confounding and fractional replication in factorial experiments.   *Biometrika*, **34**, 255–272, 1947.
8. KISHEN, K.   On a general method of expressing a single degree of freedom in an s^m factorial arrangement in terms of main effects and interactions.   *Sankhyā*, **6**, 133–140, 1942.
9. BOSE, R. C.   Mathematical theory of the symmetrical factorial design.   *Sankhyā*, **8**, 107–166, 1947.

CHAPTER 18

Other Factorial Experiments

18.1 INTRODUCTION

In the previous chapters we have considered the more important types of factorial experiment: namely, when the number of levels is the same prime number for all the factors. We have also considered briefly in the last chapter the case when the number of levels of all the factors is the same power of a prime. In this way we have dealt with the 2^n, 3^n, 4^n, 5^n, and 7^n systems, and these are the only systems with the same number of levels per factor that are likely to be of interest to experimenters. In this chapter we shall discuss the following:

1. When each factor has the same number of levels, this number being a power of a prime, since this may be dealt with for most purposes in a way simpler than by recourse to Galois field theory.

2. When the number of levels for the factors are powers (not all the same) of the same prime number: e.g., a $2 \times 4 \times 4$ experiment, that is, one with 1 factor at 2 levels and 2 factors at 4 levels.

3. When the number of levels are prime numbers: e.g., a $2^2 \times 3^2$ experiment, that is, one with 2 factors at 2 levels and 2 factors at 3 levels.

4. When the number of levels is a product of different primes: e.g., a 6^2 experiment, that is, one with 2 factors each at 6 levels.

We shall also deal in this chapter with experiments that are almost factorial in structure, for instance, an experiment on quality, say, type a, b, or c by rates of 0, 1, 2 units of a stimulus in which certain factorial combinations that are formally different are, in fact, the same.

It is not intended to give an exhaustive description of all these cases. On the one hand, some of them are rather difficult for the ordinary experimenter to understand and to interpret, and experimenters do not find it necessary in the author's experience to have recourse to them at all frequently. The advantages that accrue from using the simpler types of experiment will become evident from the descriptions that follow.

342

The importance of using experimental designs that are fairly easily understood cannot be emphasized too strongly.   With the complex designs, there is considerable danger of the experimenter becoming lost in the intricacies of the design and analysis and losing sight of his main objective.

18.2 THE NUMBER OF LEVELS BEING THE SAME PRIME POWER

We have dealt with this case in the previous chapter from the point of view of Galois fields.   The treatment given below is not quite so general but is simpler.   A further advantage is that it enables the examination of designs, say, for factors with 8 levels in blocks of 4 plots.

Suppose the number of levels is k which equals p^m, p being a prime number and m being some integer greater than unity.   We can set up a correspondence between the k levels of the 1 factor and the p^m combinations of m pseudofactors each at p levels as exemplified in Table 18.1 for the case of $k = 8 = 2^3$.

TABLE 18.1

Level of Factor	Levels of Pseudofactors		
	(1)	(2)	(3)
0	0	0	0
1	1	0	0
2	0	1	0
3	1	1	0
4	0	0	1
5	1	0	1
6	0	1	1
7	1	1	1

In the design of an experiment with 2 factors, x and y, each at 8 levels, we replace x by a, b, c and y by d, e, f, so that we have an experiment on 6 factors each at 2 levels.   The analogy is not perfect, however, for we must remember that some components of the main effect of either original factor will appear formally as 2- and 3-factor interactions: for example, the interaction ABC is a contrast among the levels of the x factor: namely,

$$(-x_0 + x_1 + x_2 - x_3 + x_4 - x_5 - x_6 + x_7)$$

If we wish to use blocks of 16 plots we can confound the following:

$$ABD, \ CEF, \ \text{and} \ ABCDEF$$

and main effect comparisons are not confounded. If information were desired on all interaction components, and it would generallly be advisable in such a case as the one under discussion, 2 replicates with different confounding would be used. The system of confounding for 6 factors in blocks of 8 (Chapter 14) may be used to give a design in blocks of 8. The composition of the blocks is easily obtained in the usual way.

The most frequently used design of this type is that for 2 factors each at 4 levels in blocks of 4 plots. Let the factors be a and b. The 3 degrees of freedom for each main effect may be represented by

$$A' = a_3 + a_2 - a_1 - a_0$$
$$A'' = a_3 - a_2 - a_1 + a_0 \qquad (1)$$
$$A''' = a_3 - a_2 + a_1 - a_0$$

by setting $a_0 = (1)$, $a_1 = x$, $a_2 = y$, $a_3 = xy$, so that $2X = A'''$, $2Y = A'$, $2XY = A''$. The representation we use here has a little interest, from the point of view of the linear, quadratic, and cubic effect of the factor. Supposing the levels to be *equally* spaced, then the linear quadratic and cubic comparisons, A_L, A_Q, and A_C, respectively, are, apart from constant divisors, as follows:

$$A_L = -3a_0 - a_1 + a_2 + 3a_3$$
$$A_Q = a_0 - a_1 - a_2 + a_3 \qquad (2)$$
$$A_C = -a_0 + 3a_1 - 3a_2 + a_3$$

Therefore, A'' measures the quadratic effect, and

$$A_L = 2A' + A'''$$
$$A_C = -A' + 2A'''$$

or $\qquad (3)$

$$5A' = 2A_L - A_C$$
$$5A''' = A_L + 2A_C$$

With similar expressions for the b factor, a design in blocks of 8 is given by confounding any one interaction degree of freedom, say, $A'''B'''$, and, to obtain the blocks, we need merely to expand the expression

$$A'''B''' = (a_3 - a_2 + a_1 - a_0)(b_3 - b_2 + b_1 - b_0)$$

and place combinations with a positive sign in one block and those with a negative sign in the other block.

Two replicates with such differing systems would yield full information on main effects and on 7 of the 9 interaction degrees of freedom, with half information on the other 2 interaction degrees of freedom.

With 3 replicates a balanced design in blocks of 4 plots exists (Table 18.2).

TABLE 18.2

Replicate	Confounding
1	$A'B'$, $A''B''$, $A'''B'''$
2	$A'B''$, $A''B'''$, $A'''B'$
3	$A'B'''$, $A''B'$, $A'''B''$

The first replicate may be constructed by expanding the expressions,

$$A'B' = (a_3 + a_2 - a_1 - a_0)(b_3 + b_2 - b_1 - b_0)$$

$$A''B'' = (a_3 - a_2 - a_1 + a_0)(b_3 - b_2 - b_1 + b_0)$$

and taking as the first block those combinations that are positive in both expressions, as the second block those positive in $A'B'$ and negative in $A''B''$, etc.   This gives the following blocks:

a_0b_0	a_0b_1	a_0b_3	a_0b_2
a_1b_1	a_1b_0	a_1b_2	a_1b_3
a_2b_2	a_2b_3	a_2b_1	a_2b_0
a_3b_3	a_3b_2	a_3b_0	a_3b_1

The other replicates are similarly constructed.   It should be noted that this design may be derived from the completely orthogonalized 4×4 square (cf. Chapter 17).

With 3 factors each at 4 levels and 64 treatment combinations in all, the following system of confounding in blocks of 8 plots confounds three 2-factor interaction degrees of freedom:

$$A'B''C''', \qquad A''B'''C' \qquad A'''B'C''$$

$$A''B''C''', \qquad A'''C', \qquad B'C''', \qquad A'B'''$$

For the derivation of this and other systems of confounding, one may note that

$$A'A'' = A'''$$

$$A''A''' = A'$$

and

$$A'A''' = A''$$

With a second replicate with the following confounding,

$$A'B'''C'', \qquad A''B'C''', \qquad A'''B''C'$$

$$A'''B'''C''', \qquad A''C', \qquad A'B'', \qquad B'C''$$

the experiment would yield full information on main effects, on 21 of the 27 two-factor interaction degrees of freedom, and on 19 of the 27 three-factor interaction degrees of freedom, with half information on all other contrasts.

The derivation of other designs in blocks of 4 plots and the analysis of all these designs are left as an exercise to the reader. A simple way of analysis, though possibly tedious in some cases, is to utilize the pseudo-factors in the analysis also. This method of analysis is quite suitable to routine calculations and keeps to the front the different degrees of freedom which may have been confounded. The addition-subtraction process may be applied to the total yields and then adjustments, obtained from block totals, applied to the partially confounded interactions.

18.3 NUMBER OF LEVELS EQUAL TO DIFFERENT POWERS OF SAME PRIME

This case follows easily by the same methods as the previous one. As an example, we can consider a design for 3 factors, a at 2 levels, b and c at 4 levels each. This may be represented as an experiment on five 2-level factors, a, b_1, b_2, c_1, c_2, and it is easily seen that, with blocks of 16 plots, only a 3-factor interaction degree of freedom need be confounded. With blocks of 8, it is necessary to confound 1 degree of freedom of an interaction of 2 factors: for example, we may confound

$$AB'C', \ AB''C'', \ B'''C'''$$

As a second example, we consider a $2^2 \times 4^2$ experiment. We represent the factors by a, b, c_1, c_2, d_1, d_2, and to obtain blocks of 8 we must confound 7 degrees of freedom with blocks. A possibility would be to confound two 2-factor interaction contrasts and other interactions in each replicate, thus: $AC''D''$, $BC''D'''$, $ABC''D'$, $AC''D'$, $C'''D'''$, ABD'', BC'. With blocks of 16 plots, there is no particular difficulty, as we may confound, for example,

$$AC'D'', \ BC''D''', \ ABC'''D'$$

18.4 NUMBER OF LEVELS EQUAL TO DIFFERENT PRIME NUMBERS

Insofar as general rules may be obtained for this case, we may suppose we have a $p^m q^n$ experiment, that is, one involving m factors each at p levels and n factors each at q levels, both p and q being prime numbers. We may denote a treatment combination by $(x_1, x_2, \cdots, x_m, y_1, y_2, \cdots, y_n)$ when $x_1, x_2, \cdots, x_m$ may take on the values 0, 1, 2, $\cdots$, $p - 1$ and $y_1, y_2, \cdots, y_n$ may take on the values 0, 1, 2, $\cdots$, $q - 1$. Main effects and interactions within either of the 2 groups of factors may be defined as in the pure system. The difficulties with this mixed system arise when we consider interactions of factors in the first group with factors in the second group. The $(p - 1)(q - 1)$ degrees of freedom for the interaction XY are the $(p - 1)(q - 1)$ degrees of freedom for interaction in the $p \times q$ table (Table 18.3).

TABLE 18.3

y_1	x_1				
	0	1	2	$\cdots$	$p - 1$
0					
1					
2					
$\cdot$					
$\cdot$					
$\cdot$					
$q - 1$					

These degrees of freedom arise only by comparisons among pq sets of $p^{m-1}q^{n-1}$ treatment combinations. Therefore, if the interaction of a factor of the first group and a factor of the second group is confounded, using equal-sized blocks, the main effects of these factors must also be confounded. In general, if r independent effects and interactions of the first group and s independent effects or interactions of the second group are completely confounded with blocks, the block size must be $p^{m-r}q^{n-s}$. The possibilities of confounding the higher-order interactions only are, therefore, somewhat limited.

As an example, we may consider the $2^2 \times 3^2$ experiment, and we denote the factors by a, b, c, and d in order. The possible block sizes are the factors of 36: that is, 6, 9, 12, 18. We consider, for the moment only, complete confounding with blocks. With blocks of 6 plots we may confound any one of A, B, or AB and any one of C, D, CD, or CD^2, and, of course, their interaction in one replicate. With blocks of 9 A, B, or AB must be confounded, because 9 is not an even number. With a block size of 12, we may confound CD or CD^2, and, with a block size of 18, we may confound AB.

Since most experiments are on a few factors, say, 5 or less, the above considerations result in the necessity of considering partial confounding. The type of partial confounding we shall consider is not quite of the same type as in previous chapters, because, in the designs discussed therein, an effect was either completely confounded or unconfounded with blocks in any one replicate. We shall consider designs in which effects or interactions are correlated as little as possible with block effects. The general methods by which the device of partial confounding is used are illustrated in the examples that follow.

18.4.1 The $3 \times 2 \times 2$ Experiment

Let the factors be a, b, and c with 3, 2, and 2 levels, respectively. Frequently there will be no experimental difficulties in using blocks of 12 units, and the consequent ease of analysis because of the absence of confounding will often offset the loss of precision resulting from blocks of this size compared to those of small sizes. In other cases, it will be important to use smaller blocks. The use of blocks of 6 plots confounding the main effect B, the main effect C, or the interaction BC presents no difficulty, but these designs are more properly classified as split-plot designs, which will be discussed in Chapter 19. Similar remarks hold for the use of blocks of 4 plots confounding A. In order that main effects be unconfounded, the block size must be 6.

The design for blocks of 6 plots given by Yates [1] is the only one that does not result in the confounding of main effects. To obtain this design, we note that interaction BC is given by the comparison

$$(b_1 - b_0)(c_1 - c_0)$$

i.e.,

$$b_1c_1 + b_0c_0 - b_1c_0 - b_0c_1$$

Let us denote by α the pair of treatment combinations b_1c_1 and b_0c_0 and by β the pair b_1c_0 and b_0c_1. Because the interaction BC is estimated by comparison among the 4 possible combinations on factors b and c, this interaction comparison must be partially confounded with blocks of 6. The BC interaction is, in fact, the comparison of α with

β, so that we are led to the design in Table 18.4, the first symbol of a treatment combination denoting the level of the factor a.

TABLE 18.4

Replicate

I		II		III	
0α	0β	0β	0α	0β	0α
1β	1α	1α	1β	1β	1α
2β	2α	2β	2α	2α	2β

Each block contains the levels of each factor equally frequently for each factor separately, but the 2 groups of treatment combinations α and β must be distributed unequally. The 3 replicates give a design which appears balanced in that main effects are unconfounded. The degree of confounding that actually results from this design will be shown by the corresponding analysis, which will be worked out from the basic mathematical model.

Consider the true yields of each treatment combination which we may denote by (ijk), the levels of the 3 factors. We define

$$\mu = \tfrac{1}{12} \sum_{ijk} (ijk)$$

$$a_i = \tfrac{1}{4} \sum_{jk} (ijk) - \mu$$

$$b_j = \tfrac{1}{6} \sum_{ik} (ijk) - \mu$$

$$c_k = \tfrac{1}{6} \sum_{ij} (ijk) - \mu$$

$$(ab)_{ij} = \tfrac{1}{2} \sum_{k} (ijk) - a_i - b_j - \mu$$

$$(ac)_{ik} = \tfrac{1}{2} \sum_{j} (ijk) - a_i - c_k - \mu$$

$$(bc)_{jk} = \tfrac{1}{3} \sum_{i} (ijk) - b_j - c_k - \mu$$

$$(abc)_{ijk} = (ijk) - a_i - b_j - (ab)_{ij} - c_k - (ac)_{ik} - (bc)_{jk} - \mu$$

In the present case, we may reduce the number of parameters:

$b_0 + b_1 = 0$ so we put $-b_0 = +b_1 = b$

$c_0 + c_1 = 0$ so we put $-c_0 = +c_1 = c$

$\sum_j (ab)_{ij} = 0$ so we put $-(ab)_{i0} = +(ab)_{i1} = (ab)_i$

$\sum_k (ac)_{ik} = 0$ so we put $-(ac)_{i0} = +(ac)_{i1} = (ac)_i$

$\sum_j (bc)_{jk} = \sum_k (bc)_{jk} = 0$

so we put $(bc)_{00} = -(bc)_{01} = -(bc)_{10} = (bc)_{11} = (bc)$

$\sum_i (abc)_{ijk} = \sum_j (abc)_{ijk} = \sum_k (abc)_{ijk} = 0$

so we put $(abc)_{i00} = -(abc)_{i01} = -(abc)_{i10} = (abc)_{i11} = (abc)_i$

We note also that

$$\sum_i a_i = 0, \quad \sum_i (ab)_i = 0, \quad \sum_i (ac)_i = 0, \quad \sum_i (abc)_i = 0$$

The plan in full is as shown in Table 18.5.

TABLE 18.5

Replicate 1		Replicate 2		Replicate 3	
Block 1	Block 2	Block 1	Block 2	Block 1	Block 2
000	001	001	000	001	000
011	010	010	011	010	011
101	100	100	101	101	100
110	111	111	110	110	111
201	200	201	200	200	201
210	211	210	211	211	210

We denote the actual yields by y_{ijklm} where i, j, k are the levels of the 3 factors, l ($= 1, 2, 3$) is the replicate number and m ($= 1, 2$) is the block number. The mathematical model with additivity of treatment effects is

$$y_{ijklm} = \mu + a_i + b_j + (ab)_{ij} + c_k + (ac)_{ik} + (bc)_{jk} + (abc)_{ijk}$$
$$+ r_l + (-1)^m g_l + e_{ijklm} \quad (4)$$

where r_l is the effect of the lth replicate, g_l is the effect of block within the replicate (positive for block 2 and negative for block 1), and the e_{ijklm}'s may be regarded as uncorrelated and distributed with mean zero and the same variance σ^2. Clearly not all possible combinations of subscripts occur. The estimates of the parameters are obtained by minimizing

$$\Sigma e^2_{ijklm}$$

The first term of this sum of squares of deviations, if unnecessary subscripts are eliminated, is

$$[y_{00011} - \mu - a_0 + b + (ab)_0 + c + (ac)_0 - (bc) - (abc)_0 - r_1 + g_1]^2$$

The resulting equations, imposing the condition $\Sigma r_l = 0$, are of a simple form, obtained by equating contrasts of yields with their expectations (Table 18.6).

TABLE 18.6

Equation for	LHS	RHS	
μ	36μ	$Y\ldots\ldots$	$= T$
a_i	$12\mu + 12a_i$	$Y_i\ldots\ldots$	$= [A]_i$
b	$36b$	$Y_{\cdot 1}\ldots - Y_{\cdot 0}\ldots$	$= [B]$
$(ab)_i$	$12b + 12(ab)_i$	$Y_{i1}\ldots - Y_{i0}\ldots$	$= [AB]_i$
c	$36c$	$Y_{\cdot\cdot 1}\ldots - Y_{\cdot\cdot 0}\ldots$	$= [C]$
$(ac)_i$	$12c + 12(ac)_i$	$Y_{i\cdot 1}\ldots - Y_{i\cdot 0}\ldots$	$= [AC]_i$
(bc)	$36(bc) + 4g_1 + 4g_2 + 4g_3$	$Y_{\cdot 00}\ldots - Y_{\cdot 01}\ldots - Y_{\cdot 10}\ldots + Y_{\cdot 11}\ldots$	$= [BC]$
$(abc)_0$	$12(abc)_0 + 12(bc) - 4g_1 + 4g_2 + 4g_3$	$Y_{000}\ldots + Y_{011}\ldots - Y_{001}\ldots - Y_{010}\ldots$	$= [ABC]_0$
$(abc)_1$	$12(abc)_1 + 12(bc) + 4g_1 - 4g_2 + 4g_3$	$Y_{100}\ldots + Y_{111}\ldots - Y_{101}\ldots - Y_{110}\ldots$	$= [ABC]_1$
$(abc)_2$	$12(abc)_2 + 12(bc) + 4g_1 + 4g_2 - 4g_3$	$Y_{200}\ldots + Y_{211}\ldots - Y_{201}\ldots - Y_{210}\ldots$	$= [ABC]_2$
r_l	$12\mu + 12r_l$	$Y\ldots_l\cdot$	$= [R]_l$
g_1	$12g_1 + 4(bc) - 4(abc)_0 + 4(abc)_1 + 4(abc)_2$	$Y\ldots_{12} - Y\ldots_{11}$	$= [G]_1$
g_2	$12g_2 + 4(bc) + 4(abc)_0 - 4(abc)_1 + 4(abc)_2$	$Y\ldots_{22} - Y\ldots_{21}$	$= [G]_2$
g_3	$12g_3 + 4(bc) + 4(abc)_0 + 4(abc)_1 - 4(abc)_2$	$Y\ldots_{32} - Y\ldots_{31}$	$= [G]_3$

These equations may be written down very simply by noting that all the coefficients in the model are plus or minus unity, so that the equations are of the form,

Total of yields that contain a parameter positively −

     total of yields that contain a parameter negatively = its expectation

The solutions of the equations are:

$$
\left.
\begin{aligned}
\hat{\mu} &= \frac{T}{36} \\
12\hat{a}_i &= [A]_i - \frac{T}{3} \\
36\hat{b} &= [B] \\
12\widehat{(ab)}_i &= [AB]_i - \tfrac{1}{3}[B] \\
36\hat{c} &= [C] \\
12\widehat{(ac)}_i &= [AC]_i - \tfrac{1}{3}[C] \\
32\widehat{(bc)} &= [BC] - \tfrac{1}{3}\{[G]_1 + [G]_2 + [G]_3\} \\
32\widehat{(bc)} + 20\widehat{(abc)}_0 &= 3[ABC]_0 + [G]_1 - [G]_2 - [G]_3 \\
32\widehat{(bc)} + 20\widehat{(abc)}_1 &= 3[ABC]_1 - [G]_1 + [G]_2 - [G]_3 \\
32\widehat{(bc)} + 20\widehat{(abc)}_2 &= 3[ABC]_2 - [G]_1 - [G]_2 + [G]_3
\end{aligned}
\right\} \quad (5)
$$

We note that $\hat{b}$, $\hat{c}$, $\widehat{(bc)}$, $\widehat{(ab)}_i$, $\widehat{(ac)}_i$, and $\widehat{(abc)}_i$ are expressed on the basis of the difference of half-plot yields. On a plot-yield basis, these effects and interactions would take twice the value indicated by the equations.

We see, from the form of the normal equations, that the interactions BC and ABC are partially confounded with blocks, so that we will have to obtain a sum of squares for blocks and a sum of squares for treatments eliminating blocks. The total sum of squares removed by fitting all the constants is equal to

$$\hat{\mu}T + \sum_i \hat{a}_i[A]_i + \hat{b}[B] + \Sigma\widehat{(ab)}_i[AB]_i + \hat{c}[C] + \sum_i \widehat{(ac)}_i[AC]_i$$

$$+ \widehat{(bc)}[BC] + \sum_i \widehat{(abc)}_i[ABC]_i + \Sigma\hat{g}_i[G]_i + \Sigma\hat{r}_i[R]_i \quad (6)$$

which equals

$$\frac{T^2}{36} + \left\{\frac{1}{12}\sum_i [R]^2_i - \frac{T^2}{36}\right\} + \left\{\frac{1}{12}\Sigma[A]^2_i - \frac{T^2}{36}\right\} + \left\{\frac{[B]^2}{36}\right\}$$

$$+ \left\{\frac{1}{12}\sum_i [AB]^2_i - \frac{1}{36}[B]^2\right\} + \left\{\frac{[C]^2}{36}\right\} + \left\{\frac{1}{12}\sum_i [AC]^2_i - \frac{[C]^2}{36}\right\}$$

$$+ \widehat{(bc)}[BC] + \sum_i \widehat{(abc)}_i[ABC]_i + \sum_i \hat{g}_i[G]_i \quad (7)$$

Apart from the last 3 terms in this sum, the terms are the quantities one would ordinarily calculate for the correction sum of squares, sum of squares for replicates, A, B, AB, C, and AC, respectively. The last three terms can be manipulated to a simpler form, thus:

$$\sum_i \hat{g}_i[G]_i + \widehat{(bc)}[BC] + \sum_i \widehat{(abc)}_i[ABC]_i$$

$$= \tfrac{1}{12}[G]_1\{[G]_1 - 4\widehat{(bc)} + 4\widehat{(abc)}_0 - 4\widehat{(abc)}_1 - 4\widehat{(abc)}_2\}$$

$$+ \tfrac{1}{12}[G]_2\{[G]_2 - 4\widehat{(bc)} - 4\widehat{(abc)}_0 + 4\widehat{(abc)}_1 - 4\widehat{(abc)}_2\}$$

$$+ \tfrac{1}{12}[G]_3\{[G]_3 - 4\widehat{(bc)} - 4\widehat{(abc)}_0 - 4\widehat{(abc)}_1 + 4\widehat{(abc)}_2\}$$

$$+ \widehat{(bc)}[BC] + \sum_i \widehat{(abc)}_i[ABC]_i$$

$$= \tfrac{1}{12}\{[G]^2{}_1 + [G]^2{}_2 + [G]^2{}_3\}$$

$$+ (\widehat{bc})\{[BC] - \tfrac{1}{3}[G]_1 - \tfrac{1}{3}[G]_2 - \tfrac{1}{3}[G]_3\}$$

$$+ (\widehat{abc})_0\{[ABC]_0 + \tfrac{1}{3}[G]_1 - \tfrac{1}{3}[G]_2 - \tfrac{1}{3}[G]_3\}$$

$$+ (\widehat{abc})_1\{[ABC]_1 - \tfrac{1}{3}[G]_1 + \tfrac{1}{3}[G]_2 - \tfrac{1}{3}[G]_3\}$$

$$+ (\widehat{abc})_2\{[ABC]_2 - \tfrac{1}{3}[G]_1 - \tfrac{1}{3}[G]_2 + \tfrac{1}{3}[G]_3\}$$

$$= \tfrac{1}{12}\{[G]^2{}_1 + [G]^2{}_2 + [G]^2{}_3\} + 32(\widehat{bc})^2$$

$$+ (\widehat{abc})_0 \cdot \tfrac{1}{3}[32(\widehat{bc}) + 20(\widehat{abc})_0] + (\widehat{abc})_1 \cdot \tfrac{1}{3}[32(\widehat{bc}) + 20(\widehat{abc})_1]$$

$$+ (\widehat{abc})_0\tfrac{1}{3}[32(\widehat{bc}) + 20(\widehat{abc})_2]$$

$$= \tfrac{1}{12}\Sigma[G]^2{}_i + 32(\widehat{bc})^2 + \tfrac{20}{3}\sum_i (\widehat{abc})^2{}_i \tag{8}$$

The first term is the sum of squares for blocks ignoring treatments, the second the sum of squares for BC eliminating blocks, and the third the sum of squares for ABC eliminating blocks. The sum of squares for BC can, of course, be written in the form

$$\tfrac{1}{32}\{[BC] - \tfrac{1}{3}[G]_1 - \tfrac{1}{3}[G]_2 - \tfrac{1}{3}[G]_3\}^2 \tag{9}$$

with a similar expression for the sum of squares for ABC. The analysis of variance takes then the form given in Table 18.7.

TABLE 18.7   ANALYSIS OF VARIANCE FOR 3×2^2 EXPERIMENT

Due to	df	Sum of Squares
Replicates	2	As usual
Blocks	3	As usual
A	2	As usual
B	1	As usual
AB	2	As usual
C	1	As usual
AC	2	As usual
BC	1	$32(\widehat{bc})^2$
ABC	2	$\tfrac{20}{3}\sum_i (\widehat{abc})^2{}_i$
Error	19	By subtraction
Total	35	Sum of squares about mean

Finally, we may examine the variance of the partially confounded interactions, that of the unconfounded effects and interactions being the usual one. The estimate $(\widehat{bc})$ of the interaction (bc) may be expanded as a linear function of the yields, and the variance of this linear function obtained. Consider $96\widehat{(bc)}$ which equals $3[BC] - [G]_1 - [G]_2 - [G]_3$.

The coefficients of the plot yields in this linear function are as shown in Table 18.8.

TABLE 18.8

Replicate 1		Replicate 2		Replicate 3	
Block 1	Block 2	Block 1	Block 2	Block 1	Block 2
4	−4	−2	2	−2	2
4	−4	−2	2	−2	2
−2	2	4	−4	−2	2
−2	2	4	−4	−2	2
−2	2	−2	2	4	−4
−2	2	−2	2	4	−4

The sum of squares of these coefficients is $(12 \times 4^2 + 24 \times 2^2) = 288$, and so the variance of $\widehat{(bc)}$ is $(1/96^2)288\sigma^2 = \sigma^2/32$. If we require the interaction BC to be on a per plot basis, we use $2\widehat{(bc)}$ which has a variance of $\sigma^2/8$. This variance may be compared with the variance if no confounding were used, namely, $\sigma^2/9$, and it is seen that the partial confounding has resulted in a loss of $\frac{1}{9}$ information on BC. We can see that the variance we have obtained for $\widehat{(bc)}$ is correct by noting that, for example,
$$\widehat{(bc)} = (bc) + \text{error}$$
and
$$E32\widehat{(bc)}^2 = 32E\,(\text{error})^2 + 32(bc)^2 = \sigma^2 + 32(bc)^2$$
so that
$$E\,(\text{error})^2 = \frac{\sigma^2}{32}$$

Now, considering the ABC interaction, we note that
$$\widehat{(abc)}_0 + \widehat{(abc)}_1 + \widehat{(abc)}_2 = 0$$
so that $\widehat{(abc)}_0$, $\widehat{(abc)}_1$, and $\widehat{(abc)}_2$ are correlated. The variance of any linear contrast
$$\lambda_0\widehat{(abc)}_0 + \lambda_1\widehat{(abc)}_1 + \lambda_2\widehat{(abc)}_2, \quad \lambda_0 + \lambda_1 + \lambda_2 = 0$$
is easily found by noting that
$$20[\lambda_0\widehat{(abc)}_0 + \lambda_1\widehat{(abc)}_1 + \lambda_2\widehat{(abc)}_2]$$
$$= 3\lambda_0[ABC]_0 + 3\lambda_1[ABC]_1 + 3\lambda_2[ABC]_2 + (\lambda_0 - \lambda_1 - \lambda_2)[G]_1$$
$$+ (-\lambda_0 + \lambda_1 - \lambda_2)[G]_2 + (-\lambda_0 - \lambda_1 + \lambda_2)[G]_3$$
$$= 3\lambda_0[ABC]_0 + 3\lambda_1[ABC]_1 + 3\lambda_2[ABC]_2 + 2\lambda_0[G]_1 + 2\lambda_1[G]_2 + 2\lambda_2[G]_3$$

When this is expressed in terms of the plot yields, and the expectation of the square is calculated, we obtain as the variance of $\lambda_0\widehat{(abc)}_0 + \lambda_1\widehat{(abc)}_1 + \lambda_2\widehat{(abc)}_2$ the quantity

$$\frac{1}{400}(108\Sigma\lambda^2_i + 96\Sigma\lambda_i\lambda_j)\sigma^2 = (\Sigma\lambda^2_i)\frac{60}{400}\sigma^2 = (\Sigma\lambda^2_i)\frac{3\sigma^2}{20}$$

It should be remembered that the $\widehat{(abc)}_i$'s are correlated, and we can verify that

$$\text{var }\widehat{(abc)}_i = \frac{\sigma^2}{10}$$

and (10)

$$\text{cov }[\widehat{(abc)}_i, \widehat{(abc)}_j] = -\frac{\sigma^2}{20}$$

We are, for most purposes, interested only in comparisons of the $\widehat{(abc)}_i$'s, and, for such purposes, we may, as a trick, say that the variance of each $\widehat{(abc)}_i$ is $\frac{3}{20}\sigma^2$, and we shall obtain the correct answer. On a per plot basis we estimate the ABC interaction by $2\widehat{(abc)}_i$, which has a variance of $\frac{3}{5}\sigma^2$. It is easily verified that, in the absence of confounding, the corresponding variance would be $\sigma^2/12$, so that the relative information on this interaction is

$$\tfrac{1}{12}/\tfrac{3}{20} = \tfrac{5}{9}$$

and the relative loss in information is $\frac{4}{9}$. There is a curious property of designs, which is exemplified by this case, that the total relative loss in information is equal to the number of degrees of freedom confounded per replicate; thus,

$$1 \times \tfrac{1}{9} + 2 \times \tfrac{4}{9} = 1$$

18.4.2 The 3 × 3 × 2 Experiment

Denoting the factors by a, b, and c, respectively, a design which gives full information on main effects in blocks of 6 plots is given in Table 18.9, where AB_i is the set of combinations of a and b, for which $x_1 + x_2 = i \bmod 3$.

TABLE 18.9 DESIGN FOR 3 × 3 × 2 EXPERIMENT IN BLOCKS OF 6 PLOTS

Level of Third Factor	I_a	I_b	I_c	II_a	II_b	II_c
c_0	AB_1	AB_2	AB_0	AB_2	AB_0	AB_1
c_1	AB_2	AB_0	AB_1	AB_1	AB_2	AB_0

By examination of the least squares equations obtained from a model with mean, block, treatment, and error terms, or by visual inspection, it is seen that the design gives ¾ information on AB; ¼ information on the interaction of AB and C, denoted by ABC; and full information on all other effects and interactions. If a second pair of replicates based on AB^2 is added, the information on all components of the interaction of a and b is

$$\tfrac{7}{8}[= \tfrac{1}{2}(1 + \tfrac{3}{4})]$$

and of the interaction of a, b, and c is

$$\tfrac{5}{8}[= \tfrac{1}{2}(1 + \tfrac{1}{4})]$$

A reparametrization based on the 3^2 system leads to a simplification of the derivation of the analysis.

For the case of the first 2 replicates, and using the notation,

$[I_a]$ = total of block I_a, etc.

$[AB_i]$ = total of treatments for which $x_1 + x_2 = i \bmod 3$

$[ABC]_i$ = total of treatment combinations for which $x_1 + x_2 = i \bmod 3$

        and for which factor c takes the level 1 minus those for which

$x_1 + x_2 = i \bmod 3$ and c takes level 0

it is found (cf. Yates [1]) that, with

$$2Q_0 = 2[AB_0] - [I_b] - [I_c] - [II_b] - [II_c] \tag{11}$$

and similar expressions for $2Q_1$, $2Q_2$, the estimate of AB is equal to

$$\tfrac{1}{18}(2Q_0, 2Q_1, 2Q_2) \tag{12}$$

each component being subject to a variance of $\sigma^2/9$ for comparisons with each other, and the sum of squares for AB is

$$\tfrac{1}{36}[(2Q_0)^2 + (2Q_1)^2 + (2Q_2)^2] \tag{13}$$

Similarly, with

$$2R_0 = 2[ABC_0] - [I_b] + [I_c] + [II_b] - [II_c] \tag{14}$$

and similar expressions for $2R_1$ and $2R_2$, the estimate of (ABC_0, ABC_1, ABC_2) is

$$\tfrac{1}{6}(2R_0 - \overline{2R},\ 2R_1 - \overline{2R},\ 2R_2 - \overline{2R}) \tag{15}$$

and the sum of squares for the 2 degrees of freedom is

$$\frac{1}{12} \sum_i (2R_i - \overline{2R})^2 \tag{16}$$

With the 4 replicates confounding AB and AB^2 equally, the expressions remain the same, except that there are analogous expressions for AB^2 and AB^2C, the expressions $[AB_0]$, $[ABC_0]$, etc., are calculated over the whole experiment, and that the divisor for the expressions $2Q$ is 42; for $\Sigma(2Q - 2\overline{Q})^2$ it is 84; for the expressions $2R$ it is 30; and for $\Sigma(2R - \overline{2R})^2$ it is 60.

18.4.3 The $3 \times 3 \times 3 \times 2$ Experiment

Let the factors be denoted by a, b, c, and d. If we consider the first group of factors a, b, and c, the systems of confounding in blocks of 3 plots which do not result in confounding of main effects are as follows:

$$AB, \ AC, \ AB^2C^2, \ BC^2$$

$$AB, \ AC^2, AB^2C, \ BC$$

$$AB^2, AC, \ ABC^2, \ BC$$

$$AB^2, AC^2, ABC, \ BC^2$$

Taking one of these systems of confounding, we may attach the sets of 3 treatment combinations it gives to the levels of d, in such a way as to give blocks of 6 plots in which all the main effects are unconfounded, and the particular 3-factor interaction of a, b, and c is completely confounded. For the first system this leads to the 9 blocks in Table 18.10.

TABLE 18.10

	I	II	III	IV	V	VI	VII	VIII	IX
d_0	000	012	021	002	011	020	001	022	010
	122	101	110	121	100	112	120	111	102
	211	220	202	210	222	201	212	200	221
d_1	012	021	000	011	020	002	022	010	001
	101	110	122	100	112	121	111	102	120
	220	202	211	222	201	210	200	221	212

The other 3 designs may be obtained in order by interchanging 1 and 2 for the levels of a, of b, and of c, respectively, as may be seen from examining the equations that define the symbols AB, AC, etc.

This design may be analyzed in the same way as the 3×2^2 design. With the above replicate, it will be found that the relative information on the effects and interactions is as given in Table 18.11.

TABLE 18.11   RELATIVE INFORMATION

A, B, C, D	1
AB, AC, BC^2	$\frac{3}{4}$
ABD, ACD, BC^2D	$\frac{1}{4}$
AB^2, AC^2, BC^2	1
AB^2D, AC^2D, BC^2D	1
AB^2C^2	0
ABC^2, AB^2C, ABC	1
AB^2C^2D	1
$ABC^2D, AB^2CD, ABCD$	1

It is left as an exercise to the reader to derive the estimates and the analysis of variance by the methods given in section 18.6.

18.5   NUMBER OF LEVELS A PRODUCT OF DIFFERENT PRIMES

This case is somewhat intricate, because the main effects and interactions cannot be broken down into orthogonal contrasts as in the case of a prime number of levels. To take an example, if the number of levels is 6, we strike difficulties because there do not exist 2 mutually orthogonal Latin squares of side 6, so that we cannot obtain 2 systems of confounding, apart from the confounding of main effects, for two 6-level factors in blocks of 6 which result in different confounding. If we choose the letters of one square for the confounding in one replicate and of another square for the confounding in the second replicate, the degrees of freedom completely confounded in the first square will be partially confounded in the second square. This may be easily verified. It is left as a somewhat awkward exercise to the reader to examine the analysis of such an experiment. It is sufficient here to state that the experimenter is usually not in the position of having to use a definite number of levels such as 6, but can take his choice among 5 or 7 levels, for which cases simple systems of confounding exist.

A formal way out of the difficulty in the case of 6 levels is to regard each factor as arising from 2 pseudofactors, one with 2 levels and one with 3 levels. In this way, some of the designs of the previous class may be used. In the case of a 6×9 experiment, if the need for such should arise, we could regard the experiment as a $3^3 \times 2$ experiment formally, with modifications in the design and analysis.

18.6   THE GENERAL METHOD OF ANALYZING PARTIALLY CONFOUNDED DESIGNS

We have given a complete derivation of the analysis for the $3 \times 2 \times 2$ design and sketched the results for the other designs discussed. The analysis for the $3 \times 2 \times 2$ design was given because it is illustrative of a process that is sometimes valuable, particularly when there are missing data.

We can, however, utilize the formulation of Chapter 6 for the whole problem, and this leads to rules by which the estimates of effects and interactions can be written down merely by looking at the design. To obtain these rules we use, as in that chapter, a model containing μ, the constant contribution, b_i, the contribution of block i, the blocks being numbered from 1 to the total number of blocks in the experiment, t_j, the treatment contribution, where j runs from 1 to the total number of treatment combinations $= t$, say, and an error. We obtained the equations,

$$\left(N_{\cdot j} - \sum_i \frac{n^2_{ij}}{N_{i\cdot}} \right) t_j - \sum_{k \neq j} \left(\sum_i \frac{n_{ij} n_{ik}}{N_{i\cdot}} \right) t_k = Q_j, \qquad j = 1, 2, \cdots, t \quad (17)$$

where

$$Q_j = Y_{\cdot j} - \sum_i \frac{n_{ij}}{N_{i\cdot}} Y_{i\cdot\cdot}$$

that is, the actual total for the treatment adjusted by the block means for the block effects that that total contains. For the designs we discuss in this chapter, and assuming no missing data, we always have $N_{i\cdot}$ equal to k the size of the block, $N_{\cdot j}$ equal to r the number of replicates, and n_{ij} equal to unity if treatment j occurs in block i, and otherwise equal to zero. The equations reduce, therefore, to

$$r\left(1 - \frac{1}{k} \right) t_j - \frac{1}{k} \text{ (sum of } t\text{'s that occur in a block with } t_j) = Q_j \quad (18)$$

We know also that the best linear unbiased estimate of a linear function of the t's is the same linear function of the best linear unbiased estimates of the t's.

Consider now a function of the t's such as the expansion of $(AB_0 - AB_1)(c_0 + c_1)$ in terms of treatment combinations for the $3 \times 3 \times 2$

design given above. The quantity Q for this treatment comparison is given in the table below, the coefficients of plot yields only being given:

	I_a	I_b	I_c	II_a	II_b	II_c
c_0	$(-1 + \frac{1}{2})$	$(-\frac{1}{2})$	$(1 - \frac{1}{2}) + \frac{1}{2}$	$\frac{1}{2}$	$1 - \frac{1}{2}$	$-\frac{1}{2} - (1 - \frac{1}{2})$
c_1	$(+\frac{1}{2})$	$(1 - \frac{1}{2})$	$-\frac{1}{2} - (1 - \frac{1}{2})$	$-(1 - \frac{1}{2})$	$-\frac{1}{2}$	$1 - \frac{1}{2} + \frac{1}{2}$

which reduces to

	I_a	I_b	I_c	II_a	II_b	II_c
c_0	$-\frac{1}{2}$	$-\frac{1}{2}$	1	$\frac{1}{2}$	$\frac{1}{2}$	-1
c_1	$\frac{1}{2}$	$\frac{1}{2}$	-1	$-\frac{1}{2}$	$-\frac{1}{2}$	1

This linear function of the yields is then equated to its expectation, which is

$$-\tfrac{1}{2}(AB_1)c_0 + \tfrac{1}{2}(AB_2)c_1 - \tfrac{1}{2}(AB_2)c_0 + \tfrac{1}{2}(AB_0)c_1$$
$$+ (AB_0)c_0 - (AB_1)c_1 + \tfrac{1}{2}(AB_2)c_0 - \tfrac{1}{2}(AB_1)c_1$$
$$+ \tfrac{1}{2}(AB_0)c_0 - \tfrac{1}{2}(AB_2)c_1 - (AB_1)c_0 + (AB_0)c_1$$

which equals

$$\tfrac{3}{2}[(AB_0)c_0 + (AB_0)c_1 - (AB_1)c_0 - (AB_1)c_1]$$

The expectation of the expression reduces to a multiple of the comparison we wish to estimate, because we are working with groups of 3 plots, each group containing the levels of a, and b and, in a sense AB^2, equally frequently. The expression which estimates $\tfrac{1}{6}(AB_0 - AB_1) \times (c_0 + c_1)$ is then $\tfrac{1}{9}(Q_0 - Q_1)$, where Q_0, Q_1 are defined as before.

To obtain the variance of this estimate, we note that the true treatment comparison is a linear function of the true treatment effects, say, $\lambda_1\tau_1 + \lambda_2\tau_2 + \cdots + \lambda_t\tau_t$, and that it is estimated by $\rho_1 Q_{t_1} + \rho_2 Q_{t_2} + \cdots + \rho_t Q_{t_t}$, where Q_{t_1} is the Q expression for treatment 1, and so on. From the results of Chapter 6 the variance of the estimate is $(\lambda_1\rho_1 + \lambda_2\rho_2 + \cdots + \lambda_t\rho_t)\sigma^2$. The variance of $\tfrac{1}{9}(Q_0 - Q_1)$ is therefore $\tfrac{2}{9}\sigma^2$. The sum of squares for this comparison will therefore be $\tfrac{9}{2} \times 1/9^2 (Q_0$

$- Q_1)^2 = \frac{1}{18}(Q_0 - Q_1)^2$. In a similar way we would find that $\frac{1}{12}(AB_0 + AB_1 - 2AB_2)(c_0 + c_1)$ is estimated by $\frac{1}{9}(Q_0 + Q_1 - 2Q_2)$, and that the variance of this comparison is $\frac{6}{9}\sigma^2$, so that the sum of squares is

$$\frac{(Q_0 + Q_1 - 2Q_2)^2}{9 \times 6}$$

The total sum of squares for the AB interaction is, therefore,

$$\tfrac{1}{9}[(Q_0 - \bar{Q})^2 + (Q_1 - \bar{Q})^2 + (Q_2 - \bar{Q})^2]$$

For purposes of comparison of the Q_i's we may regard the Q_i's as each having a variance of $\frac{1}{9}\sigma^2$ and zero correlation. The factor $\frac{1}{9}$ is also the multiplier of the particular Q function, which is used to estimate the corresponding parameters. This illustrates a general rule of the relation among the variance of the Q_i's, the divisor in the sum of squares, and the relative information.

For the general case, suppose that we wish to estimate

$$\sum_1^t \lambda_i \tau_i \tag{19}$$

where

$$\Sigma \lambda_i = 0$$

the λ_i's are all 0, $+1$, or -1 and the τ_i is the effect of the ith treatment combination. As an estimate of this quantity, we shall use

$$\frac{1}{K}\left(\sum_1^t \lambda_i Q_i\right) \tag{20}$$

where Q_i is the Q for the ith treatment combination and K is some constant. Then the variance of the estimate is $(1/K)(\Sigma \lambda^2_i)\sigma^2$, and the sum of squares is

$$\frac{K}{\sum_1^t \lambda^2_i}\left[\frac{1}{K}\left(\sum_1^t \lambda_i Q_i\right)\right]^2$$

If there were no confounding, the quantities Q_i would be the total yields of the ith treatment combination, and K would equal r the number of replicates, and the variance of the estimate would be

$$\frac{1}{r}\left(\sum_1^t \lambda^2_i\right)\sigma^2$$

The relative information on the comparison is equal to

$$\left(\frac{\text{variance without confounding}}{\text{variance with confounding}}\right)$$

assuming σ^2 to be the same in both cases. This is equal to K/r, and, if we denote it by I, we have the relations given in Table 18.12.

TABLE 18.12

	No Confounding	Confounding
Divisor for $\Sigma\lambda_i Q_i$	r	$K = r \times I$
Variance/σ^2	$\dfrac{\Sigma\lambda^2_i}{r}$	$\dfrac{\Sigma\lambda^2_i}{K} = \dfrac{\Sigma\lambda^2_i}{r} \times \dfrac{1}{I}$
Divisor of $(\Sigma\lambda_i Q_i)^2$ for sum of squares	$r(\Sigma\lambda^2_i)$	$K(\Sigma\lambda^2_i) = r(\Sigma\lambda^2_i) \times I$

Actually, the divisor for $\Sigma\lambda_i Q_i$ necessary to express the comparison on the basis of the difference of a plot yield positive for the comparison and of a plot yield negative for the comparison is $\dfrac{2}{r\Sigma|\lambda_i|}$ or $\dfrac{2}{K\Sigma|\lambda_i|}$, in the two cases. This rule is not followed strictly in some publications, but the reader should have no difficulty in reconciling the statements given here with others if this is taken into account.

As an example of the utilization of this procedure, we shall consider the estimation of the ABC interaction for the $3 \times 3 \times 2$ design. The interaction, which we may denote by AB^2C, is unconfounded. We confine ourselves to 1 degree of freedom of the partially confounded interaction: namely, the expansion in terms of treatment combinations of

$$(AB_0 - AB_1)(c_0 - c_1)$$

The expression in the Q's is represented diagrammatically in Table 18.13.

TABLE 18.13

	I_a	I_b	I_c	II_a	II_b	II_c
c_0	$-1 + \frac{1}{2}$	$+\frac{1}{2}$	$1 - \frac{1}{2} - \frac{1}{2}$	$-\frac{1}{2}$	$1 - \frac{1}{2}$	$-1 + \frac{1}{2} + \frac{1}{2}$
	$= -\frac{1}{2}$	$= \frac{1}{2}$	$= 0$	$= -\frac{1}{2}$	$= \frac{1}{2}$	$= 0$
c_1	$+\frac{1}{2}$	$-1 + \frac{1}{2}$	$1 - \frac{1}{2} - \frac{1}{2}$	$1 - \frac{1}{2}$	$-\frac{1}{2}$	$-1 + \frac{1}{2} + \frac{1}{2}$
	$= \frac{1}{2}$	$= -\frac{1}{2}$	$= 0$	$= \frac{1}{2}$	$= -\frac{1}{2}$	$= 0$

The expectation of the whole expression is readily seen to be

$$\tfrac{1}{2}(AB_0c_0 - AB_0c_1 - AB_1c_0 + AB_1c_1)$$

The divisor on this expression is therefore 3, and, with no confounding, we would have used a divisor of 12, so that we have $\frac{1}{4}$ relative information on the comparison. The variance of the comparison would have been $\frac{1}{6}\sigma^2$, so that, with confounding, it is $\frac{2}{3}\sigma^2$, and the sum of squares for the comparison is $(\text{Expression})^2/6$. From the point of view of computation, we note that we may calculate $2R_0$, $2R_1$, and $2R_2$ as given earlier, the expression above being equal to $(R_0 - R_1)$. The sum of squares for the 1 degree of freedom comparison is $\frac{1}{6}(R_0 - R_1)^2$, so that by symmetry the sum of squares for the 2 degrees of freedom for ABC is

$$\tfrac{1}{3}\Sigma(R_i - \bar{R})^2 = \tfrac{1}{12}\Sigma(2R_i - 2\bar{R})^2$$

18.7 OTHER MIXED FACTORIAL DESIGNS

A general procedure for obtaining designs of the mixed factorial type, that is, of type $p^m q^n$, has been exemplified in the foregoing examples. The guiding principle is to consider the two component pure systems and confounding with as low block size with each of these. For the $3^2 2^2$ factorial experiment, we examine therefore the 3^2 system in blocks of 3, and the 2^2 system in blocks of 2. If we denote the factors in order by a, b, c, d, we can make up blocks of 3 on the first 2 factors by confounding AB or AB^2, and blocks of 2 on the second pair of factors by confounding CD. Thus we are led to the following design for 4 replicates partially confounding AB and $ABCD$:

I_a	I_b	I_c	I_d	I_e	I_f	II_a	II_b	II_c	II_d	II_e	II_f
0α	1α	2α	0β	1β	2β	1α	2α	0α	1β	2β	0β
1β	2β	0β	1α	2α	0α	0β	1β	2β	0α	1α	2α

in which

0 denotes the combinations on a and b: 00, 12, 21
1 denotes the combinations on a and b: 01, 10, 22
2 denotes the combinations on a and b: 02, 20, 11

and

α denotes the combinations on c and d: 00, 11
β denotes the combinations on c and d: 01, 10

A second pair of replicates based on AB^2 could be used to give balance on the interaction of a and b.

Numerous investigations have been made of other cases, for example, Li,[2] Nair and Rao.[3-6] The reader may refer to these publications. The occasion will not arise frequently when designs other than those given here or easily derivable from those given here are desired. Frequently, when other cases are dealt with, a split-plot design or some other type of design is preferable. For example, a 5×2 experiment can be performed with a 5×5 Latin square with the plots split into 2 parts for the 2-level factor. Apart from familiarity with all the types of design, the only solution of this problem would be a dictionary of designs according to the structure of the treatments, but the value of such a dictionary, if constructed, would be somewhat doubtful unless it indicated the value of designs and how minor modifications in the structure of the treatments would enable a much better design to be used.

18.8 PARTIALLY FACTORIAL EXPERIMENTS

There is a class of experiments in which the treatment combinations have an appearance of consisting of a full set of factorial combinations, but are not in fact so. The simplest example of this type is that in which there are, say, 3 equally spaced amounts, including a zero amount of a particular treatment administered in 3 forms. If none of the amounts is zero, no new difficulty arises.

	Form		
Amount	1	2	3
0	x	x	x
1	x	x	x
2	x	x	x

At first sight there appear to be 9 treatment combinations, but there are, in fact, only 7 different ones, as the 3 forms at zero amounts consist each of zero application and are identical. The experimenter must consider whether he should use all 9 treatment combinations as though they are distinct or only the 7 distinct combinations, and further he should consider the method of analysis in each case.

First, assume that all 9 treatment combinations are used and analyzed in the usual way. The 8 degrees of freedom would then be partitioned as follows:

	df
Amount	2
Form	2
Interaction	4
Total	8

We notice that the comparison of forms will include a comparison of the zero treatment plots, which can contribute only experimental error. We make up the set of 8 orthogonal comparisons given in Table 18.14, the first subscript of the treatment symbol representing the form and the second the amount to indicate the defects of the above partitioning:

TABLE 18.14 TREATMENT COMPARISONS

Contrast	10	20	30	11	21	31	12	22	32
A_1	2	2	2	−1	−1	−1	−1	−1	−1
A_2	0	0	0	1	1	1	−1	−1	−1
F_1	2	−1	−1	2	−1	−1	2	−1	−1
F_2	0	1	−1	0	1	−1	0	1	−1
$A_1 \times F_1$	4	−2	−2	−2	1	1	−2	1	1
$A_1 \times F_2$	0	2	−2	0	−1	1	0	−1	1
$A_2 \times F_1$	0	0	0	2	−1	−1	−2	1	1
$A_2 \times F_2$	0	0	0	0	1	−1	0	−1	1

Because 10, 20, and 30 are, in fact, identical treatments, we see that F_1 and $A_L \times F_1$ estimate the same contrast of real treatments, apart from sign and different errors, and, likewise, F_2 and $A_L \times F_2$ estimate the same contrast.   Thus, if we made an analysis in the above way, the sum of squares for interaction would include a component arising directly from the differences between forms.   There are, of course, only 2 degrees of freedom for the interaction of amounts and forms: namely, the interaction of the table:

Forms

Amount	1	2	3
1	x	x	x
2	x	x	x

The best method of analysis for data of this type depends on the response law and how it may vary for each form.   The situation may be represented as in Figure 20.

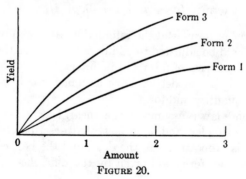

FIGURE 20.

If the response curves were straight lines, the hypothesis would be

$$y_{ij} = \mu + f_i x + e_{ij} \text{ (plus replicate effects)}$$

$$= \mu + \bar{f}x + (f_i - \bar{f})x + e_{ij} \tag{21}$$

The experimenter would then be interested in testing whether the $(f_i - \bar{f})$'s are all zero. It would be advisable to include in the model a term for curvilinearity in the response, i.e., use the model

$$y_{ij} = \mu + f_i x + g_i x^2 + e_{ij} \tag{22}$$

If f_i and g_i are without restriction, we would be fitting 7 constants μ, f_i, g_i to the 7 distinct yields, and there is little new to be said about the matter. It may be more reasonable to suppose that

$$y_{1j} = \mu + f_1 x + g_1 x^2 + e_{1j}$$

$$y_{2j} = \mu + \lambda f_1 x + \lambda^2 g_1 x^2 + e_{2j}$$

$$y_{3j} = \mu + \tau f_1 x + \tau^2 g_1 x^2 + e_{3j}$$

that is, that the basic response law is

$$y_{ij} = \mu + fx + gx^2 \tag{23}$$

and that the forms differ in containing different concentrations of the basic causative factor.

With the modification of the interaction given above, we would obtain the following estimates, for each of which we give the expectation:

Linear effect of quantity: $\frac{2}{3}(1 + \lambda + \tau)f_1 + \frac{4}{3}(1 + \lambda^2 + \tau^2)g_1$

Quadratic effect of quantity: $\frac{2}{3}(1 + \lambda^2 + \tau^2)g_1$

Effect of forms: $3f_1 + 5g_1, 3\lambda f_1 + 5\lambda^2 g_1, 3\tau f_1 + 5\tau^2 g_1$

Quantity $\times$ form: $f_1 + 3g_1, \lambda f_1 + 3\lambda^2 g_1, \tau f_1 + 3\tau^2 g_1$

where the effect of forms and the interaction are each given by 3 quantities which would be adjusted to add to zero. We see that this method of expressing the effects of form and its interaction with quantity is not satisfactory with the model we have assumed, for if $g_1 = 0$, there is interaction of quantity and form.

If the response law is assumed to be linear, i.e., that g_1 above is zero, the situation is simpler, and is, in fact, that described by Yates.[1] The effect of form is proportional to the dose, and the best estimates of the differences between forms are given by the differences of the yield at level 1 plus twice the yield at level 2. The interaction will then be twice the yield at level 1 minus the yield at level 2. With this method of estimation, the expectations of the estimates including quadratic terms are as follows:

Linear effect of quantity: $\frac{2}{3}(1 + \lambda + \tau)f_1 + \frac{4}{3}(1 + \lambda^2 + \tau^2)g_1$

Quadratic effect of quantity: $\frac{2}{3}(1 + \lambda^2 + \tau^2)g_1$

Effect of forms: $5f_1 + 9g_1, 5\lambda f_1 + 9\lambda^2 g_1, 5\tau f_1 + 9\tau^2 g_1$

Quantity $\times$ form: $2g_1, 2\lambda^2 g_1, 2\tau^2 g_1$

We note that if the relationships are in fact linear, i.e., $g_1 = 0$, there is no quadratic effect of quantity, and also no interaction of form and quantity. If, however, there is curvature in the response law, the interaction of form and quantity will contain some contribution arising from this source, when we would prefer it to be zero. This example is important in indicating that a definition of interaction is a consequence of the definition of the main effect. A similar procedure may be used with any number of levels, equally or unequally spaced.

Satisfactory methods for the analysis of such data have not been evolved for more or less general situations. The reader may refer to Finney [7] for a discussion of some of these questions in relation to biological assay. The essential fact is that the experimenter should have ideas on response laws with his particular experimental material, because, otherwise, it is impossible for him to characterize accurately the differences in forms. In the absence of such knowledge, he can always make the simple statement that, at particular dosages, one form gives a response a stated amount different from that due to another form, and, in order to make such statements, it will be necessary to remove main effects of blocks and any other removable environmental effects. An important point in the design of such experiments is that the zero treatments be adequately represented because the yield in question forms the base point for the curves of the 3 forms. If the response law is known, this is not necessarily so. It is also important that no effects be confounded. It would, for example, be very unwise to test the forms on different groups of experimental units. If experimental circumstances necessitate the testing of forms on different groups, the zero treatment, or even all the rates for one form, should be tested in each group.

Of the same type, but giving more identical treatments, is the case mentioned by Yates [1] when we have levels of a treatment, form, and method of application if the lowest level is zero amount. For example, with 2 levels, zero = (1) and l; 2 forms, f_1, f_2; and 2 methods, m_1, m_2; the 8 combinations are

$$m_1f_1, \; m_1f_1l, \; m_1f_2, \; m_1f_2l$$

$$m_2f_1, \; m_2f_1l, \; m_2f_2, \; m_2f_2l$$

The combinations m_1f_1, m_1f_2, m_2f_1, and m_2f_2 are identical and consist, in fact, of zero treatment. The appropriate method of analysis in such cases depends on whether the zero treatment is represented 4, 3, 2 times or only once but, in all cases, amounts to a suitable choice of individual degrees of freedom. For example, with 2 replicates, each of 7 plots, the control being represented 3 times, we have the 6 contrasts among the 7 treatments or quasitreatments in a block shown in Table 18.15.

TABLE 18.15

	c_1	c_2	c_3	m_1f_1l	m_1f_2l	m_2f_1l	m_2f_2l
Forms F				-1	$+1$	-1	$+1$
Methods M				-1	-1	$+1$	$+1$
Forms $\times$ Methods FM				$+1$	-1	-1	$+1$
Levels L	-4	-4	-4	$+3$	$+3$	$+3$	$+3$
Error E_1	1	-1					
Error E_2	1	1	-2				

The structure of the analysis of variance will be:

	df
Replicate R	1
F	1
M	1
FM	1
L	1
Error E_1, $E_1 \times R$	
E_2, $E_2 \times R$	8
$F \times R$, $M \times R$	
$FM \times R$, $L \times R$	
Total	13

The sums of squares are calculated in the usual way.

As a general conclusion for this type of experiment, in the absence of other overriding facets of the experimental situation, it is probably best to retain the full factorial structure which will allow use of the standard systems of confounding to reduce block size. In some cases, as in the second case discussed above, it may be possible to obtain a set of orthogonal contrasts which are reasonable to the experimenter. In other cases, when the response law is unknown, the best procedure is to estimate the yield of each treatment combination removing block effects. If there are dummy treatments which appear in the factorial structure to be different, the mean of their adjusted values may be used as an estimate of the yield of the one distinct combination.

REFERENCES

1. YATES, F. *The design and analysis of factorial experiments.* Imp. Bur. Soil Sci., Harpenden, England. 1937.
2. LI, J. Design and statistical analysis of some confounded factorial experiments. *Iowa Agr. Exp. Sta. Res. Bull.*, **333**, 1944.
3. NAIR, K. R., and RAO, C. R. Confounded designs for asymmetrical factorial experiments. *Sci. and Cult.*, **7**, 313–314, 1941.
4. NAIR, K. R., and RAO, C. R. Confounded designs for the $k \times p^m \times q^n \cdots$ type of factorial experiment. *Sci. and Cult.*, **7**, 361–362, 1942.
5. NAIR, K. R., and RAO, C. R. A general class of quasi-factorial designs leading to confounded designs for factorial experiments. *Sci. and Cult.*, **7**, 457–458, 1942.
6. NAIR, K. R., and RAO, C. R. Confounding in asymmetrical factorial experiments. *Jour. Roy. Stat. Soc. B*, **10**, 109–131, 1948.
7. FINNEY, D. J. The principles of biological assay. *Suppl. Jour. Roy. Stat. Soc.*, **9**, 46–91, 1947.

CHAPTER 19

Split-Plot Experiments

19.1 THE SIMPLE SPLIT-PLOT EXPERIMENT

In the previous chapters we have covered the great bulk of experiments involving several factors which are likely to be of practical importance. For all these experiments, the main problem is to devise arrangements in small blocks, because the error variance of an experiment increases markedly with the size of block. The device of confounding is used to give arrangements in small blocks. In this way, we sacrifice information on some effects and interactions (preferably high-order interactions) which the experimenter regards as trivial or unimportant, in order that we can obtain more information on the more interesting questions. With this exception, the experiments are so planned that the information (as measured by the reciprocal of the true variance) on effects and interactions is the same. In the case when an effect or interaction is confounded with blocks, we have ignored the fact that the block comparisons contain some information. Block comparisons, in fact, contain some information on treatment comparisons, which can be extracted if we can estimate the variance between blocks within a replicate which are treated alike. With a number of replicates of a confounded design, this is, of course, possible, as the reader will have already noted, because we could, with some designs, obtain a test of significance of confounded effects or interactions. We shall strike the problem of the combination of this type of information, known as *interblock* or *between-block* information, with the other type of information, known as *intra-block* or *within-block* information when we discuss quasifactorial and incomplete block designs in later chapters. For most of the designs discussed in previous chapters, the amount of interblock information is very small, and we did not consider its utilization. For designs using blocks of 2 or 4 plots with several replicates, however, it might be well worth while to do so, and the appropriate methods will be given.

We now come to a class of designs in which, for one reason or another, we plan to utilize the interblock information from the start and for which the interblock information is an essential part of the body of information provided by the experiment. The structure of the experiments will be that of plots within blocks and blocks within replicates. The usual terminology is to refer to the blocks as whole plots and the plots as split plots. There is nothing essentially new in the design or analysis of such experiments, but they are sufficiently distinctive to merit separate consideration. These experiments are known as split-plot experiments.

As an example, we could have the arrangement shown in Figure 21 for testing 5 varieties each at 5 rates of planting. The basic unit or split plot would be chosen in the usual way; the plot would consist of 5 split plots, and the replicate of 5 plots, with, say, 4 replicates. If rates of planting were the whole-plot treatment and varieties the split-plot treatment, each split plot within a whole plot would have the same rate of planting but a different variety. One replicate could look like Figure 21 in plan, the first symbol denoting the variety, and the second the rate of planting.

11	34	25	52	13
31	24	15	32	43
41	54	35	12	53
21	44	55	42	23
51	14	45	22	33

FIGURE 21.

The double lines correspond to a grouping of the plots or experimental units on the usual basis for making up blocks, and the single lines separate the split plots. In a field experiment it is natural to make up the split plots within a whole plot in such a way as to sample best the whole plot, i.e., in the direction with the greater trend, and to lay out the whole plots within a replicate in such a way as to sample the replicate best. The randomization procedure is to allot whole-plot treatments at random to the whole plots, and then to allot the split-plot treatments at random within the whole plot. It is usually desirable to have rectangular plots for field experiments, and a split-plot experiment in the field looks like the above plan. The effects of the restrictions in the design on the accuracy of estimates will suggest the principles on which the design is based.

The analysis of such an experiment will be based on the additive model

$$y_{ijk} = \mu + r_i + t_{jk} + \text{error} \qquad (1)$$

where

Replicate number $= i = 1, 2, \cdots, r$

Whole-plot treatment number $= j = 1, 2, \cdots, t$

Split-plot treatment number $= k = 1, 2, \cdots, s$

The important question is the assumption that may be made about the error term. As in the case of randomized blocks and Latin squares, we regard this error term as arising because the treatment combination t_{jk} falls on one particular plot rather than another. We note immediately that we cannot assume the errors to be homogeneous for all the treatment combinations. The treatment combinations with the same whole-plot treatment are restricted to lie within the same whole plot for each replicate. To elucidate the matter, we shall follow the same procedure that we used for the randomized block design. Suppose that the plots have basic yields x_{iuv}, u, v being the whole-plot and split-plot numbers, and that the yield of treatment combination (jk) on this plot x_{iuvjk} is expressible as

$$x_{iuvjk} = x_{iuv} + t_{jk} \qquad (2)$$

Then, as for the randomized blocks, we have the identity

$$x_{iuvjk} = x_{\ldots\ldots} + (x_{i\ldots\ldots} - x_{\ldots\ldots}) + (x_{\ldots jk} - x_{\ldots\ldots})$$
$$+ (x_{i\cdot\cdot jk} - x_{i\ldots\ldots} - x_{\ldots jk} + x_{\ldots\ldots}) + (x_{iuvjk} - x_{i\cdot\cdot jk}) \qquad (3)$$

which reduces to

$$x_{iuvjk} = x_{\ldots} + t_{\cdot\cdot} + (x_{i\cdot\cdot} - x_{\ldots}) + (t_{jk} - t_{\cdot\cdot}) + (x_{iuv} - x_{i\cdot\cdot}) \qquad (4)$$

The treatment combination occurs on a randomly chosen plot, and we denote its actual yield by y_{ijk} so that we have

$$y_{ijk} = \mu + r_i + (t_{jk} - t_{\cdot\cdot}) + (x_{iuv} - x_{i\cdot\cdot}) \qquad (5)$$

We may, furthermore, write

$$t_{jk} = t_{\cdot\cdot} + (t_{j\cdot} - t_{\cdot\cdot}) + (t_{\cdot k} - t_{\cdot\cdot}) + (t_{jk} - t_{j\cdot} - t_{\cdot k} + t_{\cdot\cdot})$$
$$= t_{\cdot\cdot} + t_j + s_k + (ts)_{jk} \quad \text{say} \qquad (6)$$

and, noting that

$$x_{iuv} - x_{i\cdot\cdot} = (x_{iu\cdot} - x_{i\cdot\cdot}) + x_{iuv} - x_{iu\cdot}) \qquad (7)$$

we have, on rearrangement,

$$y_{ijk} = \mu + r_i + t_j + (x_{iu\cdot} - x_{i\cdot\cdot}) + s_k + (ts)_{jk} + (x_{iuv} - x_{iu\cdot}) \qquad (8)$$

The observed yield may then be written

$$y_{ijk} = \mu + r_i + t_j + \eta_{ij} + s_k + (ts)_{jk} + e_{ijk} \qquad (9)$$

where

$$\eta_{ij} = \Sigma \delta_{iu}^j (x_{iu\cdot} - x_{i\cdot\cdot})$$

$$e_{ijk} = \Sigma \delta_{iuv}^{jk} (x_{iuv} - x_{iu\cdot})$$

δ_{iu}^j = a random variable which takes the value of unity if treatment j occurs on whole plot u, in replicate i

and

δ_{iuv}^{jk} = a random variable which takes the value of unity if treatment combination (jk) occurs on plot (uv), in replicate i

The errors η_{ij} are correlated with each other, and the errors e_{ijk} are correlated with each other, as in the case of randomized blocks. The above discussion dealt only with the plot errors, but, as in the case of randomized blocks, we may regard the other errors as being included in the η_{ij} and e_{ijk}.

To obtain the analysis of variance by the present approach, we make up a set of s orthogonal linear functions of the split-plot yields within each whole plot as follows:

$$c_{ij1} = \lambda_{11} y_{ij1} + \lambda_{12} y_{ij2} + \cdots + \lambda_{1s} y_{ijs}$$

$$c_{ij2} = \lambda_{21} y_{ij1} + \lambda_{22} y_{ij2} + \cdots + \lambda_{2s} y_{ijs}$$

$$\cdots \cdots \cdots \cdots \cdots \cdots \cdots \cdots \quad (10)$$

$$c_{ijs} = \lambda_{s1} y_{ij1} + \lambda_{s2} y_{ij2} + \cdots + \lambda_{ss} y_{ijs}$$

where

$$\lambda_{11} = \lambda_{12} = \cdots = \lambda_{1s} = \frac{1}{\sqrt{s}}$$

$$\sum_{k=1}^{s} \lambda_{ik} = 0 \quad \text{for} \quad i = 2, 3, \cdots, s$$

$$\sum_{k=1}^{s} \lambda_{ik} \lambda_{i'k} = 0 \quad \text{for} \quad i \neq i' \quad (11)$$

$$\sum_{k=1}^{s} \lambda^2_{ik} = 1$$

These comparisons are equal to the same comparisons of the t_{jk}'s plus errors, which we proceed to examine. For any c_{ij1}, we find that

$$c_{ij1} = \sqrt{s}(\mu + r_i + t_j + \eta_{ij}) \quad (12)$$

so that the quantities $c_{ij1}/\sqrt{s}$ which equal the whole-plot means are given by

$$\frac{c_{ij1}}{\sqrt{s}} = \mu + r_i + t_j + \eta_{ij} \quad (12a)$$

This is a model exactly the same as for the randomized block experiment for t treatments in r blocks of t plots, so that we know that the estimate of any comparison of the t's is given by the comparison of the whole-plot means, and we obtain the analysis of variance:

	df
Replicates	$r - 1$
Treatment	$t - 1$
Error	$(r - 1)(t - 1)$

Considering now the other functions c_{ijk}, k being unequal to unity, we note that the quantity $(x_{iu\cdot} - x_{i\cdot\cdot})$ is the same for all split plots of the same whole plot, so that, as regards the errors, we have orthogonal contrasts of the quantities $(x_{iuv} - x_{iu\cdot})$. We found in the case of randomized blocks that orthogonal comparisons of quantities such as these are uncorrelated. Again, therefore, we may obtain estimates of the comparisons of the t_{jk}'s, by taking the corresponding comparisons of the observed means of the comparisons over all replicates. The estimates of whole-plot mean comparisons and split-plot comparisons will be best linear unbiased estimates if the variance of the $(x_{iu\cdot} - x_{i\cdot\cdot})$ is the same for all replicates and the variance of the $(x_{iuv} - x_{iu\cdot})$ is the same for all whole plots. An analysis of variance may be made for the split-plot comparisons as for the whole-plot comparisons, and, if the whole plots are analyzed on a split-plot basis, that is, if the quantities c_{ij1} are analyzed, the two analyses of variance may be combined into one, in such a way that the constituent parts add up to the total sum of squares about the mean.

TABLE 19.1 ANALYSIS OF VARIANCE FOR A SPLIT-PLOT EXPERIMENT

Due to	df	Sum of Squares
Replicates R	$r - 1$	$\sum_i \dfrac{Y^2_{i\cdot\cdot}}{ts} - \dfrac{Y^2_{\cdots}}{rts}$
Whole-plot treatments T	$t - 1$	$\sum_j \dfrac{Y^2_{\cdot j\cdot}}{rs} - \dfrac{Y^2_{\cdots}}{rts}$
$R \times T$	$(r - 1)(t - 1)$	$\sum_{ij} \dfrac{Y^2_{ij\cdot}}{s} - \sum_i \dfrac{Y^2_{i\cdot\cdot}}{ts} - \sum_j \dfrac{Y^2_{\cdot j\cdot}}{rs} + \dfrac{Y^2_{\cdots}}{rts}$
Split-plot treatments S	$s - 1$	$\sum_k \dfrac{Y^2_{\cdot\cdot k}}{rt} - \dfrac{Y^2_{\cdots}}{rts}$
$S \times T$	$(t - 1)(s - 1)$	$\sum_{jk} \dfrac{Y^2_{\cdot jk}}{r} - \sum_j \dfrac{Y^2_{\cdot j\cdot}}{rs} - \sum_k \dfrac{Y^2_{\cdot\cdot k}}{rt} + \dfrac{Y^2_{\cdots}}{rts}$
Remainder	$(r - 1)t(s - 1)$	By subtraction
Total	$rts - 1$	$\sum_{ijk} y^2_{ijk} - \dfrac{Y^2_{\cdots}}{rts}$

If we denote the expectation of the whole-plot mean square by σ^2 and of the split-plot mean square by σ^2_s, we find that the expectations of the mean squares are as indicated in Table 19.2.

TABLE 19.2

	Mean Square	Expectation of Mean Square
Whole-plot treatments T	T	$\sigma^2 + \dfrac{rs}{t-1}\sum_j t^2_j$
$R \times T$	W	σ^2
Split-plot treatments S	S	$\sigma^2_s + \dfrac{rt}{s-1}\Sigma s^2_k$
$S \times T$	I	$\sigma^2_s + \dfrac{r}{(t-1)(s-1)}\sum_{jk} (ts)^2_{jk}$
Remainder	E	σ^2_s

The results we have obtained could have been obtained from the model

$$y_{ijk} = \mu + r_i + t_j + \eta_{ij} + s_k + (ts)_{jk} + e_{ijk} \qquad (13)$$

in which the η_{ij}'s are normally and independently distributed with mean zero and variance σ^2_w, and the e_{ijk}'s are normally and independently distributed with mean zero and variance σ^2_s. In that case, we would have

$$\sigma^2 = \sigma^2_s + s\sigma^2_w$$

In passing, it may be noted that the use of the finite model obviates one difficulty that arises with the infinite model: namely, that, apart from sampling errors, the whole-plot error mean square must be greater than E. With the finite model, this need not necessarily happen. The infinite model approach does, however, indicate that this will generally be the case. The expectations of the mean squares, which are the same for both finite and infinite models, indicate the appropriate tests of significance:

1. To test $t_j = 0$, $j = 1, \cdots, t$, i.e., that $\Sigma t^2_j = 0$, or that there are no differences between whole-plot treatments *averaged over all the split-plot treatments*, test T/W against the F distribution with $(t-1)$ and $(r-1)(t-1)$ degrees of freedom.

2. To test $s_k = 0$, $k = 1, \cdots, s$, i.e., that $\Sigma s^2_k = 0$, or that there are no differences between split-plot treatments *averaged over all the whole-plot treatments*, test S/E against the F distribution with $(s-1)$ and $(r-1)t(s-1)$ degrees of freedom.

3. To test that the interactions of whole-plot treatments and split-plot treatments are zero, i.e., that the $(ts)_{jk}$'s are all zero, test I/E against the F distribution with $(t-1)(s-1)$ and $(r-1)t(s-1)$ degrees of freedom.

As with randomized blocks or Latin squares, we rely on the approximation by the F test to the randomization test and perform the tests as stated.

It may be noted that, if the third test of significance gives the result that the interaction cannot be regarded as zero, the other 2 tests of significance may be somewhat irrelevant. If there is an interaction, both whole-plot treatments and split-plot treatments have an effect, but not in an additive way. Whether the whole-plot treatments averaged over the split-plot treatments or vice-versa differ insignificantly or not, when there is an interaction, may be of little interest because both sets of treatments have an effect. It should also be noted that there is no justification for testing the split-plot treatment mean square against the interaction mean square, unless the interaction is, in fact, zero. If this were the case, this interaction sum of squares would not have been separated from the error mean square in the first place. A test against interaction is valid if the whole-plot treatments are a random sample of an infinite population of treatments, and this would then test for the existence of split-plot treatment effects averaged over the population of whole-plot treatments (see Chapter 28).

If there are no missing data, all treatment comparisons are estimated directly as the corresponding comparison of observed means. Finally, in the interpretation of results, it is necessary to obtain the appropriate standard error for any comparison of the treatments. The general procedure for this follows from the above description of the analysis. Any comparison of treatments can be expressed as a linear function of comparisons of the two types, whole-plot and split-plot comparisons, given above. We list the types of comparison that can be made, all being expressed on the basis of a split-plot yield:

1. A comparison of whole-plot treatment means: Each whole-plot mean has a variance of $\dfrac{\sigma^2}{s}\left(=\dfrac{\sigma^2_s + s\sigma^2_w}{s}\right)$, so that each whole-plot treatment mean has a variance of σ^2/rs for comparison with other whole-plot treatment means.

2. A comparison of split-plot treatment means: This comparison is estimated by the comparison of actual means, each mean being the mean of rt split plots and, therefore, having a variance of σ^2_s/rt.

3. A component of the interaction of whole-plot and split-plot treatments will have an error calculated in the usual way with a variance of σ^2_s per split plot. For such comparisons, each treatment combination mean has a variance of σ^2_s/r.

4. The comparison of whole-plot treatments averaged over a set of d of the split-plot treatments, e.g., a comparison between the t quantities

$$\alpha_i = \frac{1}{d}(t_{i1} + t_{i2} + \cdots + t_{id}), \qquad i = 1, 2, \cdots, t$$

has an error variance depending on both σ^2 and σ^2_s. To obtain the variance of each of these quantities we note that:

(a) The estimate of $X = (t_{i1} + t_{i2} + \cdots + t_{id}) + (t_{i,d+1} + \cdots + t_{is})$ has a variance of $s\sigma^2/r$.

(b) The estimate of $Y = (s - d)(t_{i1} + t_{i2} + \cdots + t_{id}) - d(t_{i,d+1} + \cdots + t$ has a variance of $(\sigma^2_s/r)[(s - d)^2 d + d^2(s - d)] = (\sigma^2_s/r)(s - a)as$.

These two linear functions of the parameters are uncorrelated, and

$$\frac{t_{i1} + t_{i2} + \cdots + t_{id}}{d} = \frac{dX + Y}{ds}$$

It, therefore, has a variance

which equals

$$\frac{1}{d^2 s^2}\left(\frac{d^2 s\sigma^2}{r} + \frac{s - d}{r} ds\sigma^2_s\right)$$

$$\frac{1}{rs}\left(\sigma^2 + \frac{s - d}{d}\sigma^2_s\right) \tag{14}$$

The estimated variance is then

$$\frac{1}{rs}\left(W + \frac{s - d}{d}E\right) \tag{15}$$

Tests of significance for comparisons 1, 2, and 3 above are made by replacing true variances by estimated variances and using the t test with the appropriate number of degrees of freedom. For comparison 4 an exact test of significance does not exist. The theoretical problem involved with the infinite model is: What is the distribution of

$$t \ \text{(say)} \ = \frac{\lambda_1 x + \lambda_2 y}{\lambda^2_1 s^2_1 + \lambda^2_2 s^2_2}$$

where x, y are independent normal deviates with estimated variances s^2_1 and s^2_2, known to be estimates of different variances σ^2_s and σ^2, based on their respective degrees of freedom, and λ_1, λ_2 are fixed constants. This has been given attention in the noted Behrens-Fisher problem, but the solution given by the Behrens-Fisher test is subject to considerable controversy as it involves the fiducial argument. A test that is possibly too conservative but otherwise seems reasonable is the t test based on $(r - 1)$ degrees of freedom. Better still, a test of the comparison should be made by evaluating it in each replicate, and thus obtaining the estimated variance, based on $(r - 1)$ degrees of freedom.

The errors of the various types of comparison give an indication of the relative statistical value of the split-plot design. In general, σ^2 will be greater than σ^2_s, so that split-plot treatment comparisons are estimated more accurately than whole-plot treatment comparisons. In the absence of other conditions, this suggests which factor should be applied to the whole plots. We shall discuss the efficiency of split-plot designs later.

19.2　ARRANGEMENT OF WHOLE-PLOT TREATMENTS IN A LATIN SQUARE

If the number of whole-plot treatments is less than 9, say, and the number of replicates can be made equal to the number of these treatments, it is possible to arrange the whole-plot treatments according to a Latin square, each whole plot being divided into the requisite number of split plots for the split-plot treatments. With 4 whole-plot treatments, t_1, t_2, t_3, and t_4, and 2 split-plot treatments, s_1 and s_2, in a field plot test, we could have a random arrangement as shown in Figure 22 where whole plots are demarcated by double lines.

$t_1 s_1$	$t_1 s_2$	$t_3 s_2$	$t_3 s_1$	$t_2 s_2$	$t_2 s_1$	$t_4 s_2$	$t_4 s_1$
$t_3 s_1$	$t_3 s_2$	$t_4 s_1$	$t_4 s_2$	$t_1 s_2$	$t_1 s_1$	$t_2 s_2$	$t_2 s_1$
$t_2 s_1$	$t_2 s_2$	$t_1 s_1$	$t_1 s_2$	$t_4 s_1$	$t_4 s_2$	$t_3 s_1$	$t_3 s_2$
$t_4 s_1$	$t_4 s_2$	$t_2 s_1$	$t_2 s_2$	$t_3 s_2$	$t_3 s_1$	$t_1 s_2$	$t_1 s_1$

FIGURE 22.

The whole-plot treatments are arranged at random in a Latin square in the usual way, each whole plot is divided into 2 split plots, and the split-plot treatments are randomized within whole plots. The model for this experiment with t rows, t columns, t whole-plot treatments, and s split-plot treatments is

$$y_{ijkl} = \mu + r_i + c_j + t_k + \eta_{ijk} + s_l + (ts)_{kl} + e_{ijkl} \qquad (16)$$

where $i = 1, 2, \cdots, t; j = 1, 2, \cdots, t; k = 1, 2, \cdots, t; l = 1, 2, \cdots, s$. The parameters t_k, s_l, $(ts)_{kl}$ are defined as previously, and r_i is the effect of the ith row, c_j is the effect of the jth column; the η_{ijk}'s are uncorrelated variables with mean zero and variance σ^2_w and the e_{ijkl}'s are uncorrelated variables with mean zero and variance σ^2_s. As a handy device we can also regard the distributions as being normal.

We obtain the analysis of variance given in Table 19.3.

TABLE 19.3 ANALYSIS OF VARIANCE FOR SPLIT-PLOT EXPERIMENT ARRANGED IN A LATIN SQUARE

Due to	df	Sum of Squares
Rows R	$t - 1$	$\sum_i \dfrac{Y^2_{i\cdots}}{ts}$ — correction
Column C	$t - 1$	$\sum_j \dfrac{Y^2_{\cdot j\cdot\cdot}}{ts}$ — correction
Whole-plot treatments T	$t - 1$	$\sum_k \dfrac{Y^2_{\cdot\cdot k\cdot}}{ts}$ — correction
Whole-plot error W	$(t - 1)(t - 2)$	By subtraction
Total for whole plots	$t^2 - 1$	$\sum_{ij} \dfrac{Y^2_{ij\cdot\cdot}}{s}$ — correction
Split-plot treatments S	$s - 1$	$\sum_l \dfrac{Y^2_{\cdots l}}{t^2}$ — correction
Interaction ST	$(t - 1)(s - 1)$	$\sum_{kl} \dfrac{Y^2_{\cdot\cdot kl}}{r}$ — correction — SS for T — SS for S
Error	By subtraction	By subtraction
Total	$t^2 s - 1$	$\sum_{ijkl} y^2_{ijkl}$ — correction

$$\text{Correction} = \frac{Y^2_{\cdots}}{t^2 s}$$

The tests of significance, estimates, and variances of estimates are as for the case of the randomized block arrangement of whole plots. The expectations of the mean squares for whole-plot error and split-plot error are, respectively, σ^2 and $\sigma^2{}_s$ as before. If the infinite model is used, $\sigma^2 = \sigma^2{}_s + s\sigma^2{}_w$, where $\sigma^2{}_w$ is the variance common to split plots in the same whole plot.

19.3 EXTENSION OF THE SPLIT-PLOT PRINCIPLE

The possible extensions and variations on the split-plot principle are too numerous to enumerate completely, and for the rest of the chapter we shall give some examples which illustrate the main points.

With 3 factors denoted by the letters a, b, and c with levels a, b, and c, respectively, we may arrange the levels of the factor c on split-split plots, and the levels of factor b on split plots within whole plots to which levels of factor a are allocated. The method of analysis is entirely analogous to that for the case of 2 factors. The analysis consists of 3 parts, between whole plots, between split plots within whole plots, between split-split plots within split plots, each part being put on the basis of a split-split plot in order that the parts may be combined into one complete analysis.

If t_{jkl} is the true yield of the combination with factor a at the jth level, b at the kth level, and c at the lth level, we make up treatment comparisons as follows:

$$a_j = t_{j..} - t_{...}$$

$$b_k = t_{.k.} - t_{...}$$

$$(ab)_{jk} = t_{jk.} - t_{j..} - t_{.k.} + t_{...}$$

$$c_l = t_{..l} - t_{...}$$

$$(ac)_{jl} = t_{j.l} - t_{j..} - t_{..l} + t_{...}$$

$$(bc)_{kl} = t_{.kl} - t_{.k.} - t_{..l} + t_{...}$$

$$(abc)_{jkl} = t_{jkl} - t_{jk.} - t_{j.l} - t_{.kl} + t_{j..} + t_{.k.} + t_{..l} - t_{...}$$

Then we may write the model for the analysis as

$$y_{ijkl} = \mu + r_i + a_j + (ra)_{ij} + b_k + (ab)_{jk} + (rab)_{ijk}$$
$$+ c_l + (ac)_{jl} + (bc)_{kl} + (abc)_{jkl} + e_{ijkl} \quad (17)$$

where i is the replicate number, μ is the mean, r_i is the effect of the ith replicate, and $(ra)_{ij}$, $(rab)_{ijk}$, e_{ijkl} are error variables with mean zero and variances $\sigma^2{}_w$, $\sigma^2{}_s$, and $\sigma^2{}_{ss}$, respectively. With the finite model, the mean of whole plots, $y_{ij..}$, follows the model

$$y_{ij\cdots} = \mu + r_i + a_j + (ra)_{ij}$$

Comparisons of split-plot means within whole plots will not involve the error terms $(ra)_{ij}$, and these lead to the split-plot analysis. Finally, comparisons between split-split plots within split plots will not involve the error terms $(ra)_{ij}$ and $(rab)_{ijk}$, and these give the third part of the analysis of variance. The analysis of variance will have the structure shown in Table 19.4, the expectations of the mean squares for the infinite model being given in parentheses.

TABLE 19.4

Due to	df	Mean Square	Expectation of Mean Square
Replicates	$r - 1$		
A	$a - 1$		
Error	$(r - 1)(a - 1)$	E	$\sigma^2(= \sigma^2_{ss} + c\sigma^2_s + bc\sigma^2_w)$
B	$b - 1$		
AB	$(a - 1)(b - 1)$		
Error	$(r - 1)a(b - 1)$	S	$\sigma^2_s(= \sigma^2_{ss} + c\sigma^2_s)$
C	$c - 1$		
AC	$(a - 1)(c - 1)$		
BC	$(b - 1)(c - 1)$		
ABC	$(a - 1)(b - 1)(c - 1)$		
Error	$(r - 1)ab(c - 1)$	SS	σ^2_{ss}
Total	$rabc - 1$		

As for the case of split-plot experiments, there are several errors applicable to mean yields, depending on the nature of the comparison being made. As an example, we may take the comparison obtained by expanding

$$a_0(b_0 + b_1)(c_0 + c_1) - a_1(b_0 + b_1)(c_0 + c_1)$$

i.e.,

$$a_0b_0c_0 + a_0b_1c_0 + a_0b_0c_1 + a_0b_1c_1 - a_1b_0c_0 - a_1b_1c_0 - a_1b_0c_1 - a_1b_1c_1$$

This will be estimated by

$$y_{\cdot 000} + y_{\cdot 010} + y_{\cdot 001} + y_{\cdot 011} - y_{\cdot 100} - y_{\cdot 110} - y_{\cdot 101} - y_{\cdot 111}$$

The error part in this expression may be written out rather quickly using the infinite model, thus,

$$4(ra)_{\cdot 0} + 2(rab)_{\cdot 00} + 2(rab)_{\cdot 01} + e_{\cdot 000} + e_{\cdot 010} + e_{\cdot 001} + e_{\cdot 011}$$

$$- 4(ra)_{\cdot 1} - 2(rab)_{\cdot 10} + 2(rab)_{\cdot 11} - e_{\cdot 100} - e_{\cdot 110} - e_{\cdot 101} - e_{\cdot 111}$$

The expectation of the square of this is

$$\frac{32\sigma^2_w}{r} + \frac{16\sigma^2_s}{r} + \frac{8\sigma^2_{ss}}{r}$$

which may be estimated by $\dfrac{8}{r}\left(SS + 2\,\dfrac{S - SS}{c} + 4\,\dfrac{E - S}{bc}\right)$.

In general, the variance of the estimated difference between two whole-plot treatments, averaged over b' of the split-plot treatments in combination with c' of the split-split-plot treatments, is

$$\frac{2}{r}\left(\sigma^2_w + \frac{\sigma^2_s}{b'} + \frac{\sigma^2_{ss}}{b'c'}\right)$$

from which the estimated variance may be obtained easily, using negative estimates of variance components if such occur. As degrees of freedom for a t test in these cases, the author favors the number $(r - 1)(a - 1)$, though this possibly results in slight underestimation of the level of significance.

19.4 THE EFFICIENCY OF SPLIT-PLOT DESIGNS RELATIVE TO RANDOMIZED BLOCKS

Under many circumstances the experimenter utilizes a split-plot design for technical reasons. For example, one of the factors in an agronomic experiment may be such that it can be applied only to larger areas of land and not to the usual size of plot. In that case, the plots could be split for the other factor or factors. It is, however, of interest to evaluate the relative efficiency of the split-plot design, as this evaluation will suggest circumstances under which the design is more appropriate than randomized blocks. The analysis of variance with whole-plot treatments arranged in r randomized blocks is given in Table 19.5.

TABLE 19.5

Due to	df	Mean Square
Blocks	$r - 1$	
Whole-plot treatments T	$t - 1$	
Error	$(r - 1)(t - 1)$	W
Split-plot treatments S	$s - 1$	
$T \times S$	$(t - 1)(s - 1)$	
Error	$(r - 1)t(s - 1)$	E
Total	$rts - 1$	

The estimated information on whole-plot treatments is proportional to $1/W$, and on split-plot treatments and interaction to $1/E$. An estimate of the error variance E', which would have been obtained with randomized blocks of size ts, and 1 plot for each treatment combination per replicate, can be obtained by replacing the treatment mean squares by their appropriate error mean squares and evaluating the consequent mean square for treatments and error combined *within* replicates. Thus,

$$E' = \frac{r(t-1)W + rt(s-1)E}{rts - r} = \frac{(t-1)W + t(s-1)E}{ts - 1} \qquad (18)$$

The information on all treatment comparisons would then have been proportional to $1/E'$. E' is a weighted average of W and E, and, because W will be usually greater than E (except for sampling errors), E' will be intermediate in size between W and E. The information on whole-plot treatments relative to randomized blocks is then E'/W which is less than 1. For split-plot treatments and interactions the relative information is E'/E which is greater than 1. These results express the obvious: that the arrangement of split-plot treatments together within a whole plot results in a lower accuracy on whole-plot treatment comparisons and an increased accuracy on other treatment comparisons. The formulas enable a quantitative evaluation of these effects. Recourse should be taken to a split-plot design when experimental conditions necessitate the special arrangement, or when the experimenter is more interested in one factor, which he arranges within whole plots, than in the other. The use of a Latin square for the whole-plot treatments will tend, to a considerable degree, to lessen the differences in accuracy of the 2 types of comparison, because of the effect of the 2-fold restriction in reducing error variance. Yates[1] has published an examination of experimental data, mainly agronomic, from the point of view of the efficiency of split-plot designs. A possible disadvantage under some circumstances, for example, when a partitioning of the treatment mean square into components of variance is contemplated, is the fact that whole-plot and split-plot comparisons may be of widely differing accuracies.

19.5 THE 2-FACTOR EXPERIMENT WITH BOTH FACTORS IN STRIPS

Instead of the usual 2-factor split-plot arrangement, with the levels of one factor arranged at random within plots, the whole of which is receiving a constant level of the other factor, it is sometimes convenient to have both sets of treatments arranged as whole-plot treatments, also arranged according to a pattern. Agronomic experiments in which both experimental factors are not easily applied to small areas are of this type. If the factors have a and b levels, respectively, the plan of 1 replicate might be as shown in Figure 23.

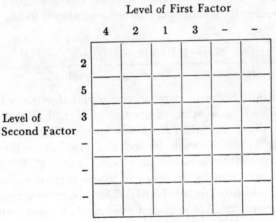

FIGURE 23.

Levels of one factor are applied to rows at random and of the other factor to columns at random. At least 2 replicates are necessary, in order to provide estimates of error. With additivity of treatment effects, the model will be

$$y_{ijk} = \mu + r_i + a_j + (ra)_{ij} + b_k + (rb)_{ik} + (ab)_{jk} + (rab)_{ijk}$$

The terms in the model are defined analogously to the previous cases, but we may simplify matters by using the infinite model and suppose that the errors $(ra)_{ij}$, $(rb)_{ik}$, and $(rab)_{ijk}$ are normally, independently distributed with means zero and variances σ^2_r, σ^2_c, and σ^2_s, respectively.

The structure of the analysis of variance is given in Table 19.6.

TABLE 19.6   ANALYSIS FOR 2-FACTOR EXPERIMENT IN STRIPS

Due to	df	Expectation of Mean Square
Replicates R	$r - 1$	
Treatments A	$a - 1$	$\sigma^2_s + b\sigma^2_r + \dfrac{rb}{a - 1}\sum_j a^2_j$
$R \times A$	$(r - 1)(a - 1)$	$\sigma^2_s + b\sigma^2_r$
Treatments B	$b - 1$	$\sigma^2_s + a\sigma^2_c + \dfrac{ra}{b - 1}\sum_k b^2_k$
$R \times B$	$(r - 1)(b - 1)$	$\sigma^2_s + a\sigma^2_c$
Interactions AB	$(a - 1)(b - 1)$	$\sigma^2_s + \dfrac{r}{(a - 1)(b - 1)}\sum_{jk} (ab)^2_{jk}$
$R \times AB$	$(r - 1)(a - 1)(b - 1)$	σ^2_s
Total	$rab - 1$	

Such a design gives relatively low accuracy on both main effects with relatively high accuracy on the interactions. For example, the variance of the mean for each level of the first factor averaging over the levels of the second factor, for comparison with any other levels of the first factor, is

$$\frac{\sigma^2_s + b\sigma^2_r}{rb} = \frac{\sigma^2_r}{r} + \frac{\sigma^2_s}{rb}$$

which will generally be dominated by the first term with a low number of replicates. The variance of any treatment comparison may be obtained by noting that the best estimate with complete data will be the same comparison of treatment means, and the variance of this comparison is easily obtained from the model, as in previous cases. Estimates of variance components from the analyses of variance are then substituted.

19.6 SPLIT-PLOT CONFOUNDING

So far in our use of the split-plot principle, we have assumed that plots are split into a number of parts equal to the number of levels of the split-plot treatment factor. This is frequently an overrestrictive condition on the design: for example, if the whole plot is a litter of mice and split plots are mice within the litter, it may well be the case that we can have a large number of litters with 4 mice, and we wish to test as split-plot treatments, say, 3 factors each with 2 levels, or 8 combinations in all. The procedure under such conditions is quite straightforward, following from the descriptions of confounding in earlier chapters. Suppose there are 3 whole-plot treatments. It will usually be reasonable to assume that the 3-factor interaction of the 3 split-plot factors is of less interest than other comparisons. This interaction may then be confounded with whole plots. If the whole-plot treatments are t_1, t_2, and t_3 and the split-plot factors are a, b, and c, one replicate would contain 6 whole plots each split into 4 split plots as follows before randomization:

t_1		t_1		t_2		t_2		t_3		t_3	
a	b	(1)	ab	a	b	(1)	ab	a	b	(1)	ab
c	abc	ac	bc	c	abc	ac	bc	c	abc	ac	bc

Comparisons of t_1, t_2, and t_3 averaged over the split-plot treatments will then be whole-plot comparisons, as will be the interaction ABC and the interaction of ABC with t_1, t_2, and t_3. Effects A, B, C and interactions AB, AC, BC and the interactions of these 6 comparisons with t_1, t_2, and t_3 will be comparisons among split plots. The analysis of variance will have the structure shown in Table 19.7.

TABLE 19.7

Due to	df	Expectation of Mean Square
Replicates	$r - 1$	
$t_1 v t_2 v t_3 (T)$	2	
ABC	1	
$T \times ABC$	2	
Whole-plot error	$5(r - 1)$	$\sigma^2_s + r\sigma^2_w$
A, B, C AB, AC, BC	6	
$T \times A, T \times B, T \times C$ $T \times AB, T \times AC, T \times BC$	12	
Split-plot error	$18(r - 1)$	σ^2_s
Total	$24r - 1$	

All other details of this design follow readily by the usual methods, the analogy with factorial experiments being complete, except that interblock (= whole-plot) information is utilized. There are numerous extensions of this approach, which can be devised, given a particular investigation with formulated aims.

An example with a Latin square is of some combinatorial interest (Finney [2]). Suppose 4 treatments are being compared by a Latin square, and it is desired also to test 2 factors, a, b, each at 2 levels by splitting the plots, but that the plots can be divided into halves only, smaller units being impractical. The interaction AB must then be confounded with whole plots, and it is desirable that it be unconfounded with rows and columns. That this is possible follows from the possibility of inserting rings in a 4×4 square, such that 2 rings occur in each row, in each column, and with each treatment (Figure 24).

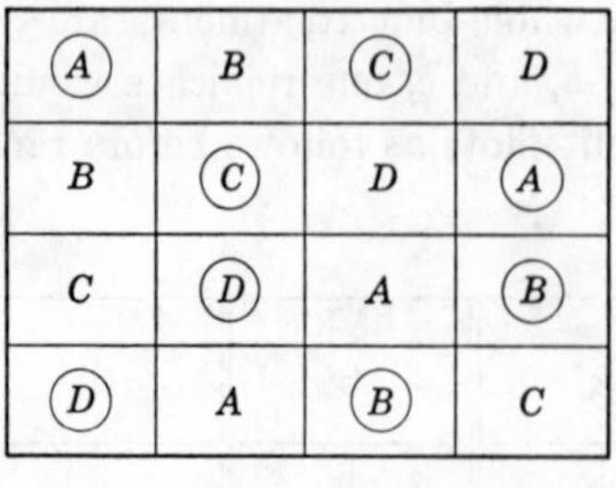

FIGURE 24.

The ringed squares would contain one of the 2 sets of treatments, (1) and ab, or a and b. The same device may be used with 3 split-plot factors a, b, and c and the plots split into 4 parts confounding ABC. This type of design is possible only with squares of the first transformation set. Similarly, for some 6×6 Latin squares, it is possible to assign rings to letters such that 3 rings occur with each row, column, and letter, leading to a corresponding design. It has not been verified that these designs are unbiased, and this is not an entirely obvious property.

19.7   THE ANALYSIS OF COVARIANCE IN SPLIT-PLOT DESIGNS

The theory of the analysis of covariance for split-plot designs follows directly from the case of the analysis of covariance in a 2-way classification, in the same way as does the analysis of variance. It will be remembered (cf. Chapter 8) that the infinite model must be used. In the case of the analysis of variance of split-plot designs, the original general linear hypothesis which contained correlated errors was partitioned into 2 independent general linear hypotheses, one for the analysis of whole plots and one for the analysis of split plots.

The structure of the analysis of covariance for the split-plot design will be identical to that of the analysis of variance and may be regarded as 2 separate analyses of covariance, one for whole-plot treatments and one for split-plot treatments (Table 19.8).

TABLE 19.8

Whole Plots	df	y^2	xy	x^2
Reps	$r - 1$			
Treatments A	$t - 1$	T_{yy}	T_{xy}	T_{xx}
Error a	$(r - 1)(t - 1)$	W_{yy}	W_{xy}	W_{xx}
Split Plots				
Treatments B	$s - 1$	S_{yy}	S_{xy}	S_{xx}
Interaction AB	$(t - 1)(s - 1)$	I_{yy}	I_{xy}	I_{xx}
Error b	$(r - 1)t(s - 1)$	E_{yy}	E_{xy}	E_{xx}

Again to facilitate the computation of the error b sums of squares and products, the whole-plot analysis is done on a split-plot basis; i.e., the sums of squares and products are computed from the whole-plot totals and then divided by s.

In the case of split-plot experiments, we find that there are 2 error regressions of y on x, one for each error, say, β_w and β_s. It may be noted, for example, that a regression common to all the split plots of a whole plot in no way affects split-plot comparisons. It is found that

$$\hat{\beta}_w = \frac{W_{xy}}{W_{xx}} \tag{19}$$

with estimated variance

$$\frac{1}{(r-1)(t-1)-1} \frac{1}{W_{xx}} \left(W_{yy} - \frac{W^2_{xy}}{W_{xx}} \right) \tag{20}$$

and that

$$\hat{\beta}_s = \frac{E_{xy}}{E_{xx}} \tag{21}$$

with estimated variance

$$\frac{1}{(r-1)t(s-1)-1} \frac{1}{E_{xx}} \left(E_{yy} - \frac{E^2_{xy}}{E_{xx}} \right) \tag{22}$$

The plot yields may be adjusted to the same value of x by calculating

$$y_{ijk} - \hat{\beta}_w(x_{ij.} - x_{i..}) - \hat{\beta}_s(x_{ijk} - x_{ij.}) \tag{23}$$

We note that $\hat{\beta}_s$ does not enter into whole-plot comparisons and $\hat{\beta}_w$ does not enter into split-plot comparisons. The errors of adjusted treatment comparisons may be evaluated by the usual rules. Tests of significance are made in the way usual for the analysis of covariance.

19.8 MISSING DATA

In the case of one missing split plot, the experiment may be analyzed by the analysis of covariance with a concomitant variable which takes the value of 0 for the plots with actual yields and -1 for the plot with missing yield. The above procedure then completes the analyses. This procedure actually amounts to the estimation of one missing value for the particular split plot and one for the whole plot containing the missing split plot. This should not be a source of confusion when one considers the structure of the analysis of variance. It would be possible, with the infinite model, to obtain one solution only by maximum likelihood, but the process would be very tedious, and we would then be unable to use the analysis of variance technique for testing purposes.

The case of one missing whole plot has been examined (see also by Anderson [3]). In this case, the whole-plot analysis is performed as if there were no split-plot treatments, and the missing value is estimated in the usual way. Split-plot treatment comparisons that do not involve the treatments of the missing whole plot are evaluated in the ordinary way: that is, by taking a mean over all the replicates. Split-plot comparisons that involve the treatments of the missing whole plot are obtained by taking a mean of the comparison of observed yields over the replicates other than the one containing the missing plot. As a simple computational procedure for the estimation of split-plot comparisons and the split-plot error variance, values may be inserted for the missing plots equal to their mean over the replicates containing these treatments, the analysis of variance completed, and the error degrees of freedom reduced by the number of missing plots. Comparisons are then estimated by the comparison of treatment means of the augmented table. For the estimation of errors of treatment comparisons, it is necessary to evaluate the error as a linear function of the plot errors and evaluate its variance. The usual formulas, ignoring the fact that data were missing, probably underestimate the error only slightly.

For the case of one missing split plot, an analogous procedure may be used. The whole-plot analysis is performed with a missing plot, and the split-plot analysis with a value inserted equal to (mean of actual split plots in whole plot) plus (mean of the missing plot treatment over other replicates) minus (mean of other split plots of whole plots in which this treatment occurs).

The possible cases of missing data in split-plot experiments are very numerous. The number of configurations in which only 3 split plots are missing is large, including the cases of all in 1 whole plot, 1 in 1 whole plot and 2 in another with the same split-plot treatment on 1, 2, or all of the 3 missing split plots, and so on. Whether the expenditure of the necessary labor on obtaining accurate (in terms of general linear hypothesis theory) solutions for the ordinary experiment is worth while may be doubted. The best suggestion is that the experimenter make a guess by looking at the plan and yields of the experiment and thenceforward ignore the fact that data were missing. The field of statistics must, like all other sciences, exercise some criteria of value of particular types of work, and it is not worth while generally to use what would be a complicated procedure on a small experiment.

REFERENCES

1. YATES, F. Complex experiments. *Suppl. Jour. Roy. Stat. Soc.*, **2**, 181–247, 1935.
2. FINNEY, D. J. Orthogonal partitions of the 6 × 6 Latin squares. *Ann. Eug.*, **13**, 184–196, 1946.
3. ANDERSON, R. L. Missing-plot techniques. *Biometrics*, **2**, 41–47, 1946.

FURTHER READING

4. YATES, F. *The design and analysis of factorial experiments.* Imp. Bur. Soil Sci., Harpenden, England. 1937.
5. COCHRAN, W. G., and COX, G. M. *Experimental designs.* John Wiley & Sons, New York. 1950.

CHAPTER 20

Fractional Replication

20.1 INTRODUCTION

So far in this book, we have considered possible arrangements of the complete factorial system; that is, we have considered only arrangements in which each individual treatment combination of the factorial set is represented the same number of times. For example, with 5 factors each at 2 levels, we have discussed arrangements of the 32 treatment combinations in blocks of 2 plots, blocks of 4 plots, 8×8 Latin squares, and so on, but always with the restriction that each of the 32 combinations is to be tested an equal number of times. Such a restriction is practicable with a small number of factors, but, when we consider the case of, say, 10 factors each at 2 levels, it would result in the necessity of our testing 1024 combinations or a multiple of these. The main reason for imposing the restriction is that it results in the estimates of effects and interactions having maximum precision and being uncorrelated. Thus, to take a simple example, suppose we are evaluating 2 factors, a and b, each at 2 levels, and test the treatment combination (1), a, b, ab with n_1, n_2, n_3, n_4 repetitions, respectively, in a single randomized block. Then each effect and interaction is estimated with variance

$$\frac{\sigma^2}{4}\left(\frac{1}{n_1} + \frac{1}{n_2} + \frac{1}{n_3} + \frac{1}{n_4}\right)$$

but the estimates are correlated thus:

$$\mathrm{cov}\,(\hat{A},\, \hat{B}) = \frac{\sigma^2}{4}\left(\frac{1}{n_1} - \frac{1}{n_2} - \frac{1}{n_3} + \frac{1}{n_4}\right)$$

$$\mathrm{cov}\,(\hat{A},\, \widehat{AB}) = \frac{\sigma^2}{4}\left(-\frac{1}{n_1} - \frac{1}{n_2} + \frac{1}{n_3} + \frac{1}{n_4}\right)$$

and

$$\mathrm{cov}\,(\hat{B},\, \widehat{AB}) = \frac{\sigma^2}{4}\left(-\frac{1}{n_1} + \frac{1}{n_2} - \frac{1}{n_3} + \frac{1}{n_4}\right)$$

These covariances will be zero if $n_1 = n_2 = n_3 = n_4$. Furthermore, if we fix $(n_1 + n_2 + n_3 + n_4)$, the total number of observations, we obtain minimum variance for each of the effects and interaction with $n_1 = n_2 = n_3 = n_4$.

As we have seen throughout the general problem of the design of experiments, we are given a model, and we wish to determine the parameters of the model with as low variance as possible. There are two methods by which this may be accomplished: namely, by choosing the pattern of observations, for example, equal n's above, or by reducing the error variance σ^2 by choice of design.

The question we ask in this chapter is whether it is always necessary to test all the factorial combinations equally frequently or whether we can omit some of them. The question is of considerable relevance, for factorial experiments are most appropriate for exploratory research, and in such research the number of possible factors that should be tested is by no means so small as 2 or 3. For example, in research into the possible importance of the various vitamins in the nutrition of an organism, the number of factors that should be used is at least of the order of 10. It is, furthermore, important to use a factorial system because we cannot assume all interactions to be negligible. The testing of 1024 treatment combinations may be virtually impossible from the practical viewpoint. If the whole 1024 combinations were tested, the subdivision of the 1023 treatment comparisons would be:

Main effects	10
2-factor interactions	45
3-factor interactions	120
4-factor interactions	210
5-factor interactions	252
6-factor interactions	210
7-factor interactions	120
8-factor interactions	45
9-factor interactions	10
10-factor interactions	1
Total	1023

It may well be reasonable to assume that high-order interactions are negligible, and, if for instance all interactions involving 3 or more factors could be ignored, the testing of the 1024 combinations would give an estimate of error based on about 950 degrees of freedom. The accuracy that would result for the estimation of main effects and interactions (a variance of $\sigma^2/256$ where σ^2 is the experimental error variance) might well be unnecessarily high. We may then ask what information can be obtained from the testing of a lesser number of combinations. We shall, in fact, find that information on main effects and interactions for all the 10 factors can be obtained under some mild assumptions from the testing of 512, 256, or perhaps even 128 of the total of 1024 combinations. The general process by which this is accomplished is known as fractional replication.

20.2 A SIMPLE EXAMPLE OF FRACTIONAL REPLICATION

Suppose we are testing 3 factors, a, b, and c, which are known not to interact. For example, we might wish to weigh 3 small objects by a chemical balance, the procedure being to place the objects in the right-hand pan and then to place known weights in the left-hand pan to bring the pointer to the zero position. The treatment combinations will then consist of:

	Objects in Right-Hand Pan
(1)	None
a	1
b	2
ab	1 and 2
c	3
ac	1 and 3
bc	2 and 3
abc	1, 2, and 3

The relation between the true yields and the effects and interactions in the ordinary 3-factor situation is shown in Table 20.1.

TABLE 20.1

True Yield	μ	$\frac{1}{2}A$	$\frac{1}{2}B$	$\frac{1}{2}AB$	$\frac{1}{2}C$	$\frac{1}{2}AC$	$\frac{1}{2}BC$	$\frac{1}{2}ABC$
(1)	+	−	−	+	−	+	+	−
a	+	+	−	−	−	−	+	+
b	+	−	+	−	−	+	−	+
ab	+	+	+	+	−	−	−	−
c	+	−	−	+	+	−	−	+
ac	+	+	−	−	+	+	−	−
bc	+	−	+	−	+	−	+	−
abc	+	+	+	+	+	+	+	+

Suppose that we test only the 4 combinations, a, b, c, and abc. Then we see from the table that we can estimate the quantities $(\mu + \frac{1}{2}ABC)$,

$\frac{1}{2}(A + BC)$, $\frac{1}{2}(B + AC)$ and $\frac{1}{2}(C + AB)$, but that it is impossible to separate the A effect from the BC interaction, the B effect from the AC interaction, the C effect from the AB interaction, or the mean μ from the ABC interaction. In fact, we have the following 4 estimating relations:

$$\mu + \tfrac{1}{2}ABC \text{ is estimated by } \tfrac{1}{4}(a + b + c + abc)$$

$$\tfrac{1}{2}(A + BC) \text{ is estimated by } \tfrac{1}{4}(a - b - c + abc)$$

$$\tfrac{1}{2}(B + AC) \text{ is estimated by } \tfrac{1}{4}(-a + b - c + abc) \tag{1}$$

$$\tfrac{1}{2}(C + AB) \text{ is estimated by } \tfrac{1}{4}(-a - b + c + abc)$$

where a, b, c, etc., are now the observed yields. We may say that, with these 4 observations only, A is completely confounded with BC, because there is no possibility of estimating A alone and BC alone but only their sum. Similarly, B is completely confounded with AC, C with AB, and ABC with μ. This confounding, however, need not cause the experimenter any worry if he is prepared to assume that the interactions are negligible. The second, third, and fourth comparisons may be used to estimate the 3 main effects, and the estimates are uncorrelated. In this simple example, there is not, of course, any possibility of estimating the error variance, and we would not use this design for any practical purpose. It serves, however, to bring out the main idea of fractional replication, that a suitably chosen subset of the full factorial set can provide worth-while information. The above example utilizes $\frac{1}{2}$ replication of the 2^3 system, because we have tested only 4 of the 8 combinations.

We could equally well have used the set of treatment combinations (1), ab, ac, and bc, and it may be verified that the estimating equations will be:

$$\mu - \tfrac{1}{2}ABC = \tfrac{1}{4}[(1) + ab + ac + bc]$$

$$\tfrac{1}{2}(A - BC) = \tfrac{1}{4}[-(1) + ab + ac - bc]$$

$$\tfrac{1}{2}(B - AC) = \tfrac{1}{4}[-(1) + ab - ac + bc] \tag{2}$$

$$\tfrac{1}{2}(C - AB) = \tfrac{1}{4}[-(1) - ab + ac + bc]$$

The confounding among mean, effects, and interaction is almost the same as before.

The dominant feature of this example is the choice of the interaction ABC and the selection of either the treatments entering positively in this interaction or those entering negatively. For most purposes, we may disregard which half of the treatment combinations we choose, because we shall always choose an interaction in such a way that those interactions that are completely confounded with the effects or interactions we wish to estimate are assumed on the basis of prior knowledge to be negligible.

If we use the equality sign to denote "completely confounded with," we may write the confounding relations above in the form:

$$A = BC$$
$$B = CA \tag{3}$$
$$C = AB$$

and, if by convention we denote μ by I, also

$$I = ABC \tag{4}$$

We note that the first 3 equalities are obtained from the fourth by regarding the relationship as an algebraic identity and I as unity and using multiplication with the rule that the square of any letter is to be replaced by unity. Thus,

$$I = ABC$$

when multiplied by A gives

$$A = A^2BC = BC \quad \text{since} \quad A^2 = 1$$

when multiplied by B gives

$$B = AB^2C = AC \quad \text{since} \quad B^2 = 1$$

and when multiplied by C gives

$$C = ABC^2 = AB \quad \text{since} \quad C^2 = 1$$

Thus, we can treat these effect and interaction symbols as ordinary algebraic quantities except that the square of any letter is unity.

Another example would perhaps be instructive. Suppose then that we select those treatments that appear positively in the AB interaction. We shall then have 4 observations:

$$(1) = \mu - \tfrac{1}{2}A - \tfrac{1}{2}B + \tfrac{1}{2}AB - \tfrac{1}{2}C + \tfrac{1}{2}AC + \tfrac{1}{2}BC - \tfrac{1}{2}ABC + e_1$$
$$ab = \mu + \tfrac{1}{2}A + \tfrac{1}{2}B + \tfrac{1}{2}AB - \tfrac{1}{2}C - \tfrac{1}{2}AC - \tfrac{1}{2}BC - \tfrac{1}{2}ABC + e_2$$
$$c = \mu - \tfrac{1}{2}A - \tfrac{1}{2}B + \tfrac{1}{2}AB + \tfrac{1}{2}C - \tfrac{1}{2}AC - \tfrac{1}{2}BC + \tfrac{1}{2}ABC + e_3 \tag{5}$$
$$abc = \mu + \tfrac{1}{2}A + \tfrac{1}{2}B + \tfrac{1}{2}AB + \tfrac{1}{2}C + \tfrac{1}{2}AC + \tfrac{1}{2}BC + \tfrac{1}{2}ABC + e_4$$

or

$$(1) = (\mu + \tfrac{1}{2}AB) - \tfrac{1}{2}(A + B) - \tfrac{1}{2}(C + ABC) + \tfrac{1}{2}(AC + BC) + e_1$$
$$ab = (\mu + \tfrac{1}{2}AB) + \tfrac{1}{2}(A + B) - \tfrac{1}{2}(C + ABC) - \tfrac{1}{2}(AC + BC) + e_2$$
$$c = (\mu + \tfrac{1}{2}AB) - \tfrac{1}{2}(A + B) + \tfrac{1}{2}(C + ABC) - \tfrac{1}{2}(AC + BC) + e_3$$
$$abc = (\mu + \tfrac{1}{2}AB) + \tfrac{1}{2}(A + B) + \tfrac{1}{2}(C + ABC) + \tfrac{1}{2}(AC + BC) + e_4$$

$$(6)$$

The confounding relations are given by the equations:

$$A = B$$
$$C = ABC$$
$$AC = BC$$

$$(7)$$

and

$$I = AB$$

The first 3 of these relations may be obtained from the fourth by multiplying both sides of the fourth equation by A, C, and AC, respectively, with the rule that $A^2 = B^2 = C^2 = 1$.

In each of these two examples we have used a ½ replicate of the full set of factorial combinations. Our original assumption was that we were testing 3 factors which do not interact: that is, that the true interactions AB, AC, BC, and ABC are zero. The first ½ replicate we considered is then a satisfactory experiment (apart from the fact that no estimate of error can be made) because we can estimate each of the 3 effects, A, B, and C. In the second ½ replicate design considered, however, the effect A is confounded with effect B, and this is entirely contradictory to the aim of the experimenter.

The crucial part of the specification of the design is clearly the choice of the relationship $I = ABC$ or $I = AB$. This relation is known as the defining relation or identity relationship. Once this relationship is chosen, we can specify the functions of the parameters which can be estimated, and the choice of a relationship is based on this fact. Thus, we would not use a relationship that results in the confounding of main effects with each other. We now proceed to a more realistic case.

20.3 ½ REPLICATION OF A 2^6 EXPERIMENT

Suppose we have 6 factors, a, b, c, d, e, f, each at 2 levels, and wish to test only 32 of the total of 64 possible treatment combinations. We follow the lines of previous examples in testing those treatment combinations that appear positively in the expression for the 6-factor interaction: that is, the treatment combinations that contain an even number of letters (zero being regarded as even). The confounding relations are then as in Table 20.2.

TABLE 20.2   CONFOUNDING RELATIONS IN $\frac{1}{2}$ REPLICATE OF 2^6 FACTORIAL
EXPERIMENT

$I = ABCDEF$	$E = ABCDF$
$A = BCDEF$	$AE = BCDF$
$B = ACDEF$	$BE = ACDF$
$AB = CDEF$	$ABE = CDF$
$C = ABDEF$	$CE = ABDF$
$AC = BDEF$	$ACE = BDF$
$BC = ADEF$	$BCE = ADF$
$ABC = DEF$	$ABCE = DF$
$D = ABCEF$	$DE = ABCF$
$AD = BCEF$	$ADE = BCF$
$BD = ACEF$	$BDE = ACF$
$ABD = CEF$	$ABDE = CF$
$CD = ABEF$	$CDE = ABF$
$ACD = BEF$	$ACDE = BF$
$BCD = AEF$	$BCDE = AF$
$ABCD = EF$	$ABCDE = F$

We have thus accounted for the 64 parameters, the mean μ, and the 63 main effects and interactions, and each one is confounded with the one with name complementary to it in $ABCDEF$. Each of the 31 comparisons between the yields of the 32 treatment combinations, which have the property of being linear with coefficients of plus or minus unity, measures the sum of an effect and an interaction or of 2 interactions. The 2 effects or interactions estimated by the same contrast are said to be aliases of each other. Now, suppose all interactions involving 3 or more factors are zero. We may then use the comparisons to estimate main effect, 2-factor interactions, or error, as the case may be. We have, in all, 10 comparisons which may be used to estimate the experimental error: namely, $ABC = DEF$, $ABD = CEF$, $ACD = BEF$, $BCD = AEF$, $ABE = CDF$, $ACE = BDF$, $BCE = ADF$, $ADE = BCF$, $BDE = ACF$, $CDE = ABF$. The following breakdown in the analysis of variance may then be made:

	df
Main effects	6
2-factor interactions	15
Error	10
Total	31

In this way we have obtained a satisfactory design for estimating the parameters in the following mathematical model:

$$)-2a_ib_jc_kd_le_mf_n = 2\mu \pm A \pm B \pm AB \pm C \pm AC \pm BC \pm D \pm AD$$

$$\pm BD \pm CD \pm E \pm AE \pm BE \pm CE \pm DE \pm F \pm AF \pm BF$$

$$\pm CF \pm DF \pm EF + 2e_{ijklmn} \quad (8)$$

where the sign for each of the letters A, B, C, D, E, F is plus if the corresponding subscript on the left is 1 (i.e., the factor is at the higher level) and minus otherwise; the signs on interaction terms are the product of the signs on the main effects, μ is the mean, and the e_{ijklmn}'s are uncorrelated with a mean of zero and a variance of σ^2.

The experimenter would probably regard the experiment given in the previous paragraphs as rather unsatisfactory because it utilizes a randomized block of 32 plots. Let us examine the possibility of using blocks of 16 plots and blocks of 8 plots. If we are to use blocks of 16 plots, one of the 31 possible comparisons must be confounded with blocks, and we can choose any one of the 10 comparisons which we have used above for the estimation of error. Suppose we confound the comparison that estimates ABC and DEF. The structure of the experiment will, apart from randomization, be as in Table 20.3.

TABLE 20.3 ½ REPLICATE OF 2^6 DESIGN IN 2 BLOCKS OF 16 PLOTS

Block I	(1)	ab	ac	bc
	de	abde	acde	bcde
	ef	abef	acef	bcef
	df	abdf	acdf	bcdf

Block II	ad	bd	cd	abcd
	ae	be	ce	abce
	adef	bdef	cdef	abcdef
	af	bf	cf	abcf

The analysis of the experiment will consist of the evaluation of the 31 comparisons, and this may be done by the addition-subtraction process described in Chapter 14 for the complete 2^n factorial system. For the arrangement of the yields in the standard pattern, one factor, say, f, is ignored completely. In this way, all 31 contrasts will be estimated, but some of them will have to be renamed, as, for example, the contrast computed as $ABCD$ which will be renamed EF.

If we consider now the possibilities of blocks of 8 plots, it will be necessary to confound between blocks 3 comparisons, each of which is the product of the other 2. Some care is necessary in the choice of these 3 comparisons. If, for example, we confound $ABCD$, $ABEF$, and $CDEF$, then we are, in fact, also confounding EF, CD, and AB, because

$$I = ABCDEF$$

$$ABCD = EF$$

$$ABEF = CD \tag{9}$$

and

$$CDEF = AB$$

Such a system of confounding is unsatisfactory because 3 of the 15 2-factor interactions are confounded, and they involve all the 6 factors. An alternative system is the following, in which are confounded

$$ABC = DEF$$

and

$$ABD = CEF \tag{10}$$

and

$$CD = ABEF$$

This is the best that can be obtained with blocks of 8 plots. The reader may verify easily that any other system would result in the confoundings of some main effects or main effects and interactions or more 2-factor interactions. The actual design before randomization will be as in Table 20.4.

TABLE 20.4   ½ REPLICATE OF 2^6 DESIGN IN 4 BLOCKS OF 8 PLOTS

Block I	Block II	Block III	Block IV
(1)	ac	ad	ae
ab	bc	bd	be
acde	de	ce	cd
bcde	abde	abce	abcd
acdf	df	cf	cdef
bcdf	abdf	abcf	abcdef
ef	acef	adef	af
abef	bcef	bdef	bf

The method of obtaining the contents of each block easily is:

1. Form the intrablock subgroup which consists of all treatment combinations that have an even number of letters in common with $ABCDEF$, ABC, and ABD. The first block is made up of the intrablock subgroup combinations. In obtaining these, it is useful to note that the elements in the intrablock subgroup form a group in that the product of any 2 elements in the subgroup is also in the subgroup. In forming the prod-

uct, the usual rule of replacing the square of a letter by unity is to be observed. Thus, $ab \times acde = a^2bcde = bcde$, etc.

2. Form the other blocks by multiplying the elements of the first block by a treatment combination that does not already occur in previous blocks and that has an even number of letters in common with $ABCDEF$.

20.4 A SIMPLE EXAMPLE OF ¼ REPLICATION

We take the case of 5 factors, a, b, c, d, and e, each at 2 levels, for purposes of illustration. We may select half of the treatment combinations on the basis of one interaction, and among these select half on the basis of another interaction. For example, suppose we select first on the basis of the ABC interaction: then we would have the treatment combinations (or its complement, and we consider only the one case),

$$(1),\ ab,\ ac,\ bc,\ d,\ abd,\ acd,\ bcd$$

$$e\ abe,\ ace,\ bce,\ de,\ abde,\ acde,\ bcde$$

Now, from these we select those treatment combinations that occur with the same sign (negative, say) in the interaction ADE. We have, finally, the following 8 combinations:

$$(1),\ bc,\ abd,\ acd,\ abe,\ ace,\ de,\ bcde$$

Note that these treatment combinations have the same sign in the interaction $BCDE$ (they all occur positively). It is a general rule that we have used previously in our discussion of confounding that, if a treatment combination has an even number of letters in combination with an interaction X and with an interaction Y, then it also has an even number of letters in common with XY, the generalized interaction of X and Y. If we examine the expected value of each of the selected treatment combinations, in terms of the full factorial model, we find the following:

$$(1) = \mu' - \tfrac{1}{2}A' - \tfrac{1}{2}B' - \tfrac{1}{2}C' - \tfrac{1}{2}D' - \tfrac{1}{2}E' + \tfrac{1}{2}(BD)' + \tfrac{1}{2}(BE)'$$

$$bc = \mu' - \tfrac{1}{2}A' + \tfrac{1}{2}B' + \tfrac{1}{2}C' - \tfrac{1}{2}D' - \tfrac{1}{2}E' - \tfrac{1}{2}(BD)' - \tfrac{1}{2}(BE)'$$

$$abd = \mu' + \tfrac{1}{2}A' + \tfrac{1}{2}B' - \tfrac{1}{2}C' + \tfrac{1}{2}D' - \tfrac{1}{2}E' + \tfrac{1}{2}(BD)' - \tfrac{1}{2}(BE)'$$

$$acd = \mu' + \tfrac{1}{2}A' - \tfrac{1}{2}B' + \tfrac{1}{2}C' + \tfrac{1}{2}D' - \tfrac{1}{2}E' - \tfrac{1}{2}(BD)' + \tfrac{1}{2}(BE)'$$

$$abe = \mu' + \tfrac{1}{2}A' + \tfrac{1}{2}B' - \tfrac{1}{2}C' - \tfrac{1}{2}D' + \tfrac{1}{2}E' - \tfrac{1}{2}(BD)' + \tfrac{1}{2}(BE)' \quad (11)$$

$$ace = \mu' + \tfrac{1}{2}A' - \tfrac{1}{2}B' + \tfrac{1}{2}C' - \tfrac{1}{2}D' + \tfrac{1}{2}E' + \tfrac{1}{2}(BD)' - \tfrac{1}{2}(BE)'$$

$$de = \mu' - \tfrac{1}{2}A' - \tfrac{1}{2}B' - \tfrac{1}{2}C' + \tfrac{1}{2}D' + \tfrac{1}{2}E' - \tfrac{1}{2}(BD)' - \tfrac{1}{2}(BE)'$$

$$bcde = \mu' - \tfrac{1}{2}A' + \tfrac{1}{2}B' + \tfrac{1}{2}C' + \tfrac{1}{2}D' + \tfrac{1}{2}E' + \tfrac{1}{2}(BD)' + \tfrac{1}{2}(BE)'$$

where

$$\mu' = \mu - \tfrac{1}{2}ABC - \tfrac{1}{2}ADE + \tfrac{1}{2}BCDE$$

$$A' = A - BC - DE + ABCDE$$

$$B' = B - AC - ABDE + CDE$$

$$C' = C - AB - ACDE + BDE$$

$$D' = D - ABCD - AE + BCE \tag{12}$$

$$E' = E - ABCE - AD + BCD$$

$$(BD)' = BD - ACD - ABE + CE$$

$$(BE)' = BE - ACE - ABD + CD$$

Formally these expressions may be written $A(1 - ABC - ADE + BCDE)$, $B(1 - ABC - ADE + BCDE)$, etc.

With these 8 observations, we can estimate the 8 new parameters, μ, A', B', C', D', E', $(BD)'$, and $(BE)'$. Clearly estimates of these new parameters are of no value to the experimenter unless we can isolate one of the terms in each of A', B', C', etc., and assume that all the other terms are zero. If the experimenter is prepared to assume that all interactions are zero, the 8 treatment combinations are sufficient to give estimates of the effects A, B, C, D, and E. In fact, it is obvious and may be verified easily by least squares that, under this condition, the best estimate of A by $\hat{A}$ is given by

$$4\hat{A} = -(1) - bc + abd + acd + abe + ace - de - bcde$$

that is, $4\hat{A}$ equals the sum of plots containing a minus the sum of those not containing a. The other effects are estimated similarly, and the corresponding estimators of $(BD)'$ and $(BE)'$ provide an estimate of error based on 2 degrees of freedom.

The whole of the design and analysis of this trial may be simply deduced from the identity

$$\mathbf{I} = -ABC = -ADE = +BCDE \tag{13}$$

We interpret this identity relationship as follows: The treatment combinations that are used are those that occur negatively in the ABC interaction, negatively in the ADE interaction, and positively in the $BCDE$ interaction. As a result, any effect or interaction X is inseparable from or completely confounded with the generalized interaction of X with ABC, of X with ADE, and of X with $BCDE$, and the comparison of combinations positive for X minus those negative for X in fact estimates $X - XABC - XADE + XBCDE$. The 8 treatments are said to constitute a ¼ replicate of the 2^5 experiment on a, b, c, d, e, based on the identity relationship or defining relation

$$I = -ABC = -ADE = +BCDE$$

There are, in all, 4 possible ¼ replicate designs which result in the same interconfounding: namely, those based on the above identity and the following identities:

$$I = +ABC = +ADE = +BCDE$$

$$I = +ABC = -ADE = -BCDE \tag{14}$$

and

$$I = -ABC = +ADE = -BCDE$$

The 4 possible ¼ replicates are not generally worth distinguishing from the practical viewpoint, because one may be changed into the other by suitable interchanging of the levels of the factors, and it is usually sufficient to consider any of the 4 as being given by the relationship

$$I = ABC = ADE = BCDE$$

20.5 ¼ REPLICATION OF A 2^8 EXPERIMENT

The ¼ replicate design in the previous paragraphs is of little practical use except in a problem for which interactions are zero: for example, in the weighing of small objects. We proceed to discuss an example that will be of considerable utility in many fields of research.

Consider an experiment on 8 factors, a, b, c, d, e, f, g, h. We shall attempt to find a design using only 64 of the possible 256 combinations. If we can assume that all interactions involving 3 or more factors are zero, but 2-factor interactions must be included in the model, we must use an identity relationship such that all the terms in it apart from the identity involve at least 5 letters. A possible one is

$$I = ABCDE = ABFGH = CDEFGH$$

We wish the terms to involve at least 5 letters, because, with each term that has 4 letters, six 2-factor interactions will be mutually confounded in pairs. If any term has only 3 letters, a main effect will be confounded with a 2-factor interaction. The above identity relationship is then a suitable one, and we may choose any one of the 4 possible ¼ replicates based on it.

We must now examine the possibilities of arranging the 64 chosen treatment combinations in blocks of 16 or, if possible, 8 units. Consider first the case of blocks of 16 units: Any interaction confounded with blocks must be such that the other interactions confounded with blocks by virtue of the identity relationship also involve at least 3 letters. Below is given the identity relationship followed by 3 comparisons suitable for confounding:

$$I = ABCDE = ABFGH = CDEFGH$$
$$ACF = BDEF = BCGH = ADEGH$$
$$BDG = ACEG = ADFH = BCEFH$$
$$ABCDFG = EFG = CDH = ABEH$$

(15)

These relations give us 4 possible designs in blocks of 16 units, and we may take which one we please. For convenience, we take that design which includes the control treatment and construct the intrablock subgroup which is then one of the 4 blocks. The following rules are sufficient to determine the intrablock subgroup:

1. All the treatment combinations are even with respect to $ABCDE$ and $ABFGH$ (and therefore $CDEFGH$), and with ACF and BDG and therefore with respect to all the interactions in the four relations.

2. The treatment combinations in the intrablock subgroup form a group in that, if x and y are in the group, so is the product xy obtained by combining x and y, dropping common letters. (Other properties are also necessary in order that they form a group, but these are of no concern in the present problem.)

With these rules, we find that the intrablock subgroup consists of the following treatment combinations:

$$(1), \quad ach, \quad aef, \quad cefh$$
$$bdh, \quad abcd, \quad abdefh, \quad bcdef$$
$$beg, \quad abcegh, \quad abfg, \quad bcfgh$$
$$degh, \quad acdeg, \quad adfgh, \quad cdfg$$

These were generated by noting that each of ach, aef, bdh and beg has 2 letters in common with all the interactions in the 4 identities, and they are not obtainable from each other by taking products.

The whole design (Table 20.5) before randomization is obtained by writing down the intrablock subgroup as block I; multiplying its elements by an element (ab, say) which is known, from the identity relationship to be included in the experiment, to give block II; multiplying the elements of intrablock subgroup by another element not already enumerated which must be included (ce, say) to give block III; and, likewise, with a multiplier of, say, de to give block IV.

TABLE 20.5   ¼ REPLICATE OF 2^8 DESIGN IN 4 BLOCKS OF 16 PLOTS

Block I	Block II	Block III	Block IV
(1)	ab	ce	de
ach	bch	aeh	acdeh
aef	bef	acf	adf
cefh	abcefh	fh	cdfh
bdh	adh	bcdeh	beh
abcd	cd	abde	abce
abdefh	defh	abcdfh	abfh
bcdef	acdef	bdf	bcf
beg	aeg	bcg	bdg
abcegh	cegh	abgh	abcdgh
abfg	fg	abcefg	abdefg
bcfgh	acfgh	befgh	bcdefgh
degh	abdegh	cdgh	gh
acdeg	bcdeg	adg	acg
adfgh	bdfgh	acdefgh	aefgh
cdfg	abcdfg	defg	cefg

The analysis may be performed by dropping the letters a and f from the treatment combinations, thus regarding the experiment as a full replicate on 6 factors, b, c, d, e, g, h, and using the addition-subtraction process to obtain the values for the 63 comparisons of the 64 yields. These will have names involving 1 to 6 of the letters B, C, D, E, G, H, and they may then be renamed by the use of the identity relationship

$$I = -ABCDE = -ABFGH = CDEFGH \qquad (16)$$

in which it is necessary to insert the appropriate signs on the terms. The signs are determined by the fact that we have used the ¼ replicate which contains the control, so that we have taken the negative part of the first 2 interactions and the positive part of the third. In this way, assuming interactions involving 3 factors or more to be zero, we rename for example $BCDE$ to be $-A$, $CDEGH$ to be F, and BGH to be $-AF$. The analysis of variance will have the structure:

	df
Blocks	3
Main effects	8
2-factor interactions	28
Error	24
	—
Total	63

The variance of each estimated effect or interaction will be $\sigma^2/16$, where σ^2 is the error variance.

Now let us consider blocks of 8 units for this ¼ replicate experiment. There is no simple set of rules that lead us to a design, but there does not appear to be a design in which no 2-factor interactions are confounded with blocks. The following set of equations define a design in which two 2-factor interactions are confounded with blocks:

$$I = ABCDE = ABFGH = CDEFGH$$

confounding with blocks the following comparisons:

$$ACF = BDEF = BCGH = ADEGH$$
$$BDG = ACEG = ADFH = BCEFH$$
$$ABCDFG = EFG = CDH = ABEH$$
$$CDF = ABEF = ABCDGH = EGH$$
$$AD = BCE = BDFGH = ACEFGH$$
$$BCFG = ADEFG = ACH = BDEH$$
$$ABG = CDEG = FH = ABCDEFH$$

The contents of each block are given in Table 20.6.

TABLE 20.6   ¼ REPLICATE OF 2^8 DESIGN IN 8 BLOCKS OF 8 PLOTS

I	II	III	IV	V	VI	VII	VIII
(1)	ab	ce	de	fg	gh	acf	bdh
abcd	cd	abde	abce	abcdfg	abcdgh	bdf	ach
cefh	abcefh	fh	cdfh	cegh	cefg	aeh	bcdef
abdefh	defh	abcdfh	abfh	abdegh	abdefg	bcdeh	aef
beg	aeg	bcg	bdg	bef	beh	abcefg	degh
acdeg	bcdeg	adg	acg	acdef	acdeh	defg	abcegh
bcfgh	acfgh	befgh	bcdefgh	bch	bcf	abgh	cdfg
adfgh	bdfgh	acdefgh	aefgh	adh	adf	cdgh	abfg

The analysis of variance may be performed as with blocks of 16: namely, by dropping the letters a and f, performing the addition-subtraction process, and renaming according to the identity $I = -ABCDE = -ABFGH = CDEFGH$. The structure of the analysis of variance will be

	df
Interactions AD, FH	2
Block error	5
Main effects	8
2-factor interactions	26
Error (within block)	22
Total	63

The 2 confounded interactions will be estimated with a variance equal to (block error mean square/16) and all the main effects and the other interactions with a variance equal to (within block error mean square/16).

20.6 ONE-IN-2^p REPLICATION OF THE 2^n FACTORIAL SYSTEM

The extensions to higher degrees of fractional replication are intuitively obvious. If a fraction one in 2^p of a 2^n factorial system is used, there will be 2^{n-p} treatment combinations actually tested with $(2^{n-p} - 1)$ degrees of freedom among them. Of the total of $(2^n - 1)$ effects and interactions in the full model, $2^p - 1$ will be confounded with the total, and the remaining $2^n - 2^p$ will be mutually confounded in groups of 2^p, there being $(2^{n-p} - 1)$ such groups. The identity relationship will be of the form

$$I = X = Y = XY = Z = XZ = YZ = XYZ = U = \cdots \quad (17)$$

there being p interactions X, Y, Z, U, etc., none of which is obtainable from the others by multiplication. We give the following designs which may have some value.

With 10 or more factors, it is possible to estimate main effects and 2-factor interactions from $\frac{1}{8}$ of a replicate if 3-factor and higher-order interactions are negligible. A suitable identity relationship with 10 factors, a, b, c, d, e, f, g, h, j, k, is:

$$I = ABCDE = ABFGH = CDEFGH = ACGJK = BDEGJK$$
$$= BCFHJK = ADEFHJK \quad (18)$$

Thus the 10 main effects and the 45 two-factor interactions are obtained by testing 128 of the possible 1024 combinations. These may be arranged in blocks of 32 units by confounding comparisons which may be denoted by ABJ, ADF, and $BDFJ$. The intrablock subgroup for this design is:

(1), *cek*, *abcd*, *abdek*, *abfg*, *abcefgk*, *cdfg*, *defgk*, *ghk*, *cegh*, *abcdghk*, *abdegh*, *abfhk*, *abcefh*, *cdfhk*, *defh*, *begj*, *bcgjk*, *acdegj*, *adgjk*, *aefj*, *acfjk*, *bcdefj*, *bdfjk*, *behjk*, *bchj*, *acdehjk*, *adhj*, *aefghjk*, *acfghj*, *bcdefghjk*, *bdfghj*.

Arrangements in blocks of 16 units for which main effects and 2-factor interactions are not confounded with blocks have not been found.

A second example is a $\frac{1}{16}$ replication of a 2^{12} experiment. If the factors are denoted by a, b, c, d, e, f, g, h, j, k, l, m, a suitable identity relationship is

$$I = ABCDE = ABFGH = CDEFGH = ABJKL = CDEJKL$$

$$= FGHJKL = ABCDEFGHJKL = ACFJM = BDEFJM$$

$$= BCGHJM = ADEGHJM = BCFKLM = ADEFKLM$$

$$= ACGHKLM = BDEGHKLM \quad (19)$$

If comparisons denoted by ABM, DFH, and $ABDFGM$ are confounded, we have a design in 4 blocks of 64 plots which enables estimation of all main effects and 2-factor interactions. The intrablock subgroup consists of the treatment combinations which have an even number of letters in common with $ABCDE$, $ABFGH$, $ABJKL$, $ACFJM$, ABM, and DFH.

20.7 THE VALUE OF FRACTIONAL DESIGNS

It is difficult to place a value on the individual experiment. A good experiment may be characterized to some extent by a good choice of factors to be tested and by good experimental technique. There are other imponderables such as the value of the aims of the experiment, whether the experiment is likely to lead to a clearer understanding of basic processes, and so on. For purposes of discussion let us suppose that the object of the experimenter is to determine the factors that produce a certain result and the relative importance of these factors. In such circumstances the experimenter must obtain by observation and intuition an idea of the factors that may possibly influence the character in which he is interested. When the experimenter has reached this situation, fractional designs are of real value. They may be used to determine which of the possible factors are of importance relative to a given error of prediction. Once these factors have been discovered, it is necessary to perform detailed work on the factors, possibly even one at a time in order to formulate a law relating response to dosage for each factor. Only when the response to dosage is known as a mathematical relationship does a branch of enquiry resemble an exact science. One difference between the biological and physical sciences lies in the fact that in the physical sciences the experimental material can often be brought to any desired degree of purity and can be examined by varying one factor at a time, the errors of prediction being small relative to the magnitudes of the effects involved, whereas in the biological sciences this is not possible. A further difference between the physical sciences and the biological sciences is that the experimental unit in the biological sciences is much more complex than the physical science unit and cannot easily, if at all, be broken down into simpler units.

If the criterion of value of the experiment is related to the number of main effects and low-order interactions discovered by the experimenter, fractionally replicated designs may have considerable value, for a large number of effects and low-order interactions may be estimated. A difficulty in the evaluation of an experiment is the value to be attributed to information on the various effects and interactions, and the relative value to be attributed to estimates applicable to limited situations and estimates of perhaps lower precision applicable to less limited situations.

We have discussed fractionally replicated designs which are suitable if the experimenter can assume interactions between 3 or more factors to be negligible. Many of the designs we have given can be used if a few of the 3-factor interactions cannot be assumed negligible. A more detailed examination of possible identity relationships and systems of confounding will be necessary, but, apart from this, there is no further difficulty.

The principle of fractional replication may strike the reader as being based on unwarranted assumptions. It should be pointed out that the necessary assumptions are no more exacting than the assumptions made, for example, with a single replicate of a 2^6 factorial experiment: namely, that all interactions involving 3 or more factors are negligible or that a specified set of the 3-factor interactions and all interactions involving more than 3 factors are negligible.

The value of fractionally replicated designs lies in the same phenomena which make the factorial design valuable, in that the experimenter can rarely assume that interactions between the factors which themselves affect a characteristic, biological or physical, do not exist, before he has conducted experiments. On the other hand, what we know about response curves suggests that high-order interactions will be small relative to the experimental errors usually encountered. If high-order interactions are important, the experimenter will soon discover the fact by any design in which the factors are varied simultaneously. An experimental check is perhaps advisable in most cases when a highly fractional design is used, for example, by the use of two repetitions of the basic fractional replicate. In this way an estimate of experimental error uncontaminated by high-order interactions would be obtained, and this could be compared with the estimate of error obtained from the high-order interactions.

Usually the experimenter is in the position of being able to impose treatments on and to examine a certain number of experimental units. He is also in the position that he can think of many factors which should be investigated. We may, therefore, ask whether we can apply any criteria of value to possible experiments on this fixed number of experimental units. To be specific, let us suppose that 128 experimental units are available; then the experimenter can use any of the following designs, staying within the 2^n factorial system:

Number of Factors	Number of Replicates
1	64
2	32
3	16
4	8
5	4
6	2
7	1
8	½
9	¼
10	⅛

Of course, in some situations, there are not more than 3 factors that the experimenter considers worth examining, and, even if there are 10 factors, the experimenter can possibly guess very accurately which 5, say, of the 10 factors are really important. On the other hand, there appears to be a little evidence, for example in nutritional work on biological organisms, that the "best" experimenter's guess in such a situation turns out, with the accumulation of research results, to be not at all accurate. The comparison of the possible designs listed above is, at best, a hazardous procedure. It is, however, the responsibility of the experimenter and statistician to attempt to make the comparison, particularly as the experimenter alone may be unaware of all the possibilities.

As regards the amount of information given by the above possible designs, we can state that the 1-factor experiment will determine the effect of the chosen factor over a limited range of circumstances with a variance of $\sigma^2/32$. The effect of each factor will be determined with the same variance for all the designs listed, but, as more factors are introduced, the effect is estimated for the average of a wider set of conditions specified by the other factors that are varied. The fact that the estimate is for a wider set of circumstances may be an advantage or disadvantage, depending on the circumstances and aims of the experimenter, but it will usually be advantageous in the long view. In evaluating the designs, it is also necessary to put a value on the knowledge obtained about interactions, particularly 2-factor interactions, which we regard a priori as likely to be of greater importance. The lower the number of replicates used in the above designs, the higher will be the value of the designs, if knowledge of the existence of interactions is of some value. The reader will find it instructive to consider the case when the experimenter favors the use of 2 replicates, but wishes to test 10 factors and can perform the experimental work on only 128 experimental units at a time. Considerations of this type make the fractional designs very valuable under some circumstances. The choice of a fractional design does, however, require considerable care, and the experimenter would be unwise to use this type of design at any available opportunity without examination of all the facets.

We have seen that it is difficult, if not impossible, to obtain fractional designs in small blocks without confounding important contrasts. This implies that it may be worth while under some circumstances to use what would be considered large blocks in order to include many factors and obtain comparatively precise information on the effect of each. The extent to which this will be worth while will depend partly on the relationship between error variance and size of block for the experimental material under consideration. In the discussion above we have ignored the fact that, with more factors included, the error mean square will be based on a lower number of degrees of freedom. The effect of this on the accuracy or sensitivity of the experiment will be small.

FURTHER READING

1. FINNEY, D. J. The fractional replication of factorial experiments. *Ann. Eug.*, **12**, 291–301, 1945.
2. FINNEY, D. J. Recent developments in the design of experiments. III. Fractional replication. *Jour. Agr. Sci.*, **36**, 184–191, 1946.
3. KEMPTHORNE, O. A simple approach to confounding and fractional replication in factorial experiments. *Biometrika*, **34**, 255–272, 1947.

CHAPTER 21

The General Case
of Fractional Replication

Fractional replication is of most practical utility when the factors each have 2 levels. The process, however, can be of utility for the other cases, and, in addition to giving the general theory, we shall include in this chapter an actual example on factors with 3 levels.

21.1 FACTORS AT THE SAME PRIME NUMBER (p) OF LEVELS

In Chapter 17, we gave the definitions of effects and interactions for the p^n factorial system, and found expressions for the yields in terms of effects and interactions. The latter may be expressed as follows:

$$t_{ijk}\cdots = \mu + \sum_{(\alpha_1, \alpha_2 \cdots) \text{ and } s} (\delta_s{}^{\alpha_1 i + \alpha_2 j + \cdots}) A^{\alpha_1} B^{\alpha_2} \cdots_s \qquad (1)$$

where the symbol

$$\delta_s{}^{\alpha_1 i + \alpha_2 j + \cdots} = 1, \quad \text{if} \quad \alpha_1 i + \alpha_2 j + \cdots = s \bmod p$$

$$= 0 \text{ otherwise}$$

and the summation is over the unique set of points $(\alpha_1, \alpha_2, \cdots)$ for the possible effect and interaction symbols $A^{\alpha_1} B^{\alpha_2} \cdots$.

In testing the full set of treatment combinations in a randomized block, we would have the general linear hypothesis

$$y_{ijk}\cdots = \mu + \sum_{(\alpha_1, \alpha_2 \cdots) \text{ and } s} (\delta_s{}^{\alpha_1 i + \alpha_2 j + \cdots}) A^{\alpha_1} B^{\alpha_2} \cdots_s + e_{ijk}\cdots \qquad (2)$$

This is a general linear hypothesis on $\left[1 + \left(\dfrac{p^n - 1}{p - 1}\right) p\right]$ parameters,

the parameters satisfying $\left(\dfrac{p^n - 1}{p - 1}\right)$ conditions, namely,

$$\sum_s A^{\alpha_1} B^{\alpha_2} \cdots_s = 0 \qquad (3)$$

410

for each choice of $(\alpha_1, \alpha_2, \cdots)$. The problem is to estimate μ and estimable functions of the $A^{\alpha_1}B^{\alpha_2}\cdots$, that is, the effects and interactions. Now we may suppose that only those treatment combinations that satisfy

$$\beta_1 x_1 + \beta_2 x_2 + \cdots + \beta_n x_n = 0 \bmod p$$

are tested. The following coefficients in the model will be equal for all the plots:

$$\delta_s{}^{\alpha_1 x_1 + \alpha_2 x_2 \cdots}, \qquad \delta_s{}^{(\alpha_1+\beta_1)x_1+(\alpha_2+\beta_2)x_2+\cdots}$$

$$\delta_s{}^{(\alpha_1+2\beta_1)x_1+(\alpha_2+2\beta_2)x_2+\cdots}, \quad \text{etc.} \quad \text{to} \quad \delta_s{}^{[\alpha_1+(p-1)\beta_1]x_1+[\alpha_2+(p-1)\beta_2]x_2+\cdots}$$

The effects or interactions denoted by $A^{\alpha_1}B^{\alpha_2}\cdots$, $A^{\alpha_1+\lambda\beta_1}B^{\alpha_2+\lambda\beta_2}\cdots$, for $\lambda = 1, 2, \cdots, p-1$ are, therefore, mutually confounded, that is, cannot be estimated separately, and the model may be written

$$y_{ijk\cdots} = \mu' + \Sigma'\delta_s{}^{\alpha_1 i + \alpha_2 j + \cdots}A^{\alpha_1}B^{\alpha_2}\cdots{}_s{}^* + e_{ijk\cdots} \tag{4}$$

where

$$A^{\alpha_1}B^{\alpha_2}\cdots{}_s{}^* = A^{\alpha_1}B^{\alpha_2}\cdots{}_s + \sum_{\lambda=1}^{p-1} A^{\alpha_1+\lambda\beta_1}B^{\alpha_2+\lambda\beta_2}\cdots{}_s \tag{5}$$

and Σ' denotes summation over a subset of $\dfrac{p^n-1}{p(p-1)}$ choices out of the total of $\left(\dfrac{p^n-1}{p-1}\right)$ distinct choices of $(\alpha_1, \alpha_2, \cdots, \alpha_n)$.

We may regard this design and its analysis as being given by the relationship

$$I = A^{\beta_1}B^{\beta_2}\cdots \tag{6}$$

and this relationship defining the design has the properties:

1. The treatment combinations actually tested consist of those combinations for which $\Sigma\beta_i x_i = 0 \bmod p$.

2. Any set of $(p-1)$ degrees of freedom X is completely confounded with $(A^{\beta_1}B^{\beta_2}\cdots)^\lambda X$, $\lambda = 1, 2, \cdots, p-1$, or, in other words, X and $X(A^{\beta_1}B^{\beta_2}\cdots)^\lambda$ are mutually confounded.

Corresponding to a particular choice of $(\beta_1, \beta_2\cdots)$ there are p different $(1/p)$th replicates specified by

$$\Sigma\beta_i x_i = l \bmod p \tag{7}$$

where l can take any one of the values $0, 1, 2, \cdots, p-1$. These different $(1/p)$th replicates are exactly the same as far as their practical value is concerned, and any one may be obtained from the others by interchanging the levels of one of the factors for which β is not zero.

In exactly the same way a 1-in-p^t replicate is specified by a relationship of the form

$$I = X = Y = XY = XY^2 = \cdots = XY^{p-1}$$

$$= Z = ZX = ZX^2 = \cdots = ZX^{p-1}$$

$$= ZY = ZY^2 = \cdots = ZY^{p-1}$$

$$= ZY^rX^s[r, s = 1, 2, \cdots, (p-1)]$$

$$= \text{etc.} \tag{8}$$

there being t symbols, X, Y, Z, $\cdots$, none of which is contained in the generalized interactions of any of the others.

Any effect or interaction V not contained in the identity relationship will be completely confounded with the p^t-1 generalized interactions of V with the $\left(\dfrac{p^t-1}{p-1}\right)$ symbols other than unity in the identity relationship.

Having examined the structure of the 1-in-p^t replicated factorial experiments, we may now consider the circumstances under which they may be regarded as providing good designs. If the experimental material is such that interactions involving more than 2 factors are negligible, we may use a 1-in-p^t replicate, if we can find an identity relationship that results in main effects and 2-factor interactions being confounded with high-order interactions but not with each other.

For example, with $p = 3$, $n = 3$, and the identity relationship

$$I = ABC$$

we may generate the resulting confounding:

$$A \quad = AB^2C^2 = BC$$

$$B \quad = AB^2C \ = AC$$

$$C \quad = ABC^2 \ = AB$$

$$AB^2 = AC^2 \quad = BC^2$$

In this way the 8 degrees of freedom between the 9 results are partitioned into 4 sets of 2 degrees of freedom, each line corresponding to a set of 2 degrees of freedom. Clearly this design is of no practical value unless the 2-factor interactions are zero. The situation is much the same with a $\frac{1}{3}$ replicate of a 3^4 experiment, the best that can be done being to confound 2-factor interactions with each other.

With 5 factors each at 3 levels, the $\frac{1}{3}$ replicate based on

$$I = ABCDE \tag{9}$$

(or any of the cases $I = AB^qC^rD^sE^t$, q, r, s, t all > 0, correspondingly), we have the following confounding:

$$A = AB^2C^2D^2E^2 = BCDE$$

$$AB = ABC^2D^2E^2 = CDE$$

$$AB^2 = AC^2D^2E^2 = BC^2D^2E^2$$

with similar relationships from interchanging letters A and B with C, D, or E. The model, for which any of the 3 sets of 81 of the total of 243 treatment combinations specified above would be an adequate test, is

$$y_{ijklm} = \mu + A_i + B_j + AB_{i+j} + AB^2_{i+2j} + C_k + AC_{i+k} + AC^2_{i+2k}$$

$$+ BC_{j+k} + BC^2_{j+2k} + D_l + AD_{i+l} + AD^2_{i+2l} + BD_{j+l}$$

$$+ BD^2_{j+2l} + CD_{k+l} + CD^2_{k+2l} + E_m + AE_{i+m}$$

$$+ AE^2_{i+2m} + BE_{j+m} + BE^2_{j+2m} + CE_{k+m} + CE^2_{k+2m}$$

$$+ DE_{l+m} + DE^2_{l+2m} + e_{ijklm} \tag{10}$$

where i, j, k, l, m denote the levels of the factors a, b, c, d, e and the subscripts of the terms on the right-hand side are reduced modulo 3: that is, a model in which the interactions of 2 factors do not depend on the value taken by any other factor.

The only other general aspect that needs consideration is the arrangement in blocks of the treatment combinations to be tested. If all the treatment combinations that lie in a block satisfy the relationships,

$$\Sigma\gamma_ix_i = l \bmod p$$

$$\Sigma\delta_ix_i = m \bmod p \tag{11}$$

.

.

.

then these combinations also satisfy the relations,

$$\Sigma(\gamma_i + \lambda\beta_i)x_i = l \bmod p$$

$$\Sigma(\delta_i + \lambda\beta_i)x_i = m \bmod p$$

(12)

and so on, for $\lambda = 1, 2, \cdots, p - 1$, if the fraction for which $\Sigma\beta_i x_i = 0$ mod p is used. If an effect or interaction W is confounded with blocks, then so are all the generalized interactions of W with the elements of the identity relationship.

Let us examine the $\frac{1}{3}$ replicate of a 3^5 experiment from the point of view of possible arrangements in blocks of 27 plots and blocks of 9 plots. We suppose the identity relationship chosen is

$$\mathrm{I} = ABCDE$$

If we confound ABC with blocks, we will also confound $ABC(ABCDE) = ABCD^2E^2$ and $ABC(ABCDE)^2 = DE$, which does not meet our requirements that we do not wish to confound main effects or 2-factor interactions. If we confound ABC^2, we also confound ABD^2E^2 and CD^2E^2, and these then constitute a suitable system of confounding for blocks of 27 plots. It may be verified that in order to use blocks of 9 plots it is necessary to confound at least one 2-factor interaction: The following may be confounded with blocks to give this result:

$$
\begin{aligned}
ABC^2 &= ABD^2E^2 &= CD^2E^2 \\
AB^2D &= AC^2DE^2 &= BC^2E^2 \\
ACD^2 &= AB^2CE^2 &= BD^2E \\
BCD &= AB^2C^2D^2E &= AE
\end{aligned}
$$

(13)

To specify the actual arrangement of treatment combinations, we utilize the facts that the block containing the control has all the members of the intrablock subgroup and that the other blocks may be obtained by multiplication of the intrablock subgroup by any treatment combination that occurs in the trial. The intrablock subgroup consists of the treatment combinations which satisfy

$$
\left.
\begin{aligned}
x_1 + x_2 + x_3 + x_4 + x_5 &= 0 \\
x_1 + x_2 + 2x_3 \quad\quad\quad &= 0 \\
x_1 + 2x_2 \quad\ + x_4 \quad\quad &= 0
\end{aligned}
\right\} \bmod 3
$$

(14)

These treatment combinations form a group, for, if $(y_1, \cdots, y_n)$ and $(z_1, \cdots, z_n)$ satisfy these equations, then so does $(y_1 + z_1, y_2 + z_2, \cdots,$

$y_n + z_n$), and the control $(0, 0, \cdots, 0)$ serves as the unit element, the law of combination being addition modulo 3. The intrablock subgroup is as follows, where we may adopt either form of representation:

$(0, 0, 0, 0, 0)$	(1)	$(2, 1, 0, 2, 1)$	a^2bd^2e
$(1, 0, 1, 2, 2)$	acd^2e^2	$(0, 2, 2, 2, 0)$	$b^2c^2d^2$
$(2, 0, 2, 1, 1)$	a^2c^2de	$(1, 2, 0, 1, 2)$	ab^2de^2
$(0, 1, 1, 1, 0)$	bcd	$(2, 2, 1, 0, 1)$	a^2b^2ce
$(1, 1, 2, 0, 2)$	abc^2e^2		

The other blocks are obtained by multiplying this block by c^2e, ce^2, d^2e, de^2, $c^2d^2e^2$, c^2d, cd^2, cde. It may be noted that the elements (1), c^2e, ce^2, d^2e, de^2, $c^2d^2e^2$, c^2d, cd^2, and cde form a group, the rule of combination being ordinary multiplication with the conditions that $a^3 = b^3 = c^3 = d^3 = e^3 = 1$. The product of this group and the intrablock subgroup make up all the treatment combinations tested.

A striking example of fractional replication given by Fisher [1] was devised by Tippett. Consider 5 factors, a, b, c, d, e, each at 5 levels, and suppose all interactions are zero. How many treatment combinations must be tested in order to discover which factors have effects? Suppose we have a $\dfrac{1}{5^3} = \dfrac{1}{125}$ replicate of the 3125 possible combinations based on the identity relationship consisting of ABC, AC^2D, BDE, and all their interactions. In order that the fractional design thus designated be useful for the present purpose, it is necessary that no 2-factor interactions be contained in these interactions:

1. $(ABC)(AC^2D)^r = A^{1+r}BC^{1+2r}D^r$, $r = 1$, 2, 3, 4; if $1 + r = 0$, $1 + 2r \neq 0$, all numbers being reduced modulo 5, so that any of these interaction terms contains 3 letters.

2. $(AC^2D)(BDE)^r = AB^rC^2D^{1+r}E^r$, $r = 1$, 2, 3, 4; clearly all terms certainly contain at least 4 letters.

3. $(ABC)(AC^2D)^r(BDE)^s = A^{1+r}B^{1+s}C^{1+2r}D^{r+s}E^s$, $r, s = 1, 2, 3, 4$; if $s = 4$, $1 + s = 0$, but it is then impossible for 2 of the quantities, $1 + r$, $1 + 2r$, and $r + s$, to be zero: if $s \neq 4$, at least one of $1 + r$, $1 + 2r$, and $r + s$ must be non-zero.

We have, therefore, an identity relationship which contains no 2-factor interactions. If we are sure that interactions between the factors are trivial compared to main effects, we may use the 25 treatment combinations to test the main effects of the 5 factors. The intrablock subgroup for this identity relationship may be obtained by solving the 3 equations:

$$x_1 + x_2 + x_3 = 0$$
$$x_1 + 2x_3 + x_4 = 0 \left.\right\} \bmod 5$$
$$x_2 + x_4 + x_5 = 0$$

The solutions are generated by taking $\lambda_1 X + \lambda_2 Y$ where $X = (10414)$, $Y = (01422)$ and $\lambda_1, \lambda_2 = 0, 1, 2, 3, 4$.

(00000)	(01422)	(02344)	(03211)	(04133)
(10414)	(11331)	(12203)	(13120)	(14042)
(20323)	(21240)	(22112)	(23034)	(24401)
(30232)	(31104)	(32021)	(33443)	(34310)
(40141)	(41013)	(42430)	(43302)	(44224)

The design used by Tippett brought to light immediately the factor and its level which was producing the response.

21.2 THE FORMAL EQUIVALENCE OF FRACTIONAL REPLICATION AND CONFOUNDING

The device of confounding may be represented by the addition to the factorial scheme of a number of pseudofactors whose combinations represent the blocks of the experiment. Consider the confounding of ABC for a 3^3 experiment in blocks of 9 plots. Suppose we attach to the symbols for treatments in the block containing the $(ABC)_i$ combinations the symbol d_i, thus making the experiment on 4 factors a, b, c, and d. The 27 combinations of the 4 factors actually represented are a $\frac{1}{3}$ replicate of the total of 81, given by the identity

$$I = ABCD^2$$

for the comparison represented by

$$D = ABC = ABCD$$

and is the comparison of the 3 blocks. We may, therefore, obtain the design and the arrangement in blocks immediately by specifying the identity $I = ABCD^2$, the last factor d being understood to give the blocks. The formal equivalence may be seen by noting that the combinations tested will satisfy, say,

$$x_1 + x_2 + x_3 + 2x_4 = 0 \bmod 3$$

so that, when

$$\left.\begin{array}{lll}\text{when} & x_4 = 0, & x_1 + x_2 + x_3 = 0 \\ & x_4 = 1, & x_1 + x_2 + x_3 = 1 \\ \text{and, when} & x_4 = 2, & x_1 + x_2 + x_3 = 2\end{array}\right\} \bmod 3$$

The joint problem of confounding and fractional replication for p^n systems reduces then to the enumeration of identity relationships for fractional replication. If we need a 1-in-p^t replicate of a p^n experiment in p^r blocks ($r < n - t$), we need a 1-in-p^{t+r} replicate of a p^{n+r} experiment. The requirements on the identity relationship are not quite so exacting as in a true case of fractional replication, for the identity relationship can contain terms involving only 4 letters if one of them corresponds to a block pseudofactor. Operationally the author's experience is that this equivalence is not of much help, because methods of enumeration of fractional designs with a small fraction have not been evolved. Rather, the equivalence is sometimes useful in the other direction, that, once a design with a 1-in-p^t replicate of a p^n experiment with p^r blocks is enumerated, it is easy to specify a 1-in-p^{t-1} of a p^{n+1} design with p^{r-1} blocks.

A group of designs may, for example, be deduced from that given in Chapter 20 for a $\frac{1}{16}$ replicate of a 2^{12} experiment. The identity relationship was

$$I = ABCDE = ABFGH = CDEFGH$$

$$= ABJKL = CDEJKL = FGHJKL = ABCDEFGHJKL$$

$$= ACFJM = BDEFJM = BCGHJM = ADEGHJM$$

$$= BCFKLM = ADEFKLM = ACGHKLM = BDEGHKLM$$

If the factor m is regarded as giving 2 blocks, the above identity relationship provides a $\frac{1}{8}$ replicate of a 2^{11} experiment in 2 blocks. Similarly, we may obtain a $\frac{1}{4}$ replicate of a 2^{10} in 4 blocks, a $\frac{1}{2}$ replicate of 2^9 in 8 blocks, and a full replicate of a 2^8 in 16 blocks.

21.3 THE EFFECT OF BLOCK-TREATMENT INTERACTIONS

The formalization which has been given above enables a simple examination of the possible effects of block-treatment interactions on the interpretation of a confounded experiment. Consider a 2^5 experiment on factors a, b, c, d, and e, the 32 combinations being arranged in blocks of 8 plots confounding ABC, ADE, and $BCDE$. This experiment may be represented as a $\frac{1}{4}$ replicate of a 2^7 experiment by introducing block pseudofactors f and g, say, the identity relationship being

$$I = ABCF = ADEG = BCDEFG \qquad (15)$$

If there are differential effects of the factors from block to block, the interpretation is exceedingly difficult, for we have as a result of the identity relationship the following relations:

$$AB = CF, \qquad AD = EG$$

$$AC = BF, \qquad AE = DG \qquad (16)$$

$$BC = AF, \qquad DE = AG$$

Of the total of 10 two-factor interactions, 6 could be interpreted as block-treatment interactions. If there are significant block-treatment interactions but no interactions between the factors, the usual method of analysis will tend to indicate the presence of 2-factor interactions. This is not particularly surprising in that the usual method of analysis assumes additivity of block, treatment, and error contributions and can hardly be expected to be satisfactory when additivity does not hold. The reason for stating the position is that it is important for the experimenter to be aware of the possible difficulties. In discussing the rules by which blocks of the experimental units should be chosen, we stated that as much heterogeneity of experimental material as possible should be removed by the blocks. This rule should be followed only so long as additivity can reasonably be expected to hold. Block interactions will, over a number of experiments, tend to average to zero, because groups of treatment combinations are allocated to the blocks at random, so that the problem is not so important in groups of experiments as in a single experiment. In addition to noting the effects of block-treatment interactions on estimates of effects and interactions, we may also remind the reader of the relevant discussion in Chapter 8, which amounted essentially to the fact that, with block-treatment interactions, we cannot obtain an estimate of the true error variance to which comparisons are subject.

Examination of the possible presence of block-treatment interactions for factorial experiments on some field crops (Yates,[2] Kempthorne [3]) indicated that they were fairly certainly small. This is, of course, evidence in only one small branch of the application of experimental design.

21.4   FRACTIONAL REPLICATION OF MIXED FACTORIAL SYSTEMS

By a mixed factorial system we mean the system obtained by taking all the combinations of m factors at p levels, n factors at q levels, and so on, where p and q are prime numbers. We dealt briefly with the difficulties of confounding with this system, and we shall encounter the same difficulties in fractional replication.

In order that a set of treatment combinations be a fractional replicate of the simplest type, the number of treatment combinations must be a factor of $p^m q^n$, say, equal to $p^a q^b$ which will be a 1-in-$p^{m-a} q^{n-b}$ replicate. This may be effected by picking a set of $(m - a)$ independent effects or interactions from the possible $(p^m - 1)/(p - 1)$ of the first group, and a set of $(n - b)$ independent effects or interactions from the possible $(q^n - 1)/(q - 1)$ of the second group of factors. The treatment combinations tested will then be based on 2 identities.

$$I = X = Y = Z = \text{etc.} = XY = \cdots = XY^{p-1} = \text{etc.} \tag{17}$$
and
$$I = U = V = W = \text{etc.} = UV = \cdots = UV^{q-1} = \text{etc.} \tag{18}$$

The confounding among the effects and interactions may be obtained from the identity relationships.

Suppose we have $p = 3$, $m = 4$, $q = 2$, $n = 4$ with factors a, b, c, d, e, f, g, h in order. A $\frac{1}{6}$ replicate could be based on the identity relationships,

$$I = ABCD$$

$$I = EFGH$$

There will be $3^3 \times 2^3 = 216$ treatment combinations, and it may be verified that the following confounding among effects and interactions occurs.

$$
\left.
\begin{aligned}
A \;\; &= AB^2C^2D^2 = BCD \\
AB &= ABC^2D^2 = CD \\
AB^2 &= AC^2D^2 = BC^2D^2
\end{aligned}
\right\}
\begin{aligned}
&\text{and similar relationships obtained} \\
&\text{by permuting the letters } ABCD
\end{aligned}
$$

$$
\left.
\begin{aligned}
E \;\; &= FGH \\
EF &= GH
\end{aligned}
\right\}
\begin{aligned}
&\text{and similar relationships obtained} \\
&\text{by permuting the letters } EFGH
\end{aligned}
$$

In addition, the following interactions, for example, are mutually confounded:

$$AE = AB^2C^2D^2E = BCDE$$
$$= AFGH = AB^2C^2D^2FGH = BCDFGH$$

in which, while we use the symbolism appropriate for pure systems, we must interpret a symbol such as $BCDFGH$ to be the interaction of the 3×2 table:

	$(BCD)_0$	$(BCD)_1$	$(BCD)_2$
$(FGH)_0$	x	x	x
$(FGH)_1$	x	x	x

The above example is of little practical value, for 2-factor interactions are inextricably mixed. It illustrates, however, the main difficulty with mixed systems, that one must, so to speak, work within groups of factors each at the same number of levels.

In view of this, there is little to be said on fractional replication of mixed systems. If there is a sufficient number of factors at one of the levels to enable fractional replication on that set of factors, fractional replication may be used. The advantages to the experimenter of having the same number of levels for most of the factors are rather striking. They lie in the facts that, with the same number of levels, simple systems of confounding and fractional replication exist and the analysis of the experiment is straightforward.

21.5 OTHER FRACTIONALLY REPLICATED DESIGNS

We have, in all cases so far, considered a fractional replicate of a p^n experiment which contains p^s treatment combinations, where s is less than n. It is not necessary that we restrict ourselves in this way, and we can, in fact, make up a k-in-p^r fractional design, in which k is any number between 1 and p^r. There do not appear to be any extensive investigations for cases when k is greater than unity, and the possibilities are certainly considerable, though not necessarily of practical value.

As an example, let us suppose that an experimenter wishes to test 5 factors each at 2 levels, but has only 24 experimental units. Furthermore, suppose interactions involving 3 or more factors can be assumed to be very small. As a possibility, we could suggest a $\frac{3}{4}$ design made up of a $\frac{1}{2}$ replicate based on the identity

$$I = -ABCDE \tag{19}$$

and the $\frac{1}{4}$ replicate based on the identity (note that the signs are specified)

$$I = -ABC = -CDE = ABDE \tag{20}$$

The analysis follows from the normal equations which, under the assumptions, are of the form:

$$
\begin{aligned}
6\hat{A} \quad - 2\widehat{BC} \quad\quad &= \tfrac{1}{2}[A] \\
-2\hat{A} \quad + 6\widehat{BC} \quad\quad &= \tfrac{1}{2}[BC] \\
6\hat{B} \quad - 2\widehat{AC} \quad\quad &= \tfrac{1}{2}[B] \\
6\widehat{AC} - 2\hat{B} \quad\quad &= \tfrac{1}{2}[AC] \\
6\hat{C} \quad - 2\widehat{AB} - 2\widehat{DE} &= \tfrac{1}{2}[C] \\
-2\hat{C} \quad + 6\widehat{AB} + 2\widehat{DE} &= \tfrac{1}{2}[AB] \\
-2\hat{C} \quad + 2\widehat{AB} + 6\widehat{DE} &= \tfrac{1}{2}[DE] \\
6\hat{D} \quad - 2\widehat{CE} \quad\quad &= \tfrac{1}{2}[D] \\
-2\hat{D} \quad + 6\widehat{CE} \quad\quad &= \tfrac{1}{2}[CE] \\
6\hat{E} \quad - 2\widehat{CD} \quad\quad &= \tfrac{1}{2}[E] \\
-2\hat{E} \quad + 6\widehat{CD} \quad\quad &= \tfrac{1}{2}[CD] \\
6\widehat{AD} + 2\widehat{BE} \quad\quad &= \tfrac{1}{2}[AD] \\
6\widehat{AE} + 2\widehat{BD} \quad\quad &= \tfrac{1}{2}[AE] \\
6\widehat{BD} + 2\widehat{AE} \quad\quad &= \tfrac{1}{2}[BD] \\
6\widehat{BE} + 2\widehat{AD} \quad\quad &= \tfrac{1}{2}[BE]
\end{aligned}
\tag{21}
$$

where $[A]$ denotes the sum of the combinations containing a minus those not containing a, $[BC]$ the sum of the terms whose expectations contain BC positively minus the sum of terms whose expectation contains it negatively. It follows, therefore, that

$$\text{var } (\hat{A}) = \text{var } (\hat{B}) = \text{var } (\hat{D}) = \text{var } (\hat{E}) = \text{var } (\widehat{BC}) = \text{var } (\widehat{AC})$$

$$= \text{var } (\widehat{CE}) = \text{var } (\widehat{CD}) = \frac{3\sigma^2}{16}$$

$$\text{cov}(\hat{A}, \widehat{BC}) = \text{cov}(\hat{B}, \widehat{AC}) = \text{cov}(\hat{D}, \widehat{CE}) = \text{cov}(\hat{E}, \widehat{CD}) = \frac{\sigma^2}{16}$$

$$\text{var}(\hat{C}) = \text{var}(\widehat{AB}) = \text{var}(\widehat{DE}) = \frac{\sigma^2}{5}$$

$$\text{cov}(\hat{C}, \widehat{AB}) = \text{cov}(\hat{C}, \widehat{DE}) = \frac{\sigma^2}{20}, \qquad \text{cov}(\widehat{AB}, \widehat{DE}) = \frac{\sigma^2}{20}$$

$$\text{var}(\widehat{AD}) = \text{var}(\widehat{AE}) = \text{var}(\widehat{BD}) = \text{var}(\widehat{BE}) = \frac{3\sigma^2}{16}$$

all unmentioned covariances being zero.

For the ½ replicate alone, we know that each effect and interaction will be estimated with a variance of $\sigma^2/4$ and that all the estimates will be uncorrelated. The use of the additional ¼ of a replicate has, therefore, resulted in lower variances for all the estimates, but has introduced correlations between some of the estimates of up to ⅓. These correlations will render tests of significance somewhat tedious, as they are a concomitant of the non-orthogonality present.

The example we have considered is not a ¾ replicate in the sense that ¾ of the combinations are tested. Ideally, perhaps, we would take a ½ replicate with ½ of the remaining ½ replicate. Suppose we consider the 2^6 case and take the ½ replicate based on the identity

$$I = -ABCDEF \tag{22}$$

and the ¼ replicate based on the identity

$$I = +ABCDEF = ABC = DEF \tag{23}$$

where we note that the ¼ replicate is not in the chosen ½ replicate. This set of treatment combinations will lead to the following typical normal equations:

For A:

$$12\hat{A} + 4\widehat{BC} = \tfrac{1}{2}[A]$$
$$4\hat{A} + 12\widehat{BC} = \tfrac{1}{2}[BC] \tag{24}$$

with similar equations for $\hat{B}$ and $\widehat{AC}$, $\hat{C}$ and $\widehat{AB}$, $\hat{D}$ and $\widehat{EF}$, $\hat{E}$ and $\widehat{DF}$, $\hat{F}$ and $\widehat{DE}$.

For $\widehat{AD}$:

$$12\widehat{AD} = \tfrac{1}{2}[AD] \tag{25}$$

with similar equations for $\widehat{AE}$, $\widehat{AF}$, $\widehat{BD}$, $\widehat{BE}$, $\widehat{BF}$, $\widehat{CD}$, $\widehat{CE}$, and $\widehat{CF}$.

It follows, therefore, that the variance is $3\sigma^2/32$ for each main effect, likewise for 2-factor interactions partially confounded with main effects, and $\sigma^2/12$ for all other 2-factor interactions. The covariance of an effect and interaction which are partially confounded is $-\sigma^2/32$, so that their correlation is $\tfrac{1}{3}$. It may be noted that, if we take the reciprocal of the variance as the amount of information, then the full replicate or $\tfrac{1}{2}$ replicate gives $1/4\sigma^2$ units of information per plot while the $\tfrac{3}{4}$ replicate gives $2/9\sigma^2$ units of information per plot. It will, in fact, be true always that a design that results in partial confounding between some effects and interactions will yield less information per plot, as measured above, than a design that does not have such partial confounding. For this reason and for those given above, fractional designs other than of type 1 in p^r for the p^n system are not advantageous, though in a given situation one of them may be resorted to.

21.6 WEIGHING DESIGNS

Considerable attention has been given in recent years (Hotelling,[4] Mood,[5] Plackett and Burman,[6] Kempthorne,[7] Kishen [8]) to a problem originally considered by Yates.[2] The problem is that of weighing a number of small objects by a balance, the errors of operation, reading, and balancing of which are important relative to the magnitudes of the weights of the objects. It is not our purpose here to describe this work in detail, but it is illustrative of the general process in the design of experiments.

If we put objects a, b, c, for instance, in the right-hand pan of the balance and enough known weights in the left-hand pan to balance the machine, then the observation y_{abc} may be expressed in the form

$$y_{abc} = \mu + A + B + C + e_{abc} \tag{26}$$

where μ is the bias of the machine; A, B, and C are the true weights, and e_{abc} is the error. In general, a set of weighings may be written in the form of a matrix

$$\begin{bmatrix} 1 & 0 & 1 & 0 & 0 \\ 0 & 1 & 0 & 1 & 1 \\ & & \text{etc.} & & \end{bmatrix}$$

of which the first column refers to a, the second to b, and so on, and the first row to the first weighing, etc. In the first weighing, then, objects a and c are weighed; in the second b, d, and e; and so on. If we add a column of 1's at the beginning we have a matrix X, say, and, if we denote the n observations by a column matrix y consisting of n numbers, the observations may be written

$$y = X\alpha + \epsilon \tag{27}$$

where

$$\alpha = \begin{bmatrix} \mu \\ A \\ B \\ C \\ \vdots \\ \vdots \end{bmatrix}$$

and ϵ is a column matrix of the errors of weighing. From Chapter 6, we know that the estimates $\hat{\alpha}$ are given by

$$\hat{\alpha} = S^{-1}X'y$$

where

$$S = X'X \tag{28}$$

and the variance-covariance matrix of the estimates is $(S^{-1})\sigma^2$.

The weighing problem, therefore, reduces to the consideration of the matrix S^{-1} and particular properties of it. For our purposes it is, however, simpler to redefine μ to be equal to $\mu - \frac{1}{2}A - \frac{1}{2}B - \frac{1}{2}C$, etc., and to write $\frac{1}{2}A$, $\frac{1}{2}B$, etc., for A, B, etc. With this redefinition, the elements of a row of the matrix are plus unity if the corresponding object is placed on the right-hand side of the balance and minus unity if not used in the particular weighing. With the matrix so defined and the equation

$$y = X\alpha + \epsilon$$

α will now consist of the new μ and half the true weights. The true weights are then estimated by

$$2S^{-1}X'y$$

with variance $4(S^{-1})\sigma^2$. The problem is, therefore, to maximize some chosen property of the matrix S^{-1}.

In general, the property we would maximize would be the determinant of S, and we would then obtain minimum generalized variance of the estimates (see Cramér [9] for instance). This is done very simply under certain conditions, for we note that the matrix X consists of rows each containing plus or minus unity. If there are n weighings in all, i.e., n rows in the matrix X, and p objects to be weighed so that X has $(p + 1)$ columns, the columns of the matrix can be represented as vectors in n-dimensional space. Furthermore, the vectors are all of the same length because each term in each column is plus or minus unity. The determinant of S is the volume of the parallelepiped formed by the $(p + 1)$ vectors in the n-dimensional space, and clearly the volume of the parallelepiped is a maximum when the $(p + 1)$ vectors are mutually orthogonal. The problem of evolving weighing designs reduces to the enumeration of matrices of the desired type if they exist. Otherwise one must follow trial and error methods, or rather special devices (see Mood [5]). Matrices that have the desired property are known as Hadamard matrices, and the reader may consult Plackett and Burman's paper [6] for a review of the subject and a listing of matrices. If a matrix X with the desired property exists, then $X'X$ is equal to n times the r-by-r unit matrix, so that the estimates of A, B, etc., will be subject to a variance equal to $\dfrac{4}{n} \sigma^2$. This is the minimum value of the variance of any weight that can be obtained with any weighing design of the type we are discussing. These estimates are, in this case, $\dfrac{2}{n} X'y$, which is very simply computed. Because we have considered only the case when the objects are put in the right-hand pan and the weights in the left-hand pan, the problem is known very appropriately as the spring balance problem.

The other branch of the problem is known as the chemical balance problem, in which weights and objects can be put in either pan, and the procedure will be to put a set of the objects in the right-hand pan and the remainder in the left-hand pan and add known weights to one pan or the other, as the case may be, to bring the pointer to the zero mark. Clearly the same formulation as above holds; if we replace ½A by A, the same design considerations hold; and the minimum variance that can be achieved is σ^2/n.

We may note, in conclusion, that the full set of 2^n factorial combinations gives a design with the required property, as does any fractionally replicated design that keeps main effects unconfounded with each other.

We may also note that we have shown, in a roundabout fashion, that, if the experimenter's concern is to estimate effects and interactions, the full set of factorial combinations, or a suitably chosen fractional replicate, is optimum for the purpose.

21.7 AN EXAMPLE OF THE USE OF FRACTIONAL REPLICATION

For a more complete description of the problem, the reader may refer to Tischer and Kempthorne.[10] In brief, the problem was to determine the effect of various factors on the readings given by a machine called the Adams consistometer, which is used to give a measure of the consistency of some types of canned food. The investigation was made because standards are being set up for the consistency of some canned foods, and the Adams consistometer was thought likely to be generally adopted for the purpose. The particular factors were chosen because they were thought to be of possible importance in routine use of the machine. The basic idea of the machine is that the food is emptied into a truncated cone which is in contact with a flat metal sheet, the container is raised, and the spread of the food measured. The 6 factors that were thought to have possible importance were:

(a) Rate of lifting of the cone.
(b) Temperature of material.
(d) Time allowed for spreading.
(e) Methods of cleaning the apparatus.
(f) Angle of the cone.
(g) Surface of the cone.

All cones used were of a constant volume. In addition to testing these factors, it was also necessary to determine whether their effects depended on the consistency of the material. If, for example, the factors were found to have effects independent of the level of consistency, and with no interactions, a constant correction could be used to adjust a reading made at a particular temperature to a standard temperature. Materials that were of low, medium, and high consistency and had been checked for homogeneity were selected by the use of the machine under virtually constant conditions, and these constitute the factor c. In deciding on the design for this problem, it was necessary to consider the relative merits of a series of experiments, in which only one factor is varied at a time, and a factorial experiment. Since it was desired to test each of the factors at 3 levels, a single replicate of a factorial design would require 2187 observations, and this was quite outside the bounds of practicality. On the other hand, there was no prior information that the factors were independent in their actions and that there were no interactions, but, on common sense grounds, high-order interactions were likely to be trivial. It was, therefore, natural to consider the use of a fractionally replicated design. A $\frac{1}{9}$ replicate based on the identity

$$I = ABCD^2E = CD^2E^2F^2G^2 = ABC^2DF^2G^2 = ABE^2FG$$

was used, and the 243 treatment combinations were divided into 9 blocks of 27, by confounding the 4 comparisons each with 2 degrees of freedom which have as one name

$$AB^2F^2G, \quad BCDF, \quad ACDG, \quad ABC^2D^2FG$$

It may be verified that, in this way, no 2-factor interaction is confounded. Thus, if AB^2F^2G is confounded, then so are $AC^2DE^2FG^2$, BC^2DEF^2G, $AB^2CD^2E^2F$, $AB^2C^2DEG^2$, ACD^2F^2, BCD^2G, AEG, BEF also confounded. A group of 27 combinations constituted a day's work, and within each day the 27 were arranged in random order. The intrablock subgroup for the design consists of the 27 combinations shown in Table 21.1.

TABLE 21.1

Level of

a	b	c	d	e	f	g
0	0	0	0	0	0	0
0	1	1	2	0	2	0
0	2	2	1	0	1	0
1	0	1	0	1	2	1
2	0	2	0	2	1	2
1	1	2	2	1	1	1
1	2	0	1	1	0	1
2	1	0	2	2	0	2
2	2	1	1	2	2	2
1	0	1	1	2	1	0
2	0	2	2	1	2	0
1	1	2	0	2	0	0
1	2	0	2	2	2	0
2	0	2	1	0	0	1
0	0	0	1	1	2	2
2	1	0	0	0	2	1
2	2	1	2	0	1	1
0	1	1	0	1	1	2
0	2	2	2	1	0	2
2	1	0	1	1	1	0
2	2	1	0	1	0	0
0	0	0	2	2	1	1
1	0	1	2	0	0	2
0	1	1	1	2	0	1
0	2	2	0	2	2	1
1	1	2	1	0	2	2
1	2	0	0	0	1	2

A condensed analysis of variance is given in Table 21.2. Actually,

TABLE 21.2 ANALYSIS OF VARIANCE OF EXAMPLE

	df	Sum of Squares	Mean Square	F
Blocks	8	38.98		
Main effects				
A	2	6.33	3.16	
B	2	577.93	288.96	184
C	2	6688.31	3344.16	2130
D	2	98.40	49.20	3.31
E	2	1.05	0.52	<1
F	2	17.28	8.64	5.5
G	2	16.79	8.40	5.3
2-factor interactions	84	141.80	1.69	1.1
Error	136	213.46	1.57	
Total	242	7800.33		

the sets of 4 degrees of freedom for the 21 interactions were separated, and only 2 of them, of b and c, and of f and g, were significant at the 5 percent level. There is, therefore, very little evidence of interactions, except that an interaction of b and c would be expected on general considerations. In addition, repeated observations, with all the other factors kept constant, were made on the 3 types of material. The mean square between repeated observations was 1.46, so that there is also no evidence of high-order interactions. This mean square was not entirely homogeneous, but the effect of the heterogeneity on interpretation based on the analysis of variance was thought to be small. We shall not give the estimates of the effects of the factors, because they are of no interest in the present context, nor shall we discuss some other aspects of the experimental results.

This example is disappointing in the sense that it did not bring to light any interactions, and so, for this problem, the effects of each of the factors could have been obtained by varying each factor independently. The knowledge that even 2-factor interactions are unimportant over the ranges of the factors considered, is, however, valuable and could not have been obtained without a design of the factorial type. Furthermore, the accuracy with which the effects are estimated by this design would have necessitated about 1700 (7×243) observations, if the factors had been varied one at a time.

The precision for estimates of effects given by the actual experiment is unnecessarily high, but a minimum of about 30 observations per factor would have been necessary with 7 one-factor experiments so that the fractional design is in no way inferior to the other type, and gives additional information which was desired.

REFERENCES

1. FISHER, R. A. *The design of experiments.* Oliver and Boyd, Edinburgh, 4th ed. 1947.
2. YATES, F. Complex experiments. *Suppl. Jour. Roy. Stat. Soc.*, **2**, 181–247, 1935.
3. KEMPTHORNE, O. A note on differential responses in blocks. *Jour. Agr. Sci.*, **37**, 245–248, 1947.
4. HOTELLING, H. Some problems in weighing and other experimental techniques, *Ann. Math. Stat.*, **15**, 297–306, 1944.
5. MOOD, A. M. On Hotelling's weighing problem. *Ann. Math. Stat.*, **17**, 432–446, 1946.
6. PLACKETT, R. L., and BURMAN, J. P. The design of optimum multifactorial experiments. *Biometrika*, **33**, 305–325, 1946.
7. KEMPTHORNE, O. The factorial approach to the weighing problem. *Ann. Math. Stat.*, **19**, 238–245, 1948.
8. KISHEN, K. On the design of experiments for weighing and making other types of measurement. *Ann. Math. Stat.*, **14**, 294–301, 1945.
9. CRAMÉR, H. *Mathematical methods of statistics.* Princeton University Press, Princeton. 1945.
10. TISCHER, R. G., and KEMPTHORNE, O. Influence of variations in technique and environment on the determination of consistency of canned sweet corn. *Food Technology*, **5**, 200–203, 1951

CHAPTER 22

Quasifactorial or Lattice
and Incomplete Block Designs

22.1 INTRODUCTION

The problem we shall be discussing in this and the following chapters is the comparison of a number of treatments, which are not related in a special way as are a factorial set of treatments, with blocks the size of which is less than the number of treatments. For example, plant breeders are frequently in the position of having to compare, say, 100 varieties or first crosses of inbred lines. In earlier chapters we discussed the effect of size of block on the variance of treatment comparisons and described Fairfield Smith's empirical law according to which the within-block variance increases to a varying degree, depending on the nature of the experimental material, with increasing number of experimental units per block. We also obtained a view of the effect on the sensitivity of tests of hypotheses of the size of the experimental error variance. As a result of these considerations, we devoted some chapters to a discussion of confounding, a device by which the size of block within which comparisons are made may be reduced, with resulting gain in precision on the comparisons of interest to the experimenter, and at the expense of information on comparisons that the experimenter thinks to be unimportant. The problem we shall discuss is therefore an important one.

The size of block that should be achieved depends markedly on the experimental material and the cost of achieving this size. For example, in nutritional experiments on young sheep, it might well be advisable to make comparisons within pairs, because pairs of lambs are frequently obtained, and the pair of lambs, although not genetically identical (unless the twins are identical), will be the result of the same cross and will have been subjected to the same intrauterine environment as well as, presumably, similar postnatal environments. They may be expected then to be much more similar than a pair of lambs taken at random from a flock. In an experiment on young cattle, the same considerations hold, and, in recent years, it has been found that the frequency of identical twins is sufficiently high to make the consideration of the use of blocks of two identical twins important. The gain in accuracy that may be expected by the use of twins in these cases, for example, over the use of larger blocks may be estimated from experimental data in which twins have been used, as we shall indicate later.

In the case of field plot experiments, the size of plot is usually, though by no means always, fairly well determined by experimental and agronomic techniques, and the experimenter usually aims toward a block size of less than 12 plots. In some circumstances this is impossible and in other cases possibly not worth while. If this arbitrary rule is accepted, and we wish to compare 100 varieties, we might use for example 10 blocks of 10 plots for each replicate. If this is done, it is obvious we can make up 99 treatment comparisons in a replicate to consist of 90 comparisons which are entirely comparisons within blocks and 9 comparisons which are between blocks. These between-block comparisons will be less accurate than the within-block comparisons, for they will be subject to an error based on the failure of blocks of 10 plots treated alike to yield the same results. The blocks could be made up so badly that the between-block error will not be greater than the within-block error, but the former error will not usually be less than the latter. In general, if blocks are made up on the basis of contiguity of plots or on the basis of prior information about the fertility of the plots, the between-block error will be considerably greater than the within-block error. Furthermore, more than one replicate will be necessary in order that the experimental error may be estimated. It is therefore appropriate to consider how the replicates should differ from each other, in order that the information on all possible comparisons shall be as large as possible.

There are two main groups of designs which may be distinguished:

1. In which a correspondence may be established between the treatments and the treatment combinations of a factorial set, and, when the treatments are renamed according to this correspondence, the methods for factorial experiments we have discussed may be used. Designs of this group are known as quasifactorial or lattice designs.

2. In which, although it may be possible to set up the sort of correspondence mentioned in 1, the correspondence is of little or no help in devising the design or simplifying the analysis. This group of designs will be denoted by the term incomplete block designs.

It should be pointed out that the distinction we make is not a hard and fast one but is of value in describing the designs. Under most circumstances, the designs that will be discussed under 1, which will be obtained by the use of a factorial correspondence, could have been obtained in other ways. Their derivation from a corresponding factorial model is, however, quite straightforward, and it would be unnecessarily tedious not to adopt this procedure. The next few chapters will deal with the first group of designs and later chapters with the second group. This order has the possible virtue of conforming largely to the chronological order of the development of the designs.

22.2 THE SIMPLEST QUASIFACTORIAL DESIGN

With perhaps a little risk of another design being regarded as the simplest, we consider the testing of 4 treatments t_1, t_2, t_3, t_4 in blocks of 2 experimental units. Such a design might well be of value in a study on the nutrition of young sheep as mentioned previously.

The first step is to set up a correspondence between the 4 treatments and the treatment combinations of 2 factors, a, b, say, each at 2 levels, as in Table 22.1.

TABLE 22.1

Treatment	Quasifactorial Combination
t_1	(1)
t_2	a
t_3	b
t_4	ab

In Chapter 14 we discussed the arrangement of 2 factors at 2 levels in blocks of 2 plots. There are, in fact, 3 possible arrangements:

Confounding	Blocks
A	(1), b and a, ab
B	(1), a and b, ab
AB	(1), ab and a, b

and we may use these arrangements for the 4 treatments so that we have 3 types of replicate (Figure 25).

Replicate I   Replicate II   Replicate III

t_1	t_3
t_2	t_4

t_1	t_2
t_3	t_4

t_1	t_4
t_2	t_3

FIGURE 25.

Now let us make r repetitions of each of these replicates, so that we have $3r$ replicates in all, and consider the estimation of the effects and interactions. This is quite straightforward, namely, that we estimate A from the replicates of types II and III, B from the replicates of types I and III, and AB from the replicates of types I and II. Each effect and the interaction will be estimated with a variance of $\sigma^2/2r$, where σ^2 is the variance within blocks of 2 units.

Our object in setting up the experiment in the first instance was to estimate the differences among the treatments t_1, t_2, t_3, and t_4. If we denote the yields of (1), a, b, and ab by the same symbols, we have

$$(1) = \mu - \tfrac{1}{2}A - \tfrac{1}{2}B + \tfrac{1}{2}AB$$

$$a = \mu + \tfrac{1}{2}A - \tfrac{1}{2}B - \tfrac{1}{2}AB$$

$$b = \mu - \tfrac{1}{2}A + \tfrac{1}{2}B - \tfrac{1}{2}AB$$

$$ab = \mu + \tfrac{1}{2}A + \tfrac{1}{2}B + \tfrac{1}{2}AB$$

Any comparison among the 4 treatments is expressible in terms of A, B, and AB, for instance,

$$t_1 - t_2 = (1) - a = -A + AB$$

$$t_1 + t_2 - 2t_3 = (1) + a - 2b = A - 2B + AB$$

and so on. We have obtained estimates of A, B, and AB, so that we can substitute these estimates to obtain the estimate of the treatment comparison. Thus:

$$(t_1 \overset{\frown}{-} t_2) = -\hat{A} + \widehat{AB}$$

$$(t_1 \overset{\frown}{-} t_3) = -\hat{B} + \widehat{AB}$$

$$(t_1 \overset{\frown}{-} t_4) = -\hat{A} - \hat{B}$$

and any other comparison may be computed from these differences.

Now let us examine the variances of these differences. Each of the estimates $\hat{A}$, $\hat{B}$, and $\widehat{AB}$ has a variance of $\sigma^2/2r$, and the estimates are independent, so that we have

$$\operatorname{var}(t_1 \overset{\frown}{-} t_2) = \frac{\sigma^2}{r}$$

$$\operatorname{var}(t_1 \overset{\frown}{-} t_3) = \frac{\sigma^2}{r}$$

$$\operatorname{var}(t_1 \overset{\frown}{-} t_4) = \frac{\sigma^2}{r}$$

It is easily verified that the estimate of the difference between any 2 treatments has a variance of σ^2/r.

This may be compared with the variance that would have held if we had used blocks of 4 plots, for then, with the total of $3r$ replicates, any treatment difference would have a variance of $2\sigma^2/3r$. In the latter case, however, the σ^2 refers to the variance within blocks of 4 plots and should be written σ^2_4, whereas, in the former case, it should be written as σ^2_2. In general, we know that σ^2_4 will be greater than σ^2_2, and, if σ^2_4 is greater than $\frac{3}{2}\sigma^2_2$, the confounded design will have resulted in a lower variance for the estimate of a treatment difference. If the reduction from blocks of 4 plots to blocks of 2 plots had not reduced the experimental error variance, the quasifactorial design would have given $\frac{2}{3}\left(= \frac{r}{\sigma^2} \div \frac{3r}{2\sigma^2} \right)$ of the information given by the design with no confounding. This factor of 2/3 is known as the efficiency factor of the particular incomplete block design.

The analysis of variance of the yields of the $3r$ replicates has the structure shown in Table 22.2.

TABLE 22.2

Due to	df	Expectation of Mean Square
Replicates	$3r - 1$	
Blocks	$3r$	
A	1	
B	1	
AB	1	
Error (intrablock)	$6r - 3$	σ^2
Total	$12r - 1$	

So far we have utilized only information given by comparisons within blocks.

To utilize the between-block information, we note that the block sum of squares may be partitioned in the following way:

	df
A	1
B	1
AB	1
$A \times$ reps I	$r - 1$
$B \times$ reps II	$r - 1$
$AB \times$ reps III	$r - 1$

Replicates of type I, therefore, contain some information on the A effect, and, similarly, replicates of type II on the B effect, and replicates of type III on the AB effect. An important question is then the combination of this information with the information given by within-block comparisons, and the process by which this is done is known as the recovery of interblock information.

The basis of this method is as follows. It is assumed that the yield of a plot is made up of a quantity μ constant for all plots, a quantity r constant for all plots of the same replicate, a quantity t due to the particular treatment, a quantity b common to all the plots of the same block, and a quantity e varying from plot to plot, thus,

$$y = \mu + r + t + b + e$$

There are, of course, a number of quantities r equal to the number of replicates, of quantities t equal to the number of treatments, and so on. The quantities μ, r, t are assumed to be fixed unknown parameters, whereas the quantities b are assumed to be uncorrelated with mean of zero and variance $\sigma^2{}_b$, and the quantities e to be uncorrelated with each other and with the b's with a mean of zero and variance σ^2. The assumptions about the e's follow from the assumption of additivity, and the assumptions about the b's follow from the assumed additivity of block effects, and the fact that groups of treatments specified to be together in a block are assigned to a block at random (cf. Chapter 8).

Consider the two possible estimates of the A effect. The estimate from a replicate in which it is unconfounded will be a within-block estimate and will have a variance of σ^2. For a replicate in which A is confounded, i.e., of the form

Block 1	$1_{(1)}$	2_b
Block 2	3_a	4_{ab}

where the number in the plot is the plot number

the estimate of A is

$$\tfrac{1}{2}(-y_1 - y_2 + y_3 + y_4)$$

which is equal to A plus an error of

$$\tfrac{1}{2}(-2b_1 + 2b_2 - e_1 - e_2 + e_3 + e_4)$$

The estimate, therefore, has a variance of

$$\sigma^2 + 2\sigma^2{}_b$$

Now we noted in the early chapters, that, if x_1 is an estimate of a parameter μ, say, with variance $\sigma^2{}_1$, and x_2 is an uncorrelated estimate of μ with variance $\sigma^2{}_2$, the best combined estimate of μ is

$$\frac{\dfrac{x_1}{\sigma^2{}_1} + \dfrac{x_2}{\sigma^2{}_2}}{\dfrac{1}{\sigma^2{}_1} + \dfrac{1}{\sigma^2{}_2}}$$

which has a variance of

$$\frac{1}{\dfrac{1}{\sigma^2{}_1} + \dfrac{1}{\sigma^2{}_2}}$$

Applying this rule to the present situation, we have an estimate, say, A_I of the effect of A from replicates of type I with variance $(\sigma^2 + 2\sigma^2{}_b)/r$, and from replicates of type II and type III we have estimates A_II and A_III each with variance σ^2/r. The best estimate of the A effect is then

$$\frac{\dfrac{r}{\sigma^2 + 2\sigma^2{}_b} A_\mathrm{I} + \dfrac{r}{\sigma^2} A_\mathrm{II} + \dfrac{r}{\sigma^2} A_\mathrm{III}}{\dfrac{r}{\sigma^2 + 2\sigma^2{}_b} + \dfrac{r}{\sigma^2} + \dfrac{r}{\sigma^2}}$$

which may be written

$$\frac{W'A_\mathrm{I} + WA_\mathrm{II} + WA_\mathrm{III}}{W' + 2W}$$

where

$$W' = \frac{1}{\sigma^2 + 2\sigma^2{}_b} \quad \text{and} \quad W = \frac{1}{\sigma^2}$$

The variance of this estimate is

$$\frac{1}{r(W' + 2W)}$$

In the above we assume that we know σ^2 and $\sigma^2 + 2\sigma^2{}_b$, whereas in a practical situation we shall not. The procedure that is followed is to obtain estimates $\hat{\sigma}^2$ and $(\widehat{\sigma^2 + 2\sigma^2{}_b})$, say, and to use, as weights,

$$w' = \frac{1}{\sigma^2 \hat{+} 2\sigma^2{}_b}, \qquad w = \frac{1}{\hat{\sigma}^2}$$

We shall use capital W, W' for the true weights, and w, w' for estimated weights throughout. This procedure is an approximation, and the validity of the approximation will be examined later.

Now,

$$\frac{W'A_I + WA_{II} + WA_{III}}{W' + 2W} = \frac{1}{3}(A_I + A_{II} + A_{III})$$

$$+ \frac{W' - W}{3(W' + 2W)}(2A_I - A_{II} - A_{III})$$

or

$$\hat{A} = A_T + A_C$$

where $\hat{A}$ is the best estimate of the effect A, A_T is the estimate of the effect A obtained from the whole of the $3r$ replicates, and A_C is an adjustment. Similarly,

$$\hat{B} = B_T + B_C$$

where

$$B_C = \frac{W' - W}{3(W' + 2W)}(-B_I + 2B_{II} - B_{III})$$

and

$$\widehat{AB} = AB_T + AB_C$$

where

$$AB_C = \frac{W' - W}{3(W' + 2W)}(-AB_I - AB_{II} + 2AB_{III})$$

Considering the yield of any one treatment, say, t_1 which is the control (1), and is given by

$$(1) = \mu - \tfrac{1}{2}A - \tfrac{1}{2}B + \tfrac{1}{2}AB$$

we find, on inserting the values for $\hat{A}$, $\hat{B}$, and $\widehat{AB}$, that

$$(\hat{1}) = \hat{\mu} - \tfrac{1}{2}A_T - \tfrac{1}{2}B_T + \tfrac{1}{2}AB_T - \tfrac{1}{2}A_C - \tfrac{1}{2}B_C + \tfrac{1}{2}AB_C$$

or, using the observed mean for $\hat{\mu}$,

$$\hat{t}_1 = \text{mean yield of } t_1 \text{ in whole experiment} - \tfrac{1}{2}A_C - \tfrac{1}{2}B_C + \tfrac{1}{2}AB_C$$

Similarly, the yields of t_2, t_3, and t_4 may be obtained by applying adjustments to their mean yields over the whole of the experiment.

We may now consider the accuracy of treatment comparisons. The estimates of the possible comparisons of two treatments are:

$$(t_1 \overset{\frown}{-} t_2) = -\hat{A} + \widehat{AB}$$

$$(t_1 \overset{\frown}{-} t_3) = -\hat{B} + \widehat{AB}$$

$$(t_1 \overset{\frown}{-} t_4) = -\hat{A} - \hat{B}$$

$$(t_2 \overset{\frown}{-} t_3) = \hat{A} - \hat{B}$$

$$(t_2 \overset{\frown}{-} t_4) = -\hat{B} - \widehat{AB}$$

$$(t_3 \overset{\frown}{-} t_4) = -\hat{A} - \widehat{AB}$$

Now the variances of $\hat{A}$, $\hat{B}$, and $\widehat{AB}$ are each $1/r(W' + 2W)$, and they are uncorrelated, and so the variance of each treatment difference is $2/r(W' + 2W)$. If randomized blocks of 4 plots had been used, the variance of each treatment difference would have been $(2/3r)\sigma^2{}_4$. The variance $\sigma^2{}_4$ is equal to $\dfrac{1}{3}\left(\dfrac{1}{W'} + \dfrac{2}{W}\right)$, for of the 3 degrees of freedom in a replicate, supposing there were no treatment effects, one has a variance of $1/W'$ and two a variance of $1/W$. The variance of each treatment comparison with blocks of 4 plots would then have been

$$\frac{2\sigma^2{}_4}{3r} = \frac{2}{9r}\left(\frac{1}{W'} + \frac{2}{W}\right)$$

The relative efficiency of the quasifactorial design is defined to be

$$\frac{\left\{\begin{array}{l}\text{Average variance of a treatment difference with complete}\\ \quad\text{randomized blocks}\end{array}\right\}}{\text{Average variance of a treatment difference in the experiment}}$$

In this case, the relative efficiency is

$$\frac{2}{9r}\left(\frac{1}{W'} + \frac{2}{W}\right) \bigg/ \frac{2}{r}\left(\frac{1}{W' + 2W}\right) = \frac{(1 + 2x)(x + 2)}{9x} \quad \text{where} \quad x = \frac{W'}{W}$$

The ratio x is positive and less than or equal to unity, under most circumstances, for it equals $\sigma^2/(\sigma^2 + 2\sigma^2{}_b)$. The efficiency then has a minimum value of unity or 100 percent when $W' = W$, and under all other possible circumstances is greater than 100 percent. If W' is not much less than W, the efficiency will be near 100 percent, as would be expected intuitively, for then $\sigma^2{}_b\left[= \dfrac{1}{2}\left(\dfrac{1}{W'} - \dfrac{1}{W}\right)\right]$ is close to zero, and there is little variation between blocks additional to that within blocks. As we have noted before in other connections (cf. Chapter 19), the variance between blocks could be less than the variance within blocks on the same basis, though this should not happen often, if competition is eliminated.

22.2.1 The Estimation of the Weights W and W'

The main problem remaining for this simple example of a lattice design is the estimation of the weights W and W'. We have already stated that the expectation of the usual mean square ($\mathbf{E}$, say) which is called the intrablock mean square is σ^2, so that W may be estimated by $w = 1/\mathbf{E}$.

Now consider the estimation of $W' = 1/(\sigma^2 + 2\sigma^2{}_b)$. If we consider the estimate of the A effect in those replicates in which it is confounded, we note that the estimate in each replicate has a variance of $\sigma^2 + 2\sigma^2{}_b$, and so we may take the mean square between these r estimates, and this mean square with $(r-1)$ degrees of freedom will have an expectation of $\sigma^2 + 2\sigma^2{}_b$. Similarly, the mean square of the estimates of B between the r replicates in which it is confounded gives an estimate of $\sigma^2 + 2\sigma^2{}_b$ based on $(r-1)$ degrees of freedom. The variation of AB also gives an estimate based on $(r-1)$ degrees of freedom. Finally, consider the quantities:

$$2A_\mathrm{I} - A_\mathrm{II} - A_\mathrm{III}$$

$$-B_\mathrm{I} + 2B_\mathrm{II} - B_\mathrm{III}$$

$$-AB_\mathrm{I} - AB_\mathrm{II} + 2AB_\mathrm{III}$$

The first, for example, may be expressed in terms of the block errors and within-block errors, thus,

$$\frac{1}{r}\,[2\ (\text{sum of } rb\text{'s} - \text{sum of } rb\text{'s}) + (\text{sum of } 2re\text{'s} - \text{sum of } 2re\text{'s})$$

$$- \tfrac{1}{2}(\text{sum of } 2re\text{'s} - \text{sum of } 2re\text{'s}) - \tfrac{1}{2}(\text{sum of } 2re\text{'s} - \text{sum of } 2re\text{'s})]$$

The expectation of its square is then

$$\frac{1}{r^2}\left[8r\sigma^2{}_b + \sigma^2\left(2r + 2r + \frac{2r + 2r + 2r + 2r}{4}\right)\right] = \frac{1}{r^2}\,(8r\sigma^2{}_b + 6r\sigma^2)$$

The expectation then of

$$\frac{r}{6}\,(2A_\mathrm{I} - A_\mathrm{II} - A_\mathrm{III})^2$$

is equal to

$$\sigma^2 + \tfrac{4}{3}\sigma^2{}_b$$

This is also the expectation of

$$\frac{r}{6}(-B_{\text{I}} + 2B_{\text{II}} - B_{\text{III}})^2 \quad \text{and of} \quad \frac{r}{6}(-AB_{\text{I}} - AB_{\text{II}} + 2AB_{\text{III}})^2$$

The complete analysis of variance for the experiment may then be written as in Table 22.3.

TABLE 22.3 ANALYSIS OF VARIANCE FOR BALANCED 2^2 LATTICE DESIGN

Due to	df	Expectation of Mean Square	Observed Mean Square
Replicates	$3r - 1$		
Blocks eliminating treatments			
$\left.\begin{array}{l} A \times \text{reps I} \\ B \times \text{reps II} \\ AB \times \text{reps III} \end{array}\right\}$	$3(r-1)$	$\sigma^2 + 2\sigma^2_b$	B_1
			B
$\left.\begin{array}{l} 2A_{\text{I}} - A_{\text{II}} - A_{\text{III}} \\ -B_{\text{I}} + 2B_{\text{II}} - B_{\text{III}} \\ -AB_{\text{I}} - AB_{\text{II}} + 2AB_{\text{III}} \end{array}\right\}$	3	$\sigma^2 + \frac{4}{3}\sigma^2_b$	B_2
Treatments ignoring blocks			
$\left.\begin{array}{l} A \\ B \\ AB \end{array}\right\}$	3		
Intrablock error	$3(2r-1)$	σ^2	E
Total	$12r - 1$		

The expectation of B, the pooled between-block mean square, is equal to

$$\frac{3(r-1)(\sigma^2 + 2\sigma^2_b) + 3(\sigma^2 + \frac{4}{3}\sigma^2_b)}{3r} = \sigma^2 + 2\left(1 - \frac{1}{3r}\right)\sigma^2_b$$

We may, therefore, estimate σ^2 by E, and $\sigma^2 + 2\sigma^2_b$ by

$$\left(B - \frac{1}{3r}E\right) \Big/ \left(1 - \frac{1}{3r}\right)$$

and we may use the reciprocals of these as estimates of W and W', respectively. If r were large, say, above 5, it would be nearly as satisfactory to use $1/B_1$ as an estimate of W'.

An examination will be made in a later chapter of the loss in efficiency due to inaccuracies in the weights. In the case we have examined, the estimation of the relative weights with a small number of replicates (say, less than 4) would be so inaccurate as to render the procedure of utilization of the interblock information unsatisfactory. Our purpose, however, is to illustrate the process.

22.3 TYPES OF LATTICE DESIGN

The general theory of lattice designs will be given in the next chapter, and we will conclude the present chapter with an elementary discussion of the types of lattice design and incomplete block designs. In this section we shall describe types of lattice design.

We have already given the basic property of lattice designs, that they are based on a factorial correspondence. In the first place, we may classify designs according to the number of restrictions imposed in the randomization. For the example discussed above, the randomization within a replicate is restricted in one way: namely, by blocks. The procedure in setting up an actual experiment is to obtain the groups of treatments that are to lie in a block, to allocate these groups to blocks at random, and to randomize the position of the treatments within the block. The only restriction is then that the placement of treatment combinations is restricted so that they occur in specified blocks. These designs will be referred to as lattice designs in conformity with the literature.

The Latin square principle may also be used, resulting in a design with two restrictions. Groups of treatment combinations are specified that must occupy rows of plots, and other groups are specified that must occupy columns. For example, consider the pattern in Figure 26 for 2 replicates of 9 treatments.

I

1	2	3
4	5	6
7	8	9

II

1	5	9
6	7	2
8	3	4

FIGURE 26.

The squares may be interpreted as a 2-way classification of the experimental units of each replicate: If the units are field plots, Figure 26 would be the pattern on the ground, if the 2-way classification of plots is based on contiguity. The classification will always be referred to as rows and columns as though the experiment were a field experiment. In this pattern each treatment occurs with any other treatment either once in a row or once in a column. Consider the quantity

$$T_1 = (1 + 2 + 3)_{\text{II}} + (1 + 4 + 7)_{\text{II}} + (1 + 5 + 9)_{\text{I}} + (1 + 6 + 8)_{\text{I}}$$

where $(1 + 2 + 3)_{\text{II}}$ equals the total of the yield of treatments 1, 2, and 3 in replicate II, and so on. This sum contains all the row and column effects of each square, and, if the yield of any one plot is regarded as made up of a replicate effect, a row effect, a column effect, a treatment effect, and a within row and column error, the above quantity is equal to $(3t_1 + 9t.)$ plus a certain linear function of the errors plus the replicate, row, and column effects in equal proportions, where t_1 is the effect of treatment 1 and $t.$ is the mean treatment effect. Similarly,

$$T_2 = (1 + 2 + 3)_{\text{II}} + (2 + 5 + 8)_{\text{II}} + (2 + 4 + 9)_{\text{I}} + (2 + 6 + 7)_{\text{I}}$$

is equal to $(3t_2 + 9t.)$ plus a linear function of the errors, plus the same linear function of the replicate, row, and column effects. The quantity

$$\tfrac{1}{3}(T_1 - T_2)$$

is then an estimate of $(t_1 - t_2)$ with a variance depending only on the variance of the within-row-and-column errors. Under the same circumstances that the Latin square of side k is useful in comparing k treatments, because the removal of row and column differences produces a reduction in the error variance to which treatment differences are subject, the above type of lattice design will be effective for comparing the corresponding number of treatments. Such designs are known as lattice square designs.

This hierarchy of designs may, in a sense, be continued, for it is possible to specify the groups of treatment combinations that are to be together in a block and then to place a double restriction on the allocation of the groups to the blocks. An example of this type will be discussed in a later chapter. This design may be regarded as being subject to three restrictions on the randomization of the position of the treatment combinations.

Within the set of designs with one restriction, we may classify designs according to the number of treatments relative to the block size and to the number of different confoundings used. If the number of treatments is the square of the size of block, the designs are known as 2-dimensional. In the example we discussed for 4 treatments, 3 different confoundings were used, and these were all the possible ones. If 2 different confoundings are used, the design is known as a simple lattice, the name being used also if the basic 2 replicates are repeated any number of times. If 3 different confoundings are used, the design is known as a triple lattice. With k^2 treatments, k being a prime number or a power of a prime number, up to $(k + 1)$ different confoundings may be used, and, if a complete set of $(k + 1)$ different confoundings is used, the design is known as a completely balanced lattice. If k is not a prime number or a power of a prime, in general, only 3 different confoundings are possible, being based on the rows, columns, and letters of a $k \times k$ Latin square. In the case of k equal to 12, four different confoundings are possible.

With k^3 treatments in blocks of k plots, the design is known as a 3-dimensional lattice. Such designs with 3 different confoundings exist for all values of k. If more than 3 different confoundings are desired, the position is a little more complex. If k is a prime number or a power of a prime number, the examination of possibilities is relatively straightforward and will be given in the following chapter.

This process may be extended indefinitely, and a few examples will be given in the following chapter. For instance, the testing of 32 ($= 2^5$) treatments in blocks of 4 ($= 2^2$) plots may be examined as a quasifactorial design.

Within the set of designs with 2 restrictions which may be used for k^2 treatments in $k \times k$ squares, the situation is as follows. If k is a prime number or a power of a prime number, there are $(k + 1)$ orthogonal groupings into k groups of k treatments, and it is possible to arrange the treatment combinations in $(k + 1)$ replicates, so that each orthogonal grouping is confounded once with rows and once with columns over the set of $(k + 1)$ replicates. This design is known as a completely balanced lattice square. If each orthogonal grouping is confounded once with rows or once with columns in $\left(\dfrac{k + 1}{2}\right)$ replicates, the design is known as a semibalanced lattice square. A lattice square design other than these may be termed an unbalanced lattice square. If k is not a prime number or a power of a prime number, in general, only 3 orthogonal groupings into k groups of k treatments are possible (except $k = 12$ as far as is known), and only 3 basic replicates are possible.

There is another type of design for $k(k + 1)$ treatments, which is somewhat similar to lattice designs and is known as rectangular lattices. The number of replicates clearly possible is a multiple of 2 or 3 basic replicates.

22.4 TYPES OF INCOMPLETE BLOCK DESIGN

The simplest type of incomplete block design for t treatments is that in which there is a block for each possible pair of treatments. This is, of course, possible with any number of treatments, but the number of blocks is $t(t-1)/2$, and the number of replicates is $(t-1)$, which is often inordinately large. This is the simplest type of balanced incomplete block design which is defined to consist of a number, say, r replicates of each treatment, in blocks of, say, k plots, the balanced property being that each possible pair of treatments occurs together in the same number of blocks (always denoted by λ). The example of a lattice design that we used has this property and may therefore be regarded in either way. Such designs are, however, with a reasonable number of replicates, often unavailable, and recourse is then made to partially balanced incomplete blocks. The definition of these is somewhat lengthy and is postponed to the appropriate chapter. In addition, there are incomplete block designs with a double restriction, known as Youden squares.

FURTHER READING

The designs discussed in this chapter, with the exception of rectangular lattices and partially balanced incomplete block designs were introduced by Yates in a series of papers from 1935 onward. Extensive work on the enumeration of balanced incomplete block designs has been done by the Indian school under the leadership of R. C. Bose, and partially balanced incomplete block designs were developed by the same group.

1. YATES, F. A new method of arranging variety trials involving a large number of varieties. *Jour. Agr. Sci.*, **26**, 424–455, 1936.
2. YATES, F. A further note on the arrangement of variety-trials: Quasi-Latin squares. *Ann. Eug.*, **7**, 319–331, 1937.
3. YATES, F. Incomplete randomised blocks. *Ann. Eug.*, **7**, 121–140, 1936.
4. YATES, F. Lattice squares. *Jour. Agr. Sci.*, **30**, 672–687, 1940.
5. YATES, F. The recovery of inter-block information in balanced incomplete block designs. *Ann. Eug.*, **10**, 317–325, 1940.
6. YATES, F. The recovery of inter-block information in variety trials arranged in three-dimensional lattices. *Ann. Eug.*, **9**, 136–156, 1939.
7. BOSE, R. C. On the construction of balanced incomplete block designs. *Ann. Eug.*, **9**, 353–400, 1939.
8. BOSE, R. C. On some new series of balanced incomplete block designs. *Bull. Calçutta Math. Soc.*, **34**, 17–31, 1942.
9. BOSE, R. C., and NAIR, K. R. Partially balanced incomplete block designs. *Sankhyā*, **4**, 337–372, 1939.
10. HARSHBARGER, B. Rectangular lattices. *Virginia Agr. Exp. Sta. Mem.*, **1**, 1947.

CHAPTER 23

Lattice Designs

The theory on which this chapter will be based is that of Chapter 17 on the general prime-power factorial system. In that chapter we noted that the cases of p equal to a prime and p equal to a power of a prime were identical if the Galois field of p elements was used for the representation. We shall here devote our attention mainly to the case when p is a prime number, as the other case may be developed in the same fashion. For the rest of this chapter, therefore, p will be used to denote a prime number, and, except for the last section, we shall be discussing the case of p^n treatments.

23.1 TYPES OF LATTICE DESIGNS

23.1.1 2-Dimensional Lattices

These are designs for p^2 treatments in blocks of p plots, and we may represent the p^2 treatments by the combinations of 2 factors, say, a and b, each at p levels, so that the quasifactorial name of a treatment is a set of 2 numbers (ij), both i and j taking on the values 0 to $(p-1)$. We know that there are $(p+1)$ possible orthogonal groupings which we may represent by the symbols A, B, AB, AB^2, $\cdots$, AB^{p-1}. If we are using a simple lattice, we may confound A in one replicate and B in the other. There is, as we shall see later, no point in choosing any other set of 2 groupings. This is, in any case, obvious since our correspondence between the treatments and the quasifactorial treatment combinations is entirely formal and arbitrary. If 3 orthogonal groupings are to be used, we may choose A, B, and AB in our factorial representation, to give us a triple lattice. A quadruple lattice is given by 4 groupings, say, A, B, AB, and AB^2. If we use a balanced lattice with $(p+1)$ replicates, we would confound each of A, B, AB, AB^2, $\cdots$, AB^{p-1} in one of the replicates.

445

23.1.2 3-Dimensional Lattices

In this case, we have p^3 treatments arranged in p^2 blocks of p plots. We may represent the treatments by the combinations resulting from 3 factors each with p levels: namely, 0, 1, 2, $\cdots$, $p - 1$. In order to have p^2 blocks of p plots, we must confound 2 effects or interactions and their generalized interactions. Thus, with $p = 3$, there are 13 possible systems of confounding. In general, there are $(p^2 + p + 1)$ different schemes of confounding.

It may be noted that, if it is desired that each effect or interaction be unconfounded in at least one of the replicates used, at least 3 replicates are necessary. A set of 3 replicates may be specified as follows:

Replicate	Confound
I	$A, B, AB, AB^2, \cdots, AB^{p-1}$
II	$A, C, AC, AC^2, \cdots, AC^{p-1}$
III	$B, C, BC, BC^2, \cdots, BC^{p-1}$

In this case, which is the one described by Yates,[1] all main effects are confounded in 2 out of the 3 replicates, all 2-factor interactions in 1 of the 3 replicates, and the 3-factor interactions are completely unconfounded.

If 4 replicates are used for the case of 3^3, we may add to the above

$$\text{Replicate IV: Confound } AB, AC, BC^2, AB^2C^2$$

The usual practice with 6 replicates is to repeat replicates I, II, and III above. It will be seen later, however, that a more efficient design is obtained by using different schemes of confounding in each replicate.

23.1.3 4-Dimensional Lattices

In this case we have p^4 treatments to be arranged in p^3 blocks of p plots. If 4 pseudofactors, a, b, c, d, are used to give the pseudofactorial treatment combinations, we may enumerate the possible schemes of confounding as in the 3-dimensional case. From Chapter 17 we know that there are $(p^4 - 1)/(p - 1)$ possible schemes of confounding. With $p = 3$, there are 40 schemes of confounding, and they are specified in Table 23.1. The confounded effects and interactions will consist of those given in the table with all their possible products.

TABLE 23.1 SCHEMES OF CONFOUNDING FOR 3^4 SYSTEM IN BLOCKS OF 3 PLOTS

Generators of Set of Confounded Interactions

Number	Generators	Number	Generators
1	A, B, C	21	B, AC^2, AD
2	A, B, D	22	B, AC^2, AD^2
3	A, B, CD	23	AB, C, D
4	A, B, CD^2	24	AB, C, AD
5	A, C, D	25	AB, C, AD^2
6	A, C, BD	26	AB, AC, D
7	A, C, BD^2	27	AB, AC, AD
8	A, BC, D	28	AB, AC, AD^2
9	A, BC, BD	29	AB, AC^2, D
10	A, BC, BD^2	30	AB, AC^2, AD
11	A, BC^2, D	31	AB, AC^2, AD^2
12	A, BC^2, BD	32	AB^2, C, D
13	A, BC^2, BD^2	33	AB^2, C, AD
14	B, C, D	34	AB^2, C, AD^2
15	B, C, AD	35	AB^2, AC, D
16	B, C, AD^2	36	AB^2, AC, AD
17	B, AC, D	37	AB^2, AC, AD^2
18	B, AC, AD	38	AB^2, AC^2, D
19	B, AC, AD^2	39	AB^2, AC^2, AD
20	B, AC^2, D	40	AB^2, AC^2, AD^2

23.1.4 5-Dimensional Lattices

This case is possibly not of great practical value but is rather instructive from the point of view of the analysis of variance and is, therefore, included. There are p^5 treatments, and it is desired to arrange them in blocks of p plots, for example, 32 treatments in blocks of 2 plots. At least 5 replicates will be desirable in order that each effect and interaction shall be unconfounded with blocks in one of the replicates. If the pseudofactors are denoted by a, b, c, d, e, we may confound 4 of the main effects and all their interactions in a replicate, giving 5 different replicates in all.

23.2 THE GENERAL METHOD OF ANALYSIS

In Chapter 17, we gave the expressions for effects and interactions in terms of the yields of the treatment combinations and for the yields of the treatment combinations in terms of the effects and interactions. This formalization is the basis of the analysis which will be described for the designs described above. It was seen in that chapter that the difference in yield of any 2 treatment combinations could be expressed in terms of the effects and interactions. The general method of analysis will be then to obtain the best estimates of the effects and interactions. As we saw in the previous chapter, it is necessary, in order to do this, to know the relative weights to be assigned to estimates based on comparisons within and between blocks.

The yield of any plot is assumed to be made up of the following components:

A general mean.
A replicate effect, say, r.
A treatment effect, say, t.
An error common to all plots of the same block, say, η, which has a mean of zero and a variance of $\sigma^2{}_b$.
An error particular to the plot, say, e, which has a mean of zero and a variance of σ^2.

The errors e and η may, under the additive model, be taken to be uncorrelated because of the randomization procedure used. The treatment effect is reparametrized in terms of effects and interactions for convenience of analysis.

To recapitulate for the p^n system, there are $\left(\dfrac{p^n - 1}{p - 1}\right)$ sets of $(p - 1)$ degrees of freedom, and each set of $(p - 1)$ degrees of freedom is given by the comparisons among p totals, each of (p^{n-1}) treatment combinations. If the treatment combinations are denoted by $(x_1, x_2, x_3, \cdots, x_n)$, where each x_i runs from 0 to $(p - 1)$, any set of p totals is given by the treatment combinations which satisfy

$$\alpha_1 x_1 + \alpha_2 x_2 + \cdots + \alpha_n x_n = i \bmod p$$

i taking the values 0, 1, 2, $\cdots$, $(p - 1)$, and the α's also being in this range. The deviation of the mean of the combinations satisfying this relation from the general mean was denoted by $A^{\alpha_1} B^{\alpha_2} \cdots_i$. Denoting the yield of the combination $(x_1, \cdots, x_n)$ by $t_{x_1, \cdots, x_n}$, we found the relation

$$t_{x_1, \cdots, x_n} = \mu + \sum_{\alpha, r} A^{\alpha_1} B^{\alpha_2} \cdots_r \delta^r_{\alpha_1 x_1 + \alpha_2 x_2 + \cdots + \alpha_n x_n}$$

where the summation is over the $\left(\dfrac{p^n - 1}{p - 1}\right)$ possible choices of the α's and over r from 0 to $(p - 1)$, with

$$\delta^r_{\alpha_1 x_1 + \alpha_2 x_2 + \cdots + \alpha_n x_n} = 1 \quad \text{if} \quad \alpha_1 x_1 + \alpha_2 x_2 + \cdots + \alpha_n x_n = r \bmod p$$

$$= 0 \text{ otherwise}$$

Consider now the estimation of the quantities,

$$A^{\alpha_1}B^{\alpha_2}\cdots{}_r, \qquad r = 0, 1, 2, \cdots, (p-1)$$

If the corresponding effect or interaction is unconfounded in a particular replicate, the estimate of each of the quantities $A^{\alpha_1}B^{\alpha_2}\cdots{}_r$ from that replicate is the same function of the observed yields and will be subject to a variance of $\dfrac{\sigma^2}{p^{n-1}}\left(\dfrac{p-1}{p}\right)$. Any comparison

$$\Sigma\lambda_r A^{\alpha_1}B^{\alpha_2}\cdots{}_r \quad \text{with} \quad \Sigma\lambda_r = 0$$

will have a variance of

$$(\Sigma\lambda^2{}_r)\,\frac{\sigma^2}{p^{n-1}}$$

The quantity $(\Sigma\lambda^2{}_r)$ depends only on the comparison and not on the design, and so we may say that the variance of the estimate of any $A^{\alpha_1}B^{\alpha_2}\cdots{}_r$ is σ^2/p^{n-1}. Similarly, if the effect or interaction is confounded with blocks in a replicate, the estimate of each quantity $A^{\alpha_1}B^{\alpha_2}\cdots{}_r$ will be subject to a variance of

$$\frac{1}{p^{n-1}}(\sigma^2 + k\sigma^2{}_b)$$

where k is the size of the block and is, of course, equal to some power of p. For the total of the plots for which $\Sigma\alpha_i x_i = r \bmod p$ will contain p^{n-1} different within-block errors, and k times the sum of p^{n-1}/k block errors, there being p^{n-1}/k blocks which contain the plots that make up the total. The variance of the mean on a per-plot basis is then

$$\frac{1}{(p^{n-1})^2}\left(p^{n-1}\sigma^2 + \frac{p^{n-1}}{k}k^2\sigma^2{}_b\right) = \frac{1}{p^{n-1}}(\sigma^2 + k\sigma^2{}_b)$$

We now suppose that we know σ^2 and $(\sigma^2 + k\sigma^2{}_b)$, and we may obtain the best estimate of any effect or interaction by weighting the estimate in each replicate by $W = 1/\sigma^2$, if the effect or interaction is unconfounded, and by $W' = 1/(\sigma^2 + k\sigma^2{}_b)$ if it is confounded. We need be concerned only with relative weights obviously.

It is not always necessary, computationally, to go through this procedure of obtaining the best estimate of each effect and interaction. For, what is needed eventually is the best estimate of treatment comparisons, and, although this may be obtained by estimates of the effects and interactions, in many cases a short-cut method may be used. Particular cases will be illustrated below, together with examples of the estimation of W and W'.

23.3 THE ANALYSIS OF 2-DIMENSIONAL LATTICES

We suppose that the 2 pseudofactors are a and b each with p levels, and that the effect A is confounded in one replicate I, and effect B in the second replicate II. Since A is confounded in replicate I and unconfounded in replicate II, any component of the A effect is best estimated by

$$\hat{A} = \frac{W'A_{\mathrm{I}} + WA_{\mathrm{II}}}{W' + W} = \frac{1}{2}(A_{\mathrm{I}} + A_{\mathrm{II}}) + \frac{W' - W}{2(W' + W)}(A_{\mathrm{I}} - A_{\mathrm{II}})$$

$$= A_T + \frac{W' - W}{2(W' + W)}(A_{\mathrm{I}} - A_{\mathrm{II}}) \tag{1}$$

where A_{I}, A_{II}, A_T are the component estimated in replicates I, II, and both replicates, respectively, and $W = 1/\sigma^2$, $W' = 1/(\sigma^2 + p\sigma^2_b)$. Similarly, the best estimate of any component of the B effect is

$$\hat{B} = B_T + \frac{W' - W}{2(W' + W)}(-B_{\mathrm{I}} + B_{\mathrm{II}}) \tag{2}$$

whereas for any component of the interaction, say, AB^λ, $\lambda = 1, 2, \cdots,$ $(p - 1)$,

$$\widehat{AB^\lambda} = AB^\lambda{}_T \tag{3}$$

We now wish to combine these estimates of the effects and interactions to obtain the estimates of the yields of each treatment. The expression for the yield of a treatment combination is

$$\mu + \hat{A} + \hat{B} + \widehat{AB} \tag{4}$$

where the suitable components of $\hat{A}$, $\hat{B}$, and $\widehat{AB}$ are used, and this equals

$$\mu + A_T + B_T + AB_T + \frac{W' - W}{2(W' + W)}(A_{\mathrm{I}} - A_{\mathrm{II}})$$

$$+ \frac{W' - W}{2(W' + W)}(-B_{\mathrm{I}} + B_{\mathrm{II}}) \tag{5}$$

But $\mu + A_T + B_T + AB_T$ is equal to the observed mean of the yield of the particular treatment, and so we have

$$\hat{t}_{ij} = \bar{t}_{ij} + c_{ai} + c_{bj} \tag{6}$$

where

$$\hat{t}_{ij} = \text{the best estimate of the yield of treatment } (ij)$$

$$\bar{t}_{ij} = \text{the observed mean yield}$$

$$c_{ai} = \frac{W' - W}{2(W' + W)} [(i\cdot)_\text{I} - (\cdot\cdot)_\text{I} - (i\cdot)_\text{II} + (\cdot\cdot)_\text{II}]$$

$$c_{bj} = \frac{W' - W}{2(W' + W)} [-(\cdot j)_\text{I} + (\cdot\cdot)_\text{I} + (\cdot j)_\text{II} - (\cdot\cdot)_\text{II}]$$

$$(7)$$

and

$$(i\cdot)_\text{I} = \text{mean of treatments with } a \text{ at level } i \text{ in replicate I}$$

$$(\cdot\cdot)_\text{I} = \text{mean of all treatments in replicate I}$$

and so on.

Finally, it is necessary to consider the estimation of W and W'. The partition of the analysis of variance in Table 23.2 may be obtained.

TABLE 23.2   STRUCTURE OF ANALYSIS OF VARIANCE FOR SIMPLE LATTICE

Due to	df	Expectation of Mean Square
Replicates	1	
Blocks eliminating treatments	$2(p-1)$	$\sigma^2 + \dfrac{p}{2}\sigma^2_b$
Treatments ignoring blocks	$p^2 - 1$	
Error (intrablock)	$(p-1)^2$	σ^2
Total	$2p^2 - 1$	

The replicate and treatment sums of squares are obtained in the usual way. Of the $2(p-1)$ degrees of freedom for blocks eliminating treatments, $(p-1)$ arise from the quantities $(A_\text{I} - A_\text{II})$, and $(p-1)$ from the quantities $(B_\text{I} - B_\text{II})$. The quantity

$$[(i\cdot)_\text{I} - (\cdot\cdot)_\text{I} - (i\cdot)_\text{II} + (\cdot\cdot)_\text{II}]$$

is orthogonal to replicates and treatments and, expressed in terms of block errors and within-block errors, is equal to

$$\left[\eta_i \left(\frac{p-1}{p}\right) - \frac{1}{p} (\text{sum of all other } \eta\text{'s}) \right] + \left(\frac{p-1}{p^2}\right) (\text{sum of } pe\text{'s})$$

$$- \frac{1}{p^2} [\text{sum of } (p^2 - p)e\text{'s}] - \left(\frac{p-1}{p^2}\right) (\text{sum of } pe\text{'s})$$

$$+ \frac{1}{p^2} [\text{sum of } (p^2 - p)e\text{'s}]$$

The expectation of the square is then

$$\left(\frac{p-1}{p}\right)\sigma^2{}_b + 2\left(\frac{p-1}{p^2}\right)\sigma^2$$

and, summing over the values of i, we get

$$(p-1)\sigma^2{}_b + 2\left(\frac{p-1}{p}\right)\sigma^2$$

The expectation then of

$$\frac{p}{2}\sum_i [(i\cdot)_\mathrm{I} - (\cdot\cdot)_\mathrm{I} - (i\cdot)_\mathrm{II} + (\cdot\cdot)_\mathrm{II}]^2$$

which is the sum of squares for the comparisons $(A_\mathrm{I} - A_\mathrm{II})$, is

$$(p-1)\left(\sigma^2 + \frac{p}{2}\sigma^2{}_b\right)$$

Similarly, the expectation of the sum of squares for $(B_\mathrm{I} - B_\mathrm{II})$

$$\frac{p}{2}\sum_j [-(\cdot j)_\mathrm{I} + (\cdot\cdot)_\mathrm{I} + (\cdot j)_\mathrm{II} - (\cdot\cdot)_\mathrm{II}]^2$$

is

$$(p-1)\left(\sigma^2 + \frac{p}{2}\sigma^2{}_b\right)$$

These two quantities together make up the sum of squares for blocks eliminating treatments, and their mean square, say, **B**, has an expectation of $\sigma^2 + \frac{p}{2}\sigma^2{}_b$.

The sum of squares for intrablock error may be obtained by subtraction. The expectation of the mean square **E**, say, is σ^2, as may be verified, for example, by noting that the total of $(p-1)^2$ degrees of freedom consist of $(p-1)$ degrees of freedom for the interaction of AB^λ with replicates, $\lambda = 1, 2, \cdots, p-1$.

We may then estimate W and W' by

$$w = \frac{1}{\mathbf{E}}, \qquad w' = \frac{1}{2\mathbf{B} - \mathbf{E}}$$

and $\dfrac{W' - W}{2(W' + W)}$ is estimated by $\dfrac{\mathbf{E} - \mathbf{B}}{2\mathbf{B}}$. Computationally, it is simpler to work in totals over the two replicates. With this method we interpret $(i\cdot)_\mathrm{I}$, for instance, as the total over j for replicate I, and use a multiplier for the adjustment of $\dfrac{E - B}{2B} \times \dfrac{1}{p} \times 2$, i.e., $\dfrac{E - B}{pB}$. Also, we need not bother with the terms $(\cdot\cdot)_{\mathrm{I}}$ and $(\cdot\cdot)_{\mathrm{II}}$, which cancel out in the summation.

23.3.1 Repetition of the Simple Lattice

If the above simple lattice is repeated $r/2$ times, the estimation of the yields of each treatment combination proceeds in exactly the same way, except that the quantities $(i\cdot)_{\mathrm{I}}$, etc., are averaged (or totaled) over all the repetitions of the replicate type. The only new feature arises in the analysis of variance and the estimation of the weights. The structure of the analysis of variance is now as in Table 23.3.

TABLE 23.3 STRUCTURE OF ANALYSIS OF VARIANCE FOR SIMPLE LATTICE WITH $r/2$ REPETITIONS

Due to	df	Mean Square	Expectation of Mean Square
Replicates	$r - 1$		
Blocks eliminating treatments			
Component a	$(r - 2)(p - 1)$	B_1	$\sigma^2 + p\sigma^2_b$
Component b	$2(p - 1)$	B_2	$\sigma^2 + \dfrac{p}{2}\sigma^2_b$
Treatments	$p^2 - 1$		
Error (intrablock)	$\dfrac{r}{2}(p-1)^2 + (\dfrac{r}{2} - 1)(p^2 - 1)$	E	σ^2
Total	$rp^2 - 1$		

The component b for blocks eliminating treatments is the same as before, if we take account of the fact that there are $r/2$ times as many replicates. Component a is obtained by noting that A is completely confounded in $r/2$ replicates, of type I, say, and therefore the interaction A by replicates I has $(r/2 - 1)(p - 1)$ degrees of freedom, with mean square of $\sigma^2 + p\sigma^2_b$. The actual sum of squares may be written

$$\frac{1}{p}\sum_{ik}(i\cdot)^2_{\mathrm{I}k} - \left(\frac{1}{p\dfrac{r}{2}}\right)\sum_i(i\cdot)^2_{\mathrm{I}\cdot} - \frac{1}{p^2}\sum_k(\cdot\cdot)^2_{\mathrm{I}k} + \left(\frac{1}{p^2\dfrac{r}{2}}\right)(\cdot\cdot)^2_{\mathrm{I}\cdot}. \quad (8)$$

where $(i\cdot)_{\mathrm{I}k}$ = the *total* yield for level i of factor a in the kth replicate of type I

$(\cdot\cdot)_{\mathrm{I}k}$ = the *total* yield of the kth replicate of type I

$(i\cdot)_{\mathrm{I}\cdot}$ = the *total* yield with level i of factor a in all the replicates of type I

and

$(\cdot\cdot)_I\cdot$ = the *total* of all yields in the replicates of type **I**

Similarly, the interaction B by (replicates of type II) gives $(r/2 - 1)$ $\times (p - 1)$ degrees of freedom, with a sum of squares obtained by interchanging i and j and I and II.

As an estimate of W we use $1/\mathsf{E}$, and of W' we may use $1/\mathsf{B}_1$. We may, however, combine components a and b to give a mean square, **B**, say, with expectation $\sigma^2 + \left(\dfrac{r - 1}{r}\right) p\sigma^2{}_b$. In that case the expectation of $\dfrac{r\mathsf{B} - \mathsf{E}}{r - 1}$ is $\sigma^2 + p\sigma^2{}_b$, so that an estimate of W' is $\dfrac{r - 1}{r\mathsf{B} - \mathsf{E}}$, and this is the estimate generally used.

23.4 THE ANALYSIS OF OTHER LATTICE DESIGNS

23.4.1 The Triple Lattice

In this case with 3 replicates, we confound A in replicate I, B in replicate II, and AB, say, in replicate III. As in the case of the simple lattice, the best estimate of the A effect is

$$\frac{W'A_I + WA_{II} + WA_{III}}{W' + 2W} \tag{9}$$

which equals

$$\frac{1}{3}(A_I + A_{II} + A_{III}) + \frac{W' - W}{3(W' + 2W)}(2A_I - A_{II} - A_{III}) \tag{10}$$

where A_I is any component of the effect of factor a. Following the same lines as before, we find that the estimate of the yield of a treatment is the mean of the treatment in the 3 replicates plus 3 corrections, say, c_{ai}, c_{bj}, c_{abk}, where, if a treatment is denoted by (ijk), i being the level of factor a, j of factor b, and k of AB (i.e., equal to $i + j \bmod p$),

$$c_{ai} = \lambda[2(i\cdot\cdot)_I - (i\cdot\cdot)_{II} - (i\cdot\cdot)_{III}]$$

$$c_{bj} = \lambda[-(\cdot j\cdot)_I + 2(\cdot j\cdot)_{II} - (\cdot j\cdot)_{III}] \tag{11}$$

$$c_{abk} = \lambda[-(\cdot\cdot k)_I - (\cdot\cdot k)_{II} + 2(\cdot\cdot k)_{III}]$$

where $\lambda = (W' - W)/3(W' + 2W)$, the terms $(i\cdot\cdot)_I$, etc., being means.

The analysis of variance has the structure given in Table 23.4.

TABLE 23.4 STRUCTURE OF ANALYSIS OF VARIANCE FOR TRIPLE LATTICE

Due to	df	Mean Square	Expectation of Mean Square
Replicates	2		
Blocks eliminating treatments	$3(p-1)$	B	$\sigma^2 + \frac{2}{3}p\sigma^2{}_b$
Treatments	$p^2 - 1$		
Error (intrablock)	$(2p-1)(p-1)$	E	σ^2
Total	$3p^2 - 1$		

The sum of squares for blocks eliminating treatments is obtained by considering the quantities, as totals:

$$2(i\cdot\cdot)_\mathrm{I} - (i\cdot\cdot)_\mathrm{II} - (i\cdot\cdot)_\mathrm{III}$$

$$-(\cdot j\cdot)_\mathrm{I} + 2(\cdot j\cdot)_\mathrm{II} - (\cdot j\cdot)_\mathrm{III}$$

$$-(\cdot\cdot k)_\mathrm{I} - (\cdot\cdot k)_\mathrm{II} + 2(\cdot\cdot k)_\mathrm{III}$$

We form the sums of squares about the mean of each of these quantities for the possible values of i, j, k, respectively, and divide by $6p$. We may then use as estimates of the weights: $w' = 1/\mathsf{E}$ and $w' = 2/(3\mathsf{B} - \mathsf{E})$.

With repetitions, say, $r/3$, of the 3 basic replicates, the only modifications in the analysis are:

1. That the quantities $(i\cdot\cdot)_\mathrm{I}$, etc., are totals over all replicates of type I, etc., and the divisor in the sum of squares is $6p\,\dfrac{r}{3} = 2pr$.

2. That there is an additional component of the sum of squares for blocks eliminating treatments: namely, the variation of the A effect over replicates of type I, the B effect over replicates of type II, and the AB interaction over replicates of type III. This sum of squares will have $(r-3)(p-1)$ degrees of freedom, with a mean square B_2, which has an expectation of $(\sigma^2 + p\sigma^2{}_b)$.

3. For w', if we denote the mean square for the total sum of squares for blocks eliminating treatments by B, we may use

$$w' = \frac{r-1}{r\mathsf{B} - \mathsf{E}}$$

an expression formally identical with that for the simple lattice.

23.4.2 The 3-Dimensional Lattice

Here we shall consider the 3-dimensional lattice with 3 replicates in which the confounding is:

Replicate	Confounding
I	B, C, and BC interactions
II	C, A, and AC interactions
III	A, B, and AB interactions

The best estimates of effects and interactions are exemplified by

$$\hat{A} = \frac{WA_I + W'A_{II} + W'A_{III}}{W + 2W'}$$

$$= A_T + \frac{(W - W')}{3(W + 2W')}(2A_I - A_{II} - A_{III})$$

$$\widehat{AB} = \frac{WAB_I + WAB_{II} + W'AB_{III}}{2W + W'} \tag{12}$$

$$= AB_T + \frac{(W - W')}{3(2W + W')}(AB_I + AB_{II} - 2AB_{III})$$

$$\widehat{ABC} = ABC_T$$

The computational procedure given by Yates [1] may be used for this particular case. This procedure consists essentially of obtaining an adjustment for each of the possible 2-way tables and is possible because no 3-factor interactions are confounded. We shall give an alternative method later.

23.4.3 The 5-Dimensional Lattice

As a final example which presents the problems in full complexity, we may consider the 5-dimensional lattice with 5 replicates, each having a different scheme of confounding. The p^5 treatments are represented by the levels of 5 factors each at p levels, say, a, b, c, d, e, and the confounding in the 5 replicates may be taken to be as shown in Table 23.5.

TABLE 23.5

Replicate	Confounding
I	B, C, D, E and all interactions
II	A, C, D, E and all interactions
III	A, B, D, E and all interactions
IV	A, B, C, E and all interactions
V	A, B, C, D and all interactions

Given the weights W and W', the estimation of all the effects and interactions is exemplified by the following:

$$\hat{A} = \frac{WA_{\mathrm{I}} + W'A_{\mathrm{II}} + W'A_{\mathrm{III}} + W'A_{\mathrm{IV}} + W'A_{\mathrm{V}}}{W + 4W'}$$

$$\widehat{AB} = \frac{WAB_{\mathrm{I}} + WAB_{\mathrm{II}} + W'AB_{\mathrm{III}} + W'AB_{\mathrm{IV}} + W'AB_{\mathrm{V}}}{2W + 3W'}$$

$$\widehat{ABC} = \frac{WABC_{\mathrm{I}} + WABC_{\mathrm{II}} + WABC_{\mathrm{III}} + W'ABC_{\mathrm{IV}} + W'ABC_{\mathrm{V}}}{3W + 2W'}$$

$$\widehat{ABCD} = \frac{WABCD_{\mathrm{I}} + WABCD_{\mathrm{II}} + WABCD_{\mathrm{III}} + WABCD_{\mathrm{IV}} + W'ABCD_{\mathrm{V}}}{4W + W'}$$

$$\widehat{ABCDE} = ABCDE_{\mathrm{T}}$$

(13)

for any component of the respective interactions.

The combination of the effects and interactions to give the estimates of the yields of the treatments will be tedious, but straightforward.

The estimation of the weights is the only new problem, and this is the reason for describing this design. The analysis of variance has the structure shown in Table 23.6.

TABLE 23.6

	df
Replicates	4
Blocks eliminating treatments	$5(p^4 - 1)$
Treatments	$p^5 - 1$
Error (intrablock)	$4p^5 - 5p^4 + 1$
Total	$5p^5 - 1$

The analysis of variance is itself a problem, and the expectation of the mean square for blocks eliminating treatments an allied one.

If we consider the A effect, it is confounded in replicates II, III, IV, and V, and the interaction of the A effect with these replicates with $3(p - 1)$ degrees of freedom will have a mean square of $\sigma^2 + p\sigma^2{}_b$, for its sum of squares consists of a sum of squares between block totals. The other main effects contribute $3(p - 1)$ degrees of freedom each with the same expectation. There are in all 10 possible choices of 2 letters from the 5 letters, A, B, C, D, E, and, given any 2 letters, there are $(p - 1)$ sets of $(p - 1)$ degrees of freedom for the interaction of the 2 factors corresponding to the 2 letters. Any of these sets of $(p - 1)$ degrees of freedom is confounded in 3 of the replicates, so that the interaction of the particular 2-factor interaction with replicates in which it is confounded gives a sum of squares with $2(p - 1)$ degrees of freedom and a mean square with expectation $\sigma^2 + p\sigma^2{}_b$. All the 3-factor interactions are confounded in 2 of the given replicates, and these give a similar contribution.

Corresponding to the above comparison, there are comparisons between the mean of effects (or interactions) when confounded and the mean of the same effects when unconfounded. For example, we may consider

$$A_{\mathrm{I}} - \tfrac{1}{4}(A_{\mathrm{II}} + A_{\mathrm{III}} + A_{\mathrm{IV}} + A_{\mathrm{V}})$$

this quantity contains only block errors η and within-block errors e. These quantities squared, and added over the possible A comparisons, give, with the appropriate divisor, a sum of squares with $(p-1)$ degrees of freedom, for which the expectation of the mean square is $\sigma^2 + \tfrac{1}{5}p\sigma^2{}_b$. Similarly, with the AB interaction, we may consider

$$\frac{AB_{\mathrm{I}} + AB_{\mathrm{II}}}{2} - \frac{AB_{\mathrm{III}} + AB_{\mathrm{IV}} + AB_{\mathrm{V}}}{3}$$

which contains only η's and e's. These quantities lead to a mean square with expectation $\sigma^2 + \tfrac{2}{5}p\sigma^2{}_b$.

In general, we may compare the mean of an interaction over the n_c replicates, in which it is confounded, with the mean of the same interaction over the n_u replicates, in which it is unconfounded. Let X be the interaction, and suppose it corresponds to the equations,

$$\sum_i \alpha_i x_i = 0, 1, 2, \cdots, (p-1) \bmod p$$

and let X_{jk} be the total of the plots for which

$$\sum_i \alpha_i x_i = j \bmod p$$

in the kth replicate in which X is confounded. Let X_{jl} be the corresponding total in the lth replicate in which X is unconfounded. Here k will run from 1 to n_c and l from 1 to n_u. Consider the quantity

$$\sum_j \left(\frac{1}{n_c} \sum_k X_{jk} - \frac{1}{n_u} \sum_l X_{jl} - \frac{1}{n_c p} \sum_{jk} X_{jk} + \frac{1}{n_u p} \sum_{jl} X_{jl} \right)^2$$

which is the sum of squares of comparisons orthogonal to treatment comparisons. The expectation of the whole is easily found to be

$$(p-1)p \left(\frac{n_u + n_c}{n_u n_c} \right) \left(\sigma^2 + \frac{n_u}{n_u + n_c} p\sigma^2{}_b \right)$$

The divisor to give the sum of squares is $p\left(\dfrac{n_u + n_c}{n_u n_c}\right)$, and the expectation of the mean square is therefore

$$\sigma^2 + \frac{n_u}{n_u + n_c}\, p\sigma^2{}_b$$

From this result Table 23.7 may be completed, it being a simple mat-

TABLE 23.7 PARTITION OF BLOCK DEGREES OF FREEDOM FOR p^5 TREATMENTS IN BLOCKS OF p WITH 5 REPLICATES

	df	Expectation of Mean Square
Comparison between replicates of effects or interactions which are confounded in these replicates:		
Main effects	$15(p-1)$	
2-factor interactions	$20(p-1)^2$	$\sigma^2 + p\sigma^2{}_b$
3-factor interactions	$10(p-1)^3$	
Comparisons between mean of confounded effects and mean of unconfounded effects:		
Main effects	$5(p-1)$	$\sigma^2 + \frac{1}{5}p\sigma^2{}_b$
2-factor interactions	$10(p-1)^2$	$\sigma^2 + \frac{2}{5}p\sigma^2{}_b$
3-factor interactions	$10(p-1)^3$	$\sigma^2 + \frac{3}{5}p\sigma^2{}_b$
4-factor interactions	$5(p-1)^4$	$\sigma^2 + \frac{4}{5}p\sigma^2{}_b$

ter to verify the orthogonality of the comparisons. This result may also be used to show that, for any lattice design arranged in replicates, the expectation of the quantity $\dfrac{r\mathbf{B} - \mathbf{E}}{r - 1}$, where $\mathbf{B}$ is the mean square for blocks eliminating treatments and $\mathbf{E}$ is the error mean square, is an expectation of $\sigma^2 + k\sigma^2{}_b$, where k is the size of block.

23.5 THE VARIANCE OF TREATMENT COMPARISONS

We have used the fact that yields may be expressed in terms of the effects and interactions in the setting up of the designs, and we now turn to the consideration of treatment differences and the accuracy with which they are estimated. Any treatment difference may be expressed in terms of effects and interactions: for example, with $p = 7$, and 2 pseudofactors,

$$t_{00} = \mu + A_0 + B_0 + AB_0 + AB^2{}_0 + AB^3{}_0 + AB^4{}_0 + AB^5{}_0 + AB^6{}_0$$
$$t_{01} = \mu + A_0 + B_1 + AB_1 + AB^2{}_2 + AB^3{}_3 + AB^4{}_4 + AB^5{}_5 + AB^6{}_6$$

$$(14)$$

and

$$t_{00} - t_{01} = (B_0 - B_1) + (AB_0 - AB_1) + (AB^2_0 - AB^2_2)$$
$$+ (AB^3_0 - AB^3_3) + (AB^4_0 - AB^4_4) + (AB^5_0 - AB^5_5)$$
$$+ (AB^6_0 - AB^6_6) \quad (15)$$

Since the errors of each of the estimates of the differences $B_0 - B_1$, $AB_0 - AB_1$, $AB^2_0 - AB^2_2$, etc., are uncorrelated, the variance of $(t_{00} - t_{01})$ is the sum of the variances of the differences. With the simple lattice with 2 replicates the variances of the differences are:

$$B_0 - B_1 : \text{variance } \frac{2}{7(W + W')}$$

$$\left.\begin{array}{c} AB_0 - AB_1 \\ AB^2_0 - AB^2_2 \\ \cdot \qquad \cdot \\ \cdot \qquad \cdot \\ \cdot \qquad \cdot \\ AB^6_0 - AB^6_6 \end{array}\right\} : \text{variance } \frac{2}{14W}$$

The variance of the difference $(\hat{t}_{00} - \hat{t}_{01})$ is then

$$\frac{2}{7}\left(\frac{1}{W + W'} + \frac{6}{2W}\right)$$

If $W' = W = 1/\sigma^2$ this variance becomes $\frac{2}{7} \cdot 7/2W = \sigma^2$, as we would expect.

In the case of the simple lattice, the same variance will hold for any 2 treatments that occur together in a block in 1 of the 2 replicates. If 2 treatments do not occur together in a block in either of the replicates, the variance is $\frac{2}{7}\left(\frac{2}{W + W'} + \frac{5}{2W}\right)$, because their difference contains differences from both main effects. Rather than consider all the possible treatment differences and their errors, it is usually satisfactory to obtain an average variance of the possible treatment differences, and its square root, which may be used as an average standard error. We therefore find the average variance of the differences between one treatment and all the others. For the case of p^n treatments, any treatment difference will involve a difference with respect to an effect or interaction for $(p^n - p^{n-1})$ other treatments. For example, with the 7^2 lattice, the treatments (ij), such that the difference between them and the control contains a difference with respect to AB^2, are those that satisfy

$$i + 2j \neq 0 \bmod 7$$

to which there are $(7^2 - 7)$ solutions. If, then, we form all the $(p^n - 1)$ differences between the control and the other treatments and average their variances, we shall have

$$\left(\frac{p^n - p^{n-1}}{p^n - 1}\right) [\text{var } (A) + \text{var } (B) + \text{var } (AB) + \text{var } (AB^2) + \cdots$$

$$+ \text{var } (AB^{p-1}) + \text{var } (C) + \text{var } (AC) + \cdots + \text{var } (ABC) + \cdots$$

$$+ \text{var } (AB^{p-1}C^{p-1}) + \text{etc.}] \quad (16)$$

there being $(p^n - 1)/(p - 1)$ symbols in the square brackets, and each var (A), etc., being the variance of a difference of 2 of the quantities $A_0, A_1, A_2, \cdots, A_{p-1}$.

If an effect or interaction X is confounded in n_c replicates and unconfounded in n_u replicates, var (X) is $\dfrac{2}{p^{n-1}}\left(\dfrac{1}{n_u W + n_c W'}\right)$.

In general, therefore, the mean variance is

$$\frac{2(p - 1)}{(p^n - 1)}\left[\frac{n_0}{rW'} + \frac{n_1}{W + (r - 1)W'} + \cdots + \frac{n_s}{sW + (r - s)W'} + \cdots + \frac{n_r}{rW}\right]$$

$$(17)$$

where n_s is the number of sets of $(p - 1)$ degrees of freedom confounded in $(r - s)$ of the total of r replicates. The n_s satisfy the relations:

$$n_0 + n_1 + \cdots + n_r = \frac{p^n - 1}{p - 1} \quad (18)$$

and

$$n_0 r + n_1(r - 1) + n_2(r - 2) + \cdots + n_r = r\left(\frac{p^n - 1}{p - 1}\right) \quad (19)$$

Thus, with 3^3 treatments and 4 replicates, $p = 3$, $n = 3$, $r = 4$ and confounding as follows: replicate I: A, B, AB, AB^2; replicate II: A, C, AC, AC^2; replicate III: B, C, BC, BC^2; and replicate IV: AB, AC, BC^2, AB^2C^2; we have $n_0 = n_1 = 0$, $n_2 = 6$, $n_3 = 4$, and $n_4 = 3$, so that the mean variance is

$$\frac{2}{13}\left(\frac{6}{2W + 2W'} + \frac{4}{3W + W'} + \frac{3}{4W}\right) \quad (20)$$

We have, therefore, the following mean variances of treatment differences:

Simple lattice with 2 replicates:

$$\frac{2}{p+1}\left(\frac{2}{W+W'}+\frac{p-1}{2W}\right) \tag{21}$$

Simple lattice with 4 replicates:

$$\frac{1}{p+1}\left(\frac{2}{W+W'}+\frac{p-1}{2W}\right) \tag{22}$$

Triple lattice with 3 replicates:

$$\frac{2}{p+1}\left(\frac{3}{2W+W'}+\frac{p-2}{3W}\right) \tag{23}$$

3-dimensional lattice with 3 replicates:

$$\frac{2(p-1)}{(p^3-1)}\left[\frac{3}{W+2W'}+\frac{3(p-1)}{2W+W'}+\frac{(p-1)^2}{3W}\right] \tag{24}$$

4-dimensional lattice with 4 replicates:

$$\frac{2(p-1)}{(p^4-1)}\left[\frac{4}{W+3W'}+\frac{6(p-1)}{2W+2W'}+\frac{4(p-1)^2}{3W+W'}+\frac{(p-1)^3}{4W}\right] \tag{25}$$

Frequently W' will be small relative to W, and the contribution to the mean variance of effects or interactions which are confounded in all the replicates would be correspondingly large. For this reason it is usual to insist on the condition that no effect be confounded with blocks in all replicates of a practical design.

It will usually be advisable as a check on the use of the average variance, to calculate the variance of a treatment difference separately for the cases when the 2 treatments occur zero, once, twice, etc., times together in a block. These variances are as follows:

Simple lattice with 2 replicates:

    Together in a block once: $\dfrac{2}{p}\left(\dfrac{1}{W+W'}+\dfrac{p-1}{2W}\right)$

    Together in a block zero times: $\dfrac{2}{p}\left(\dfrac{2}{W+W'}+\dfrac{p-2}{2W}\right)$

Triple lattice with 3 replicates:

    Together in a block once: $\dfrac{2}{p}\left(\dfrac{2}{2W+W'}+\dfrac{p-2}{3W}\right)$

    Together in a block zero times: $\dfrac{2}{p}\left(\dfrac{3}{2W+W'}+\dfrac{p-3}{3W}\right)$

3-dimensional lattice with 3 replicates:

2 levels of pseudofactors common:

$$\frac{2}{p^2}\left[\frac{1}{2W' + W} + \frac{2(p - 1)}{W' + 2W} + \frac{(p - 1)^2}{3W}\right]$$

1 level of pseudofactors common:

$$\frac{2}{p^2}\left[\frac{2}{2W' + W} + \frac{3p - 4}{W' + 2W} + \frac{(p - 1)(p - 2)}{3W}\right]$$

0 level of pseudofactors common:

$$\frac{2}{p^2}\left[\frac{3}{2W' + W} + \frac{3(p - 2)}{W' + 2W} + \frac{p^2 - 3p + 3}{3W}\right]$$

The variances for any other design may be evaluated easily by noting how many main effect, 2-factor interaction, 3-factor interaction comparisons enter into the comparison of 2 treatments.

23.6 THE EFFECTS OF INACCURACIES IN THE WEIGHTS

We shall suppose that the analysis of variance of the experiment contains a component for blocks with N degrees of freedom the expectation of whose mean square, B, say, is $\sigma^2 + p\sigma^2{}_b$. The weights that will be used are $w = 1/E$, E being the intrablock error mean square based on N degrees of freedom, and $w' = 1/B$. The distinction we have used between true weights (capitals) and estimated weights (lower case) should be noted.

In order to make any investigation at all, we must use the infinite model at least to the extent of assuming that the actual sum of squares is distributed as χ^2. In this case, NW/w is distributed according to the χ^2 distribution with N degrees of freedom, and $N'W'/w'$ is distributed independently of W/w, according to the χ^2 distribution with N' degrees of freedom. The ratio $\dfrac{W'}{w'}\dfrac{w}{W}$ is then distributed according to the F distribution with N' and N degrees of freedom.

If an effect or interaction X is confounded in n_c replicates and unconfounded in n_u replicates, the estimate of a difference $X_i - X_j$ we have used is

$$\hat{X} = \frac{n_c w' X_c + n_u w X_u}{n_c w' + n_u w} \tag{26}$$

where X_c is the mean of $(X_i - X_j)$ over the replicates in which X is confounded, and X_u the mean over the replicates in which X is unconfounded. The true variance of X_c is $1/n_c W'$, and of X_u is $1/n_u W$, so the true variance of $\hat{X}$ is

$$\frac{n_c \dfrac{w'^2}{W'} + n_u \dfrac{w^2}{W}}{(n_c w' + n_u w)^2} \tag{27}$$

the constant of proportionality $2/p^{n-1}$ being omitted.

Note that, if w' actually equals W', and w actually equals W, this becomes

$$\frac{1}{n_c W' + n_u W}$$

Now,

$$\frac{\left(n_c \dfrac{w'^2}{W'} + n_u \dfrac{w^2}{W} \right)}{(n_c w' + n_u w)^2} = \frac{1}{n_c W' + n_u W} + \frac{n_c n_u W \dfrac{w'^2}{W'} (F - 1)^2}{(n_c w' + n_u w)^2 (n_c W' + n_u W)} \tag{28}$$

where

$$F = \frac{W'}{w'} \frac{w}{W}$$

Then, if we put $W' = kW$, the variance of the actual estimate

= variance without inaccuracies in weights

$$+ \frac{1}{W} \frac{n_c n_u k (F - 1)^2}{(n_c k + n_u F)^2 (n_c k + n_u)} \tag{29}$$

If w/w' is found to be less than unity, the value of unity is used. Since

$$F = \frac{W'}{W} \frac{w}{w'} = k \frac{w}{w'} \tag{30}$$

equal weights are used if F is less than k, and, in this case, the increase in variance for the estimate of the effect is

$$\frac{n_u n_c (k - 1)^2}{kW(n_c + n_u)^2 (n_c k + n_u)} = \frac{n_u n_c (k - 1)^2}{r^2 kW(n_c k + n_u)} \tag{31}$$

Adding over all the possible effects and interactions, we shall obtain the increase in average variance due to inaccuracies in the weights, which is a constant if F is less than k, and is a function of F if F is greater than k. The percentage loss in information due to the inaccuracies in the weights may then be obtained.

In the case of the 3-dimensional lattice with 3 replicates given earlier in the chapter, the average variance using the true weights W and W' is

$$\frac{2(p - 1)}{(p^3 - 1)} \left[\frac{3}{W + 2W'} + \frac{3(p - 1)}{2W + W'} + \frac{(p - 1)^2}{3W} \right]$$

that is,

$$\frac{2(p-1)}{(p^3-1)} \cdot \frac{1}{W} \left[\frac{3}{1+2k} + \frac{3(p-1)}{2+k} + \frac{(p-1)^2}{3} \right] \tag{32}$$

The increase in variance due to inaccuracies in the weights is

$$\frac{2(p-1)}{(p^3-1)} \cdot \frac{1}{W} \left[\frac{3\cdot2\cdot1k(F-1)^2}{(2k+F)^2(2k+1)} + \frac{3(p-1)1\cdot2k(F-1)^2}{(k+2F)^2(k+2)} \right]$$

$$F > k$$

and

$$\frac{2(p-1)}{(p^3-1)} \cdot \frac{1}{W} \left[\frac{3\cdot2\cdot1\cdot(k-1)^2}{k\cdot9\cdot(2k+1)} + \frac{3(p-1)1\cdot2\cdot(k-1)^2}{k\cdot9(k+2)} \right]$$

$$F \le k \tag{33}$$

If k equals unity, these expressions reduce to

$$\frac{4(p-1)}{(p^3-1)} \cdot \frac{1}{W} \cdot (F-1)^2 \left[\frac{1}{(2+F)^2} + \frac{(p-1)}{(1+2F)^2} \right] \qquad F > 1$$

and 0, $F < 1$

Since, with k equal to unity $W' = W$, the best estimates have an average variance of differences of $2/3W$, the proportional increase in average variance is

$$\frac{6(p-1)}{(p^3-1)} (F-1)^2 \left[\frac{1}{(2+F)^2} + \frac{(p-1)}{(1+2F)^2} \right] \tag{34}$$

if F is greater than unity. With the more particular case of $p = 3$, the proportional increase is

$$\frac{6}{13} (F-1)^2 \left[\frac{1}{(2+F)^2} + \frac{2}{(1+2F)^2} \right] \tag{35}$$

if F is greater than unity. The result of Yates [1] for this case appears to be in error.

If the weight W' is not estimated so simply as in the above discussion, the problem becomes more complex. For example, suppose we have a 3-dimensional lattice and use the pooled mean square for blocks B eliminating treatments to estimate W'. This mean square is obtained from the 3 components (Table 23.8).

TABLE 23.8

Component	df	Mean Square	Expectation of Mean Square
a	$3(p-1)$	B_a	$\sigma^2 + p\sigma^2_b$
b	$3(p-1)$	B_b	$\sigma^2 + \frac{1}{3}p\sigma^2_b$
c	$3(p-1)^2$	B_c	$\sigma^2 + \frac{2}{3}p\sigma^2_b$

Then,

$$B = \frac{3(p-1)B_a + 3(p-1)B_b + 3(p-1)^2 B_c}{3(p^2-1)}$$

and has an expectation of $\sigma^2 + \tfrac{2}{3}p\sigma^2{}_b$.

The estimate of W' which is used is then

$$w' = \frac{2}{3B - E}$$

The examination of inaccuracies in the weights does not proceed in the simple fashion outlined for the previous case, because $3(p^2-1)B$ is not distributed as $\chi^2(\sigma^2 + \tfrac{2}{3}p\sigma^2{}_b)$ with $3(p^2-1)$ degrees of freedom.

For we have:

$3(p-1)B_a$ is distributed as $\chi^2(\sigma^2 + p\sigma^2{}_b)$ with $3(p-1)$ df

$3(p-1)B_b$ is distributed as $\chi^2(\sigma^2 + \tfrac{1}{3}p\sigma^2{}_b)$ with $3(p-1)$ df

$3(p-1)^2 B_c$ is distributed as $\chi^2(\sigma^2 + \tfrac{2}{3}p\sigma^2{}_b)$ with $3(p-1)^2$ df

The evaluation of the loss in information in this case, therefore, requires the use of distributions which are not simple nor tabulated. The work of Robbins and Pitman [2] may possibly be applied to the problem: They have obtained a general solution for the distribution of B and B/E, E being the error mean square.

As the simple and triple lattices with 2 and 3 replicates, respectively, are perhaps the most widely used designs, it seems advisable to make an examination in their case. We suppose then that we have mean squares B and E with expectations $(\sigma^2 + \rho p\sigma^2{}_b)$ and σ^2, respectively, and that $N'B$ is distributed as $\chi^2(\sigma^2 + \rho p\sigma^2{}_b)$ with N' degrees of freedom and NE as $\chi^2\sigma^2$ with N degrees of freedom, independently of each other.

The weights that will be used are then $w = 1/E$ and $w' = \dfrac{\rho}{B + (\rho - 1)E}$.

The variance of the estimate of an effect confounded in n_c replicates and unconfounded in n_u replicates is

$$\frac{\left(n_c \dfrac{w'^2}{W'} + n_u \dfrac{w^2}{W}\right)}{(n_c w' + n_u w)^2}$$

which equals

$$\frac{1}{n_c W' + n_u W} + \frac{n_c n_u W \dfrac{w'^2}{W'}\left(\dfrac{W'}{W}\dfrac{w}{w'} - 1\right)^2}{(n_c w' + n_u w)^2(n_c W' + n_u W)} \quad \text{as before}$$

In this case $N\mathsf{E}/\sigma^2$ is distributed as χ^2 with N degrees of freedom, and $N'\mathsf{B}/(\sigma^2 + \rho p \sigma^2{}_b)$ is distributed as χ^2 with N' degrees of freedom.

Therefore, $(\sigma^2/\mathsf{E}) \times [\mathsf{B}/(\sigma^2 + \rho p \sigma^2{}_b)]$ is distributed as F with N' and N degrees of freedom. But

$$\mathsf{B} + (\rho - 1)\mathsf{E} = \frac{\rho}{w'}$$

or

$$\mathsf{B} = \frac{\rho}{w'} - \frac{(\rho - 1)}{w}$$

and

$$\frac{\sigma^2}{\mathsf{E}} = \frac{w}{W} \tag{36}$$

so

$$\frac{w}{W} \frac{\left(\dfrac{\rho}{w'} - \dfrac{\rho - 1}{w} \right)}{\left(\dfrac{\rho}{W'} - \dfrac{\rho - 1}{W} \right)}$$

is distributed as F, i.e.,

$$\frac{w\rho}{w'W \left(\dfrac{\rho}{W'} - \dfrac{\rho - 1}{W} \right)} - \frac{(\rho - 1)}{W \left(\dfrac{\rho}{W'} - \dfrac{\rho - 1}{W} \right)}$$

is distributed as F. If we let $W' = kW$, the quantity w/w' is distributed as

$$\left(\frac{\dfrac{\rho}{k} - (\rho - 1)}{\rho} \right) \left(F + \frac{\rho - 1}{\dfrac{\rho}{k} - (\rho - 1)} \right) \tag{37}$$

where F is distributed according to the F distribution with N' and N degrees of freedom. The increase in variance for the particular effect is then

$$\frac{n_c n_u \left(k \dfrac{w}{w'} - 1 \right)^2}{kW \left(n_c + n_u \dfrac{w}{w'} \right)^2 (n_c k + n_u)}$$

The expected value of this increase may be obtained by numerical integration over the F distribution, and the expected increase in the mean variance of comparisons may be estimated for any particular design. In performing the integration, it should be noted that, if W' is estimated to be greater than W, the estimated value is not used, but it is assumed that $W = W'$. When equal weights are used, the increase in variance of an effect or interaction is

$$\frac{n_u n_c (k - 1)^2}{W k (n_c + n_u)^2 (n_c k + n_u)}$$

In the case of the triple lattice for p^2 treatments, we had

$$N' = 3(p - 1)$$

$$N = (2p - 1)(p - 1)$$

$$\rho = \tfrac{2}{3}$$

so that w/w' is distributed as $\dfrac{1}{2}\left(\dfrac{2}{k} + 1\right)\left(F - \dfrac{1}{2/k + 1}\right)$.

The increase in average variance of treatment differences is

$$\frac{12}{(p + 1)} \cdot \frac{\left(k \dfrac{w}{w'} - 1\right)^2}{kW\left(1 + 2\dfrac{w}{w'}\right)^2 (k + 2)} \quad \text{for} \quad \frac{w}{w'} > 1$$

and

$$\frac{12}{(p + 1)} \cdot \frac{(k - 1)^2}{kW \cdot 9 \cdot (k + 2)} \quad \text{for} \quad \frac{w}{w'} \leq 1 \tag{38}$$

The average proportional increase in variance for the case $p = 5$ was obtained approximately by numerical integration and was found to be as follows:

$\dfrac{W}{W'}$	1	2	3	4	5	10
Percent	1.2	2.3	2.7	2.7	2.3	0.8

The results published by Yates,[1] together with this case, indicate that the effect of inaccuracies of the weights on the variance of treatment comparisons is of the order of 1, 2, or 3 percent, and, therefore, trivial. The effect of inaccuracies of the weights will increase as the number of degrees of freedom for interblock and intrablock error decrease. Usually the number of degrees of freedom for intrablock error is sufficiently large, and, as a practical rule with lattice designs, it is probably safe to say that the effect of inaccuracies will be inappreciable if the interblock mean square is based on 10 or more degrees of freedom. With a smaller number of degrees of freedom, it is best to assume that $W' = 0$, and to utilize only intrablock information.

So far we have examined the effects of inaccuracies in the weights on the average variance of treatment differences in terms of the true weights W and W', and there still remains the question of the extent to which the estimated variance in terms of w and w' is a reasonable estimate of the variance of the differences actually estimated. The estimated variance will be used to test single degree of freedom comparisons, by what amounts to a normal theory test. Since the calculated variance will be less than the true variance of the actual estimate, the normal theory test will tend to give too high a significance level. It does not appear easy to determine the bias in the calculated significance level.

23.7 THE ANALYSIS OF LATTICE DESIGNS AS COMPLETE RANDOMIZED BLOCK DESIGNS

It was shown by Yates [1] that a p^2 and a p^3 lattice design in blocks of p plots may be analyzed as a complete randomized block experiment. His method of proof depends on the fact that, if, under a particular analysis, the expectation of the treatment mean square, in the absence of treatment effects, is equal to expectation of the error mean square, this analysis gives an unbiased estimate of the error to which treatment comparisons will be subject. This is not necessarily true, for the error sum of squares must be homogeneous.

Suppose we have an experiment on p^n treatments in a lattice design with blocks of p plots and r replicates, and consider an effect or interaction X which is confounded in n_c replicates and unconfounded in $n_u [= (r - n_c)]$ replicates. Let X_{ik} be the sum of the plot yields with the ith level of factor x (or of the interaction) in the kth replicate. Then the sum of squares for X is equal to

$$\frac{1}{rp^{n-1}} \sum_{i=0}^{p-1} \left(\sum_k X_{ik} - \frac{1}{p} \sum_i \sum_k X_{ik} \right)^2$$

Apart from the treatment constants, the expectation of the square of any quantity in brackets is

$$[(n_c p^{n-2}(p-1)^2 + n_c(p^{n-1} - p^{n-2})]\sigma^2{}_b$$

$$+ \left[rp^{n-1} \left(\frac{p-1}{p} \right)^2 + r(p^n - p^{n-1}) \frac{1}{p^2} \right] \sigma^2$$

which equals

$$n_c p^{n-1}(p-1)\sigma^2{}_b + rp^{n-2}(p-1)\sigma^2$$

The expectation of the sum of squares for X is then

$$(p-1)\left(\sigma^2 + \frac{n_c}{r} p\sigma^2{}_b \right)$$

We may use previous results to obtain the sum of squares for X by replicates (Table 23.9).

	df	Expected Mean Square
X by replicates in which confounded versus replicates in which unconfounded	$p - 1$	$\sigma^2 + \dfrac{n_u}{r} p\sigma^2_b$
X by replicates in which confounded	$(n_c - 1)(p - 1)$	$\sigma^2 + p\sigma^2_b$
X by replicates in which unconfounded	$(n_u - 1)(p - 1)$	σ^2

The mean square for the error of X is then

$$\sigma^2 + p\sigma^2_b \left[\frac{1}{(r-1)} \left(\frac{n_u}{r} + n_c - 1 \right) \right]$$
$$= \sigma^2 + p\sigma^2_b \left[\frac{n_u + rn_c - r}{r(r-1)} \right]$$
$$= \sigma^2 + \frac{n_c}{r} p\sigma^2_b \quad \text{since} \quad n_u + n_c = r \quad (39)$$

The set of $(p^n - 1)$ degrees of freedom for treatments ignoring blocks is partitioned into $(p^n - 1)/(p - 1)$ sets of $(p - 1)$ degrees of freedom, and the error sum of squares with a complete randomized block analysis may be partitioned into $(p^n - 1)/(p - 1)$ sets of $(r - 1)(p - 1)$ degrees of freedom. The above shows that the expectation of the mean square for a set of $(p - 1)$ degrees of freedom belonging to treatments is the same, apart from true treatment effects, as the expectation of the mean square of the corresponding $(r - 1)(p - 1)$ degrees of freedom for error (replicate by treatment).

An ordinary randomized block analysis of a quasifactorial design with one restriction is, therefore, valid insofar as the expectation of the treatment mean squares is the same as the expectation of the randomized block error mean square. It follows then, from consideration of the randomization test, that the complete randomized block analysis gives a reasonably valid test of the null hypothesis that there are no treatment effects. A test may also be made, of course, with the intrablock treatment and error mean squares. Difficulties do arise, however, as soon as we wish to ascribe errors to treatment comparisons obtained from the ordinary treatment averages, because we have shown that the complete error sum of squares with $(r - 1)(p^n - 1)$ degrees of freedom is not homogeneous if σ^2_b is greater than zero.

We may examine the true errors of the possible types of comparison among 2 treatments, whether they occur in a block together, not at all, once, twice, etc. If 2 treatments occur together in a block in s out of r of the replicates, the variance of the difference of the treatment averages is

$$\frac{1}{r^2}[2r\sigma^2 + 2(r - s)\sigma^2{}_b] = \frac{2}{r^2}[r\sigma^2 + (r - s)\sigma^2{}_b]$$

$$= \frac{2}{r}\left(\sigma^2 + \frac{r - s}{r}\sigma^2{}_b\right)$$

The average error variance from the complete randomized block analysis is the average over the $(p^n - 1)/(p - 1)$ effects or interactions, each with $(p - 1)$ degrees of freedom, of $\sigma^2 + \frac{n_c}{r}p\sigma^2{}_b$. The sum of n_c over all the effects and interactions is $r\left(\dfrac{p^{n-1} - 1}{p - 1}\right)$, because $\left(\dfrac{p^{n-1} - 1}{p - 1}\right)$ sets of $(p - 1)$ degrees of freedom are confounded in each replicate, and so the average of $\sigma^2 + \frac{n_c}{r}p\sigma^2{}_b$ is

$$\sigma^2 + \frac{p(p^{n-1} - 1)}{p^n - 1}\sigma^2{}_b$$

which equals

$$\sigma^2 + \sigma^2{}_b\left(1 - \frac{p - 1}{p^n - 1}\right)$$

In using the complete randomized block analysis, we attribute to the difference of any 2 treatments a variance with expectation

$$\frac{2}{r}\left[\sigma^2 + \sigma^2{}_b\left(1 - \frac{p - 1}{p^n - 1}\right)\right]$$

The deviation of the true variance of the treatment difference from the expectation of the actual variance attributed to the treatment comparison by the randomized block analysis is then equal to

$$\frac{2}{r}\left(\frac{s}{r} - \frac{p - 1}{p^n - 1}\right)\sigma^2{}_b$$

We now consider two special cases:

(a) *Simple Lattice*: $n = 2$, $r = 2$, $s = 0$ or 1

$s = 0$: true variance $= (\sigma^2 + \sigma^2{}_b)$

$s = 1$: true variance $= (\sigma^2 + \frac{1}{2}\sigma^2{}_b)$

Variance from randomized block analysis

$$= \left[\sigma^2 + \sigma^2{}_b\left(1 - \frac{1}{p + 1}\right)\right]$$

Therefore, the variance for a difference between 2 treatments not occurring in a block together is underestimated by $\left(\dfrac{1}{p+1}\right)\sigma^2{}_b$. The variance for treatments occurring in a block is overestimated by

$$\left(\frac{1}{2}-\frac{1}{p+1}\right)\sigma^2{}_b = \frac{(p-1)}{2(p+1)}\,\sigma^2{}_b$$

or approximately $\frac{1}{2}\sigma^2{}_b$. The overestimation of the latter variance is the more important practically. If, however, $\sigma^2{}_b$ is small, the errors of the variances given by the randomized block analysis will be small, and, if $\sigma^2{}_b$ is not small, the recovery of interblock information should be performed.

   (b) *Triple Lattice*: $n = 2$, $r = 3$, $s = 0$ or 1

     $s = 0$: true variance $= \frac{2}{3}(\sigma^2 + \sigma^2{}_b)$

     $s = 1$: true variance $= \frac{2}{3}(\sigma^2 + \frac{2}{3}\sigma^2{}_b)$

   Variance from randomized block analysis

$$= \frac{2}{3}\left[\sigma^2 + \sigma^2{}_b\left(1 - \frac{1}{p+1}\right)\right]$$

In this case the overestimation of variance of differences of type $s = 1$ is less.

It appears, as a general rule with the simple lattice design and to a less extent with the triple lattice design, that the ordinary randomized block analysis is not satisfactory for comparison of treatments occurring together within a block. For designs with more than 3 replicates with different confounding, the discrepancies will be small.

23.8 THE EFFICIENCY OF LATTICE DESIGNS RELATIVE TO COMPLETE RANDOMIZED BLOCKS

We saw in the previous sections that the true mean variance of treatment comparisons, estimated with true weights, was

$$\frac{2(p-1)}{(p^n-1)}\left[\frac{n_0}{rW'} + \frac{n_1}{W+(r-1)W'} + \frac{n_2}{2W+(r-2)W'} + \cdots + \frac{n_r}{rW}\right]$$

whereas the true mean variance with the complete randomized block analysis is

$$\frac{2}{r}\left(\sigma^2 + p\,\frac{p^{n-1}-1}{p^n-1}\,\sigma^2{}_b\right)$$

which equals

$$\frac{2}{r(p^n - 1)}\left[(p^n - 1)\frac{1}{W} + (p^{n-1} - 1)\left(\frac{1}{W'} - \frac{1}{W}\right)\right]$$

that is,

$$\frac{2}{r(p^n - 1)}\left(\frac{p^{n-1} - 1}{W'} + \frac{p^n - p^{n-1}}{W}\right)$$

The efficiency of the lattice in blocks of p plots relative to complete randomized blocks (i.e., blocks of p^n plots) is

$$\frac{\left(\dfrac{p^{n-1} - 1}{W'} + \dfrac{p^n - p^{n-1}}{W}\right)}{r(p - 1)\left[\dfrac{n_0}{rW'} + \dfrac{n_1}{W + (r - 1)W'} + \dfrac{n_2}{2W + (r - 2)W'} + \cdots + \dfrac{n_r}{rW}\right]} \quad (40)$$

This quantity has been evaluated for the range of values of W/W' and is given in Table 23.10. The designs considered are n-dimensional lat-

TABLE 23.10 EFFICIENCY OF n-DIMENSIONAL LATTICE DESIGNS FOR p^n VARIETIES WITH n REPLICATES RELATIVE TO RANDOMIZED COMPLETE BLOCKS

			W/W'									
p	n	p^n	1	2	3	4	5	6	7	8	9	10
2	2	4	100	109	125	143	162	181	200	220	239	259
2	3	8	100	110	127	146	165	185	205	225	245	266
2	4	16	100	110	127	146	165	185	205	225	245	266
2	5	32	100	110	128	147	166	186	206	226	246	266
2	6	64	100	111	128	147	167	187	208	228	248	269
2	7	128	100	111	129	148	168	189	209	230	251	271
2	8	256	100	111	129	149	170	190	211	232	253	274
2	9	512	100	111	130	150	170	192	213	234	256	277
2	10	1024	100	111	130	150	171	193	214	236	258	280
3	2	9	100	107	120	135	150	166	182	198	214	231
3	3	27	100	108	123	139	156	173	191	208	226	244
3	4	81	100	109	124	141	159	177	195	213	232	250
3	5	243	100	109	125	142	161	179	198	217	236	255
3	6	729	100	110	126	144	162	182	201	220	240	259
5	2	25	100	105	114	125	136	148	160	172	184	196
5	3	125	100	106	117	129	142	155	168	182	196	209
5	4	625	100	106	118	131	144	158	172	186	200	215
7	2	49	100	104	111	120	129	138	147	157	167	176
7	3	343	100	105	113	123	133	143	154	165	176	186
11	2	121	100	103	108	114	120	127	133	140	147	154
13	2	169	100	102	107	112	117	123	129	135	141	147

tices in blocks of p plots with n replicates, $(n - 1)$ of the main effects and their interactions being confounded. These designs are in a sense balanced. It should be noted that W/W' will not be comparable from line to line in the table. The relation obtained by Fairfield Smith

(Chapter 11) could be used to give an idea of relative efficiencies for the different cases, but this would necessarily be in terms of the parameter b of that relation.

This evaluation of the relative efficiency of lattice designs assumes that the same size, shape, and orientation of the plots is used in the two cases and that the replicates are the same, the difference being merely in the allocation of treatments. Such a comparison is not always entirely justified, because, with a completely randomized design, one might use a plot of different relative dimensions.

It should also be noted that we have expressed the efficiency in terms of the true weights W and W', and not of the estimated weights w and w'. It may be suspected that the use of the estimated weights tends to overestimate the relative efficiency of an actual experiment.

The relative efficiency of the design will be lowered considerably by allowing some effects or interactions to be confounded in all the replicates, and this is particularly so if it should happen that W/W' is large. This case is not included in the table.

23.9 THE COMPARISON OF p^n TREATMENTS IN BLOCKS OF p^s PLOTS ($s > 1$)

There are no difficulties in extending the methods of the present chapter to the case of comparing p^n treatments in blocks the size of which is a power of p. As an example which is reasonably practical, suppose we wish to compare 32 ($= 2^5$) treatments in blocks of 4 ($= 2^2$) plots, and denote the pseudofactors by a, b, c, d, e. There are 155 possible systems of confounding for the 2^5 system in blocks of 4. At least 3 replicates must be used if no effect or interaction is to be confounded in all replicates. A set of 3 replicates is the following:

Replicate	Confounding
I	A, B, AB, C, AC, BC, ABC
II	A, D, AD, E, AE, DE, ADE
III	B, D, BD, E, BE, DE, BDE

The estimate of A is

$$\hat{A} = \frac{W'A_\mathrm{I} + W'A_\mathrm{II} + WA_\mathrm{III}}{2W' + W}$$

$$= A_T + \frac{(W' - W)}{3(2W' + W)}(A_\mathrm{I} + A_\mathrm{II} - 2A_\mathrm{III}) \tag{41}$$

and so on.

The structure of the analysis of variance is given in Table 23.11.

TABLE 23.11

Due to	df	Expectation of Mean Square
Replicates	2	
Blocks eliminating treatments		
Effects X confounded in 2 replicates:		
X by (replicates in which confounded versus replicates in which unconfounded)	5	$\sigma^2 + \frac{1}{3} \cdot 4\sigma^2_b$
Effects X confounded in 1 replicate:		
X by (replicates in which confounded versus replicates in which unconfounded)	11	$\sigma^2 + \frac{2}{3} \cdot 4\sigma^2_b$
Effects X confounded in 2 replicates:		
X by (replicates in which confounded)	5	$\sigma^2 + 4\sigma^2_b$
Treatments	31	
Error intrablock	41	σ^2
Total	95	

The analysis presents no new difficulties.

If it is the case that n is a multiple of s, say, ks, the experiment may be represented as one on k factors each with p^s levels. The representation based on the Galois field of p^s elements, as discussed in Chapter 17, may be used, to give directly schemes of confounding in blocks of p^s plots. These schemes will be a subset of the schemes obtained by consideration of the ks factors each at p levels. The only virtue of using the more complex representation is that from it we may obtain a set of schemes of confounding which is balanced in the sense of every effect and interaction (each with $p^s - 1$ degrees of freedom) being confounded equally frequently, this set being a subset of all the schemes of confounding derived from the simpler representation, which uses the Galois field of p elements.

There remains only the question of the relative values of designs using varying sizes of block. For example, with 81 treatments, there are 2 possibilities which are of importance, with blocks of 9 plots and blocks of 3 plots. We have seen that, with blocks of 9 plots, multiples of a simple lattice, or of a triple lattice, and so on may be used. With blocks of 3 plots, it is necessary to use at least 4 replicates. It would be desirable, for example, to compare 2 multiples of a simple lattice in blocks of 9 plots with 4 replicates of the 4-dimensional lattice using blocks of 3 plots. Such a comparison is rendered difficult because of the fact that a relation between W and W' for the 2 designs is necessary. No satisfactory answer has been obtained.

23.10 THE NON-PRIME CASE

We shall deal in this section with the comparison of k^n treatments, where k is not a prime or a power of a prime. The main difference is that the number of possible designs is considerably less, because of the non-existence of a $k \times k$ completely orthogonalized square. We shall find that the analysis and estimates will be the same as in the prime case, with k substituted for p, for the designs that exist.

The model that is used is again the additive one, the yield being made up of a constant contribution, treatment effect, block error, and plot error, these being uncorrelated as before.

23.10.1 The Simple Lattice

Denoting the k^2 treatments by (ij), i and j running from 1 to k, we may place treatments with the same i together in a block in the first replicate, say, replicate I, and treatments with the same j together in a block in the second replicate, say, replicate II. The analysis may be derived very simply by utilizing the identity

$$\tau_{ij} - \tau_{..} = (\tau_{i\cdot} - \tau_{..}) + (\tau_{\cdot j} - \tau_{..}) + (\tau_{ij} - \tau_{i\cdot} - \tau_{\cdot j} + \tau_{..}) \quad (42)$$

where τ_{ij} is the true effect of treatment (ij), $\tau_{i\cdot} = \dfrac{1}{k} \sum_j \tau_{ij}$, etc. The

terms on the right-hand side are, in order, a comparison confounded with blocks in replicate I, a comparison confounded with blocks in replicate II, and a comparison unconfounded in both replicates. If we use the notation that $(i\cdot)_\text{I}$ is the observed mean of treatments with first number equal to i, in replicate I and so on, the comparison $(\tau_{i\cdot} - \tau_{..})$ is estimated by $[(i\cdot)_\text{I} - (\cdot\cdot)_\text{I}]$ with variance proportional to $\sigma^2 + k\sigma^2{}_b$, and by $[(i\cdot)_\text{II} - (\cdot\cdot)_\text{II}]$ with variance proportional to σ^2. If we put $W = 1/\sigma^2$, and $W' = 1/(\sigma^2 + k\sigma^2{}_b)$, the best estimate of $(\tau_{i\cdot} - \tau_{..})$ is then

$$\frac{W'[(i\cdot)_\text{I} - (\cdot\cdot)_\text{I}] + W[(i\cdot)_\text{II} - (\cdot\cdot)_\text{II}]}{(W' + W)}$$

and this equals

$$\tfrac{1}{2}\{[(i\cdot)_\text{I} - (\cdot\cdot)_\text{I}] + [(i\cdot)_\text{II} - (\cdot\cdot)_\text{II}]\}$$

$$- \frac{(W - W')}{2(W + W')}\{[(i\cdot)_\text{I} - (\cdot\cdot)_\text{I}] - [(i\cdot)_\text{II} - (\cdot\cdot)_\text{II}]\}$$

Similarly, the best estimate of $(\tau_{\cdot j} - \tau_{..})$ is

$$\tfrac{1}{2}\{[(\cdot j)_\text{I} - (\cdot\cdot)_\text{I}] + [(\cdot j)_\text{II} - (\cdot\cdot)_\text{II}]\}$$

$$- \frac{(W - W')}{2(W + W')}\{-[(\cdot j)_\text{I} - (\cdot\cdot)_\text{I}] + [(\cdot j)_\text{II} - (\cdot\cdot)_\text{II}]\}$$

The comparison $(\tau_{ij} - \tau_{i\cdot} - \tau_{\cdot j} + \tau_{\cdot\cdot})$ is unconfounded with blocks in both replicates, so that the best estimate of it is

$$\tfrac{1}{2}\{[(ij)_{\mathrm{I}} - (i\cdot)_{\mathrm{I}} - (\cdot j)_{\mathrm{I}} + (\cdot\cdot)_{\mathrm{I}}] + [(ij)_{\mathrm{II}} - (i\cdot)_{\mathrm{II}} - (\cdot j)_{\mathrm{II}} + (\cdot\cdot)_{\mathrm{II}}]\}$$

The best estimate of $(\tau_{ij} - \tau_{\cdot\cdot})$ is, therefore, identical with that obtained before, since

$$\tfrac{1}{2}[(i\cdot)_{\mathrm{I}} - (\cdot\cdot)_{\mathrm{I}} + (i\cdot)_{\mathrm{II}} - (\cdot\cdot)_{\mathrm{II}}] + \tfrac{1}{2}[(\cdot j)_{\mathrm{I}} - (\cdot\cdot)_{\mathrm{I}} + (\cdot j)_{\mathrm{II}} - (\cdot\cdot)_{\mathrm{II}}]$$

$$+ \tfrac{1}{2}[(ij)_{\mathrm{I}} - (i\cdot)_{\mathrm{I}} - (\cdot j)_{\mathrm{I}} + (\cdot\cdot)_{\mathrm{I}} + (ij)_{\mathrm{II}} - (i\cdot)_{\mathrm{II}} - (\cdot j)_{\mathrm{II}} + (\cdot\cdot)_{\mathrm{II}}]$$

$$= \tfrac{1}{2}[(ij)_{\mathrm{I}} + (ij)_{\mathrm{II}} - (\cdot\cdot)_{\mathrm{I}} - (\cdot\cdot)_{\mathrm{II}}]$$

that is, the observed mean yield of treatment (ij) as a deviation from the observed mean, and the correction terms are as before. The variance of the estimated difference between 2 treatments occurring together in a block is, for example, the variance of the estimate of

$$(\tau_{\cdot j} - \tau_{\cdot j'}) + (\tau_{ij} - \tau_{\cdot j} - \tau_{ij'} + \tau_{\cdot j'})$$

which is

$$\frac{2}{k}\left(\frac{1}{W + W'} + \frac{k-1}{2W}\right)$$

The variance of the estimated difference of 2 treatments that do not occur together in a block is

$$\frac{2}{k}\left(\frac{2}{W + W'} + \frac{k-2}{2W}\right)$$

Combining these 2 variances according to the relative frequencies, we find that the average variance of treatment differences is

$$\frac{2}{k+1}\left(\frac{2}{W + W'} + \frac{k-1}{2W}\right)$$

The analysis of variance and estimation of the weights are identical with that given for the prime case.

23.10.2 The Triple Lattice

This design is possible for k^2 treatments where k is any number because a $k \times k$ Latin square exists for any number k. We may denote a treatment by (ijl), i being the row, j the column, and l the letter in the Latin square on which the treatments are superimposed. The analysis is based on the identity

$$\tau_{ijl} - \tau_{\ldots} = (\tau_{i\cdot\cdot} - \tau_{\ldots}) + (\tau_{\cdot j\cdot} - \tau_{\ldots}) + (\tau_{\cdot\cdot l} - \tau_{\ldots})$$

$$+ (\tau_{ijl} - \tau_{i\cdot\cdot} - \tau_{\cdot j\cdot} - \tau_{\cdot\cdot l} + 2\tau_{\ldots}) \quad (43)$$

If rows, columns, and letters are confounded in replicates I, II, and III, respectively, the comparisons $(\tau_i.. - \tau...)$ are confounded in replicate I, $(\tau._j. - \tau...)$ in replicate II, and $(\tau.._l - \tau...)$ in replicate III, while $(\tau_{ijl} - \tau_i.. - \tau._j. - \tau.._l + 2\tau...)$ is completely unconfounded. The analysis and estimation are clearly the same as for the prime case, k being substituted for p, and we shall not go through the details.

23.10.3   The 3-Dimensional Lattice

A 3-dimensional lattice for k^3 treatments in blocks of k plots with 3 replicates (or a multiple of these 3) exists for any k, because we may arrange the treatments on the points of a $k \times k \times k$ cubic lattice. A replicate of k^2 blocks of k plots is obtained by taking the lines parallel to one of the 3 possible directions, and we may, for purposes of nomenclature, suppose that j and k are constant within blocks of replicate I, i and k within blocks of replicate II, and i and j within blocks of replicate III. The analysis is simply derived by utilizing the identity

$$(\tau_{ijk} - \tau...) = (\tau_i.. - \tau...) + (\tau._j. - \tau...)$$
$$+ (\tau_{ij}. - \tau_i.. - \tau._j. + \tau...)$$
$$+ (\tau.._k - \tau...) + (\tau_i._k - \tau_i.. - \tau.._k + \tau...)$$
$$+ (\tau._{jk} - \tau._j. - \tau.._k + \tau...)$$
$$+ (\tau_{ijk} - \tau_{ij}. - \tau_i._k - \tau._{jk} + \tau_i.. + \tau._j. + \tau.._k - \tau...) \quad (44)$$

The main effect terms, 2-factor interaction terms, and 3-factor interaction terms are confounded in 2, 1, and 0 of the replicates, respectively. Estimates of the differences of the τ_{ijk} may be obtained by computing

$$\hat{\tau}_{ijk} = \bar{\tau}_{ijk} + \frac{W - W'}{3(2W' + W)} \{[2(i\cdot\cdot)_\mathrm{I} - (i\cdot\cdot)_\mathrm{II} - (i\cdot\cdot)_\mathrm{III}]$$
$$+ [-(\cdot j\cdot)_\mathrm{I} + 2(\cdot j\cdot)_\mathrm{II} - (\cdot j\cdot)_\mathrm{III}]$$
$$+ [-(\cdot\cdot k)_\mathrm{I} - (\cdot\cdot k)_\mathrm{II} + 2(\cdot\cdot k)_\mathrm{III}]\}$$
$$+ \frac{W - W'}{3(W' + 2W)} \{[(ij\cdot)_\mathrm{I} + (ij\cdot)_\mathrm{II} - 2(ij\cdot)_\mathrm{III} - (i\cdot\cdot)_\mathrm{I} - (i\cdot\cdot)_\mathrm{II}$$
$$+ 2(i\cdot\cdot)_\mathrm{III} - (\cdot j\cdot)_\mathrm{I} - (\cdot j\cdot)_\mathrm{II} + 2(\cdot j\cdot)_\mathrm{III} + (\cdot\cdot\cdot)_\mathrm{I} + (\cdot\cdot\cdot)_\mathrm{II}$$
$$- 2(\cdot\cdot\cdot)_\mathrm{III}] + [(i\cdot k)_\mathrm{I} - 2(i\cdot k)_\mathrm{II} + (i\cdot k)_\mathrm{III} - (i\cdot\cdot)_\mathrm{I}$$
$$+ 2(i\cdot\cdot)_\mathrm{II} - (i\cdot\cdot)_\mathrm{III} - (\cdot\cdot k)_\mathrm{I} + 2(\cdot\cdot k)_\mathrm{II} - (\cdot\cdot k)_\mathrm{III} + (\cdot\cdot\cdot)_\mathrm{I}$$
$$- 2(\cdot\cdot\cdot)_\mathrm{II} + (\cdot\cdot\cdot)_\mathrm{III}] + [-2(\cdot jk)_\mathrm{I} + (\cdot jk)_\mathrm{II} + (\cdot jk)_\mathrm{III}$$
$$+ 2(\cdot j\cdot)_\mathrm{I} - (\cdot j\cdot)_\mathrm{II} - (\cdot j\cdot)_\mathrm{III} + 2(\cdot\cdot k)_\mathrm{I} - (\cdot\cdot k)_\mathrm{II} - (\cdot\cdot k)_\mathrm{III}$$
$$- 2(\cdot\cdot\cdot)_\mathrm{I} + (\cdot\cdot\cdot)_\mathrm{II} + (\cdot\cdot\cdot)_\mathrm{III}]\} \quad (45)$$

where τ_{ijk} is the observed mean of treatment (ijk).

This expression may be simplified somewhat by putting

$$\lambda = \frac{(W - W')}{3(2W' + W)}, \qquad \mu = \frac{(W - W')}{3(W' + 2W)}$$

and collecting terms, thus:

$$\hat{\tau}_{ijk} = \bar{\tau}_{ijk} + (\lambda - \mu)\{[+2(i\cdot\cdot)_{\mathrm{I}} - (i\cdot\cdot)_{\mathrm{II}} - (i\cdot\cdot)_{\mathrm{III}}]$$

$$+ [-(\cdot j\cdot)_{\mathrm{I}} + 2(\cdot j\cdot)_{\mathrm{II}} - (\cdot j\cdot)_{\mathrm{III}}]$$

$$+ [-(\cdot\cdot k)_{\mathrm{I}} - (\cdot\cdot k)_{\mathrm{II}} + 2(\cdot\cdot k)_{\mathrm{III}}]\}$$

$$- \mu\{[-(ij\cdot)_{\mathrm{I}} - (ij\cdot)_{\mathrm{II}} + 2(ij\cdot)_{\mathrm{III}}]$$

$$+ [-(i\cdot k)_{\mathrm{I}} + 2(i\cdot k)_{\mathrm{II}} - (i\cdot k)_{\mathrm{III}}]$$

$$+ [2(\cdot jk)_{\mathrm{I}} - (\cdot jk)_{\mathrm{II}} - (\cdot jk)_{\mathrm{III}}]\} \qquad (46)$$

The same formulas as for the prime case may easily be shown to hold for the variance of treatment differences. There follows a worked example.

23.10.4 A Worked Example

The yields for the 3-dimensional lattice for 27 treatments are given in Table 23.12.

TABLE 23.12 YIELDS OF 3-DIMENSIONAL LATTICE EXPERIMENT

Replicate I			Replicate II			Replicate III		
13.9 (212)	12.1 (112)	13.1 (312)	9.2 (131)	11.1 (111)	9.6 (121)	10.3 (133)	8.1 (131)	11.1 (132)
8.7 (213)	11.2 (313)	14.4 (113)	12.3 (221)	10.8 (211)	11.1 (231)	11.2 (113)	10.4 (112)	10.0 (111)
10.4 (333)	10.5 (133)	9.7 (233)	8.1 (233)	11.3 (223)	10.4 (213)	10.3 (331)	10.8 (333)	10.8 (332)
11.1 (311)	13.0 (211)	9.2 (111)	8.8 (322)	10.7 (332)	9.3 (312)	9.2 (232)	10.9 (231)	11.4 (233)
12.0 (232)	19.4 (132)	12.4 (332)	4.2 (132)	11.3 (122)	10.9 (112)	7.9 (223)	8.6 (222)	10.0 (221)
11.1 (131)	10.0 (231)	8.5 (331)	9.4 (212)	6.1 (232)	8.3 (222)	11.6 (121)	9.9 (122)	10.6 (123)
10.5 (322)	10.4 (222)	8.5 (122)	6.4 (113)	9.2 (123)	6.9 (133)	8.2 (311)	10.5 (313)	9.9 (312)
8.4 (123)	8.8 (323)	6.5 (223)	5.5 (313)	6.9 (333)	4.5 (323)	9.4 (212)	8.0 (213)	10.7 (211)
11.8 (321)	10.9 (121)	7.4 (221)	5.9 (321)	3.0 (311)	4.8 (331)	6.1 (321)	8.4 (323)	7.7 (322)

The computations are based on equations 45 and 46 and set out in order, each item being easily identified. The only difference between the formulas and the computed values is that totals rather than means are obtained. Thus the first three tables in each of the columns are 2-way tables, obtained by summing on the treatment digit omitted. The labeling of replicates is very important, as it provides the basis for combining the 2-way tables of sums (Table 23.13).

TABLE 23.13 COMPUTATIONS FOR 3-DIMENSIONAL LATTICE

		j		
i	1	2	3	
Rep I				
1	35.7	27.8	41.0	104.5
2	35.6	24.3	31.7	91.6
3	35.4	31.1	31.3	97.8
	106.7	83.2	104.0	293.9
Rep II				
1	28.4	30.1	20.3	78.8
2	30.6	31.9	25.3	87.8
3	17.8	19.2	22.4	59.4
	76.8	81.2	68.0	226.0
Rep III				
1	31.6	32.1	29.5	93.2
2	28.1	26.5	31.5	86.1
3	28.6	22.2	31.9	82.7
	88.3	80.8	92.9	262.0
2 III-I-II				
1	-0.9	6.3	-2.3	3.1
2	-10.0	-3.2	6.0	-7.2
3	4.0	-5.9	10.1	8.2
	-6.9	-2.8	13.8	4.1

		k		
j	1	2	3	
Rep I				
1	33.3	39.1	34.3	106.7
2	30.1	29.4	23.7	83.2
3	29.6	43.8	30.6	104.0
	93.0	112.3	88.6	293.9
Rep II				
1	24.9	29.6	22.3	76.8
2	27.8	28.4	25.0	81.2
3	25.1	21.0	21.9	68.0
	77.8	79.0	69.2	226.0
Rep III				
1	28.9	29.7	29.7	88.3
2	27.7	26.2	26.9	80.8
3	29.3	31.1	32.5	92.9
	85.9	87.0	89.1	262.0
2 I-II-III				
1	12.8	18.9	16.6	48.3
2	4.7	4.2	-4.5	4.4
3	4.8	35.5	6.8	47.1
	22.3	58.6	18.9	99.8

		i		
k	1	2	3	
Rep I				
1	31.2	30.4	31.4	93.0
2	40.0	36.3	36.0	112.3
3	33.3	24.9	30.4	88.6
	104.5	91.6	97.8	293.9
Rep II				
1	29.9	34.2	13.7	77.8
2	26.4	23.8	28.8	79.0
3	22.5	29.8	16.9	69.2
	78.8	87.8	59.4	226.0
Rep III				
1	29.7	31.6	24.6	85.9
2	31.4	27.2	28.4	87.0
3	32.1	27.3	29.7	89.1
	93.2	86.1	82.7	262.0
2 II-I-III				
1	-1.1	6.4	-28.6	-23.3
2	18.6	-15.9	-6.8	-41.3
3	-20.4	7.4	-26.3	-39.3
	-40.1	-2.1	-61.7	-103.9

I–III

j	1	2	3	
	18.4	2.4	11.1	31.9

2 II–I–III

j	1	2	3	
	−41.4	−1.6	−60.9	−103.9

II–I

k	1	2	3	
	−15.2	−33.3	−19.4	−67.9

2 III–I–II

k	1	2	3	
	1.0	−17.3	20.4	4.1

III–II

i	1	2	3	
	14.4	−1.7	23.3	36.0

2 I–III–II

i	1	2	3	
	37.0	9.3	53.5	99.8

Grand total = 781.9   Correction term = 7547.75

Replicate sum of squares:

$$\frac{293.9^2 + 226.0^2 + 262.0^2}{27} - CT = 85.48$$

Blocks component a:

$$\frac{1}{18}[18.4^2 + 2.4^2 + 11.1^2 + (-15.2)^2 + \cdots + (14.4)^2 + \cdots] - \frac{1}{54}[31.9^2 + (-67.9)^2 + (36.0)^2] = 163.16 - 128.22 = 34.94$$

Blocks component b:

$$\frac{1}{54}[(-41.4)^2 + \cdots + (1.0)^2 + \cdots + (37.0)^2 + \cdots] - \frac{1}{162}[(-103.9)^2 + (4.1)^2 + (99.8)^2] = 193.69 - 128.22 = 65.47$$

Blocks component c:

$$\frac{1}{18}[(-0.9)^2 + (6.3)^2 + \cdots + (10.1)^2 + (12.8)^2 + \cdots + (6.8)^2$$
$$+ (-1.1)^2 + \cdots + (-26.3)^2] - \frac{1}{54}[(3.1)^2 + (-7.2)^2 + (8.2)^2$$
$$+ (-6.9)^2 + (-2.8)^2 + (13.8)^2 + \cdots + (18.9)^2$$
$$+ (-23.3)^2 + \cdots + (-61.7)^2] + \frac{1}{162}[(4.1)^2 + (99.8)^2 + (-103.9)^2]$$
$$= 288.82 - 341.59 + 128.22 = 75.45$$

Treatment sum of squares: sum of squares between observed treatment totals

TABLE 23.14   ANALYSIS OF VARIANCE

Due to	df	Sum of Squares	Mean Square
Replicates	2	85.48	
Blocks			
Component a	6	34.94	
Component b	6	65.47	
Component c	12	75.45	
Total for blocks	24	175.86	7.328
Treatments	26	115.45	
Error	28	107.63	3.844
Total	80	484.42	

From the mean squares, we compute

$$w = 0.260, \qquad w' = 0.110$$

and, hence,

$$\lambda = 0.104, \qquad \mu = 0.079$$

and

$$\lambda - \mu = 0.025$$

To compute the adjustments we note that equation 46 is in terms of means, but it is simpler to adjust the observed treatment total. Since we have computed totals, for example, of $[2(i\cdot\cdot)_{\mathrm{I}} - (i\cdot\cdot)_{\mathrm{II}} - (i\cdot\cdot)_{\mathrm{III}}]$, and not means, the multiplier of the total is $(\lambda - \mu)/k^2$, and this gives the correction to the treatment mean. The correction to the total is therefore obtained by multiplying the total $[2(i\cdot\cdot)_{\mathrm{I}} - (i\cdot\cdot)_{\mathrm{II}} - (i\cdot\cdot)_{\mathrm{III}}]$, for example, by $3(\lambda - \mu)/k^2$. Similarly, to obtain the μ correction, we multiply the computed 2-way interaction tables by $3\mu/k$. Now $3(\lambda - \mu)/k^2 = (3 \times 0.025)/9 = 0.008$, and $3\mu/k = (3 \times 0.079)/3 = 0.079$, so that these are the multipliers for the corresponding tables. In this way we obtain the adjustments (Table 23.15).

TABLE 23.15   TABLE OF ADJUSTMENTS TO OBSERVED TREATMENT TOTALS

		j				k					i	
i	1	2	3	j	1	2	3	k	1	2	3
1	+0.07	−0.50	+0.18	1	−1.01	−1.49	−1.31	1	+0.09	−0.50	+2.26
2	+0.79	+0.25	−0.47	2	−0.47	−0.33	+0.36	2	+1.47	+1.26	+0.54
3	−0.32	+0.47	−0.80	3	−0.38	−2.80	−0.54	3	+1.61	−0.58	+2.08

i			j			k		
	1	+0.30		1	−0.33		1	+0.01
	2	+0.07		2	−0.01		2	−0.14
	3	+0.43		3	−0.49		3	+0.16

There are 6 correction terms for each total, those for (123), for example, being $-0.50 + 0.36 + 1.61 + 0.30 - 0.01 + 0.16$.

We may combine the i, j, k adjustments with the 2-way tables (Table 23.16).

TABLE 23.16 COMBINED TABLE OF ADJUSTMENTS

	j				k				i		
i	1	2	3	j	1	2	3	k	1	2	3
1	+0.37	−0.20	+0.48	1	−1.34	−1.82	−1.64	1	+0.10	−0.49	−2.27
2	+0.86	+0.32	−0.40	2	−0.38	−0.34	+0.35	2	+1.33	+1.12	+0.40
3	+0.11	+0.90	−0.37	3	−0.87	−3.29	−1.03	3	+1.77	−0.42	+2.24

The adjustment for treatment (123) is now $-0.20 + 0.35 + 1.77$, for example.

TABLE 23.17 TREATMENT TOTALS

111	30.3	29.43	211	34.5	33.53	311	22.3	23.34
112	33.4	33.28	212	32.7	32.86	312	32.3	30.99
113	32.0	32.50	213	27.1	25.90	313	27.2	27.91
121	32.1	31.62	221	29.7	29.15	321	23.8	26.59
122	29.7	30.49	222	27.3	28.40	322	27.0	27.96
123	28.2	30.12	223	35.7	25.95	323	21.7	25.19
131	28.4	28.11	231	32.0	30.24	331	23.6	24.63
132	34.7	33.22	232	27.3	24.73	332	33.9	30.64
133	27.7	28.92	233	29.2	27.35	333	28.1	28.94

Total 781.9   781.99

Variance of differences of treatment means:

The treatments having 2 digits in common

$$= \frac{2}{9}\left(\frac{1}{0.480} + \frac{4}{0.630} + \frac{4}{0.780}\right) = 3.013$$

The treatments having one digit in common

$$= \frac{2}{9}\left(\frac{2}{0.480} + \frac{5}{0.630} + \frac{2}{0.780}\right) = 3.259$$

The treatments having no digits in common

$$= \frac{2}{9}\left(\frac{3}{0.480} + \frac{3}{0.630} + \frac{3}{0.780}\right) = 3.302$$

Average variance of treatment differences

$$= \frac{2 \times 2}{26}\left(\frac{3}{0.480} + \frac{6}{0.630} + \frac{4}{0.780}\right) = \frac{4}{26}(20.902) = 3.216$$

REFERENCES AND READING

1. YATES, F. The recovery of inter-block information in variety trials arranged in three-dimensional lattices. *Ann. Eug.*, **9**, 136–156, 1939.
2. ROBBINS, H., and PITMAN, E. J. G. Application of the method of mixtures to quadratic forms in normal varieties. *Ann. Math. Stat.*, **20**, 552–560, 1949.
3. KEMPTHORNE, O., and FEDERER, W. T. The general theory of prime-power lattice designs. *Biometrics*, **4**, 54–79, 1949.
4. COX, G. M., ECKHARD, R. C., and COCHRAN, W. G. The analyses of lattice and triple lattice experiments in corn varietal tests. *Iowa Agr. Exp. Sta. Res. Bull.*, **281**, 1940.
5. HOMEYER, P. G., CLEM, M. A., and FEDERER, W. T. Punched card and calculating machine methods for analyzing lattice experiments including lattice squares and the cubic lattice. *Iowa Agr. Exp. Sta. Res. Bull.*, **347**, 1947.
6. CORNISH, E. A. The estimation of missing values in quasi-factorial designs. *Ann. Eug.*, **10**, 137–143, 1940.
7. CORNISH, E. A. The recovery of inter-block information in quasi-factorial designs with incomplete data. 1. Square, triple, and cubic lattices. *Australian Coun. Sci. Ind. Res. Bull.*, **158**, 1943.

FURTHER NOTES

In this and previous chapters, we have used the rule that, if w/w' is found to be less than unity in a particular experiment, the value of unity should be used. This is not strictly correct on the basis of the finite model, but we have conformed to the literature in the matter. The use of unity in such instances can possibly be justified on the basis of the effects of errors in the estimation of the weights. Under infinite model theory, of course, W' cannot be greater than W.

CHAPTER 24

Lattice Designs
with Two Restrictions

In Chapter 22 we described briefly designs for k^2 treatments, in which the randomization of the treatments was restricted in 2 ways, that the rows of the experimental material should contain specified groups of the treatments and also that the columns should contain specified groups. By rows and columns we mean the 2 orthogonal ways in which the experimental units are grouped, and, in a field experiment, they will correspond to rows and columns of plots in $k \times k$ squares. The purpose of the present chapter is to give a detailed discussion of such designs.

24.1 THE COMPLETELY BALANCED LATTICE SQUARE

We first consider the case when k is a prime, say, p. Then the $(p^2 - 1)$ treatment degrees of freedom may be partitioned into $(p + 1)$ sets of $(p - 1)$ degrees of freedom, denoted by $A, B, AB, AB^2, \cdots, AB^{p-1}$, where a and b are two p-level factors used to designate the treatments. Clearly in any one square we may confound any one of these sets of $(p - 1)$ degrees of freedom with rows, and any one with columns. If each of these sets of $(p - 1)$ degrees of freedom is confounded with the rows of one replicate and with the columns of one replicate, the set of $(p + 1)$ replicates is known as a completely balanced lattice square. The $(p + 1)$ replicates form a balanced design, in that every treatment occurs with every other in one row and also in one column. For example, with $p = 5$, we may have the following 3 replicates, and another 3 replicates obtained by interchanging rows and columns:

With rows:	A					AB					AB^3				
Confounded															
With columns:	B					AB^2					AB^4				
	00	01	02	03	04	00	41	32	23	14	00	21	42	13	34
	10	11	12	13	14	24	10	01	42	33	44	10	31	02	23
	20	21	22	23	24	43	34	20	11	02	33	04	20	41	12
	30	31	32	33	34	12	03	44	30	21	22	43	14	30	01
	40	41	42	43	44	31	22	13	04	40	11	32	03	24	40

The reader should verify the balanced property mentioned above. Formally there are several such designs, for we could use the following confounding, for example:

	Replicate					
	I	II	III	IV	V	VI
Confound with rows	A	AB	AB^2	AB^4	AB^3	B
Confound with columns	AB	B	AB^4	AB^3	A	AB^2

This second design is, however, of equal value with the first under the additive model, and the one can be obtained from the other by a permutation of the allocation of treatments to the symbols (ij).

The model which is assumed with such designs is

$$y_{ijk} = m + \tau_{ij} + r_k + \rho + \gamma + e_{ijk} \tag{1}$$

where i, j are the levels of the factors, k is the replicate number, m is a constant contribution, τ_{ij} is the contribution of treatment (ij), r_k is the effect of the kth replicate, ρ is an error common to the plots of a row in the replicate, γ is an error common to the plots of a column in the replicate, and e is an error individual to the plot. It is assumed that the ρ's, γ's, and e's are uncorrelated and distributed around zero with variances σ^2_r, σ^2_c, and σ^2, respectively.

This model may be reparametrized by the use of the symbols A, B, AB, $\cdots$, AB^{p-1}, with superscripts running from 0 to $p - 1$, as in all our discussions of prime-power factorial systems. The estimation of the new parameters is very simple, and we shall use the second design above for purposes of discussion. The effect A is confounded with rows in replicate I and with columns in replicate V and is unconfounded with rows or columns in the other replicates. When an effect is confounded with rows in a replicate, a comparison of the levels of the factor, say, $A_i - A_j$, is estimated in that replicate by the same comparison of the row means, and has an error containing the difference of 2 ρ's plus $\frac{1}{5}$ of (the sum of 5 e's minus the sum of 5 e's), and, therefore, has a variance of $\frac{2}{5}(\sigma^2 + 5\sigma^2_r)$. Similarly, when confounded in a replicate with columns, the estimate from that replicate will be the same function of the column means, and will have a variance of $\frac{2}{5}(\sigma^2 + 5\sigma^2_c)$. When unconfounded in a replicate, that replicate will give an estimate with a variance of $\frac{2}{5}\sigma^2$. If then $A_{\rm I}$, $A_{\rm II}$, $\cdots$, $A_{\rm VI}$ denotes the estimates of a particular comparison of the levels of the factor a in each of the 6 replicates, and if we know σ^2, σ^2_r, and σ^2_c, the best linear unbiased estimate of the comparison of the true yields from the whole experiment is

$$\hat{A} = \frac{W_r A_\mathrm{I} + W_c A_\mathrm{V} + W(A_\mathrm{II} + A_\mathrm{III} + A_\mathrm{IV} + A_\mathrm{VI})}{W_r + W_c + 4W} \qquad (2)$$

where

$$W_r = \frac{1}{\sigma^2 + 5\sigma^2{}_r}$$

and

$$W_c = \frac{1}{\sigma^2 + 5\sigma^2{}_c}$$

$$W = \frac{1}{\sigma^2}$$

$$\qquad (2a)$$

If we denote the total for the comparison over all replicates by A_T, this may be written

$$\hat{A} = \frac{A_T}{6} + \frac{(W_r - W)}{6(W_r + W_c + 4W)} (6A_\mathrm{I} - A_T)$$

$$+ \frac{(W_c - W)}{6(W_r + W_c + 4W)} (6A_\mathrm{V} - A_T) \qquad (3)$$

Similarly, for the best estimate of any B comparison, we have

$$\hat{B} = \frac{B_T}{6} + \frac{(W_r - W)}{6(W_r + W_c + 4W)} (6B_\mathrm{VI} - B_T)$$

$$+ \frac{(W_c - W)}{6(W_r + W_c + 4W)} (6B_\mathrm{II} - B_T) \qquad (4)$$

and so on. Combining the estimates of the effects and interactions, we find that the estimates of the treatment yields measured about the observed mean are very simply obtained by calculating a correction for each row and each column of the 6 squares, and adding to the observed mean the particular corrections for the rows and columns in which the constituent yields of the observed mean lie. The correction for any plots of a particular row is equal to

$$\frac{(W_r - W)}{30(W_r + W_c + 4W)} \left(\begin{array}{l} 6 \times \text{sum of row} - \text{sum of total yields for the} \\ \text{whole experiment of the treatments occurring in} \\ \text{that row} \end{array} \right)$$

and for a column is equal to

$$\frac{(W_c - W)}{30(W_r + W_c + 4W)} \left(\begin{array}{l} 6 \times \text{sum of column} - \text{sum of total yields for} \\ \text{the whole experiment of the treatments occur-} \\ \text{ring in that column} \end{array} \right)$$

In the case of a completely balanced $k \times k$ lattice square, k of course being a prime or a power of a prime, the corrections to be applied are: For a particular row,

$$\frac{(W_r - W)}{k(k + 1)[W_r + W_c + (k - 1)W]} \left[\begin{array}{l} (k + 1) \times \text{sum of row} - \text{sum} \\ \text{of total yields of treatments} \\ \text{in the row} \end{array} \right] \quad (5)$$

and, for a particular column,

$$\frac{(W_c - W)}{k(k + 1)[W_r + W_c + (k - 1)W]} \left[\begin{array}{l} (k + 1) \times \text{sum of column} - \\ \text{sum of total yields of treat-} \\ \text{ments in the column} \end{array} \right] \quad (6)$$

The above are corrections to be applied to the mean of the observed yields of the particular treatment. The corrections to the total of the observed yields of a treatment are obtained by multiplying them by $(k + 1)$.

If we put

$$\frac{(W - W_r)}{k[W_r + W_c + (k - 1)W]} = \lambda$$

and $\qquad\qquad\qquad\qquad\qquad\qquad\qquad\qquad\qquad\qquad$ (7)

$$\frac{(W - W_c)}{k[W_r + W_c + (k - 1)W]} = \mu$$

the total correction to the total of the observed yields is equal to

$\lambda[k \text{ (observed total)} + \text{(sum of all yields)}$

$\qquad - (k + 1)\text{(sum of all rows containing the treatments)}]$

$\qquad\qquad + \mu[k \text{ (observed total)} + \text{(sum of all yields)}$

$\qquad\qquad - (k + 1)\text{(sum of all columns containing the treatment)}] \quad (8)$

because every other treatment occurs in a row once with a particular treatment.

The analysis of variance may be calculated by noting that the quantities

$R_t = (k + 1) \times$ sum of row − sum of total yields of treatments occurring in the row

do not contain any treatment effects, but contain row errors and also column errors from the replicate in which the treatments in that row occupy a column, and the sum of squares within replicates has an expectation involving σ^2, σ^2_r, and σ^2_c. The quantities

$R_{ct} = (k - 1) \times$ sum of row $-$ sum of total yields of treatments occurring in the row over replicates in which this set of treatments does not lie entirely in one row or one column

contain no treatment effects or column errors, and the sum of squares over all rows within replicates of this quantity has an expectation involving σ^2 and σ^2_r. Similar considerations hold for the columns, in that the quantities

$C_t = (k + 1) \times$ sum of column $-$ sum of total yields of treatments occurring in that column

involve plot, row, and column errors, whereas the quantities

$C_{rt} = (k - 1) \times$ sum of column $-$ sum of total yields of treatments occurring in that column over replicates in which the set of treatments in the column do not lie entirely in one row or in one column

involve plot and column errors. Furthermore, the quantities are comparisons such that any R_t and C_{rt} are orthogonal as regards plot errors, and R_{ct} and C_t are orthogonal as regards plot errors. The sum of squares of deviations of the quantities R_t within replicates gives the sum of squares for rows eliminating treatments, and of R_{ct}, the sum of squares for rows eliminating columns and treatments, and likewise for the quantities C_t and C_{rt}.

We have, therefore, the two versions of the analysis of variance given in Table 24.1.

TABLE 24.1 STRUCTURE OF ANALYSIS OF VARIANCE FOR COMPLETELY BALANCED LATTICE SQUARE

Due to	df	Due to
Squares	k	Squares
Rows eliminating treatments	$k^2 - 1$	Rows eliminating columns and treatments
Columns eliminating row and treatments	$k^2 - 1$	Columns eliminating treatments
Treatments ignoring rows and columns	$k^2 - 1$	Treatments ignoring rows and columns
Error (within row and column)	$(k - 2)(k^2 - 1)$	Error (within row and column)
	$\overline{(k + 1)k^2 - 1}$	

These two forms of the analysis of variance may be obtained directly from general linear hypothesis theory regarding the row and column errors as fixed constants. They are, however, simply represented by the use of the factorial notation, in which we exhibit clearly the orthogonality of the sums of squares. For the case of the design we are discussing, namely:

				Square			
		I	II	III	IV	V	VI
Confounded with rows		A	AB	AB^2	AB^4	AB^3	B
Confounded with columns		AB	B	AB^4	AB^3	A	AB^2

the left-hand analysis of variance may be written as in Table 24.2.

TABLE 24.2

		df
Squares		5
Rows eliminating treatments		
A	[I v rest]	4
B	[VI v rest]	4
AB	[II v rest]	4
AB^2	[III v rest]	4
AB^3	[V v rest]	4
AB^4	[IV v rest]	4
		24
Columns eliminating rows and treatments		
A	[V v II, III, IV, VI]	4
B	[II v I, III, IV, V]	4
AB	[I v III, IV, V, VI]	4
AB^2	[VI v I, II, IV, V]	4
AB^3	[IV v I, II, III, VI]	4
AB^4	[III v I, II, V, VI]	4
		24
Treatments: $(A, B, AB, AB^2, AB^3, AB^4)$		24
Error		
$A \times$ II, III, IV, VI		12
$B \times$ I, III, IV, V		12
etc.		72
Total		149

The right-hand analysis of variance is given in Table 24.3.

TABLE 24.3

Squares	df
Squares	5 as in other analysis

Rows eliminating columns and treatments

		df	
A	[I v II, III, IV, VI]	4	
B	[VI v I, III, IV, V]	4	
AB	[II v III, IV, V, VI	4	
AB^2	[III v I, II, IV, V]	4	24
AB^3	[V v I, II, III, VI]	4	
AB^4	[IV v I, II, V, VI]	4	

Columns eliminating treatments

		df	
A	[V v rest]	4	
B	[II v rest]	4	
AB	[I v rest]	4	
AB^2	[VI v rest]	4	24
AB^3	[IV v rest]	4	
AB^4	[II v rest]	4	

	df	
Treatments	24	as in other analysis
Error	72	

	df
Total	149

A quantity such as A[V v rest] is to be interpreted as the interaction of the A effect with replicate V and replicates I, II, III, IV, and VI lumped together; a quantity A[I v II, III, IV, VI] as the interaction of the A effect with replicate I and replicates II, III, IV, and VI lumped together.

The necessary quantities are simply tabulated, given the experimental yields arranged according to the field plan. The steps in the computational procedure are:

1. Compute the row and column totals for each square and place at corresponding margins.

2. Compute the totals for each treatment over the whole experiment.

3. Form at each row margin $(k + 1) \times$ row total − total of all treatments occurring in the row: call these R_t.

4. Also form at row margin: $k \times$ row total + total of column with same treatments in another square − total of all treatments occurring in the row: call these R_{ct}.

5. Obtain likewise for columns the quantities C_t.

6. Obtain likewise for columns the quantities C_{rt}.

7. Obtain sum of squares for rows eliminating treatments as the sum of squares within squares (i.e., replicates) of the quantities R_t with a divisor of $k^2(k + 1)$.

8. Obtain the sum of squares for columns eliminating rows and treatments, as the sum of squares within squares of the quantities C_{rt}, with a divisor of $k^2(k-1)$.

9. Obtain likewise the sum of squares for columns eliminating treatments from the C_t.

10. Obtain the sum of squares for rows eliminating columns and treatments from the R_{ct}.

11. Obtain the sum of squares for squares and treatments and error in the usual way, these being the same for both analyses of variance.

The computational procedure given by Yates,[1] and also described with a worked example by Cochran and Cox,[2] is somewhat simpler computationally but does not exhibit clearly the structure of the analysis.

24.1.1   The Estimation of the Weights

In the present case we must find 3 weights:

$$ W = \frac{1}{\sigma^2}, \quad W_r = \frac{1}{\sigma^2 + k\sigma^2_r}, \quad \text{and} \quad W_c = \frac{1}{\sigma^2 + k\sigma^2_c} $$

The expectation of the within-row-and-column error mean square E, say, is σ^2, so that W is estimated by $1/\mathsf{E}$. The expectation of the sum of squares for rows eliminating columns and treatments R, say, is found in the usual way to be equal to $\sigma^2 + \left(\dfrac{k-1}{k}\right) k\sigma^2_r$, as may be noted by using the formula of the previous chapter and regarding rows as blocks (ignoring the square in which an effect is confounded with columns). Similarly, the expectation of the mean square for columns eliminating rows and treatments, C, say, is equal to $\sigma^2 + \left(\dfrac{k-1}{k}\right) k\sigma^2_c$.

As estimates for W_r and W_c, we may then use

$$ w_r = \frac{k-1}{k\mathsf{R} - \mathsf{E}} $$

and

$$ w_c = \frac{k-1}{k\mathsf{C} - \mathsf{E}} \tag{9} $$

so that

$$ \lambda = \frac{(\mathsf{R} - \mathsf{E})(k\mathsf{C} - \mathsf{E})}{(k-1)(k^2\mathsf{RC} - \mathsf{E}^2)} $$

and

$$ \mu = \frac{(\mathsf{C} - \mathsf{E})(k\mathsf{R} - \mathsf{E})}{(k-1)(k^2\mathsf{RC} - \mathsf{E})^2} \tag{10} $$

24.1.2 The Variance of Treatment Comparisons

The variance of a treatment comparison may be obtained by expressing the comparison in terms of the symbols A, B, AB, etc. Because each effect and interaction is equally confounded, namely, once with rows and once with columns, the variance of any effect or interaction comparison, of the form $A_i - A_j$ or $AB_i - AB_j$, etc., is

$$\frac{2}{k}\left[\frac{1}{W_r + W_c + (k-1)W}\right]$$

and the variance of any treatment difference is, therefore,

$$\frac{2}{W_r + W_c + (k-1)W} \tag{11}$$

and this is also the average variance of treatment comparisons. This variance is estimated by $\left(\dfrac{2E}{k+1}\right)(1 + k\lambda + k\mu)$.

The completely balanced lattice square may be analyzed as a design with $(k+1)$ randomized blocks of k^2 plots, for the following relations hold:

1. The expectation of the mean square for rows eliminating columns and treatments is $\sigma^2 + \left(\dfrac{k^2}{k+1}\right)\sigma^2{}_r + \left(\dfrac{1}{k+1}\right)\sigma^2{}_c$.

2. The expectation of the randomized block analysis error mean square, that is, of the mean square obtained by pooling the sums of squares for rows eliminating columns and treatments for columns eliminating treatments, and for error (within row and column), is

$$\sigma^2 + \left(\frac{k}{k+1}\right)\sigma^2{}_r + \left(\frac{k}{k+1}\right)\sigma^2{}_c$$

3. The expectation of the mean square for treatments ignoring rows and columns where the τ_{ij}'s are true treatment yields is

$$\sigma^2 + \left(\frac{k}{k+1}\right)\sigma^2{}_r + \left(\frac{k}{k+1}\right)\sigma^2{}_c + \frac{1}{(k-1)}\sum_{ij}(\tau_{ij} - \tau..)^2$$

The reader should have little difficulty verifying these statements, by examining the constituents of the analysis of variance in factorial form. It will also be seen that the error sum of squares is homogeneous. The whole experiment may then be analyzed as one in complete randomized blocks.

The efficiency of the lattice square design to the complete randomized block design is then

$$\frac{\dfrac{2}{k+1}\left(\sigma^2 + \dfrac{k}{k+1}\sigma^2{}_r + \dfrac{k}{k+1}\sigma^2{}_c\right)}{\left(\dfrac{2}{\dfrac{1}{\sigma^2+k\sigma^2{}_r} + \dfrac{1}{\sigma^2+k\sigma^2{}_c} + \dfrac{k-1}{\sigma^2}}\right)}$$

or

$$\frac{1}{(k+1)^2}\left(\frac{k-1}{W} + \frac{1}{W_r} + \frac{1}{W_c}\right)[(k-1)W + W_r + W_c] \quad (12)$$

This may be evaluated, of course, in several ways, i.e., by estimating W, W_r, and W_c and inserting the estimated values, or by comparing the mean variance of treatment differences for the lattice with the mean variance of treatments actually obtained in a randomized block analysis. The methods will not give identical results because of the use of the two forms of the analysis of variance to obtain estimates of the weights.

24.1.3 The Effects of Inaccuracies in the Weights

To estimate the effect of inaccuracies in the weights, it is necessary to assume normality of all the errors.

An examination of the loss in information in the case of the completely balanced lattice square is, however, rendered difficult by the fact that there are 3 weights, W_r, W_c, and W, and that the estimates we have used for σ^2, $(\sigma^2 + p\sigma^2{}_r)$, and $(\sigma^2 + p\sigma^2{}_c)$ are not independent. The dependence between $\hat{\sigma}^2$ and $(\sigma^2 \stackrel{\wedge}{+} p\sigma^2{}_r)$, say, is easily obtained, but the dependence between these and $(\sigma^2 \stackrel{\wedge}{+} p\sigma^2{}_c)$ is very complicated. We rely, therefore, on an investigation made for the case of the partially balanced lattice square described below. This case is easy, since, from Cochran's theorem, the partition into the analysis of variance shows the statistical independence of the mean squares under the normality assumptions. It was shown by Yates [1] that the loss of information is negligible compared with the gains in efficiency obtained by the use of the lattice square design and analysis.

24.2 THE DESIGN AND ANALYSIS OF OTHER LATTICE SQUARES

There is no difficulty in extending the above method of design and analysis to a lattice square design that is not balanced: that is, one in which each effect and interaction is not confounded equally frequently with rows and columns. It is possible to have all possibilities from a set of 2 squares only to a completely balanced set of $k + 1$, when k is a prime or a power of a prime.

As an example, we will discuss the use of only 2 squares. Such an unbalanced lattice square design could well be of value for the comparison of 49 treatments, though the sensitivity (cf. Chapter 12) of such an experiment would be rather low. We would plan the experiment so that no effect or interaction is confounded with rows in one replicate and *also* with columns in another replicate, for reasons that are fairly obvious (cf. equation 40 of Chapter 23). Suppose then that we confound effects and interactions in the 2 squares as follows:

	Square	
	I	II
Confound with rows	A	AB
Confound with columns	B	AB^2

For the case of k equal to a prime the design may be written out very easily, and for the case of k equal to a power of a prime one may take any 4 languages of the completely orthogonalized $k \times k$ Latin square. The adjustments to a treatment total consist of one for each row and column in which the treatment lies:

For each row, the adjustment is

$$- \frac{(W - W_r)}{k(W + W_r)} R_{ct} \tag{13}$$

and, for each column, the adjustment is

$$- \frac{(W - W_c)}{k(W + W_c)} C_{rt} \tag{14}$$

where

$R_{ct} = 2 \times$ sum of row $-$ sum of total yields of the treatments in the row $\tag{15}$

and

$C_{rt} = 2 \times$ sum of column $-$ sum of total yields of the treatments in the column $\tag{16}$

It should be noted that, in this design, an effect or interaction confounded with rows (or columns) in one square is completely unconfounded in the other square. (This is the reason why we use subscripts of c and t and of r and t, respectively.) As a result, only one form of the analysis of variance is necessary: namely, that given in Table 24.4. The sum of squares for rows eliminating treatments is the sum of squares within squares of the quantities R_{ct}, divided by $2k$, and for columns eliminating treatments is the sum of squares within replicates of the C_{rt}, divided by $2k$.

TABLE 24.4   STRUCTURE OF ANALYSIS OF VARIANCE FOR DESIGN IN TEXT

Due to	df	Expectation of Mean Square
Squares	1	
Rows eliminating treatments	$2(k-1)$	$\sigma^2 + \frac{1}{2}k\sigma^2_r$
Columns eliminating treatments	$2(k-1)$	$\sigma^2 + \frac{1}{2}k\sigma^2_c$
Treatments	$k^2 - 1$	
Error (within rows and columns)	$(k-3)(k-1)$	σ^2
Total	$2k^2 - 1$	

The factor of $\frac{1}{2}$ in the expectation of mean squares arises because each effect or interaction confounded with rows (or columns) is unconfounded in the other square. The weights are estimated by equating observed mean squares to their expectations.

The variance of the estimated difference of 2 treatments depends on their relative positions in the experiment, and the various values are:

In a row together:

$$\frac{2}{k}\left(\frac{1}{W+W_r} + \frac{2}{W+W_c} + \frac{k-3}{2W}\right)$$

In a column together:

$$\frac{2}{k}\left(\frac{2}{W+W_r} + \frac{1}{W+W_c} + \frac{k-3}{2W}\right) \qquad (17)$$

Not together in a row or column:

$$\frac{2}{k}\left(\frac{2}{W+W_r} + \frac{2}{W+W_c} + \frac{k-4}{2W}\right)$$

and the average variance of all estimated differences is equal to

$$\frac{2}{(k+1)}\left(\frac{2}{W+W_r} + \frac{2}{W+W_c} + \frac{k-3}{2W}\right) \qquad (18)$$

As a more complicated case, suppose we have 3 replicates with the following confounding (such a case might arise, for instance, if several replicates were removed by some experimental hazard from a completely balanced design):

	Square		
	I	II	III
Confound with rows	A	AB	B
Confound with columns	B	AB^2	AB^3

The adjustments to a treatment total will consist of an adjustment for each row and column containing the treatment:

For any row, the treatments of which do not occur entirely in a column of another replicate, the adjustment is

$$- \frac{(W - W_r)}{k(2W + W_r)} R_t \tag{19}$$

For any row, the treatments of which occur in a column of another replicate, the adjustment is

$$- \frac{(W - W_r)}{k(W + W_c + W_r)} R_t \tag{20}$$

For any column, the treatments of which do not occur entirely in a row of another replicate, the adjustment is

$$- \frac{(W - W_c)}{k(2W + W_c)} C_t \tag{21}$$

For any column, the treatments of which occur entirely in a row of another replicate, the adjustment is

$$- \frac{(W - W_c)}{k(W + W_c + W_r)} C_t \tag{22}$$

where

$R_t = 3 \times$ row total $-$ the sum of the total yields of the treatments in the row $\tag{23}$

$C_t = 3 \times$ column total $-$ the sum of the total yields of the treatments in the column $\tag{24}$

In some cases the quantity R_t will contain column effects, namely, when its divisor involves W_c, and, similarly, some of the C_t's will contain row effects, when the divisor contains W_r. For the design we are discussing, the 2 forms of the analysis of variance will be necessary as in Table 24.1. The details of this analysis are quite mechanical in the light of the formulation we use. Finally, for the variances of treatment differences, we have the following expressions:

For 2 treatments occuring together both in a row and a column:

$$\frac{2}{k}\left(\frac{2}{2W + W_r} + \frac{2}{2W + W_c} + \frac{k - 4}{3W}\right)$$

For 2 treatments occurring together in a row only:

$$\frac{2}{k}\left(\frac{1}{W + W_r + W_c} + \frac{1}{2W + W_r} + \frac{2}{2W + W_c} + \frac{k - 4}{3W}\right)$$

For 2 treatments occurring together in a column only:

$$\frac{2}{k}\left(\frac{1}{W + W_r + W_c} + \frac{2}{2W + W_r} + \frac{1}{2W + W_c} + \frac{k - 4}{3W}\right) \quad (25)$$

and for 2 treatments not occurring together in a row or a column:

$$\frac{2}{k}\left(\frac{1}{W + W_r + W_c} + \frac{2}{2W + W_r} + \frac{2}{2W + W_c} + \frac{k - 5}{3W}\right)$$

The mean variance of all treatment differences is

$$\frac{2}{k + 1}\left(\frac{1}{W + W_r + W_c} + \frac{2}{2W + W_r} + \frac{2}{2W + W_c} + \frac{k - 4}{3W}\right)$$

The validity of analyzing a lattice square experiment as an experiment in complete randomized blocks may be examined as in previous cases. If an effect (or interaction) with $(k - 1)$ degrees of freedom is confounded with rows in n_r replicates and with columns in n_c replicates and is unconfounded in n_u replicates, it is found that the expectation of the mean square for the interaction of that effect with all replicates, which is based on $(r - 1)(k - 1)$ degrees of freedom, r being the total number of replicates, is

$$\sigma^2 + \frac{n_r}{r} k\sigma^2_r + \frac{n_c}{r} k\sigma^2_c$$

which is equal to the expectation of the mean square for the effect or interaction apart from a term involving the true effect. (In a sense, this is a trivially obvious property of the designs we are discussing.) Thus, we have the same situation as in the designs with one restriction: that the expectation of the treatment sum of squares is equal to the expectation of the error sum of squares if the treatments have no effects. Unless, however, the design is completely balanced, i.e., n_r equal to n_c

and constant for all effects and interactions, the error mean square is not homogeneous under the assumed model. The lack of homogeneity need cause no concern in the testing of the hypothesis that treatments have no effect, and probably also may be ignored in the testing of comparisons of 2 unadjusted treatment means.

It is possible to obtain what is known as a semibalanced lattice square design for k^2 treatments, if k is a prime or a power of a prime which is odd. In this design, each effect or interaction is confounded in one only of the $(k + 1)/2$ replicates or squares. In that case, the mean variance of treatment comparisons is

$$\frac{2}{k+1}\left[\frac{k+1}{2\left[W_r+\left(\frac{k-1}{2}\right)W\right]}+\frac{k+1}{2\left[W_c+\left(\frac{k-1}{2}\right)W\right]}\right] \quad (26)$$

If 2 treatments occur together in a row, the variance of their estimated difference is

$$\frac{2}{k}\left[\frac{k-1}{2\left[W_r+\left(\frac{k-1}{2}\right)W\right]}+\frac{k+1}{2\left[W_c+\left(\frac{k-1}{2}\right)W\right]}\right]$$

and, if they occur together in a column, the variance of their estimated difference is

$$\frac{2}{k}\left[\frac{k+1}{2\left[W_r+\left(\frac{k-1}{2}\right)W\right]}+\frac{k-1}{2\left[W_c+\left(\frac{k-1}{2}\right)W\right]}\right] \quad (27)$$

The analysis is similar to the previous cases discussed, especially the first unbalanced design above.

The comparison of particular lattice square designs with complete randomized blocks may be performed by the usual method of comparing the mean variance of treatment differences by the lattice square analysis and by the randomized block analysis.

24.3 THE NON-PRIME CASE

Suppose we have k^2 treatments where k is not a prime or a power of a prime. Then we may, as in the case of triple lattice arrangements described in the previous chapter, arrange the k^2 treatments in a $k \times k$

Latin square, and, in some cases (e.g., $k = 12$), we may be able to superimpose Greek letters to give a Graeco-Latin square. This square gives,
as the case may be, 3, 4 (or, if letters of further alphabets can be superimposed retaining the Latin square property, more) orthogonal classifications into k groups of k treatments. Suppose these groupings are denoted by α, β, γ, δ. Then we may make up a square design as follows:

	Square			
	I	II	III	IV
Confound with rows	α	β	γ	δ
Confound with columns	β	γ	δ	α

Such a design exists for k equal to 12. For some values of k, for example,
k equal to 6 and equal to 10, only 3 orthogonal classifications can be
obtained, say, α (= rows of square), β (= columns of square), and γ
(= letters of square), and, in these cases, we may use multiples of a
basic set of 3 replicates:

	Square		
	I	II	III
Confound with rows	α	β	γ
Confound with columns	β	γ	α

We can, of course, use any number of replicates providing each of the
3 types of confounding are represented, though, in general, it will be
better to use the 3 replicates with equal frequencies.

The analysis of this design is very similar to the analysis of the triple
lattice. The true treatment yield is denoted by τ_{ijk}, i denoting the α
group, j the β group, and k the γ group in which it lies. We use the
identity

$$\tau_{ijk} = \tau_{\ldots} + (\tau_{i..} - \tau_{\ldots}) + (\tau_{.j.} - \tau_{\ldots}) + (\tau_{..k} - \tau_{\ldots})$$

$$+ (\tau_{ijk} - \tau_{i..} - \tau_{.j.} - \tau_{..k} + 2\tau_{\ldots})$$

The component $(\tau_{i..} - \tau_{\ldots})$ is confounded with rows in square I and
with columns in square III, so that, with

$$W_r = \frac{1}{\sigma^2 + k\sigma^2_r}, \quad W_c = \frac{1}{\sigma^2 + k\sigma^2_c}, \quad \text{and} \quad W = \frac{1}{\sigma^2}$$

the best estimate of $(\tau_{i..} - \tau_{\ldots})$ is

$$\frac{W_r[(i\cdot\cdot) - (\cdot\cdot\cdot)]_\text{I} + W[(i\cdot\cdot) - (\cdot\cdot\cdot)]_\text{II} + W_c[(i\cdot\cdot) - (\cdot\cdot\cdot)]_\text{III}}{W_r + W_c + W} \quad (28)$$

or

$$(i\cdot\cdot)_T - (\cdot\cdot\cdot)_T - \frac{(W - W_r)}{3(W_r + W_c + W)} \{2[(i\cdot\cdot) - (\cdot\cdot\cdot)]_\text{I}$$

$$- [(i\cdot\cdot) - (\cdot\cdot\cdot)]_\text{II} - [(i\cdot\cdot) - (\cdot\cdot\cdot)]_\text{III}\}$$

$$- \frac{(W - W_c)}{3(W_r + W_c + W)} \{2[(i\cdot\cdot) - (\cdot\cdot\cdot)]_\text{III} - [(i\cdot\cdot) - (\cdot\cdot\cdot)]_\text{II}$$

$$- [(i\cdot\cdot) - (\cdot\cdot\cdot)]_\text{I}\} \quad (29)$$

where $[(i\cdot\cdot) - (\cdot\cdot\cdot)]_T$, $[(i\cdot\cdot) - (\cdot\cdot\cdot)]_\text{I}$, etc., are the observed means on a per plot basis of $(\tau_i\cdot\cdot - \tau\cdot\cdot\cdot)$ for the 3 replicates, for replicate I, etc. Similar arguments apply to the other components.

The adjusted yield as a total of 3 plots may be obtained by adding to the unadjusted treatment total a correction for each row and for each column of each square. If we put

$$\lambda = \frac{(W - W_r)}{k(W_r + W_c + W)} \quad \text{and} \quad \mu = \frac{(W - W_c)}{k(W_r + W_c + W)} \quad (30)$$

the correction for each of the plots of a row is $-\lambda R_t$

$$\text{and for each plot of a column is } -\mu C_t \quad (31)$$

where

$R_t = 3 \times$ row total $-$ the sum of the total yields of the treatments occurring in the row (32)

and

$C_t = 3 \times$ column total $-$ the sum of the total yields of the treatments occurring in the column (33)

The analysis of variance has the structure given in Table 24.5.

TABLE 24.5 STRUCTURE OF ANALYSES OF VARIANCE FOR UNBALANCED LATTICE SQUARE

Due to	df	Due to
Squares	2	Squares
Rows eliminating columns	$3(k - 1)$	Rows eliminating columns and treatments
Columns eliminating rows and treatments	$3(k - 1)$	Columns eliminating treatments
Treatments	$k^2 - 1$	Treatments
Error (within row and column)	$2(k - 1)(k - 2)$	Error (within row and column)
Total	$3k^2 - 1$	Total

The sums of squares are obtained in the same way as for the balanced case described above, it being necessary to form quantities R_{ct} and C_{rt} defined analogously, the divisors being $4k$ for rows eliminating columns and treatments or for columns eliminating rows and treatments, and $6k$ for rows eliminating treatments or columns eliminating treatments. The expectation of the mean square, R, say, for rows eliminating columns and treatments is $(\sigma^2 + \frac{1}{2}k\sigma^2_r)$, and, for columns eliminating rows and treatments, C, say, is $(\sigma^2 + \frac{1}{2}k\sigma^2_c)$. As estimates for the weights, then, we may use $w = 1/E$, E being the error mean square, $w_r = 1/(2R - E)$ and $w_c = 1/(2C - E)$.

The mean variance of treatment comparisons may be obtained by noting the following variances:

$$\text{var}\,(\hat{\tau}_{i\cdot\cdot} - \hat{\tau}_{i'\cdot\cdot}) = \text{var}\,(\hat{\tau}_{\cdot j\cdot} - \hat{\tau}_{\cdot j'\cdot}) = \text{var}\,(\hat{\tau}_{\cdot\cdot k} - \hat{\tau}_{\cdot\cdot k'})$$

$$= \frac{2}{k(W_r + W_c + W)} \tag{34}$$

and

$$\text{var}\,[(\hat{\tau}_{ijk} - \hat{\tau}_{i\cdot\cdot} - \hat{\tau}_{\cdot j\cdot} - \hat{\tau}_{\cdot\cdot k} + 2\hat{\tau}_{\cdot\cdot\cdot})$$

$$- (\hat{\tau}_{i'j'k'} - \hat{\tau}_{i'\cdot\cdot} - \hat{\tau}_{\cdot j'\cdot} - \hat{\tau}_{\cdot k'\cdot} + 2\hat{\tau}_{\cdot\cdot\cdot})]$$

$$= \frac{2}{3kW}\,(k-3); \quad i \neq i', j \neq j', k \neq k'$$

$$= \frac{2}{3kW}\,(k-2); \quad \begin{cases} i = i', j \neq j', k \neq k' \\ i \neq i', j = j', k \neq k' \\ i \neq i', j \neq j', k = k' \end{cases} \tag{35}$$

It follows, by simple substitution, that

$$\text{var}\,(\hat{\tau}_{ijk} - \hat{\tau}_{i'j'k'})$$

$$= \frac{2}{k}\left(\frac{2}{W_r + W_c + W} + \frac{k-2}{3W}\right); \quad \begin{cases} i = i', j \neq j', k \neq k' \\ i \neq i', j = j', k \neq k' \\ i \neq i', j \neq j', k = k' \end{cases}$$

$$= \frac{2}{k}\left(\frac{3}{W_r + W_c + W} + \frac{k-3}{3W}\right); \quad i \neq i', j \neq j', k \neq k' \tag{36}$$

In the comparisons of a particular treatment with all the others, there will be $3(k-1)$ of the upper type and $(k-1)(k-2)$ of the lower type, so that the mean variance of treatment comparisons is

$$\frac{2}{k+1}\left(\frac{3}{W_r + W_c + W} + \frac{k-2}{3W}\right) \tag{37}$$

a result identical with the prime case.

24.4 DESIGNS WITH 2-RESTRICTIONS WHICH ARE NOT SQUARE

The notion of double confounding, which was present in Chapter 15, may be used to develop a group of designs for p^n treatments, p being a prime or a power of a prime, the replicate having a rectangular pattern of the form p^r plots by p^s plots, where $r + s = n$. There are obviously many cases, and it is possible and only worth while to give one example. No aspect of the design or analysis will be unfamiliar in the light of the material of the present and previous chapters.

Suppose then that we have 32 treatments and wish to use a design with 2 restrictions. A correspondence of the 32 treatments to the case of 5 factors each at 2 levels, say, a, b, c, d, e, is set up. Any 1 replicate can consist of a rectangular pattern of 8 plots by 4 plots or 16 plots by 2 plots. In the case of an 8×4 arrangement, we confound a set of 7 degrees of freedom with rows and a set of 3 degrees of freedom with columns or vice-versa. For example, with field plots whose relative dimensions are 1 to 5, it might be advantageous to have replicates of relative dimensions 8 to 20 by such an arrangement. The following 3 replicates are such that each effect or interaction is unconfounded with rows or columns in at least 1 replicate:

I   Confound with rows: A, B, AB, C, AC, BC, ABC

   Confound with columns: D, E, DE

II   Confound with rows: $AB, AC, BC, AE, BE, CE, ABCE$

   Confound with columns: ACD, BD, ABC

III   Confound with rows: $A, BE, ABE, CD, ACD, BCDE, ABCDE$

   Confound with columns: AE, BDE, ABD

In this case a model consisting of a mean, treatment effect, row error, column error, and treatment error would be used, and there would be 3 weights:

$$W = \frac{1}{\sigma^2}, \qquad W_r = \frac{1}{\sigma^2 + 4\sigma^2_r}, \qquad W_c = \frac{1}{\sigma^2 + 8\sigma^2_c}$$

The analysis, although rather intricate computationally, may be obtained by an approach identical with that used for lattice squares.

The enumeration of designs will be greatly facilitated by the use of factor groups. We may note, for instance, that, if unit elements are added to the confounded effects and interactions, 2 groups are obtained, one for rows and one for columns and that the product of these groups gives the whole group of effects and interactions together with a unit element.

24.5 FURTHER DESIGNS

There is a group of designs for p^3 treatments, where p is a prime or a power of a prime which is of some interest and value. They consist of blocks of p plots, each block being arranged according to a lattice square pattern, and are analogous to split-plot experiments. With the usual factorial notation, the scheme shown in Table 24.6 may be used.

TABLE 24.6

Replicate	Confounded with Rows	Columns	Lattice Square Plots Split for
I	A	B	C
II	C	A	B
III	B	C	A

Information will be of 4 types:

1. Interrow with variance proportional to $W_r = \dfrac{1}{\sigma^2{}_s + k\sigma^2 + k^2\sigma^2{}_r}$

2. Intercolumn with variance proportional to $W_c = \dfrac{1}{\sigma^2{}_s + k\sigma^2 + k^2\sigma^2{}_c}$

3. Intrarow and column with variance proportional to $W = \dfrac{1}{\sigma^2 + k\sigma^2{}_s}$

4. Intrawhole plots with variance proportional to $W_s = \dfrac{1}{\sigma^2{}_s}$

With such a design the variance of the A, B, and C effects will be $1/p^2(W_r + W_c + W_s)$ the variance of the interactions AB, AB^2, AB^3, AB^4, AC, AC^2, AC^3, AC^4, BC, BC^2, BC^3, BC^4, etc., will be $1/p^2(W + 2W_s)$, and, for all interactions involving 3 factors, the variance will be $1/p^2(3W_s)$. The mean variance of varietal comparisons will be

$$\frac{2}{31}\left(\frac{3}{W_r + W_c + W_s} + \frac{12}{W + 2W_s} + \frac{16}{3W_s}\right) \qquad (38)$$

The analysis will follow the general lines of the present and previous chapters. The weights for row comparisons, column comparisons, whole-plot and split-plot comparisons may be obtained from:

1. The mean square for rows eliminating varieties and columns and whole plots, which is obtained from the comparison of main effects in

squares in which they are confounded with rows with the same main effects in squares in which they are unconfounded with rows, columns, or whole plots.

2. The mean square for columns, eliminating varieties and rows and whole plots obtained likewise.

3. The error mean square for whole plots, obtained from the comparison of 2-factor interactions in the squares in which they are confounded with whole plots with the same interactions in the other 2 squares in which they are unconfounded.

4. The split-plot error mean square, obtained from the comparison of 2-factor interactions among squares in which they are unconfounded, and the interaction of the 3-factor interactions with the 3 squares.

This design appears to be eminently suited for corn breeding work in which the basic plot is long and narrow. It is customary to use plots of size 2 by 10 hills, and the arrangement of p of these (for small p) in a whole plot would result in a whole plot that is more or less square, and the full advantages of the Latin square control of row and column effects would be utilizable.

Alternative to the above split-plot design for p^3 varieties, we may, as Yates[3] pointed out, divide the varieties into p groups of p^2 varieties and test each group of p^2 varieties with $p \times p$ lattice squares, of which only 2 are absolutely necessary for each group. The division into p groups of p^2 varieties may be made by choosing one effect or interaction to be confounded with groups in each replicate, and a large number of possible groupings are available. If the pseudofactors are denoted by a, b, c, the possible replicates are obtained by choosing one effect or interaction to be confounded with squares and other interactions to be confounded with rows and columns within squares: If the factors each have 5 levels, for example, Table 24.7 gives 9 suitable replicates:

TABLE 24.7

Confounded with

Squares	Rows	Columns
A	B	C
A	BC	BC^2
A	BC^3	BC^4
B	C	A
B	AC	AC^2
B	AC^3	AC^4
C	A	B
C	AB	AB^2
C	AB^3	AB^4

This table could be extended (1) by interchanging rows and columns and (2) by confounding between squares each of the possible 31 effects and interactions. The minimum number of replicates that must be used is 4, whatever the value of p, but such a design would have a low relative efficiency. Information in such a design consists of:

1. Among squares.
2. Among rows within squares.
3. Among columns within squares.
4. Within row and columns.

and the relative efficiency may be evaluated in terms of the variances of these types of information. As stated by Yates,[3] the efficiency factor of the design given above (the ratio of the mean variance of varietal comparison in complete randomized blocks to the mean variance in the design, when information other than within rows and columns is assumed to be valueless, and when the error variance is assumed to be the same in both designs) is

$$\frac{(p-1)(p^2+p+1)}{(p+1)(p^2+p+2\frac{1}{2})}$$

This factor is obtained by noting that the 3 main effects will be determined with variance $1/(p-1)W$ and the remaining (p^2+p-2) effects and interactions with variance $2/3(p-1)W$, so that the mean variance of varietal comparisons would be

$$\frac{2(p-1)}{(p^3-1)}\left[\frac{3}{(p-1)W}+\frac{2(p^2+p-2)}{3(p-1)W}\right]=\frac{4}{3W}\left[\frac{(p^2+p+2\frac{1}{2})}{(p^2+p+1)(p-1)}\right]$$

compared with $4/3(p+1)W$ with complete randomized blocks and the same error variance.

A further extension is the testing of p^4 varieties involving pseudo-factors a, b, c, and d, in which factors a and b are applied in a lattice square arrangement, the plots being split for factors c and d, which are also applied in a lattice square arrangement.

REFERENCES

1. YATES, F. Lattice squares, *Jour. Agr. Sci.*, **30**, 672–687, 1940.
2. COCHRAN, W. G., and COX, G. M. *Experimental designs.* John Wiley & Sons, New York. 1950.
3. YATES, F. *The design and analysis of factorial experiments.* Imp. Bur. Soil Sci., Harpenden, England. 1937.
4. CORNISH, E. A. The recovery of inter-block information in quasi-factorial designs with incomplete data. 2. Lattice squares. *Australian Coun. Sci. Ind. Res. Bull.*, **175**, 1944, and *Jour. Australian Inst. Agr. Sci.*, **7**, 19–26, 1941.
5. KEMPTHORNE, O. Recent developments in the design of field experiments. IV. Lattice squares with split-plots. *Jour. Agr. Sci.*, **37**, 156–161, 1947.

CHAPTER 25

Rectangular Lattices

25.1 INTRODUCTION

There is a class of designs, some members of which have been examined by Harshbarger,[1,3] called rectangular lattices. Suppose we wish to test $k(k - l)$ treatments $(k > l)$, in an incomplete block design. If k is a prime number, the only obvious factors of $k(k - l)$ are k and $(k - l)$. This suggests that we should consider a block size of $(k - l)$.

An easy way to get a design in blocks of $(k - l)$ is to arrange the $k(k - l)$ treatments in the cells of a $k \times k$ square in such a way that l of the cells in each row and column are not occupied, and to use rows and columns of the square as blocks. For example, for 3×2 treatments we arrange the treatments in a 3×3 square as follows:

	1	2
3		4
5	6	

The treatments will be denoted by (i, j), i being the row number, and j the column number of the square on which the blocks are based. The discussion of the analysis when $l = 1$ is simplified by assuming that the cells of the square that are not occupied lie on the leading diagonal, so that the treatments (ii), $i = 1, \cdots, k$ do not occur. If treatments are not numbered in this way, they may be renumbered easily to give this arrangement. Arrangements of this form, involving 2 basic replicates with as many repetitions as desired, are known as rectangular lattices, though they would better be named simple rectangular lattices to conform to the usual lattice notation.

Three groupings of the treatments may be obtained by taking a Latin square and dropping out l cells in each row and column such that l of each letter are also dropped out. In the case of $l = 1$, such arrangements obviously exist for any value of k that is a prime or a power of a prime or odd. For, when k is a prime or a power of a prime, we can construct a Latin square such that the leading diagonal contains one letter, and any square orthogonal to this one will have the required property. When k is odd, we make up a square with the desired property merely by writing down the first row as $0, 1, 2, 3, \cdots, k - 1$, and adding 1 to each element (reducing modulo k) to give the second row, adding 1 to the elements of the second row to give the third row, and so on. In all cases in which such a square is possible, we may have the design known as the triple rectangular lattice. There are 3 basic replicates, in which rows, columns, and letters of the square, respectively, are confounded, giving blocks of $(k - l)$ experimental units.

In the case when k is a prime or a power of a prime, it follows, from general theory, and from what was said above, that we may have a rectangular lattice for $k(k - 1)$ treatments in blocks of $(k - 1)$ experimental units with k basic replicates. If the 1st language is such that the letter in the diagonal is constant, the confounding will be of rows, columns, 2d language, 3d language, $\cdots$, $(k - 1)$th language, respectively, in the k replicates.

There does not seem to be a great need for discussion of cases other than $l = 1$; for $k(k - 2) = (k - 1)^2 + 1$, so that, unless the treatments are very well defined, it is likely that one may be omitted and a design for $(k - 1)^2$ treatments used. For any k, the number $k(k - 1)$ is approximately midway between $(k - 1)^2$ and k^2, and we have spent two chapters on designs for these numbers of treatments. The subject of the design of experiments can hardly be expected to deal with all possibilities, and the study of all possible numbers of treatments in all possible sizes of block would be a poor utilization of the statistician's time.

25.2 THE ANALYSIS OF A SIMPLE RECTANGULAR LATTICE FOR $k(k - 1)$ TREATMENTS

The usual additive model will be used, namely, that the yield of treatment (ij) in block k within a particular replicate s is given by the equation

$$y_{ijks} = \mu + b_{ks} + \tau_{ij} + r_s + e_{ijks} \tag{1}$$

where the e_{ijks}'s are assumed to be uncorrelated and distributed around a mean of zero with constant variance σ^2. Apart from the matter of constant variance, the assumptions are justified, because the allocation of treatments to experimental units within the block is made randomly. If the allocation to blocks of groups of treatments which are to be together in a block is made randomly, and this should be done always, we may also assume that the b_{ks}'s are uncorrelated and distributed around a mean of zero with a constant variance of $\sigma^2{}_b$. The experimental units should be chosen to have approximately constant variance within blocks.

In the simple rectangular lattice, there are 2 basic replicates, and we shall call the X replicates those in which rows of the square are confounded and the Y replicates those in which columns are confounded. In X replicates, therefore, $k = i$ and, in Y replicates, $k = j$, so that the subscript k may be dropped. The true treatment effects measured from a mean of zero are denoted by τ_{ij}, and we denote by ρ_i the mean of the τ_{ij}'s in the ith row and γ_j the mean of the τ_{ij}'s in the jth column of the square. We note that the τ_{ij}'s with $i = j$ do not occur, so that

$$\rho_i = \frac{1}{k-1} \sum_{j \neq i} \tau_{ij}, \qquad \gamma_j = \frac{1}{k-1} \sum_{i \neq j} \tau_{ij} \qquad (2)$$

and $\sum_i \rho_i = \sum_j \gamma_j = \sum_{ij} \tau_{ij} = 0$. We denote the mean yield from treatment (ij) in the X replicates by $x_{ij\cdot}$, and in the Y replicates by $y_{ij\cdot}$, and the corresponding totals by $X_{ij\cdot}$, $Y_{ij\cdot}$. The difficulty of the analysis arises from the fact that the comparisons confounded in X replicates are partially confounded in the Y replicates, because of the missing diagonal in the basic square. The estimation problem may be solved by assuming σ^2 and $\sigma^2{}_b$ to be known. For we then have a general linear hypothesis on the τ_{ij}'s, which consists of two parts, the differences within blocks and the differences between blocks. By virtue of the randomization of treatments within a block and consequent orthogonality of orthogonal comparisons (given additivity, cf. Chapter 8), we obtain the first term of equation 3 below, and, by virtue of the random allocation of groups of treatments to the blocks, we obtain the second term of equation 3. It may be of help to recall to the reader the fact that, if we make up $(n - 1)$ orthogonal comparisons of x_1, x_2, $\cdots$, x_n, say,

$$\sum_{j=1}^{n} \lambda_{ij} x_j, \qquad i = 1, \cdots, n - 1$$

with

$$\sum_{i=1}^{n} \lambda_{ij} = 0$$

and

$$\sum_{j=1}^{n} \lambda_{ij}\lambda_{i'j} = 1 \quad \text{if} \quad i = i'$$
$$= 0 \quad \text{if} \quad i \neq i'$$

then,

$$\sum_{i=1}^{n-1} \left(\sum_{j=1}^{n} \lambda_{ij}x_j \right)^2 = \Sigma(x_j - \bar{x})^2$$

This fact we have used again and again, for example, in the breaking up of the treatment sum of squares in an ordinary randomized block analysis. With r repetitious of each of the basic replicates, the best linear unbiased estimates of the τ_{ij}'s are obtained by minimizing,

$$\frac{1}{2\sigma^2} \sum_s \left[\sum_{\substack{ij \\ i \neq j}} (x_{ijs} - x_{i\cdot s} - \tau_{ij} + \rho_i)^2 + \sum_{\substack{ij \\ i \neq j}} (y_{ijs} - y_{\cdot js} - \tau_{ij} + \gamma_j)^2 \right]$$
$$+ \frac{(k-1)}{2[\sigma^2 + (k-1)\sigma^2{}_b]} \sum_s \left[\sum_i (x_{i\cdot s} - x_{\cdot\cdot s} - \rho_i)^2 + \sum_j (y_{\cdot js} - y_{\cdot\cdot s} - \gamma_j)^2 \right] \quad (3)$$

where we are supposing the same numbering of blocks within replicates of the same type, and, as usual, the replacement of a subscript by a dot denotes that a mean has been obtained over that subscript. Put $W = \frac{1}{\sigma^2}$, and $W' = \frac{1}{\sigma^2 + (k-1)\sigma^2{}_b}$.

Then, differentiating with respect to τ_{lm} and denoting estimates by $\hat{}$, we get

$$rW \left[(x_{lm\cdot} - x_{l\cdot\cdot} - \hat{\tau}_{lm} + \hat{\rho}_l) \left(-1 + \frac{1}{k-1} \right) \right.$$
$$+ \sum_{m' \neq m} (x_{lm'\cdot} - x_{l\cdot\cdot} - \hat{\tau}_{lm'} + \hat{\rho}_l) \left(\frac{1}{k-1} \right)$$
$$+ (y_{lm\cdot} - y_{\cdot m\cdot} - \hat{\tau}_{lm} + \hat{\gamma}_m) \left(-1 + \frac{1}{k-1} \right)$$
$$\left. + \sum_{l' \neq l} (y_{l'm\cdot} - y_{\cdot m\cdot} - \hat{\tau}_{l'm} + \hat{\gamma}_m) \left(\frac{1}{k-1} \right) \right]$$
$$+ r(k-1)W' \left[(x_{l\cdot\cdot} - x_{\cdot\cdot}) - \hat{\rho}_l) \left(-\frac{1}{k-1} \right) \right.$$
$$\left. + (y_{\cdot m\cdot} - y_{\cdot\cdot\cdot} - \hat{\gamma}_m) \left(-\frac{1}{k-1} \right) \right] \quad (4)$$

and, simplifying, we get

$$rW[-(x_{lm\cdot}-x_{l\cdot\cdot}-\hat{\tau}_{lm}+\hat{\rho}_l)-(y_{lm\cdot}-y_{\cdot m\cdot}-\hat{\tau}_{lm}+\hat{\gamma}_m)$$

$$+\frac{1}{(k-1)}\sum_{m'}(x_{lm'\cdot}-x_{l\cdot\cdot}-\hat{\tau}_{lm'}+\hat{\rho}_l)$$

$$+\frac{1}{(k-1)}\sum_{l'}(y_{l'm\cdot}-y_{\cdot m\cdot}-\hat{\tau}_{l'm\cdot}+\hat{\gamma}_m)\Big]$$

$$+rW'[-(x_{l\cdot\cdot}-x_{\cdots}-\hat{\rho}_l)-(y_{\cdot m\cdot}-y_{\cdots}-\hat{\gamma}_m)]\quad(5)$$

We note that

$$\sum_{m'}(x_{lm'\cdot}-x_{l\cdot\cdot}-\hat{\tau}_{lm'}+\hat{\rho}_l)=0$$

and

$$\sum_{l'}(y_{l'm\cdot}-y_{\cdot m\cdot}-\hat{\tau}_{l'm}+\hat{\gamma}_m)=0$$

where, of course, m' cannot take the value l and l' cannot take the value m.

So the equation for $\hat{\tau}_{lm}$ is

$$-rW[(x_{lm\cdot}-x_{l\cdot\cdot}-\hat{\tau}_{lm}+\hat{\rho}_l)+(y_{lm\cdot}-y_{\cdot m\cdot}-\hat{\tau}_{lm}+\hat{\gamma}_m)]$$

$$-rW'[(x_{l\cdot\cdot}-x_{\cdots}-\hat{\rho}_l)+(y_{\cdot m\cdot}-y_{\cdots}-\hat{\gamma}_m)]=0\quad(6)$$

or

$$2rW\hat{\tau}_{lm}-r(W-W')\hat{\rho}_l-r(W-W')\hat{\gamma}_m$$

$$=rW(x_{lm\cdot}+y_{lm\cdot}-x_{l\cdot\cdot}-y_{\cdot m\cdot})$$

$$+rW'(x_{l\cdot\cdot}-x_{\cdots}+y_{\cdot m\cdot}-y_{\cdots})\quad(7)$$

This equation may be written

$$rW(2\hat{\tau}_{lm}-x_{lm\cdot}-y_{lm\cdot}+x_{\cdots}+y_{\cdots})-r(W-W')\hat{\rho}_l-r(W-W')\hat{\gamma}_m$$

$$=rW(-x_{l\cdot\cdot}-y_{\cdot m\cdot}+x_{\cdots}+y_{\cdots})+rW'(x_{l\cdot\cdot}-x_{\cdots}+y_{\cdot m\cdot}-y_{\cdots})$$

$$=-r(W-W')(x_{l\cdot\cdot}-x_{\cdots}+y_{\cdot m\cdot}-y_{\cdots})\quad(8)$$

or

$$2\hat{\tau}_{lm}=(x_{lm\cdot}+y_{lm\cdot}-x_{\cdots}-y_{\cdots})+\frac{W-W'}{W}(\hat{\rho}_l-x_{l\cdot\cdot}+x_{\cdots})$$

$$+\frac{W-W'}{W}(\hat{\gamma}_m-y_{\cdot m\cdot}+y_{\cdots})\quad(9)$$

From this equation, we see that the best estimate of τ_{lm} expressed around the general mean is equal to the mean yield under this treatment plus two corrections, say,

$$c'_{xl} = \frac{W - W'}{2W}(\hat{\rho}_l - x_l.. + x...) = \frac{W - W'}{2W}d_{xl}$$

$$c'_{ym} = \frac{W - W'}{2W}(\hat{\gamma}_m - y.m. + y...) = \frac{W - W'}{2W}d_{ym}$$

(10)

All that remains then is to find explicit expressions for d_{xl} and d_{ym}. If we add equation 9 over m, remembering that m does not take the value l, we get

$$2(k - 1)\hat{\rho}_l = (k - 1)(x_l.. + y_l.. - x... - y...)$$

$$+ (k - 1)\frac{W - W'}{W}(\hat{\rho}_l - x_l.. + x...) - \frac{W - W'}{W}(\hat{\gamma}_l - y.l. + y...)$$

or, after a little simplification and rearrangement,

$$(k - 1)(W + W')(\hat{\rho}_l - x_l.. + x...) + (W - W')(\hat{\gamma}_l - y.l. + y...)$$

$$= (k - 1)W(y_l.. - y... - x_l.. + x...) \quad (11)$$

or

$$(k - 1)(W + W')d_{xl} + (W - W')d_{yl}$$

$$= (k - 1)W(t_l.. - 2x_l.. - t... + 2x...) \quad (12)$$

where

$$t_l.. = x_l.. + y_l..$$

Similarly,

$$(W - W')d_{xl} + (k - 1)(W + W')d_{yl}$$

$$= (k - 1)W(t.l. - 2y.l. - t... + 2y...) \quad (13)$$

Therefore, after adding equations 12 and 13 and then solving equations 12 and 12 + 13, we find

$$\left(\frac{W - W'}{W}\right)d_{xl} = \frac{(k - 1)(W - W')(t_l.. - 2x_l.. + t... + 2x...)}{[(k - 1)(W + W') - (W - W')]}$$

$$- \frac{(k - 1)(W - W')^2(t_l.. - 2x_l.. + t.l. - 2y.l.)}{[(k - 1)(W + W') - (W - W')][(k - 1)(W + W') + (W - W')]}$$

(14)

with an expression for d_{yl} obtained by reversing the position of l within the first two lower subscripts and interchanging x and y. The adjustments to the observed total of the yields for a particular treatment (lm) is then $c_{xl} + c_{ym}$, where, using $T_{l\cdot\cdot}$ to denote the sum of yields of all plots with a treatment whose first subscript is l, etc., and noting that the terms $t\ldots$, $x\ldots$, $y\ldots$ drop out on summation of all the appropriate adjustments, we have

$$
c_{xl} = \frac{(W - W')(T_{l\cdot\cdot} - 2X_{l\cdot\cdot} - \frac{1}{k}T\ldots + \frac{2}{k}X\ldots)}{[(k-1)(W+W') - (W-W')]}
$$
$$
- \frac{(W-W')^2(T_{l\cdot\cdot} - 2X_{l\cdot\cdot} + T_{\cdot l\cdot} - 2Y_{\cdot l\cdot})}{[(k-1)(W+W') - (W-W')][(k-1)(W+W') + (W-W')]}
$$

(15)

$$
c_{ym} = \frac{(W-W')(T_{\cdot m\cdot} - 2Y_{\cdot m\cdot} - \frac{1}{k}T\ldots + \frac{2}{k}Y\ldots)}{(k-1)(W+W') - (W-W')}
$$
$$
- \frac{(W-W')^2(T_{m\cdot\cdot} - 2X_{m\cdot\cdot} + T_{\cdot m\cdot} - 2Y_{\cdot m\cdot})}{[(k-1)(W+W') - (W-W')][(k-1)(W+W') + (W-W')]}
$$

(16)

25.2.1 The Analysis of Variance

The structure of the analysis of variance is given in Table 25.1.

TABLE 25.1 STRUCTURE OF ANALYSIS OF VARIANCE FOR r REPETITIONS OF A SIMPLE RECTANGULAR LATTICE

	df
Replicates	$2r - 1$
Blocks eliminating treatments	
Component a	$2(r-1)(k-1)$
Component b	$2(k-1)$
Treatments ignoring blocks	$k(k-1) - 1$
Error	$(2r-1)k^2 - (4r-1)k + 1$
Total	$2rk(k-1) - 1$

Component a exists only when r is greater than unity. There are, then, r replicates of type X which have identical block structure, and the interaction of these block structures with the X replicates gives a sum of squares with $(r-1)(k-1)$ degrees of freedom; similarly, $(r-1)(k-1)$ degrees of freedom arise from the Y replicates. Component a plus component b is equal to the sum of squares for blocks eliminating treatments obtained when fixed unknown block parameters are assumed and estimated. The intrablock estimates of the τ_{ij}'s are obtained by putting $W' = 0$, and the estimates of block effects are then easily obtained as the block mean minus $\hat{\rho}_i$ or $\hat{\gamma}_i$, as the case may be. The component b is

$$\frac{1}{rk(k-2)} \left\{ \sum_l \left[(k-1)(Y_l.. - X_l..) - (X._l. - Y._l.) \right] (Y_l.. - X_l..) \right.$$

$$+ \sum_l \left[(k-1)(X._l. - Y._l.) - (Y_l.. - X_l..) \right] (X._l. - Y._l.)$$

$$\left. - (Y... - X...)^2 \right\} \quad (17)$$

The expectations of the sum of squares for the components are:

Component a: $\qquad 2(r-1)(k-1)\sigma^2 + 2(r-1)(k-1)^2\sigma^2{}_b$

Component b: $\qquad 2(k-1)\sigma^2 + (k-1)^2\sigma^2{}_b$

so that the mean square for the pooled blocks eliminating treatments, $\mathbf{B}$, say, has an expectation of $\sigma^2 + \left(\dfrac{2r-1}{2r} \right)(k-1)\sigma^2{}_b$. The expectation of the error mean square $\mathbf{E}$, say, is σ^2. The weights W and W' may, therefore, be estimated by the equations,

$$w = \frac{1}{\mathbf{E}}$$

$$w' = \frac{2r-1}{2r\mathbf{B} - \mathbf{E}} \quad (18)$$

25.2.2 The Variance of Treatment Comparisons

The variance of a treatment difference is estimated by considering the equation 7 for the $\hat{\tau}_{lm}$'s. To get the variance of the estimated difference of $\hat{\tau}_{lm}$ and $\hat{\tau}_{l'm'}$, we obtain the estimate of $\hat{\tau}_{lm} - \hat{\tau}_{l'm'}$ from these equations with the right-hand sides changed, so that the right-hand side of the equation for $\hat{\tau}_{lm}$ is unity and for $\hat{\tau}_{l'm'}$ is minus unity and for all other $\hat{\tau}_{l''m''}$ is zero (cf. Chapter 6).

In this way we find that there are 4 types of comparisons exemplified by the following:

$(\hat{\tau}_{12} - \hat{\tau}_{13})$
or
$(\hat{\tau}_{21} - \hat{\tau}_{31})$
$\left.\right\}$ with variance $\dfrac{2}{2rW}\left[1 + \dfrac{(k-1)(W-W')(W+W')}{\Delta}\right]$

$(\hat{\tau}_{12} - \hat{\tau}_{23})$ with variance

$$\frac{2}{2rW}\left[1 + \frac{(W-W')[(2k-1)W + (2k-3)W']}{\Delta}\right]$$

$(\hat{\tau}_{12} - \hat{\tau}_{21})$ with variance

$$\frac{2}{2rW}\left[1 + \frac{2(W-W')[(k-1)(W+W') + (W-W')]}{\Delta}\right] \quad (19)$$

$(\hat{\tau}_{12} - \hat{\tau}_{34})$ with variance $\dfrac{2}{2rW}\left[1 + \dfrac{2(k-1)(W-W')(W+W')}{\Delta}\right]$

where

$$\Delta = (k-1)^2(W+W')^2 - (W-W')^2$$

For most purposes the use of an average variance of treatment comparisons of

$$\frac{2}{2rW}\left\{1 + \frac{(W-W')}{(k^2-k-1)\Delta}[(2k^3 - 6k^2 + 8k - 4)W\right.$$

$$\left. + (2k^3 - 6k^2 + 4k - 2)W']\right\} \quad (20)$$

which is virtually identical to the simpler expression

$$\frac{2}{2rW}\left[1 + \frac{2(k-1)^3(W-W')(W+W')}{(k^2-k-1)\Delta}\right]$$

will be satisfactory.

An examination of the effect of inaccuracies in the weights would proceed as in the previous chapter. No work on this has been reported, so far as is known.

25.3 THE ANALYSIS OF THE TRIPLE RECTANGULAR LATTICE

The procedure by which a triple rectangular lattice for $k(k-1)$ treatments will be analyzed may be derived in exactly the same manner as the above. Each treatment will have 3 subscripts, i, j, m, say, such that $i \neq m$, $j \neq m$, $i \neq j$. Three quantities, ρ_i, γ_j, and δ_m, will be defined thus:

$$\rho_i = \frac{1}{k-1} \sum_{jm} \tau_{ijm}$$

$$\gamma_j = \frac{1}{k-1} \sum_{im} \tau_{ijm} \qquad (21)$$

$$\delta_m = \frac{1}{k-1} \sum_{ij} \tau_{ijm}$$

There are 3 types of replicate, X, Y, and Z, correspondingly. If we denote yields by x_{ijms}, y_{ijms}, or z_{ijms}, s being the replicate number, the equation corresponding to equation 9 is

$$3\hat{\tau}_{lmn} = (x_{lmn\cdot} + y_{lmn\cdot} + z_{lmn\cdot} - x_{\cdots\cdots} - y_{\cdots\cdots} - z_{\cdots\cdots})$$

$$+ \frac{W-W'}{W}(\hat{\rho}_l - x_{l\cdots} + x_{\cdots\cdots}) + \frac{W-W'}{W}(\hat{\gamma}_m - y_{\cdot m\cdot\cdot} + y_{\cdots\cdots})$$

$$+ \frac{W-W'}{W}(\hat{\delta}_n' - z_{\cdot\cdot n\cdot} + z_{\cdots\cdots}) \quad (22)$$

Letting

$$d_{xl} = \hat{\rho}_l - x_{l\cdots} + x_{\cdots\cdots}$$

$$d_{ym} = \hat{\gamma}_m - y_{\cdot m\cdot\cdot} + y_{\cdots\cdots}$$

$$d_{zn} = \hat{\delta}_n - z_{\cdot\cdot n\cdot} + z_{\cdots\cdots}$$

corresponding to equations 11 and 12 for the simple rectangular lattice, we get

$$(k-1)(2W+W')d_{xl} + (W-W')d_{yl} + (W-W')d_{zl}$$

$$= (k-1)W(t_l\cdots - 3x_l\cdots - t_{\cdots\cdots} + 3x_{\cdots\cdots})$$

$$(W-W')d_{xl} + (k-1)(2W+W')d_{yl} + (W-W')d_{zl}$$

$$= (k-1)W(t_{\cdot l\cdot\cdot} - 3y_{\cdot l\cdot\cdot} - t_{\cdots\cdots} + 3y_{\cdots\cdots}) \qquad (23)$$

$$(W-W')d_{xl} + (W-W')d_{yl} + (k-1)(2W+W')d_{zl}$$

$$= (k-1)W(t_{\cdot\cdot l\cdot} - 3z_{\cdot\cdot l\cdot} - t_{\cdots\cdots} + 3z_{\cdots\cdots})$$

where $t_l\cdots = x_l\cdots + y_l\cdots + z_l\cdots$, etc., and, adding these three equations, we have

$$[(k-1)(2W+W') + 2(W-W')](d_{xl} + d_{yl} + d_{zl})$$

$$= (k-1)W(t_l\cdots - 3x_l\cdots + t_{\cdot l\cdot\cdot} - 3y_{\cdot l\cdot\cdot} + t_{\cdot\cdot l\cdot} - 3z_{\cdot\cdot l\cdot}) \quad (24)$$

The adjustment to the observed total yield under treatment (ijm) is then

$$\frac{r(W - W')}{W} (d_{xi} + d_{yj} + d_{zm}) \tag{25}$$

r being the number of times each X, Y, and Z replicate is repeated.

From the above equations, we find that

$$\frac{r(W - W')}{W} d_{xi} = \frac{(W - W')(T_{i}\cdots - 3X_{i}\cdots - \frac{1}{k}T\cdots + \frac{3}{k}X\cdots)}{[(k - 1)(2W + W') - (W - W')]}$$
$$- \frac{\left\{\begin{matrix}(W - W')^2(T_{i}\cdots - 3X_{i}\cdots + T_{\cdot i}\cdots - 3Y_{\cdot i}\cdots \\ + T_{\cdot\cdot i} - 3Z_{\cdot\cdot i}\cdot)\end{matrix}\right\}}{\left\{\begin{matrix}[(k - 1)(2W + W') - (W - W')][(k - 1)(2W + W') \\ + 2(W - W')]\end{matrix}\right\}} \tag{26}$$

where $X_{i}\cdots$, etc., are totals and $T_{i}\cdots = X_{i}\cdots + Y_{i}\cdots + Z_{i}\cdots$, with corresponding expressions for $r\left(\dfrac{W - W'}{W}\right) d_{yj}$ and $r\left(\dfrac{W - W'}{W}\right) d_{zm}$.

From the point of view of computation, as given by Cochran and Cox,[2] we note that

$$T_{i}\cdots - 3X_{i}\cdots$$

is equal to the total over the whole experiment of treatments appearing in block i of the X replicates minus 3 times the total over the X replicates of the ith block totals. If we denote these quantities by C_{xi} and use corresponding quantities for the blocks of the other replicates, that is, let

$$C_{yi} = T_{\cdot i}\cdots - 3Y_{\cdot i}\cdots$$

and

$$C_{zi} = T_{\cdot\cdot i}\cdot - 3Z_{\cdot\cdot i}\cdot \tag{27}$$

and also let

$$S_i = C_{xi} + C_{yi} + C_{zi}$$

the adjustment to the observed total yield is

$$(\lambda C_{xi} - \mu S_i) + (\lambda C_{yj} - \mu S_j) + (\lambda C_{zm} - \mu S_m) \tag{28}$$

where

$$\lambda = \frac{W - W'}{(k - 1)(2W + W') - (W - W')} = \frac{W - W'}{(2k - 3)W + kW'}$$

and

$$\mu = \frac{\lambda(W - W')}{(k - 1)(2W + W') + 2(W - W')} = \frac{\lambda(W - W')}{2kW + (k - 3)W'} \tag{29}$$

The analysis of variance is evaluated directly as in Table 25.2.

TABLE 25.2   STRUCTURE OF ANALYSIS OF VARIANCE WITH r REPETITIONS OF TRIPLE RECTANGULAR LATTICE

Due to	df	Mean Square	Expectation of Mean Square
Replicates	$3r - 1$		
Blocks component a	$3(r-1)(k-1)$ ⎫		
Blocks component b	$3(k-1)$ ⎬	B	$\sigma^2 + \left(\dfrac{3r-1}{3r}\right)(k-1)\sigma^2{}_b$
Treatments ignoring blocks	$k(k-1) - 1$		
Error	$(3r-1)k^2 - (6r-1)k + 1$	E	σ^2
Total	$3rk(k-1) - 1$		

Blocks component a is obtained in the usual way as the interaction of blocks and replicates with the same block arrangement. Blocks component b is obtained by noting that the intrablock estimates of d_{xi}, etc., are given by

$$r\tilde{d}_{xi} = \frac{1}{2k-3} C_{xi} - \frac{1}{2k(2k-3)} S_i \quad \text{etc.}$$

The estimates of block parameters are, therefore, of the form

$$\tilde{d}_{xis} = x_{1\cdots s} - x_{\cdots s} - \rho_1$$

and so on, so that the sum of squares between blocks eliminating treatments is $\Sigma \tilde{d}_{xis}$ (block total − sum of treatment means for whole experiment of treatments occurring in the block)(cf. Chapter 6).

The sum of squares for component b is then found to be equal to

$$\frac{1}{3r(2k-3)} \Sigma(C^2{}_{xi} + C^2{}_{yi} + C^2{}_{zi})$$

$$- \frac{1}{3rk(2k-3)} \left[\left(\sum_i C_{xi}\right)^2 + \left(\sum_i C_{yi}\right)^2 + \left(\sum_i C_{zi}\right)^2 \right]$$

$$- \frac{1}{3r(2k-3)2k} \left(\sum_i S^2{}_i\right) \quad (30)$$

It should be noted that r in all the formulas given is the number of repetitions of the basic pattern of 3 replicates and *not* the total number of replicates.

The expectation of the total sum of squares for blocks eliminating treatments is equal to

$$3r(k-1) \left[\sigma^2 + \left(\frac{3r-1}{3r}\right)(k-1)\sigma^2{}_b \right]$$

The weights may, therefore, be estimated by *

$$w = \frac{1}{\mathsf{E}}, \qquad w' = \frac{3r - 1}{3r\mathsf{B} - \mathsf{E}} \tag{31}$$

25.4 THE VARIANCE OF TREATMENT DIFFERENCES FOR A TRIPLE RECTANGULAR LATTICE

The true variances of estimated treatment differences are obtained by considering the original least squares equations, obtained by differentiating the sum of squares of deviations (cf. Chapter 6). To obtain the variance of $(\hat{\tau}_{lmn} - \hat{\tau}_{l'm'n'})$, we must solve the following equations:

$$3rW\hat{\tau}_{lmn} - r(W - W')\hat{\rho}_l - r(W - W')\hat{\gamma}_m - r(W - W')\hat{\delta}_n = 1$$

$$3rW\hat{\tau}_{l'm'n'} - r(W - W')\hat{\rho}_{l'} - r(W - W')\hat{\gamma}_{m'} - r(W - W')\hat{\delta}_{n'} = -1$$

and

$$3rW\hat{\tau}_{l_1m_1n_1} - r(W - W')\hat{\rho}_{l_1} - r(W - W')\hat{\gamma}_{m_1} - r(W - W')\hat{\delta}_{n_1} = 0$$

$$\tag{32}$$

for all (l_1, m_1, n_1) unequal to (l, m, n) or (l', m', n'). The estimate of $\tau_{lmn} - \tau_{l'm'n'}$ is equal to

$$\frac{2}{3rW} + \frac{(W - W')}{3W} (\hat{\rho}_l - \hat{\rho}_{l'} + \hat{\gamma}_m - \hat{\gamma}_{m'} + \hat{\delta}_n - \hat{\delta}_{n'}) \tag{33}$$

and this is the variance of the estimated difference $\hat{\tau}_{lmn} - \hat{\tau}_{l'm'n'}$.

Summing the equations 32 in the suitable way, we obtain the 3 equations:

$$\alpha\hat{\rho}_{l''} + \beta\hat{\gamma}_{l''} + \beta\hat{\delta}_{l''} = \delta_{ll''} - \delta_{l'l''}$$

$$\beta\hat{\rho}_{l''} + \alpha\hat{\gamma}_{l''} + \beta\hat{\delta}_{l''} = \delta_{ml''} - \delta_{m'l''} \tag{34}$$

$$\beta\hat{\rho}_{l''} + \beta\hat{\gamma}_{l''} + \alpha\hat{\delta}_{l''} = \delta_{nl''} - \delta_{n'l''}$$

where $\delta_{ll''}$ is the Kronecker delta, which takes the value of unity if the 2 subscripts are the same, and zero if they are different, and

* It is shown by P. M. Grundy, *Biometrics*, 6 (1950), 25–33, that this procedure for estimating the weights will in most cases lead to estimates of the variances $(1/W, 1/W')$ which have minimum variance in the class of estimates obtained by linear functions of the mean squares.

$\alpha = r(k-1)(2W + W')$ and $\beta = r(W - W')$. The solution of these equations is:

$$\hat{\rho}_{l''} = \frac{1}{\alpha - \beta}(\delta_{ll''} - \delta_{l'll''}) - \frac{\beta}{(\alpha - \beta)(\alpha + 2\beta)}(\delta_{ll''} - \delta_{l'l''} + \delta_{ml''}$$

$$- \delta_{m'l''} + \delta_{nl''} - \delta_{n'l''})$$

$$\hat{\gamma}_{l''} = \frac{1}{\alpha - \beta}(\delta_{ml''} - \delta_{m'l''}) - \frac{\beta}{(\alpha - \beta)(\alpha + 2\beta)}(\delta_{ll''} - \delta_{l'l''} + \delta_{ml''}$$

$$- \delta_{m'l''} + \delta_{nl''} - \delta_{n'l''}) \qquad (35)$$

$$\hat{\delta}_{l''} = \frac{1}{\alpha - \beta}(\delta_{nl''} - \delta_{n'l''}) - \frac{\beta}{(\alpha - \beta)(\alpha + 2\beta)}(\delta_{ll''} - \delta_{l'l''} + \delta_{ml''}$$

$$- \delta_{m'l''} + \delta_{nl''} - \delta_{n'l''})$$

Finally, we may write, for the variance of the estimate $\hat{\tau}_{lmn} - \hat{\tau}_{l'm'n'}$, the expression:

$$\frac{2}{3rW} + \frac{W - W'}{3W}\left\{\frac{2}{\alpha - \beta}[(1 - \delta_{ll'}) + (1 - \delta_{mm'}) + (1 - \delta_{nn'})]\right.$$

$$- \frac{2\beta}{(\alpha - \beta)(\alpha + 2\beta)}[(1 - \delta_{ll'}) + (1 - \delta_{mm'}) + (1 - \delta_{nn'})$$

$$\left. - \delta_{lm'} - \delta_{ln'} - \delta_{l'm} - \delta_{l'n} - \delta_{mn'} - \delta_{m'n}]\right\} \qquad (36)$$

since δ_{lm}, δ_{ln}, δ_{mn}, $\delta_{l'm'}$, $\delta_{l'n'}$, and $\delta_{m'n'}$ are zero.

We, therefore, find the following variances:

The 2 Treatments Occurring Together in a Block:

1 subscript alike: $\dfrac{2}{3rW}\left[1 + \dfrac{(4k-2)W + (2k-4)W'}{\Delta}\right]$

2 subscripts alike: $\dfrac{2}{3rW}\left[1 + \dfrac{(4k-1)W + (2k-5)W'}{\Delta}\right]$

3 subscripts alike: $\dfrac{2}{3rW}\left[1 + \dfrac{4kW + (2k-6)W'}{\Delta}\right]$

The 2 Treatments not Occurring Together in a Block:

0 subscripts alike: $\dfrac{2}{3rW}\left[1 + \dfrac{(6k-3)W + (3k-6)W'}{\Delta}\right]$

1 subscript alike: $\dfrac{2}{3rW}\left[1 + \dfrac{(6k-2)W + (3k-7)W'}{\Delta}\right]$

2 subscripts alike: $\dfrac{2}{3rW}\left[1 + \dfrac{(6k-1)W + (3k-8)W'}{\Delta}\right]$

3 subscripts alike: $\dfrac{2}{3rW}\left[1 + \dfrac{6kW + (3k-9)W'}{\Delta}\right]$

where

$$\Delta = \frac{(\alpha - \beta)(\alpha + 2\beta)}{r(W - W')} = \frac{[(2k-3)W + kW'][2kW + (k-3)W']}{W - W'}$$

In general, the variances within a group will differ by little, so that, to get an approximate average variance, we may assume that $3(k-2)$ comparisons of a treatment with treatments occurring with it in a block have a variance of

$$\frac{1}{3rW}\left[1 + \frac{(4k-2)W + (2k-4)W'}{\Delta}\right] \tag{37}$$

and $(k^2 - 4k + 5)$ have a variance of

$$\frac{1}{3rW}\left[1 + \frac{(6k-3)W + (3k-6)W'}{\Delta}\right] \tag{38}$$

This gives an average variance of

$$\frac{1}{3rW}\left[1 + \frac{3(k-1)^2}{(k^2-k-1)}\frac{2(k-1)W + (k-2)W'}{\Delta}\right] \tag{39}$$

As with all lattice designs, we may estimate the error variance to which the yields would have been subject, with complete randomized blocks, and hence the efficiency of the incomplete block arrangement. This is done by combining the sums of squares for blocks eliminating treatments and for error. The resulting mean square is an estimate of the variance in complete randomized blocks, and the mean estimated variance of treatment comparisons would be $2/3r$ times this quantity. For, if treatments are completely randomized over blocks within a replicate, of the possible $k(k-1)[k(k-1)-1]$ positions taken by the pair of treatments, $k(k-1)(k-2)$ will not involve block differences, but the remainder will do so. The average variance is then

$$\frac{1}{k(k-1)(k^2-k-1)} \{2k(k-1)(\bar{k}-2)\sigma^2$$

$$+ [k(k-1)(k^2-k-1) - k(k-1)(k-2)](2\sigma^2 + 2\sigma^2_b)\}$$

$$= 2\left[\sigma^2 + \frac{(k-1)^2}{(k^2-k-1)}\sigma^2_b\right]$$

It is readily verified that the expectation of the pooled mean square E' is equal to

$$\sigma^2 + \frac{(k-1)^2}{(k^2-k-1)}\sigma^2_b$$

The efficiency of the lattice arrangement is then estimated by comparing the actual mean variance with the estimated mean variance with randomized blocks: namely, $\frac{2}{3r}E'$.

25.5 AN EXAMPLE OF A TRIPLE RECTANGULAR LATTICE

The experiment in Table 25.3 was constructed from random normal deviates using values of unity for σ^2 and σ^2_b and a mean value of 10, treatment numbers being in parentheses.

TABLE 25.3

Block	X Replicate		
1	8.9 (132)	10.0 (143)	11.6 (124)
3	9.4 (314)	9.3 (342)	10.2 (321)
2	9.6 (213)	11.4 (234)	10.0 (241)
4	11.8 (412)	11.7 (431)	13.1 (423)
	Y Replicate		
3	11.6 (132)	12.4 (431)	10.0 (234)
1	9.6 (314)	10.0 (412)	8.4 (213)
2	10.5 (124)	11.0 (321)	10.0 (423)
4	11.5 (143)	12.6 (342)	11.8 (241)
	Z Replicate		
2	11.2 (132)	12.1 (342)	9.7 (412)
3	7.8 (143)	9.6 (423)	10.6 (213)
1	8.7 (431)	9.1 (321)	8.0 (241)
4	8.7 (124)	7.5 (314)	8.3 (234)

We find the following:

i	$X_{i..}$	$Y_{.i.}$	$Z_{..i}$
1	30.5	28.0	25.8
2	31.0	31.5	33.0
3	28.9	34.0	28.0
4	36.6	35.9	24.5
Total	127.0	129.4	111.3

(ijk)	124	132	143	213	234	241	314	321	342	412	423	431	
T_{ijk}	30.8	31.7	29.3	28.6	29.7	29.8	26.5	30.3	34.0	31.5	32.7	32.8	367.7

TABLE 25.4

i	$T_{i..}$	$T_{.i.}$	$T_{..i}$	C_{xi}	C_{yi}	C_{zi}	S_i
1	91.8	86.6	92.9	0.3	2.6	15.5	18.4
2	88.1	93.8	97.2	−4.9	−0.7	−1.8	−7.4
3	90.8	94.2	90.6	4.1	−7.8	6.6	2.9
4	97.0	93.1	87.0	−12.8	−14.6	13.5	−13.9
	367.7	367.7	367.7	−13.3	−20.5	33.8	0

TABLE 25.5   ANALYSIS OF VARIANCE

Due to	df	Sum of Squares	Mean Square	Expectation of Mean Squares
Replicates	2	16.10		
Blocks component a	0	.....		
Blocks component b	9	29.74	3.30	$\sigma^2 + (\frac{2}{3})3\sigma_b^2$
Treatments	11	15.63		
Error	13	12.57	0.97	σ^2
Total	35	74.04		

The weights are estimated as

$$w = \frac{1}{0.97} = 1.03$$

and

$$w' = \frac{2}{3 \times 3.30 - 0.97} = 0.22$$

The quantities λ and μ are estimated by

$$\lambda = \frac{1.03 - 0.22}{5 \times 1.03 - 4 \times 0.22} = \frac{0.81}{4.27} = 0.19$$

$$\mu = \lambda \frac{0.81}{8 \times 1.03 + 0.22} = 0.018$$

The adjustments are, therefore,

	i	j	k
1	−0.27	0.16	2.61
2	−0.80	0.00	−0.21
3	0.73	−1.53	1.20
4	−2.18	−2.52	2.82

The variances (approximate) of treatment comparisons are

$$\frac{1}{3 \times 1.03}\left(1 + \frac{14 \times 1.03 + 4 \times 0.22}{\Delta}\right)$$

for treatments occurring together in a block, and

$$\frac{1}{3 \times 1.03}\left(1 + \frac{21 \times 1.03 + 6 \times 0.22}{\Delta}\right)$$

for treatments not occurring together in a block, where $\Delta = 4.27 \times 8.44/0.81 = 44.49$, and are, therefore, 0.43 and 0.49, respectively. For most purposes, it will be sufficiently accurate to use a mean variance of 0.46.

If a complete randomized block design had been used, the error mean square would have been 1.92, with a mean variance of treatment comparisons of 0.64, so that the efficiency of the triple rectangular lattice in this (hypothetical) case is estimated to be 139 percent.

25.6 FURTHER NOTES

There is little need for further rectangular lattice designs, though for some values of k, quadruple lattices and so on may be written out. The analysis of these would be similar to the analysis given above, the derivation proceeding on exactly the same lines. The computation of variances of estimated differences would be rather tedious.

The case of $k(k - 2)$ treatments has not been discussed because it is considered unlikely to be important. The case of $k(k - 3)$ treatments is also not likely to be important because $k(k - 3) = (k - 1) \times (k - 2) - 2$, and the experimenter with this situation would usually be able to drop 2 treatments and use the designs described above.

We have not discussed the missing value problem, and it does not appear that a study has been made. An approximate procedure which may be suggested is to derive the intrablock estimates for the missing values and then to use these as though they were actually observed with a modification in the error degrees of freedom.

REFERENCES

1. HARSHBARGER, B. Rectangular lattices. *Virginia Agr. Exp. Sta. Mem.*, **1,** 1947.
2. COCHRAN, W. G., and Cox, G. M. *Experimental designs.* John Wiley & Sons. 1950.
3. HARSHBARGER, B. Triple rectangular lattices. *Biometrics,* **5,** 1–13, 1950.

CHAPTER 26

Balanced Incomplete Block Designs

26.1 INTRODUCTION

The previous three chapters have been concerned with the problem of arranging a number of treatments in blocks the size of which is less than the number of treatments, in such a way that an analysis is simple and gives estimates of treatment differences with variances as low and as equal as possible. In those chapters we made use of a correspondence of the treatments to the treatment combinations of a number of factors. Such a correspondence is of value only in certain cases: for example, if we wish to compare 8 treatments in blocks of 3 experimental units, a representation of the 8 treatments as treatment combinations resulting from 3 two-level factors appears to be of no help.

The designs discussed in the previous chapters are primarily suited for field plot trials, or industrial experiments, when the number of experimental units and their grouping into blocks is completely under the control of the experimenter. This is particularly the case for designs with 2 restrictions. They are also available only for specified numbers of treatments and mainly for large numbers of treatments, say, 25 or more. There is then need for designs in which rather smaller numbers of treatments may be compared in small blocks. In biological work on animals, for example, it will be desirable, if at all possible, to compare several treatments within litters, but the size of litter will depend on the particular species and will often be such that it is impossible to include all treatments within a litter. There are 2 classes of design for this situation: namely, balanced incomplete block designs which are the subject of the present chapter, and partially balanced incomplete block designs, which will be described in Chapter 27. It should be noted that there is no essential difference between the lattice designs and those to be described here. The separation was made because the lattice designs arise naturally from a factorial correspondence, and their analysis is facilitated by this correspondence.

As an example of the type of design we shall discuss in this chapter, consider the following arrangement for 6 treatments, a, b, c, d, e, f, in blocks of 3 experimental units:

$$a, b, c; \quad a, b, d; \quad a, c, e; \quad a, d, f; \quad a, e, f$$

$$b, c, f; \quad b, d, e; \quad b, e, f; \quad c, d, e; \quad c, d, f$$

Note that each treatment is represented 5 times and that every pair of treatments occurs together in a block twice. The groups of treatments making up a block are assigned to the groups of experimental units at random, and treatments are assigned within the groups at random. Designs with the above properties, that each treatment occurs equally frequently, and that each pair of treatments occurs together in a block equally frequently, were called by Yates,[1] who first proposed them, symmetrical incomplete randomized block arrangements or, more briefly, balanced incomplete block arrangements.

There are two main problems with such arrangements: the design and the analysis. The designs cannot, in general, be obtained by any formal procedure, though they may occur in related groups. The method of analysis is related to the methods by which lattice designs are analyzed, although there is no factorial analogy. The practical value of the design will be evident from the discussion of its analysis.

26.2 EXAMPLES OF INCOMPLETE BLOCK DESIGNS

As a first step in the problem of enumeration of designs, we will consider patterns, which have arisen in earlier chapters and in different connections, that may be adapted to give balanced incomplete block designs.

Consider then the 2^n factorial system, and, to be even more particular, the 2^3 system with factors a, b, and c, say. For this system we found that there were 7 distinct systems of confounding into blocks of 2 plots, those given in Table 26.1 where the crosses in a line indicate the effects and interactions confounded.

Now, if we regard the symbols A, B, AB, C, AC, BC, ABC as treatments 1, 2, 3, 4, 5, 6, 7 and the rows of the above table as blocks we have 7 blocks which may be written as (123), (145), (167), (246), (257), (347), (356).

It is obvious from the table that we have arranged the 7 treatments in blocks of 3 plots in such a way that each treatment is represented 3 times and each pair of treatments occurs together in a block once. The block arrangement is then a balanced incomplete block arrangement.

TABLE 26.1

Effect or Interaction

System	A	B	AB	C	AC	BC	ABC
	1	2	3	4	5	6	7
1	X	X	X				
2	X			X	X		
3	X					X	X
4		X		X		X	
5		X			X		X
6			X	X			X
7			X		X	X	

A balanced incomplete block arrangement for 7 treatments in blocks of 4 plots is obtained by assigning the treatments corresponding to unconfounded effects and interactions to blocks. In this case each treatment occurs 4 times, and each pair of treatments occur together in a block twice.

In this way we may obtain arrangements for $2^n - 1$ treatments in blocks of $2^s - 1$ or of $2^n - 2^s$ plots. The total number of blocks necessary is equal to the number of systems of confounding of the 2^n system in blocks of 2^{n-s}: i.e.,

$$K(n, s) = \frac{(2^n - 1)(2^n - 2) \cdots (2^n - 2^{s-1})}{(2^s - 1)(2^s - 2) \cdots (2^s - 2^{s-1})}$$

The number of times each treatment is replicated with blocks of $2^s - 1$ is

$$\left(\frac{2^s - 1}{2^n - 1}\right) K(n, s)$$

and the number of times each pair of treatments occurs together in a block is

$$\left(\frac{2^s - 1}{2^n - 1}\right)\left(\frac{2^s - 2}{2^n - 2}\right) K(n, s)$$

If we adopt Yates's notation,[1] namely:

Number of treatments: t
Number of experimental units per block: k
Number of replications of each treatment: r
Number of blocks: b
Number of times any 2 treatments occur together in a block: λ

then the above procedure leads to the designs of possible practical interest shown in Table 26.2.

TABLE 26.2

t	k	r	b	λ
3	2	2	3	1
7	3	3	7	1
7	4	4	7	2
15	3	7	35	1
15	7	7	15	3
15	8	8	15	4
31	3	15	155	1
31	7	35	155	7

In the same way we may utilize the examination that was made of systems of confounding for p^n treatment combinations in blocks of $p^{n-s}(s < n)$ to give incomplete block designs for $(p^n - 1)/(p - 1)$ treatments in blocks of $(p^s - 1)/(p - 1)$. For example, we found that there were 13 systems of confounding for the 3^3 system with factors a, b, and c in blocks of 3 plots, namely:

1. $A, B, \quad AB, \quad AB^2$
2. $A, C, \quad AC, \quad AC^2$
3. $A, BC, \quad ABC, \quad AB^2C^2$
4. A, BC^2, ABC^2, AB^2C
5. $B, C, \quad BC, \quad BC^2$
6. $B, AC, \quad ABC, \quad AB^2C$
7. B, AC^2, AB^2C, ABC^2
8. $AB, \quad C, \quad ABC, \quad ABC^2$
9. $AB, \quad AC, \quad BC^2, \quad AB^2C^2$
10. $AB, \quad AC^2, BC, \quad AB^2C$
11. $AB^2, C, \quad AB^2C, AB^2C^2$
12. $AB^2, AC, \quad BC, \quad ABC^2$
13. $AB^2, AC^2, BC^2, \quad ABC$

If we regard the symbols A, B, AB, AB^2, etc., as 13 treatments, the above gives an arrangement for the 13 treatments in blocks of 4 plots, such that each treatment is represented 4 times and every 2 treatments occur together in a block once.

In general, this procedure leads us to designs for $(p^n - 1)/(p - 1)$ treatments in blocks of $(p^s - 1)/(p - 1)$. The number of blocks is equal to the number of systems of confounding for p^n treatments in blocks of p^{n-s} plots, i.e., equal to

$$\frac{(p^n - 1)(p^n - p) \cdots (p^n - p^{s-1})}{(p^s - 1)(p^s - p) \cdots (p^s - p^{s-1})}$$

The number of times each treatment is represented is equal to the number of systems of confounding involving a specified effect or interaction, i.e., equal to

$$\frac{(p^n - p)(p^n - p^2) \cdots (p^n - p^{s-1})}{(p^s - p)(p^s - p^2) \cdots (p^s - p^{s-1})}$$

The number of times any pair of treatments occur together in a block is equal to the number of systems of confounding that involve a specified pair of effects or interactions, i.e., equal to

$$\frac{(p^n - p^2)(p^n - p^3) \cdots (p^n - p^{s-1})}{(p^s - p^2)(p^s - p^3) \cdots (p^s - p^{s-1})}$$

The following designs are of some possible practical interest:

t	k	r	b	λ
40	4	13	130	1
21	5	5	21	1
31	6	6	31	1
57	8	8	57	1

26.3 THE GENERAL CASE

With the symbols t, k, r, b, and λ defined as in the previous section, the following relationships hold:

$$bk = tr = \text{total number of plots}, \qquad \lambda = \frac{r(k - 1)}{t - 1}$$

The second relationship holds because every treatment occurs equally frequently with a specified one within a block, so that $r(k - 1)$ equals $\lambda(t - 1)$.

The simplest case is that of symmetrical pairs, i.e., with $k = 2$, for then all possible pairs of the t treatments are represented, and

$$b = \frac{t(t - 1)}{2}, \qquad r = t - 1, \qquad \lambda = 1$$

In the same way, to obtain a design in blocks of k units, we may take all the combinations of the treatments k at a time, and this gives

$$b = \frac{t!}{k!(t-k)!}, \qquad r = \frac{(t-1)!}{(k-1)!(t-k)!}, \qquad \lambda = \frac{(t-2)!}{(k-2)!(t-k)!}$$

In general, however, this procedure will lead to a very large number of replicates, and it is desirable to find designs involving a lower number of replicates. Since $\lambda = r(k-1)/(t-1)$ must be an integer, it is possible to place a lower limit on the number of replicates necessary for t treatments in blocks of k units. For example, if $t = 12$ and $k = 5$, we have that

$$\lambda = r\tfrac{4}{11}$$

and also

$$b \cdot 5 = 12r$$

so that r must be divisible by 5 and by 11 and, therefore, must be a multiple of 55. Whether a design exists for just 55 replicates must, however, be determined by enumeration methods.

An extensive list of designs is given by Fisher and Yates[2] and by Cochran and Cox.[3] Several are obtainable from completely orthogonalized squares or prime power factorial systems. Others obtained by enumeration are of cyclic nature: for example, the design for 11 treatments in 11 blocks of 5 units ($r = 5$, $\lambda = 2$) may be obtained by numbering the treatments 1, 2, 3, $\cdots$, 11, taking the first block as (1, 2, 3, 5, 8) and generating the other blocks by adding successively 1, 2, 3, to 10, reducing the sums modulo 11. For instance, the 5th block, obtained by adding 4, consists of treatments 5, 6, 7, 9, 1. Methods of enumeration are discussed by Bose,[4] Bhattacharya,[5] Hussain,[6] and Rao.[7]

In the previous section, we described some methods of enumeration of designs. We noted in Chapter 16 the representation of the effects and interactions in a p^n factorial system as a finite projective geometry and the fact that a system of confounding was given by an m flat in that geometry. The examples in section 26.2 are obtainable then by a representation of the t treatments as the elements of a finite projective geometry. Of the existing designs for a number of treatments less than 20, say, the remainder were obtained by various methods. The simplest conceptually is to determine the smallest number of replicates that is possible, because λ is an integer, and then to enumerate the design by trial and error in a systematic way. It is, for example, a simple matter to obtain the design for 6 treatments in 10 blocks of 3 in this way.

After the pioneer work of Yates,[1] the subject of the enumeration of balanced incomplete block designs has been dealt with extensively by Bose and other members of the Indian school with some work also by Fisher.[8] The account given by Bose [4] is systematic and fairly exhaustive, and the reader may refer to this paper. The two principal methods Bose describes are the use of finite geometries and the use of symmetrically repeated differences.

26.4 THE ANALYSIS OF BALANCED INCOMPLETE BLOCK EXPERIMENTS

As in the case of quasifactorial designs there are two types of information on treatment comparisons provided by the experiment: intrablock derived from comparisons within blocks, and interblock from comparisons between blocks.

The model used for the intrablock comparisons is the usual additive one,

$$y_{ij} = \mu + b_i + \tau_j + e_{ij} \tag{1}$$

where

y_{ij} = the yield in the ith block of the jth treatment (if it occurs in that block, of course)

b_i = the effect of the ith block

τ_j = the effect of the jth treatment

and the e_{ij}'s are uncorrelated and have a mean of zero and constant variance σ^2. Again the assumptions about the e_{ij}'s follow from the assumption of additivity, apart from the condition of constant variance. The situation we have is a simple case of the 2-way classification with unequal numbers and without interaction, discussed in Chapter 6. The equations for estimating treatment differences are

$$\left(N_{\cdot j} - \sum_i \frac{n^2_{ij}}{N_i \cdot}\right)\hat{\tau}_j - \sum_{j' \neq j}\left(\sum_i \frac{n_{ij}n_{ij'}}{N_i \cdot}\right)\hat{\tau}_{j'} = Q_j, \qquad j = 1, \cdots, t \tag{2}$$

where n_{ij} is the number of times the treatment j occurs in block i, $N_{\cdot j} = \sum_i n_{ij}$, and $Q_j = Y_{\cdot j} - \sum_i \frac{n_{ij}}{N_i \cdot} Y_{i \cdot \cdot}$. For the case we are considering, the design specifies that n_{ij} is either zero or unity, $N_{\cdot j}$ is equal to r for all j's, and $N_i \cdot$ is equal to k for all i's. Furthermore, the quantity $\sum_i n_{ij}n_{ij'}$ is equal to λ, for every pair (jj'), because any specified treatment occurs with another specified treatment in a block λ times. The equations 2, therefore, reduce to the following:

$$\left(r - \frac{r}{k} \right) \hat{\tau}_j - \frac{\lambda}{k} \sum_{j' \neq j} \hat{\tau}_{j'} = Q_j, \qquad j = 1, 2, \cdots, t \qquad (3)$$

or

$$\left(r - \frac{r}{k} + \frac{\lambda}{k} \right) \hat{\tau}_j - \frac{\lambda}{k} \sum_{\text{All } j} \hat{\tau}_j = Q_j, \qquad j = 1, 2, \cdots, t \qquad (4)$$

Differences of the τ_j's are, therefore, estimated by the differences of

$$\frac{Q_j}{r - \frac{r}{k} + \frac{\lambda}{k}} = \frac{Q_j}{rE} \qquad (5)$$

where

$$E = \frac{(k-1)t}{k(t-1)} \quad \text{since} \quad \lambda = \frac{r(k-1)}{t-1}$$

Furthermore,

$$Q_j = V_j - \frac{T_j}{k}$$

where

V_j = the total yield under treatment j

and

T_j = the total of blocks containing treatment j

If k is greater than $\frac{1}{2}t$, it is simpler computationally to use the differences $\frac{1}{rE} Q'_j = \frac{1}{rE} \left(V_j + \frac{T'_j}{k} \right)$, where T'_j is the total of blocks not containing treatment j, because $T_j + T'_j$ is equal to the grand total, for any j. It follows also, from the theory of Chapter 6, that the true variance of the estimated difference of 2 treatments is $2\sigma^2/rE$, and that any comparison of the treatments, say, $\Sigma\alpha_j\tau_j$, with $\Sigma\alpha_j = 0$, is estimated by

$$\Sigma\alpha_j \frac{Q_j}{rE} \qquad (6)$$

with a variance of

$$(\Sigma\alpha^2_j) \frac{\sigma^2}{rE} \qquad (7)$$

It is for this reason that the quantity $(k-1)t/k(t-1)$, which also equals $t\lambda/rk$, was denoted by E, because it measures the efficiency factor of the incomplete block design, that is, the variance of a treatment difference for a randomized block with the same number of replicates divided by the variance for the incomplete block design, assuming σ^2 to be the same in both cases.

The information on treatment comparisons given by the block totals may be extracted by noting that, under the assumptions made above, a block total B_i is given by

$$B_i = k\mu + \sum_{(i)} t_j + kb_i \tag{8}$$

where $\sum_{(i)} t_j$ is the sum of the treatment effects for the treatments occurring in block i, and the b_i's are uncorrelated, with a mean of zero and constant variance. The assumption about the b_i's is validated by the assumption of additivity plus the random allocation of groups of treatments to blocks. Equation 8 is written occasionally as

$$B_i = k\mu + \sum_{(i)} t_j + kb_i + \sum_j e_{ij} \tag{8a}$$

where the b_i's are normally and independently distributed around a mean of zero with constant variance $\sigma^2{}_b$ and the e_{ij}'s are normally and independently distributed with a mean of zero and variance σ^2, in conformity with an infinite model. Which form is followed is somewhat a matter of taste, though we prefer the form given in equation 8, for the reasons stated in Chapter 8. It is readily verified that the estimates of treatment differences based on the B_i's are given by the differences of

$$\frac{T_j}{r - \lambda} \quad \text{or} \quad \frac{T_{j'}}{r - \lambda} \tag{9}$$

and that the variance of the estimated difference of any 2 treatments is

$$\frac{2k}{(r - \lambda)} (\sigma^2 + k\sigma^2{}_b)$$

where $(\sigma^2 + k\sigma^2{}_b)$ is equal to $\frac{1}{b}\Sigma b^2{}_i$ for equation 8 or the obvious quantity for equation 8a. If we know

$$W = \frac{1}{\sigma^2} \quad \text{and} \quad W' = \frac{1}{\sigma^2 + k\sigma^2{}_b}$$

we may combine the two estimates of treatment differences weighting inversely as their variances, to give the best linear unbiased estimate.

These estimates of treatment differences are given by the differences of the quantities

$$y_j = \frac{\dfrac{Q_j}{rE} rEW + \dfrac{T_j}{r - \lambda}\left(\dfrac{r - \lambda}{k}\right)W'}{rEW + \dfrac{r - \lambda}{k}W'} \tag{10}$$

Substituting for Q_j in terms of V_j and T_j, we find

$$y_j = \frac{V_j}{r} + \frac{(W - W')}{r[Wt(k - 1) + W'(t - k)]}[(t - k)V_j - (t - 1)T_j]$$

or

$$y_j = \frac{V_j}{r} + \frac{\nu}{r}[(t - k)V_j - (t - 1)T_j] \tag{11}$$

where

$$\nu = \frac{W - W'}{Wt(k - 1) + W'(t - k)}$$

Multiplying y_j by r, and adding $\nu(k - 1)G$, where G is the grand total, we get the form given by Yates,[1]

$$Y_j = V_j + \nu W_j \tag{12}$$

where

$$W_j = (t - k)V_j - (t - 1)T_j + (k - 1)G \tag{13}$$

Treatment differences as totals of r replicates are given then by differences of the Y_j's. The total of the W_j's is zero and of the Y_j's is G.

The variance of a difference of any two Y_j's is equal to

$$2r^2 \frac{1}{rEW + \dfrac{r - \lambda}{k}W'}$$

which equals

$$\frac{2rk(t - 1)}{Wt(k - 1) + W'(t - k)}$$

Each Y_j may be regarded as having a variance of

$$\frac{rk(t - 1)}{Wt(k - 1) + W'(t - k)} \tag{14}$$

for any comparison of the t_j's.

26.4.1 The Estimation of the Weights

Following the usual procedure we estimate the weights W and W' by the analysis of variance which will have the form:

	df
Blocks eliminating treatments	$b - 1$
Treatments ignoring blocks	$t - 1$
Error	$rt - t - b + 1$
Total	$rt - 1$

The difficulty here is that the sum of squares for blocks eliminating treatments contains 2 components. The computational procedure described by Yates [9] is useful not only in obtaining the analysis of variance but also in indicating the composition of the sum of squares for blocks eliminating treatments. The notation is as follows:

$\mathrm{dev}^2 V$: sum of squares about the mean of the quantities T, etc.

B: block totals

†: obtained by addition or subtraction

*: requires checking

↔: same in both analyses

TABLE 26.3 STRUCTURE OF ANALYSES OF VARIANCE FOR BALANCED INCOMPLETE BLOCK DESIGN

Method a	df	Sum of Squares	Sum of Squares	Method b
Blocks (ignoring treatments)				Blocks (eliminating treatments)
Treatment component	$t - 1$	$\dfrac{\mathrm{dev}^2 V}{k(r - \lambda)}$	$\dfrac{\mathrm{dev}^2 W}{rt(t - k)(k - 1)}$	Treatment component
Remainder	$b - t$	†	↔ †	Remainder
Total	$b - 1$	$\dfrac{\mathrm{dev}^2 B^*}{k}$	†	Total
Treatments (eliminating blocks)	$t - 1$	$\dfrac{\mathrm{dev}^2 kQ}{k^2 rE}$	$\dfrac{\mathrm{dev}^2 V}{r}$	Treatments (ignoring blocks)
Intrablock error	$rt - t - b + 1$	†	↔ †	Intrablock error
Total	$rt - 1$	$\mathrm{dev}^2 y^*$	↔ $\mathrm{dev}^2 y^*$	Total

This analysis is self-explanatory and follows from general considerations. For example, $\mathrm{dev}^2 kQ/k^2 rE$ is of the form $\Sigma \hat{t}_j Q_j$ of Chapter 6, as is also $\mathrm{dev}^2 V/k(r - \lambda)$. The divisors may be checked with a little algebra. It is self-checking apart from the items with an asterisk as may also be proved algebraically.

The expectations of the mean squares for blocks eliminating treatments are as follows:

Treatment component	$t - 1$	$\sigma^2 + Ek\sigma^2_b$
Remainder	$v - t$	$\sigma^2 + k\sigma^2_b$
Total	$b - 1$	$\sigma^2 + \left(\dfrac{bk - t}{b - 1}\right)\sigma^2_b$

The expectation of the remainder mean square is as stated, because the sum of squares represents the sum of squares between block totals eliminating treatments with the appropriate divisor, and the variance of a block total on a per plot basis is $(\sigma^2 + k\sigma^2_b)$. The expectation of the treatment component may be obtained by subtraction.

Denoting the intrablock error mean square by **E** and the over-all mean square for blocks eliminating treatments by **B**, we may estimate W and W' by

$$w = \frac{1}{\mathbf{E}} \quad \text{and} \quad w' = \frac{t(r - 1)}{k(b - 1)\mathbf{B} - (t - k)\mathbf{E}}$$

If it is found that **B** is less than **E**, it may be assumed that σ^2_b is zero for the purposes of weighting, and, in that case, $w = w'$, and the equations for estimating differences reduced to $Y_s = V_s$.

26.4.2 Special Cases

There are two special cases.

(a) *Groups of Blocks Arranged in Replications.* In some cases it is possible to arrange the blocks in groups such that each group consists of one or more replicates of the treatments. Balanced lattices, for example, are of this type. If so, it is desirable to utilize this property in the design since the block variability as measured by σ^2_b will be less than if blocks were arranged completely at random. If there are c such groups, the block components of the analysis of variance may be further subdivided as shown in Table 26.4.

TABLE 26.4

	df	Expectation of Mean Square
Groups of blocks	$c - 1$	
Varietal component	$t - 1$	$\sigma^2 + Ek\sigma^2_b$
Remainder	$b - t - c + 1$	$\sigma^2 + k\sigma^2_b$
Varietal component and remainder	$b - c$	$\sigma^2 + \dfrac{bk - t - k(c - 1)}{b - c}\sigma^2_b$

The estimate of W' will, of course, be similarly modified.

In the special case when $c = r$, that is, when the blocks can be arranged in single replications, the expectation of the mean square for the $(b - r)$ degrees of freedom is $\sigma^2 + \dfrac{(r - 1)}{r} k\sigma^2{}_b$, and the estimate of W' is $w' = \dfrac{r - 1}{r\mathsf{B} - \mathsf{E}} \cdot$ This is the formula that we obtained for lattice designs, which are also arranged in complete replicates, and it holds for any incomplete block design with constant size of block.

Balanced incomplete block designs which may be arranged in sets of blocks, each set containing a complete replicate, are known as resolvable balanced incomplete block designs. Bose [10] obtained the result that, if a balanced incomplete block design with parameters t, b, r, k, λ is resolvable, the following inequality must hold:

$$b \geq t + r - 1$$

For, suppose the blocks of the ith set are

$$B_{i1}, B_{i2}, \cdots, B_{in}, \qquad i = 0, 1, 2, \cdots, r - 1$$

then,

$$t = nk, \qquad b = nr$$

Take a particular block, say B_{01}, and let l_{ij} be the number of treatments common to the blocks B_{01} and B_{ij}, for $i = 1, 2, \cdots, r - 1, j = 1, 2, \cdots, n$. Let m denote the mean value and s^2 the variance of the $n(r - 1)$ quantities l_{ij}. Then, it may be shown that if

$$m = \frac{k^2}{t}$$

then

$$s^2 = \frac{\Sigma(l_{ij} - m)^2}{n(r - 1)} = \frac{k(t - k)(b - t - r + 1)}{n^2(r - 1)(t - 1)}$$

The result follows since s^2 is non-negative.

If for a resolvable balanced incomplete block design the equality

$$b = t + r - 1$$

holds, the design is termed by Bose [10] an affine resolvable balanced incomplete block design. Two blocks belonging to different sets have the same number of treatments in common, for s^2 equals zero, and, conversely, a design with this property is affine resolvable.

Consider the 4 designs:

t	b	r	k	λ
6	10	5	3	2
10	18	9	5	4
28	36	9	7	2
14	26	13	7	6

The condition

$$b = t + r - 1$$

holds for all these designs, but they are not resolvable because the number of treatments common to any 2 blocks from different sets would be k^2/t always, and in no case is this an integer.

The design with parameters

$$t = 8, \quad b = 14, \quad r = 7, \quad k = 4, \quad \lambda = 3$$

is resolvable and necessarily affine resolvable. This design is, of course, the quasifactorial design corresponding to arrangements for a 2^3 system in blocks of 2^2 and is obviously resolvable from this method of construction.

(b) *Number of Blocks (b) = Number of Treatments (t).* In this case the analysis reduces to that shown in Table 26.5.

TABLE 26.5

	df	Sum of Squares
Blocks eliminating treatments	$t - 1$	$\dfrac{\text{dev}^2\, W}{rv(t - k)(k - 1)}$
Treatment ignoring blocks	$t - 1$	$\dfrac{1}{r}\,\text{dev}^2\, V$
Intrablock error	$(k - 2)t + 1$	By subtraction
Total	$kt - 1$	$\text{dev}^2\, y$

26.5 YOUDEN SQUARES

In the case of balanced incomplete block designs for which $t = b$, i.e., the number of treatments equals the number of blocks, it is possible to arrange the t blocks and treatments within the block in such a way that they form an incomplete Latin square. For example, with $t = 7$,

$k = 4$, $b = 7$, $r = 4$, the 7 treatments, say, 1, 2, 3, 4, $\cdots$, 7, may be arranged thus:

$$
\begin{array}{ccccccc}
1 & 2 & 3 & 4 & 5 & 6 & 7 \\
2 & 3 & 4 & 5 & 6 & 7 & 1 \\
4 & 5 & 6 & 7 & 1 & 2 & 3 \\
7 & 1 & 2 & 3 & 4 & 5 & 6
\end{array}
$$

If it is possible to arrange the experimental units according to a $t \times k$ classification, the rows and columns of which account for an appreciable portion of the variation of the experimental units, such an arrangement of treatments will be advantageous.

It was proved by Smith and Hartley [11] that, for all incomplete block designs in which the number of treatments is equal to the number of blocks, such an arrangement exists. These designs are known as Youden squares after Youden [12] who first discovered them. The analysis follows directly from the analysis of balanced incomplete block designs already discussed. The model that is assumed in the analysis is

$$y_{ijk} = \mu + r_i + b_j + t_k + e_{ijk} \tag{15}$$

i, j, k being the row, column, and treatment numbers, and the e_{ijk}'s being uncorrelated and distributed around zero with variance σ^2. If the intercolumn information is utilized, it is also assumed that the b_j's are uncorrelated and distributed around a mean of zero with constant variance.

The solution has already been obtained, because treatments are orthogonal to rows, namely, that the yield under treatment j is estimated to be

$$\frac{V_j}{r} + \frac{\nu}{r}[(t - k)V_j - (t - 1)T_j + (k - 1)G] \tag{16}$$

where V_j is the total under treatment k, T_j is the total of the blocks containing treatment j, and G is the grand total.

The analysis of variance is given in Table 26.6.

TABLE 26.6 ANALYSIS OF VARIANCE FOR YOUDEN SQUARES

Due to	df	Mean Square	Expectation of Mean Square
Rows	$k - 1$		
Columns eliminating treatments	$t - 1$	B	$\sigma^2 + \left(\dfrac{tk - t}{b - 1}\right)\sigma^2_b$
Treatments	$t - 1$		
Error	$(k - 2)(t - 1)$	E	σ^2
Total	$kt - 1$		

The estimation of W and W' is the same as for balanced incomplete block designs.

The Youden square design is a special case of an incomplete Latin square. We noted in Chapter 10 that a Latin square with one row removed constituted a valid experimental design. A Youden square is a Latin square with several rows removed, the remainder having the property that the columns form a set of balanced incomplete block designs. Cochran and Cox [3] give some interesting designs which consist of a Youden square adjoined to a complete Latin square. These designs are useful for a small number of treatments.

REFERENCES

1. YATES, F. Incomplete randomised blocks. *Ann. Eug.*, **7**, 121–140, 1936.
2. FISHER, R. A., and YATES, F. *Statistical tables.* Oliver and Boyd, Edinburgh. 3rd ed. 1948.
3. COCHRAN, W. G., and COX, G. M. Experimental designs. John Wiley & Sons, New York. 1950.
4. BOSE, R. C. On the construction of balanced incomplete block designs. *Ann. Eug.*, **9**, 353–400, 1939.
5. BHATTACHARYA, K. N. A new solution in symmetrical balanced incomplete block designs, *Sankhya*, **7**, 423–424, 1946.
6. HUSSAIN, Q. N. On the totality of the solutions for the symmetrical incomplete block designs. *Sankhyā*, **7**, 204–208, 1945.
7. RAO, C. R. General methods of analysis for incomplete block designs. *Jour. Amer. Stat. Assoc.*, **42**, 541–561, 1947.
8. FISHER, R. A. An examination of the different possible solutions of a problem in incomplete blocks. *Ann. Eug.*, **10**, 52–75, 1940.
9. YATES, F. The recovery of inter-block information in balanced incomplete block designs. *Ann. Eug.*, **10**, 317–325, 1940.
10. BOSE, R. C. A note on the resolvability of balanced incomplete block designs. *Sankhyā*, **8**, 249–256, 1947.
11. SMITH, C. A. B., and HARTLEY, H. O. The construction of Youden squares. *Jour. Roy. Stat. Soc. B*, **10**, 262–263, 1948.
12. YOUDEN, W. J. Experimental designs to increase accuracy of greenhouse studies. *Cont., Boyce Thompson Inst.*, **11**, 219–228, 1940.
13. CORNISH, E. A. The estimation of missing values in incomplete randomized block experiments. *Ann. Eug.*, **10**, 112–118, 1940.

CHAPTER 27

Partially Balanced
Incomplete Block Designs

27.1 INTRODUCTION

We have seen in the previous chapter that completely balanced incomplete block designs exist for certain numbers of treatments only with an inordinately large number of replicates. For example, with 8 treatments and blocks of 3 units, the lower limit to the number of replicates is 21, and with this number of replicates the blocks would consist of all combinations 3 at a time of the treatments. As a result Bose and Nair [1] were led to the consideration of partially balanced incomplete block designs. The present chapter will be based largely on the work of Bose and Nair [1] and of Rao.[2]

As a first step in the consideration of the problem, let us suppose that we have t treatments and wish to test them in b blocks of k units in such a way that each treatment is represented r times altogether. The blocks will be numbered from 1 to b, and we shall use the symbol δ_{ij} which equals unity if treatment j is in block i, and equals zero otherwise. The design is specified essentially by the numbers δ_{ij}, with $i = 1, 2, \cdots, b$ and $j = 1, 2, \cdots, t$, and we shall attempt to choose these numbers in such a way that the design has optimum properties. We consider, therefore, the estimation of treatment differences with an experiment arranged according to the set of numbers δ_{ij}. For the intrablock estimates we shall use the additive model

$$y_{ij} = \mu + b_i + \tau_j + e_{ij} \tag{1}$$

where

y_{ij} = the yield of treatment j in block i

μ = the common contribution

b_i = the contribution of block i

542

τ_j = the contribution of treatment j

e_{ij} = an error with mean zero, which we may regard as uncorrelated with all other e_{ij}'s and as having a variance of σ^2

For the interblock estimates, we use the model

$$Y_{i\cdot} = k\mu + \sum_j \delta_{ij}\tau_j + kb_i \qquad (2)$$

in which

$Y_{i\cdot}$ = the total of the block

and

b_i = an error with mean zero, uncorrelated with other b_i's and having a variance of $\dfrac{1}{k}(\sigma^2 + k\sigma^2{}_b)$

In addition, the b_i's may be regarded as being uncorrelated with the e_{ij}'s.

The intrablock estimates are obtained by minimizing

$$\sum_{ij}(y_{ij} - \mu - b_i - \tau_j)^2 \qquad (3)$$

and, since this is the ordinary 2-way classification problem, the estimates of the τ_j's are given in the notation of Chapter 6 by the equations,

$$\left(N_{\cdot j} - \sum_i \frac{n^2{}_{ij}}{N_{i\cdot}}\right)\hat{\tau}_j - \sum_{j' \neq j}\left(\sum_i \frac{n_{ij}n_{ij'}}{N_{i\cdot}}\right)\hat{\tau}_{j'} = Q_{j\cdot}, \quad j = 1, 2, \cdots, t \quad (4)$$

where

$$Q_j = Y_{\cdot j} - \sum_i \frac{n_{ij}Y_{i\cdot}}{N_{i\cdot}}$$

Applying these equations to the present problem, we have

$$n_{ij} = \delta_{ij}$$

$$N_{i\cdot} = k, \quad \text{for all } i\text{'s}$$

$$N_{\cdot j} = r, \quad \text{for all } j\text{'s}$$

so that the equations become

$$\left(r - \frac{r}{k}\right)\hat{\tau}_j - \sum_{j' \neq j}\left(\sum_i \frac{\delta_{ij}\delta_{ij'}}{k}\right)\hat{\tau}_{j'} = Q_{j\cdot}$$

$$= V_j - \frac{T_j}{k} \qquad (5)$$

where V_j is the total yield under treatment j and T_j is the total yield of the blocks containing treatment j.

The interblock estimates are obtained by minimizing

$$\sum_i \left(Y_i. - k\mu - \sum_j \delta_{ij}\tau_j \right)^2 \tag{6}$$

so that we have the equations

$$bk^2\hat{\mu} + k \sum_i \sum_j \delta_{ij}\hat{\tau}_j = kY.. \tag{7}$$

and

$$\sum_i \delta_{ij}(k\hat{\mu} + \sum_{j'} \delta_{ij'}\hat{\tau}_{j'}) = \sum_i \delta_{ij}Y_i., \qquad j = 1, 2, \cdots, t \tag{8}$$

The equations 7 and 8 reduce to the following:

$$bk^2\hat{\mu} + kr \sum_j^t \hat{\tau}_j = kY.. \tag{9}$$

$$rk\hat{\mu} + \sum_{j'} \left(\sum_i \delta_{ij}\delta_{ij'} \right) \hat{\tau}_{j'} = \sum_i \delta_{ij}Y_i., \qquad j = 1, 2, \cdots, t \tag{10}$$

We shall measure the τ's around a mean of zero, so that $\sum_j^t \hat{\tau}_j = 0$, and the equations for the $\hat{\tau}$'s are then

$$\sum_{j'} \left(\sum_i \delta_{ij}\delta_{ij'} \right) \hat{\tau}_{j'} = \sum_i \delta_{ij}Y_i. - \frac{rY..}{b} \tag{11}$$

We now note that

$$\sum_i \delta_{ij}\delta_{ij} = r$$

and that

$$\sum_i \delta_{ij}Y_i. = T_j$$

so that equation 11 may be written

$$r\hat{\tau}_j + \sum_{j' \neq j} \left(\sum_i \delta_{ij}\delta_{ij'} \right) \hat{\tau}_{j'} = T_j - \frac{rY..}{b} \tag{12}$$

and in this form the equations are strikingly similar to equation 5 for the intrablock estimates.

If we know $W = 1/\sigma^2$, and $W' = 1/(\sigma^2 + k\sigma^2{}_b)$, we can obtain the combined estimates of the τ_j's by minimizing the weighted sum of squares of deviations, that is,

$$W \sum_{ij} (y_{ij} - \mu - b_i - \tau_j)^2 + \frac{W'}{k} \sum_i (Y_i. - k\mu - \sum_j \delta_{ij}\tau_j)^2 \quad (13)$$

so that, if we combine equations 5 and 12 with the appropriate weights, the combined estimates are given by the equations

$$r \left[W \left(\frac{k-1}{k} \right) + \frac{W'}{k} \right] \hat{\tau}_j - \frac{W - W'}{k} \sum_{j' \neq j} \left(\sum_i \delta_{ij}\delta_{ij'} \right) \tau_{j'}$$

$$= WQ_j + \frac{W'}{k} \left(T_j - \frac{rY..}{b} \right) \quad (14)$$

Now, the quantity $\sum_i \delta_{ij}\delta_{ij'}$ is equal to the number of times that treatments j and j' occur together in a block, and, if we denote this by $\lambda_{jj'}$, the equations have the simple form

$$r \left[W \left(\frac{k-1}{k} \right) + \frac{W'}{k} \right] \hat{\tau}_j - \left(\frac{W - W'}{k} \right) \sum_{j' \neq j} \lambda_{jj'}\hat{\tau}_{j'}$$

$$= WQ_j + \frac{W'}{k} \left(T_j - \frac{rY..}{b} \right) \quad (15)$$

We may note in passing that these equations are particularly easy to solve in the case when $\lambda_{jj'}$ is a constant, equal to λ, say, for then they may be written as

$$\left\{ r \left[W \left(\frac{k-1}{k} \right) + \frac{W'}{k} \right] + \frac{\lambda}{k} (W - W') \right\} \hat{\tau}_j = WQ_j + \frac{W'}{k} \left(T_j - \frac{rY..}{b} \right)$$

since $\sum_j^t \hat{\tau}_j = 0$, and these equations give the estimates for differences of the τ_j's which we obtained in Chapter 26 for balanced incomplete blocks.

Given any arrangement of t treatments in b blocks of k units such that each treatment is represented r times, we may use equations 15 to obtain estimates of the τ_j's, or, by virtue of the condition we impose, of the $(\tau_j - \tau.)$'s. We now have to consider specifications of the $\lambda_{jj'}$'s and, therefore, of experimental designs. The case of $\lambda_{jj'}$, equal to λ for all j's and j''s has been discussed in Chapter 26, and we found that, for many combinations of the 2 numbers t and k, the number r necessary in order that $\lambda_{jj'}$ be constant was too big for practical purposes.

The next step is clearly to suppose that, given a treatment j, the numbers $\lambda_{jj'}$ are equal within groups of the other treatments. The $\lambda_{jj'}$'s are integers, less than or equal to r and we suppose that, over all j's and j''s, they take one of the values $\lambda_1, \lambda_2, \cdots, \lambda_s$ where $\lambda_1 > \lambda_2 > \lambda_3 \cdots > \lambda_s$. The set of treatments j', for which $\lambda_{jj'} = \lambda_1$, will be denoted by $S(j, 1)$ and called the first associates of treatment j. The set of treatments j', for which $\lambda_{jj'} = \lambda_2$, will be denoted by $S(j, 2)$ and called the second associates, and so on. With reference to any one treatment, say, j, the other treatments fall into s sets $S(j, 1), S(j, 2), \cdots, S(j, s)$, which are its first associates, its second associates, $\cdots$, its sth associates, respectively. Now we consider the equations 15 in this light, and, if we denote $r\left[W\left(\dfrac{k-1}{k}\right) + \dfrac{W'}{k}\right]$ by α, $\dfrac{W - W'}{k}$ by β, and $\left[WQ_j + \dfrac{W'}{k}\left(T_j - \dfrac{rY..}{b}\right)\right]$ by P_j, these equations may be written:

$$\alpha\hat{\tau}_1 - \beta\lambda_1 G_{11} - \beta\lambda_2 G_{12} \cdots - \beta\lambda_s G_{1s} = P_1$$

$$\alpha\hat{\tau}_2 - \beta\lambda_1 G_{21} - \beta\lambda_2 G_{22} \cdots - \beta\lambda_s G_{2s} = P_2$$

$$\cdots \cdots \cdots \cdots \cdots \cdots \cdots \cdots \cdots \quad (16)$$

$$\alpha\hat{\tau}_t - \beta\lambda_1 G_{t1} - \beta\lambda_2 G_{t2} \cdots - \beta\lambda_s G_{ts} = P_s$$

where G_{ij} = the sum of the $\hat{\tau}$'s for treatments in $S(i, j)$, and so on. The problem of design is reduced then to a choice of the sets $S(j, a)$, the ath associates of treatment j for each j, and we shall choose these sets in such a way that the equations 16 may be solved easily. The form of the equations 16 indicates that we can reduce the equations to be solved to a set of $(s + 1)$ equations in $\hat{\tau}_j, G_{j1}, G_{j2}, \cdots, G_{js}$, if certain conditions are satisfied. For, suppose we take the equation for $\hat{\tau}_1$, the sum of the equations for the group of treatments $S(1, 1)$ which are first associates of treatment 1, the sum of the equations for the group of treatments $S(1, 2)$ which are second associates of treatment 1, and so on, to the sum of the equations for the group of treatments which are sth associates of treatment 1. If the sets $S(j, a)$ are suitably chosen, this process will lead us to a set of $(s + 1)$ equations in the $(s + 1)$ unknowns $\hat{\tau}_1, G_{11}, G_{12}, \cdots, G_{1s}$. We would like, furthermore, for this set of $(s + 1)$ equations to have the same coefficients for all treatments, so that we can write down a general solution.

If we take any treatment, say, θ, and denote its first associates by $\theta^1_1, \theta^1_2, \cdots, \theta^1{}_{n_1}$, its second associates by $\theta^2_1, \theta^2_2, \cdots, \theta^2{}_{n_2}$ and so on, its sth associates being denoted by $\theta^s{}_1$, $\theta^s{}_2$, $\cdots$, $\theta^s{}_{n_s}$, we must have the following relations:

For the $\theta^1{}_j$'s:

$S(\theta^1{}_1, 1) + S(\theta^1{}_2, 1) + \cdots + S(\theta^1{}_{n_1}, 1)$
$$= k_{11}\theta + k^1{}_{11}S(\theta, 1) + k^2{}_{11}S(\theta, 2) + \cdots + k^s{}_{11}S(\theta, s)$$

$S(\theta^1{}_1, 2) + S(\theta^1{}_2, 2) + \cdots + S(\theta^1{}_{n_1}, 2)$
$$= k_{12}\theta + k^1{}_{12}S(\theta, 1) + k^2{}_{12}S(\theta, 2) + \cdots + k^s{}_{12}S(\theta, s) \quad (17a)$$

. . . .

$S(\theta^1{}_1, s) + S(\theta^1{}_2, s) + \cdots + S(\theta^1{}_{n_1}, s)$
$$= k_{1s}\theta + k^1{}_{1s}S(\theta, 1) + k^2{}_{1s}S(\theta, 2) + \cdots + k^s{}_{1s}S(\theta, s)$$

For the $\theta^2{}_j$'s:

$S(\theta^2{}_1, 1) + S(\theta^2{}_2, 1) + \cdots + S(\theta^2{}_{n_1}, 1)$
$$= k_{21}\theta + k^1{}_{21}S(\theta, 1) + k^2{}_{21}S(\theta, 2) + \cdots + k^s{}_{21}S(\theta, s)$$

$S(\theta^2{}_1, 2) + S(\theta^2{}_2, 2) + \cdots + S(\theta^2{}_{n_2}, 2)$
$$= k_{22}\theta + k^1{}_{22}S(\theta, 1) + k^2{}_{22}S(\theta, 2) + \cdots + k^s{}_{22}S(\theta, s) \quad (17b)$$

. . . .

$S(\theta^2{}_1, s) + S(\theta^2{}_2, s) + \cdots + S(\theta^2{}_{n_2}, s)$
$$= k_{2s}\theta + k^1{}_{2s}S(\theta, 1) + k^2{}_{2s}S(\theta, 2) + \cdots + k^s{}_{2s}S(\theta, s)$$

and so on. These relations must hold for any choice of θ, so that k_{11} must be constant for all θ's. Since each term of the sum $S(\theta^1{}_1, 1) + S(\theta^1{}_2, 1) + \cdots S(\theta^1{}_{n_1}, 1)$ contains θ once, k_{11} is equal to n_1, and therefore n_1, the number of 1st associates, is constant for all treatments. Similarly n_2, n_3, $\cdots$, n_s, the number of 2d, 3d, $\cdots$, sth associates, of a treatment is constant. Furthermore, k_{ij} is equal to zero for i unequal to j.

The equation 17 may be written as the single equation:

$S(\theta^i{}_1, l) + S(\theta^i{}_2, l) + \cdots + S(\theta^i{}_{n_i}, l)$
$$= \delta_{il}n_i\theta + k^1{}_{il}S(\theta, 1) + k^2{}_{il}S(\theta, 2) + \cdots + k^s{}_{il}S(\theta, s) \quad (18)$$

This states that any rth associate of θ occurs in $k^r{}_{il}$ of the sets $S(\theta^i{}_1, l)$, $S(\theta^i{}_2, l)$, $\cdots$, $S(\theta^i{}_{n_i}, l)$. We shall now prove that each of the sets $S(\theta^i{}_j, l)$, $j = 1, 2, \cdots, n_i$, contains the same number of members of any particular $S(\theta, r)$. Let $S(\theta^i{}_j, l)$ contain a_j of the elements of $S(\theta, r)$. Then a_j of the elements $\theta^r{}_y$, $y = 1, 2, \cdots, n_r$, are lth associates of $\theta^i{}_j$. Now, consider the sum of sets

$$S(\theta^r{}_1, l) + S(\theta^r{}_2, l) + \cdots + S(\theta^r{}_{n_r}, l)$$

which is equal, by equation 18, to

$$\delta_{rl} n_r \theta + k^1{}_{rl} S(\theta, 1) + k^2{}_{rl} S(\theta, 2) + \cdots + k^i{}_{rl} S(\theta, i) + \cdots + k^s{}_{rl} S(\theta, s)$$

This states that $k^i{}_{rl}$ of the $\theta^r{}_y$'s have any particular member of the set $S(\theta, i)$ as an lth associate; therefore, $a_j = k^i{}_{rl}$. Thus, we have the condition that, if any 2 treatments, θ and ϕ, are ith associates, the number of treatments common to the rth associates of θ and the lth associates of ϕ is equal to $k^i{}_{rl}$.

In this way we can say that the design is specified by t, k, n_1, n_2, $\cdots$, n_s, λ_1, λ_2, $\cdots$, λ_s, and the $k^i{}_{rl}$'s. We now proceed to determine the relationships that exist among these quantities.

Clearly,

$$n_1 + n_2 + \cdots + n_s = t - 1$$
$$n_1 \lambda_1 + n_2 \lambda_2 + \cdots + n_s \lambda_s = r(k - 1) \tag{19}$$

where r is the number of replicates, and, by symmetry,

$$k^i{}_{rl} = k^i{}_{lr} \tag{20}$$

Also from the set equations 18 and 20 and the result about $k^i{}_{rl}$, the relationship

$$n_i k^i{}_{rl} = n_r k^r{}_{il} \tag{21}$$

holds.

By summing all the s equations involving the sets $S(\theta^1{}_i, 1)$, $S(\theta^1{}_i, 2)$, we find that the sum of the left-hand sides is

$$n_1 \theta + (n_1 - 1) S(\theta, 1) + n_1 S(\theta, 2) + \cdots + n_1 S(\theta, s)$$

while the sum of the right-hand sides is

$$n_1 \theta + \left(\sum_j k^1{}_{ij} \right) S(\theta, 1) + \left(\sum_j k^2{}_{ij} \right) S(\theta, 2) + \cdots + \left(\sum_j k^s{}_{ij} \right) S(\theta, s)$$

so that

$$\sum_j k^1{}_{1j} = n_1 - 1$$
$$\sum_j k^l{}_{1j} = n_1, \qquad l \neq 1$$

Similarly, we may prove all the relations,

$$\sum_j k^l{}_{ij} = n_i - 1 \quad \text{if} \quad i = l$$
$$= n_i \quad \text{if} \quad i \neq l \tag{22}$$

27.2 THE SPECIFICATIONS OF PARTIALLY BALANCED INCOMPLETE BLOCK DESIGNS

We have, in section 27.1, obtained the specifications of partially balanced incomplete block designs as given by Bose and Nair.[1] We shall now adopt their terminology, as it is used exclusively in the literature. Summarizing the results of our discussion in section 27.1, we may state that a partially balanced incomplete block design has the properties:

1. There are t treatments in b blocks of k plots, and r replicates of each treatment.

2. With reference to any specified treatment, the remaining $(t-1)$ fall into m sets, the ith set of which occurs with the specified treatment in λ_i blocks and contains n_i treatments, the numbers n_i being the same, regardless of the treatment specified.

3. If we call the treatments that lie in a block λ_i times with a specified treatment θ, the ith associates of θ, the number of treatments common to the ith associates of θ and the jth associates of ϕ, where θ and ϕ are kth associates, is p^k_{ij}, this number being the same for any pair of kth associates.

The relationships we found are:

$$n_1 + n_2 + n_3 + \cdots + n_m = t - 1$$
$$n_1\lambda_1 + n_2\lambda_2 + n_3\lambda_3 + \cdots + n_m\lambda_m = r(k-1)$$
$$p^k_{ij} = p^k_{ji} \tag{23}$$
$$n_k p^k_{ij} = n_i p^i_{jk} = n_j p^j_{ik}$$
$$\sum_j p^k_{ij} = n_i - \delta_{ik}$$

The parameters r, b, t, λ_1, λ_2, $\cdots$, λ_m, n_1, n_2, $\cdots$, n_m are called by Bose and Nair [1] the parameters of the first kind and the p^k_{ij}'s the parameters of the second kind. It is shown by Bose and Nair that, by virtue of the relationships 23, there are, in fact, only $m\left(\dfrac{m^2-1}{6}\right)$ independent parameters of the second kind.

Let us now examine the possibilities of a partially balanced incomplete block design for 9 treatments in blocks of 3, and suppose we allow two classes of associate: namely, $\lambda_1 = 1$, $\lambda_2 = 0$. Then, the relations give

$$n_1 + n_2 = 8$$
$$n_1 = 2r$$

so that n_1 must be even.   We therefore consider the case $n_1 = 6$, $n_2 = 2$, and examine the p^k_{ij}'s.   We have the relations:

$$p^1_{11} + p^1_{12} = 5$$
$$p^1_{21} + p^1_{22} = 2$$
$$p^2_{11} + p^2_{12} = 6$$
$$p^2_{21} + p^2_{22} = 1$$

and, since

$$n_i p^i_{jk} = n_j p^j_{ik}$$

we have

$$n_1 p^1_{21} = n_2 p^2_{11} \quad \text{or} \quad 6p^1_{21} = 2p^2_{11}$$

and

$$n_1 p^1_{22} = n_2 p^2_{12} \quad \text{or} \quad 6p^1_{22} = 2p^2_{12}$$

Therefore, since each p^k_{ij} is a non-negative integer,

$$p^2_{21} = 1 \quad \text{and} \quad p^2_{22} = 0$$

or

$$p^2_{21} = 0 \quad \text{and} \quad p^2_{22} = 1$$

If $p^2_{21} = 1$, then $p^1_{22} = \frac{1}{3}$, and this is impossible.   Therefore, $p^2_{21} = 0$, and $p^2_{22} = 1$, and, therefore, $p^2_{11} = 6$, and, hence, $p^1_{21} = 2$, and $p^1_{11} = 3$.   The matrices p^k_{ij} are then

$$p^1_{ij} = \begin{pmatrix} 3 & 2 \\ 2 & 0 \end{pmatrix}, \qquad p^2_{ij} = \begin{pmatrix} 6 & 0 \\ 0 & 1 \end{pmatrix}$$

We have found, therefore, all the parameters of the design: namely, $t = 9$, $k = 3$, $r = 3$, $b = 9$, $n_1 = 6$, $\lambda_1 = 1$, $n_2 = 2$, $\lambda_2 = 0$, and the p^k_{ij} matrices above.   To obtain the actual design, we may assume that treatments 2, 3, 4, 5, 6, 7 occur with 1 in a block, and that 8 or 9 does not occur in a block with 1.   We then make up Table 27.1, in the order given, by using the matrices p^k_{ij}.

TABLE 27.1

Treatment	First Associates	Second Associates
1	2, 3, 4, 5, 6, 7	8, 9
8	2, 3, 4, 5, 6, 7	1, 9
9	2, 3, 4, 5, 6, 7	1, 8
2	1, 3, 4, 5, 8, 9	6, 7
6	1, 3, 4, 5, 8, 9	2, 7
7	1, 3, 4, 5, 8, 9	2, 6
3	1, 2, 6, 7, 8, 9	4, 5
4	1, 2, 6, 7, 8, 9	3, 5
5	1, 2, 6, 7, 8, 9	3, 4

The only arbitrary step in the formation of the table is the choice of 6 and 7 as second associates of 2, for we could have chosen any 2 of the 5 treatments 3, 4, 5, 6, and 7. The choice that we make determines the design. Given the table of associations, it is a simple matter to construct the design, which consists of the 9 blocks:

$$(123), (164), (175), (683), (695), (784), (793), (285), (294) \quad (24)$$

That the design has the required properties may be verified by the reader. Furthermore, we have shown that this is the only design, apart from permutations of the treatments, for which the parameters of the first kind are as stated. We may note that this design is identical with the one we would get by considering the 3^2 factorial system in blocks of 3 and using a set of 3 replicates, or the one we would get from the Latin square:

$$A\ (1) \quad B\ (2) \quad C\ (3)$$
$$C\ (6) \quad A\ (5) \quad B\ (9)$$
$$B\ (4) \quad C\ (8) \quad A\ (7)$$

by confounding rows, columns, and letters, respectively, in 1 of the 3 replicates.

Continuing with the same problem, we could take the case $n_1 = n_2 = 4$, and we would find that the matrices $p^k{}_{ij}$ can be

$$p^1{}_{ij} = \begin{pmatrix} 1 & 2 \\ 2 & 2 \end{pmatrix}, \qquad p^2{}_{ij} = \begin{pmatrix} 2 & 2 \\ 2 & 1 \end{pmatrix}$$

After a little enumerative work, it is found that these matrices correspond to the design in which the 9 treatments are arranged in a square, and rows are confounded in one replicate and columns in another, thus:

1	2	3
4	5	6
7	8	9

giving the blocks

$$(123), (456), (789), (147), (258), (369) \quad (25)$$

This is again a quasifactorial design: in fact, a simple lattice. In this case, with $n_1 = 4$, $n_2 = 4$, $r = 2$, $k = 3$, and $b = 6$, there are other $p^k{}_{ij}$ matrices which do not lead to a design.

As a second example, consider the case when $t = 8$ and $k = 3$, and let us see whether there is a design with $\lambda_1 = 1$ and $\lambda_2 = 0$. Since $n_1\lambda_1 + n_2\lambda_2 = r(k - 1)$, $n_1 = 2r$, we may consider the case $n_1 = 6$, $n_2 = 1$, and, consequently, $r = 3$. The $p^k{}_{ij}$ matrices are readily found to be

$$p^1{}_{ij} = \begin{pmatrix} 4 & 1 \\ 1 & 0 \end{pmatrix}, \qquad p^2{}_{ij} = \begin{pmatrix} 6 & 0 \\ 0 & 0 \end{pmatrix}$$

We may construct a table of associations, which satisfies these matrices (Table 27.2).

TABLE 27.2

Treatment	First Associates	Second Associates
1	2, 3, 4, 5, 6, 7	8
8	2, 3, 4, 5, 6, 7	1
2	1, 3, 4, 5, 6, 8	7
7	1, 3, 4, 5, 6, 8	2
3	1, 2, 5, 6, 7, 8	4
4	1, 2, 5, 6, 7, 8	3
5	1, 2, 3, 4, 7, 8	6
6	1, 2, 3, 4, 7, 8	5

The design is therefore some permutation of

$$(124), (176), (135), (825), (873), (846), (236), (745) \qquad (26)$$

27.3 DESIGNS FOR A SMALL NUMBER OF TREATMENTS

We shall not discuss in detail the problems of enumerating partially balanced incomplete block designs for any number of treatments, any size of block, and any number of replicates. Instead we shall consider the possibilities when the number of treatments is less than 10 and the block size is less than 5. The cases when the number of treatments is 4 or less are very simple, the possible designs having been discussed before.

With 5 treatments, symmetrical pairs require $(5 \times 4)/2 = 10$ blocks, and, therefore, 4 replicates, and there is little need to discuss other designs in blocks of 2 plots. All combinations 3 at a time would require $(5 \times 4 \times 3)/(3 \times 2 \times 1) = 10$ blocks, and therefore 6 replicates, so that again we need not discuss the case further, as it is unlikely that an experiment with less than 6 replicates could give sufficient accuracy of estimates or sufficient sensitivity. The testing of 5 treatments in blocks of 4 requires 5 replicates for a balanced incomplete block design, and again we do not consider the case worth discussing, though there is the possibility that the experimenter may wish to have a number of replicates that is not a multiple of 5.

With 6 treatments, symmetrical pairs require $(6 \times 5)/2 = 15$ blocks, and therefore 5 replicates, and this solution is satisfactory for most purposes. If the experimenter wishes to use blocks of 3, the design given at the beginning of Chapter 26 is a completely balanced incomplete block design with 10 blocks and 5 replicates. With blocks of 4, the minimum number of replicates for a balanced incomplete block design is 5, since $\lambda = r(k - 1)/(t - 1)$ is an integer, but actually the balanced incomplete block design includes all possible combinations of the treatments 4 at a time and involves 10 replicates. By examining the relationships 23, we can deduce the design

$$(1234), (1235), (1236), (1456), (2456), (3456) \tag{27}$$

for which

$$n_1 = 2, \qquad\qquad n_2 = 3$$

$$\lambda_1 = 3, \qquad\qquad \lambda_2 = 2$$

$$r = 4$$

$$p^1{}_{ij} = \begin{pmatrix} 1 & 0 \\ 0 & 3 \end{pmatrix}, \qquad p^2{}_{ij} = \begin{pmatrix} 0 & 2 \\ 2 & 0 \end{pmatrix}$$

This design involves 4 replicates and could be repeated if 8 (but *not* 10) replicates are desired.

For the case of 7 treatments, symmetrical pairs require 6 replicates, which is likely to be a reasonable one for most purposes. The balanced incomplete block design in blocks of 3 given in Chapter 26, namely,

$$(123), (145), (167), (246), (257), (347), (356) \tag{28}$$

requires 3 replicates and may be repeated if more replicates are necessary. From this design in blocks of 3, we obtain the balanced incomplete block design in blocks of 4 plots, namely,

$$(4567), (2367), (2345), (1357), (1346), (1256), (1247) \tag{29}$$

which requires 4 replicates.

With 8 treatments we may use symmetrical pairs if 7 replicates are possible. With r, less than 7, replicates, we may regard the 8 treatments as arising from 3 factors each at 2 levels and may therefore use any set of r of the 7 systems of confounding in blocks of 2. If blocks of

3 units are desired, the design given in the previous section may be used: namely,

$$(124), (176), (135), (825), (873), (846), (236), (745) \qquad (26)$$

To obtain arrangements in blocks of 4 units, we may again utilize a correspondence between the 8 treatments and the combinations of a 2^3 system.

With 9 treatments, symmetrical pairs require 8 replicates. A partially balanced design requiring 4 replicates is the following:

$$(12), (13), (14), (17), (23), (25), (28), (36), (39)$$
$$(45), (46), (47), (56), (58), (69), (78), (79), (89) \qquad (30)$$

which has parameters:

$$t = 9, \quad b = 18, \quad k = 2, \quad r = 4, \quad n_1 = 4, \quad \lambda_1 = 1, \quad n_2 = 4, \quad \lambda_2 = 0$$

$$p^1{}_{ij} = \begin{pmatrix} 1 & 2 \\ 2 & 2 \end{pmatrix}, \qquad p^2{}_{ij} = \begin{pmatrix} 2 & 2 \\ 2 & 1 \end{pmatrix}$$

There exist many pseudofactorial or lattice designs in blocks of 3, and there is no need to enumerate them here. With blocks of 4, a balanced incomplete block design requires 8 replicates, the blocks being

$$(1234), (1256), (1278), (1357), (1468), (1369)$$
$$(1489), (1579), (2389), (2459), (2679), (2347) \qquad (31)$$
$$(2568), (3589), (4679), (3456), (3678), (4578)$$

A partially balanced design which requires 4 replicates is the following:

$$(2347), (1358), (1269), (1567), (2468), (3459)$$
$$(1489), (2579), (3678) \qquad (32)$$

for which the parameters are:

$$t = 9, \quad b = 9, \quad k = 4, \quad r = 4, \quad n_1 = 4, \quad \lambda_1 = 2, \quad n_2 = 4, \quad \lambda_2 = 1$$

$$p^1{}_{ij} = \begin{pmatrix} 1 & 2 \\ 2 & 2 \end{pmatrix}, \qquad p^2{}_{ij} = \begin{pmatrix} 2 & 2 \\ 2 & 1 \end{pmatrix}$$

27.4 THE ANALYSIS OF PARTIALLY BALANCED INCOMPLETE BLOCK DESIGNS

The analysis of partially balanced incomplete block designs is a fairly straightforward process, particularly in view of the fact that the designs have been chosen so that the analysis is simple. We obtained equations

15 without any restriction on the design, except that the number of replicates of each treatment and the block size are to be constant. These equations would, in general, be rather difficult to solve, for, at most, they can be reduced to a set of $(t - 1)$ equations in $(t - 1)$ unknowns. To obtain the estimate of τ_j, we form $(s + 1)$ equations, of which the first is the jth equation of the set 16, namely,

$$\alpha \hat{\tau}_j - \beta\lambda_1 G_{j1} - \beta\lambda_2 G_{j2} - \cdots - \beta\lambda_s G_{js} = P_j \tag{33a}$$

the second is obtained by summing the equations of the set 16 for the first associates of treatment j, giving, because of equation 18, with $p^k{}_{ij}$'s substituted for $k^k{}_{ij}$'s,

$$\alpha G_{j1} - \beta\lambda_1(n_1\hat{\tau}_j + p^1{}_{11}G_{j1} + p^2{}_{11}G_{j2} + \cdots p^s{}_{11}G_{js})$$
$$- \beta\lambda_2(p^1{}_{12}G_{j1} + p^2{}_{12}G_{j2} + \cdots + p^s{}_{12}G_{js}) \tag{33b}$$
$$\cdots \cdots \cdots \cdots \cdots \cdots \cdots \cdots$$
$$- \beta\lambda_s(p^1{}_{1s}G_{j1} + p^2{}_{1s}G_{j2} + \cdots + p^s{}_{1s}G_{js}) = \Sigma P_{j1}$$

where ΣP_{j1} is the sum of the P_j's for the treatments that are first associates of treatment j; the third equation is obtained by summing the equations of the set 16 for the second associates of treatment j, giving

$$\alpha G_{j2} - \beta\lambda_1(p^1{}_{21}G_{j1} + p^2{}_{21}G_{j2} + \cdots + p^s{}_{21}G_{js})$$
$$- \beta\lambda_2(n_2\hat{\tau}_j + p^1{}_{22}G_{j1} + p^2{}_{22}G_{j2} + \cdots + p^s{}_{22}G_{js}) \tag{33c}$$
$$\cdots \cdots \cdots \cdots \cdots \cdots \cdots \cdots$$
$$- \beta\lambda_s(p^1{}_{2s}G_{j1} + p^2{}_{2s}G_{j2} + \cdots + p^s{}_{2s}G_{js}) = \Sigma P_{j2}$$

where ΣP_{j2} is the sum of the P_j's for the treatments that are second associates of treatment j. Continuing this process, we obtain $(s + 1)$ equations in $(s + 1)$ unknowns, $\hat{\tau}_j$, G_{j1}, G_{j2}, $\cdots$, G_{js}. By imposing the condition that the sum of the $\hat{\tau}_j$'s is to be zero, i.e., that

$$\hat{\tau}_j + G_{j1} + G_{j2} + \cdots + G_{js} = 0$$

the equations may be reduced to a set of s equations in s unknowns. We shall derive an explicit expression for the case when there are 2 classes of associates only. The reader may refer to the paper by Rao [2] for the solution for the case of 3 classes of associates.

With $s = 2$, the 3 equations in 3 unknowns are

$$\alpha \hat{\tau}_j \qquad - \beta\lambda_1 G_{j1} \qquad - \beta\lambda_2 G_{j2} = P_j$$
$$-\beta\lambda_1 n_1\hat{\tau}_j + (\alpha - \beta\lambda_1 p^1{}_{11} - \beta\lambda_2 p^1{}_{12})G_{j1} - (\beta\lambda_1 p^2{}_{11} + \beta\lambda_2 p^2{}_{12})G_{j2} = \Sigma P_{j1} \tag{34}$$
$$-\beta\lambda_2 n_2\hat{\tau}_j - (\beta\lambda_1 p^1{}_{21} + \beta\lambda_2 p^1{}_{22})G_{j1} + (\alpha - \beta\lambda_1 p^2{}_{21} - \beta\lambda_2 p^2{}_{22})G_{j2} = \Sigma P_{j2}$$

Utilizing the relation that

$$\hat{\tau}_j + G_{j1} + G_{j2} = 0 \qquad (35)$$

we have the 2 equations,

$$A'_{12}\hat{\tau}_j + B'_{12}G_{j1} = kP_j$$

$$A'_{22}\hat{\tau}_j + B'_{22}G_{j1} = k\Sigma P_{j1}$$

where

$$A'_{12} = k(\alpha + \beta\lambda_2) = r[W(k-1) + W'] + (W - W')\lambda_2$$

$$B'_{12} = k\beta(\lambda_2 - \lambda_1) = (\lambda_2 - \lambda_1)(W - W')$$

$$A'_{22} = k\beta\lambda_2 p^2_{12} - k\beta\lambda_1(n_1 - p^2_{11}) \qquad (36)$$

$$= k\beta\lambda_2 p^2_{12} - k\beta\lambda_1 p^2_{12} = k\beta(\lambda_2 - \lambda_1)p^2_{12}$$

$$= (W - W')(\lambda_2 - \lambda_1)p^2_{12}$$

and

$$B'_{22} = k\alpha - k\beta\lambda_1(p^1_{11} - p^2_{11}) - k\beta\lambda_2(p^1_{12} - p^2_{12})$$

$$= r[W(k-1) + W']$$

$$- (W - W')[\lambda_1(p^1_{11} - p^2_{11}) + \lambda_2(p^1_{12} - p^2_{12})]$$

Since

$$p^1_{11} + p^1_{12} = n_1 - 1$$

and

$$p^2_{11} + p^2_{12} = n_1$$

we have

$$(p^1_{12} - p^2_{12}) = -1 - (p^1_{11} - p^2_{11})$$

so that

$$B'_{22} = r[W(k-1) + W'] + (W - W')[\lambda_2 + (\lambda_2 - \lambda_1)(p^1_{11} - p^2_{11})]$$

The solution of the equations is then

$$\hat{\tau}_j = \frac{1}{\Delta'}[B'_{22}(kP_j) - B'_{12}(k\Sigma P_{j1})] \qquad (37)$$

where

$$\Delta' = A'_{12}B'_{22} - A'_{22}B'_{12} \qquad (38)$$

and where, recalling our definition of P_j,

$$kP_j = WkQ_j + W'\left(T_j - r\frac{Y_{..}}{b}\right)$$

$$= W(kQ_j) + W'T_j - rkW'y_{..} \qquad (39)$$

$y_{..}$ being the over-all mean.

Less work is involved computationally when n_2 is less than n_1 if we substitute for G_{j1} instead of G_{j2}. This gives the equations,

$$A'_{11}\hat{\tau}_j + B'_{11}G_{j2} = kP_j$$

$$A'_{21}\hat{\tau}_j + B'_{21}G_{j2} = k\Sigma P_{j2}$$

(40)

where

$$A'_{11} = k(\alpha + \beta\lambda_1) = r[W(k-1) + W'] + (W - W')\lambda_1$$

$$B'_{11} = k\beta(\lambda_1 - \lambda_2) = (W - W')(\lambda_1 - \lambda_2)$$

$$A'_{21} = k\beta\lambda_1 p^1{}_{21} + k\beta\lambda_2 p^1{}_{22} - k\beta\lambda_2 n_2 = k\beta(\lambda_1 p^1{}_{21} - \lambda_2 p^1{}_{12})$$

$$= (W - W')(\lambda_1 - \lambda_2)p^1{}_{12}$$

and

(41)

$$B'_{21} = k\alpha + k\beta\lambda_1(p^1{}_{21} - p^2{}_{21}) + k\beta\lambda_2(p^1{}_{22} - p^2{}_{22})$$

$$= r[W(k-1) + W']$$

$$+ (W - W')[\lambda_1(p^1{}_{21} - p^2{}_{21}) + \lambda_2(p^1{}_{22} - p^2{}_{22})]$$

$$= r[W(k-1) + W'] + (W - W')[\lambda_1 + (\lambda_1 - \lambda_2)(p^2{}_{22} - p^1{}_{22})]$$

The solution of these equations is

$$\hat{\tau}_j = \frac{1}{\Delta'}[B'_{21}(kP_j) - B'_{11}\Sigma(kP_{j2})]$$

(42)

where

$$\Delta' = A'_{11}B'_{21} - A'_{2r}B'_{11}$$

(43)

It may be noted that the two expressions for Δ' are identical algebraically.

The weights W and W' are estimated by performing the analysis of variance in 2 forms as in Table 27.3.

TABLE 27.3 ANALYSIS OF VARIANCE FOR PARTIALLY BALANCED INCOMPLETE BLOCK DESIGNS

Due to	Sum of Squares	df	Sum of Squares	Due to
Blocks ignoring treatments	B	b − 1	B'	Blocks eliminating treatments
Treatments eliminating blocks	T'	t − 1	T	Treatments ignoring blocks
Error	S_E	bk − b − t + 1	S_E	Error
Total	S	bk − 1	S	Total

In this table,

$$B = \frac{1}{k} Y^2{}_{i \cdot} - \text{CT}$$

$$T = \frac{1}{r} Y^2{}_{\cdot j} - \text{CT}$$

$$S = \sum_{ij} y^2{}_{ij} - \text{CT}$$

$$\text{CT} = \frac{(\text{grand total})^2}{bk}$$

$$T' = \Sigma \hat{t}_j Q_j$$

$\hat{t}_j$ being the intrablock estimates, and S_E and B' are obtained by subtraction.

We note that it is necessary to obtain the intrablock estimates, and these are given by the equations 37 or 42 with $W' = 0$, that is,

$$\hat{t}_j = \frac{1}{\Delta} [B_{22}(kQ_j) - B_{12}\Sigma(kQ_{j1})] \qquad (44)$$

where

$$A_{12} = r(k - 1) + \lambda_2$$

$$B_{12} = (\lambda_2 - \lambda_1) \qquad (45)$$

$$A_{22} = (\lambda_2 - \lambda_1)p^2{}_{12}$$

$$B_{22} = r(k - 1) + \lambda_2 + (\lambda_2 - \lambda_1)(p^1{}_{11} - p^2{}_{11})$$

and

$$\Delta = A_{12}B_{22} - A_{22}B_{12}$$

Alternatively, if n_2 is less than n_1, we may use the equation

$$\hat{t}_j = \frac{1}{\Delta} [B_{21}(kQ_j) - B_{11}\Sigma(kQ_{j2})] \qquad (46)$$

where

$$A_{11} = r(k - 1) + \lambda_1$$

$$B_{11} = (\lambda_1 - \lambda_2)$$

$$A_{21} = (\lambda_1 - \lambda_2)p^1{}_{12} \qquad (47)$$

$$B_{21} = r(k - 1) + \lambda_1 + (\lambda_1 - \lambda_2)(p^2{}_{22} - p^1{}_{22})$$

and

$$\Delta = A_{11}B_{21} - A_{21}B_{11}$$

The expectation of the mean squares may be seen by noting that, apart from terms involving the τ_j's,

$$E(S) = (bk - 1)\sigma^2 + k(b - 1)\sigma^2{}_b$$

$$E(S_E) = (bk - b - t + 1)\sigma^2$$

$$E(T) = (t - 1)\sigma^2 + (t - k)\sigma^2{}_b$$

so that

$$E(B') = (b - 1)\sigma^2 + (bk - t)\sigma^2{}_b$$

Denoting the mean square for error by **E** and for blocks eliminating treatments by **B**, we may then estimate W and W' by

$$w = \frac{1}{\mathbf{E}}, \qquad w' = \frac{bk - t}{k(b - 1)\mathbf{B} - (t - k)\mathbf{E}} \qquad (48)$$

The variance of an estimated treatment difference is found by the general procedure given in Chapter 6 for the 2-way classification. Considering the intrablock information, the difference of 2 treatments, j and j', is estimated to be

$$\hat{t}_j - \hat{t}_{j'} = -\frac{1}{\Delta}\{B_{22}(kQ_j - kQ_{j'}) - B_{12}[\Sigma(kQ_{j1}) - \Sigma(kQ_{j'1})]\}$$

This expression must be written in terms of the V_j's, and, if it is equal to

$$\alpha_j V_j - \alpha_{j'} V_{j'} + \text{etc.}$$

the variance of the difference is $(\alpha_j + \alpha_{j'})\sigma^2$. If j and j' are first associates, V_j occurs in $\Sigma(kQ_{j'})$ and $V_{j'}$ occurs in $\Sigma(kQ_j)$, so that the variance is

$$\frac{2k}{\Delta}(B_{12} + B_{22})\sigma^2$$

which equals

$$\frac{2k}{\Delta}B_{21}\sigma^2$$

If the j and j' are second associates, V_j and $V_{j'}$ enter only through Q_j and $Q_{j'}$, respectively, so that the variance is

$$2\frac{k}{\Delta}B_{22}\sigma^2$$

We may note that the variance of the difference is less if the 2 treatments are first associates than if they are second associates, since B_{12} ($= \lambda_2 - \lambda_1$) is negative, because we numbered the λ's so that $\lambda_1 > \lambda_2$. This merely states that the variance of the difference between 2 treatments is lower, the more times the 2 treatments occur together in a block.

By the same rule as for the intrablock estimates, the variance of the combined estimate of a treatment difference is $\dfrac{2k}{\Delta'} B'_{21}$ if the treatments are first associates, and $\dfrac{2k}{\Delta'} B'_{22}$ if the treatments are second associates.

The average variance of treatment differences, using intrablock information only, is

$$\frac{1}{(t-1)} \left(n_1 \frac{2k}{\Delta} B_{21} + n_2 \frac{2k}{\Delta} B_{22} \right) \sigma^2$$

$$= \frac{2k}{(t-1)\Delta} [(t-1)B_{22} + n_1 B_{12}]\sigma^2 \quad (49)$$

and the efficiency factor of the design is

$$\frac{(t-1)\Delta}{rk[(t-1)B_{22} + n_1 B_{12}]} \quad (50)$$

The average variance of treatment differences, using both intrablock and interblock information, is

$$\frac{2k}{(t-1)\Delta'} [(t-1)B'_{22} + n_1 B'_{12}] \quad (51)$$

27.5   A WORKED EXAMPLE

In Table 27.4 we give the results of a simulated partially balanced incomplete block design for 9 treatments in blocks of 3 plots. The results we obtained as

$$y_{in} = 50 + b_i + e_{ij}$$

where the b_i's were a random sample from a normal distribution with mean zero and variance of 100 and the e_{ij}'s a random sample from a normal population of mean zero and variance of 25.

TABLE 27.4

Block				Total
1	54 (3)	56 (8)	53 (4)	163
2	35 (2)	36 (7)	40 (4)	111
3	48 (1)	42 (7)	43 (5)	133
4	46 (7)	56 (8)	59 (9)	161
5	61 (4)	61 (5)	54 (6)	176
6	52 (3)	53 (9)	48 (5)	153
7	54 (1)	59 (8)	62 (6)	175
8	45 (2)	46 (9)	47 (6)	138
9	31 (1)	28 (2)	25 (3)	84

Grand Total 1294

The parameters of the design are:

$$t = 9, \quad k = 3, \quad r = 3, \quad b = 9$$

$$\lambda_1 = 1, \quad n_1 = 6, \quad \lambda_2 = 0, \quad n_2 = 2$$

$$p^1_{ij} = \begin{pmatrix} 3 & 2 \\ 2 & 0 \end{pmatrix}, \qquad p^2_{ij} = \begin{pmatrix} 6 & 0 \\ 0 & 1 \end{pmatrix}$$

The quantities that must be obtained to complete the intrablock estimation and analysis are as follows, where we use the formulas 46 because n_1 is greater than n_2:

$$A_{11} = r(k - 1) + \lambda_1 \qquad\qquad = 7$$
$$A_{21} = (\lambda_1 - \lambda_2)p^1_{12} \qquad\qquad = 2$$
$$B_{11} = \lambda_1 - \lambda_2 \qquad\qquad = 1$$
$$B_{21} = r(k - 1) + \lambda_1 + (\lambda_1 - \lambda_2)(p^2_{22} - p^1_{22}) = 8$$
$$\Delta = A_{11}B_{21} - A_{21}B_{11} \qquad\qquad = 54$$

The estimation equation is then

$$\hat{t}_j = \frac{8(3Q_j) - \Sigma(3Q_{j2})}{\Delta}$$

and the sum of squares for treatments eliminating blocks is $\frac{1}{3}\Sigma \hat{t}_j(3Q_j)$.

The computations are given in Table 27.5.

TABLE 27.5 COMPUTATIONS FOR THE EXAMPLE

Treatments j	V_j	T_j	$kQ_j = 3Q_j$ $= 3V_j - T_j$	2nd Associates	$\Sigma(kQ_{j2})$	Intra-block $\hat{t}_j$	P_j	ΣP_{j2}	Combined Estimate
1	133	392	7	4,9	34	0.41	0.12	0.90	0.08
2	108	333	−9	5,8	8	−1.48	−0.36	0.33	−2.31
3	131	400	−7	6,7	−33	−0.43	−0.22	−0.78	−0.75
4	154	450	12	1,9	29	1.24	0.32	0.70	1.38
5	152	462	−6	2,8	5	−0.98	−0.11	0.08	−0.69
6	163	489	0	3,7	−40	0.74	0.08	−1.08	1.20
7	124	405	−33	3,6	−7	−4.76	−0.86	−0.14	−4.89
8	171	499	14	2,5	−15	2.35	0.44	−0.47	2.87
9	158	452	22	1,4	19	2.91	0.58	0.44	3.06
Sum of column	1294	3882 $= 3 \times 1294$	0		0	0	−0.01 *	−0.02 *	−0.05 *

* Are unequal to zero because of rounding-off errors.

ANALYSIS OF VARIANCE

Due to	Sum of Squares	df	Sum of Squares	Due to
Blocks ignoring treatments	2520.52	8	1473.3	Blocks eliminating treatments
Treatments eliminating blocks	97.99	8	1145.18	Treatments ignoring blocks
Error	133.34	10	133.34	Error
Total	2751.85	26	2751.85	Total

The estimated variance of the intrablock estimate of the difference of 2 treatments is

$$2 \times 3 \times \tfrac{8}{54} \times 13.33 = 11.85 \quad \text{if they are 1st associates}$$

and

$$2 \times 3 \times \tfrac{9}{54} \times 13.33 = 13.33 \quad \text{if they are 2nd associates}$$

The efficiency factor of the design is

$$\frac{8 \times 54}{3 \times 3(8 \times 8 + 2 \times 1)} = 73\%$$

If then the reduction of block size from 9 units to 3 units resulted in a lowering of variance within block by about $\tfrac{1}{4}$, the design has proved to be of value without using the interblock information. It is not possible to estimate this reduction in variance unless the design is resolvable and the property was utilized in the experiment.

Turning now to the extraction of the interblock information, we compute the following quantities:

$$E = 13.334 \qquad\qquad B = 184.17$$

$$w = \frac{1}{13.334} \qquad\qquad = 0.0750$$

$$w' = \frac{18}{24 \times 184.17 - 6 \times 13.334} = 0.00415$$

$$r\left(w + \frac{w'}{k-1}\right) = R \qquad\qquad = 0.2312$$

$$\Lambda_2 = \lambda_2(w - w') \qquad\qquad = 0$$

$$\Lambda_1 = \lambda_1(w - w') \qquad\qquad = 0.0708$$

$$A'_{12} = R(k-1) + \Lambda_2 \qquad\qquad = 0.4624$$

$$A'_{22} = (\Lambda_2 - \Lambda_1)p^2{}_{12} \qquad\qquad = 0$$

$$B'_{12} = \Lambda_2 - \Lambda_1 \qquad\qquad = -0.0708$$

$$B'_{22} = A'_{12} + B'_{12}(p^1{}_{11} - p^2{}_{11}) \qquad = 0.6748$$

$$\Delta' = A'_{12}B'_{22} - A'_{22}B'_{12} \qquad\qquad = 0.31203$$

$$A'_{11} = R(k-1) + \Lambda_1 \qquad\qquad = 0.5332$$

$$A'_{21} = (\Lambda_1 - \Lambda_2)p^1{}_{22} \qquad\qquad = 0.1416$$

$$B'_{11} = \Lambda_1 - \Lambda_2 \qquad\qquad = 0.0708$$

$$B'_{21} = A'_{11} + B'_{11}(p^2{}_{22} - p^1{}_{12}) \qquad = 0.6040$$

$$\Delta' = A'_{11}B'_{21} - A'_{21}B'_? \qquad\qquad = 0.31203$$

The estimates are given by the equations

$$\hat{\tau}_j = \frac{k}{\Delta'}(B'_{21}P_j - B'_{11}\Sigma P_{j2})$$

where

$$P_j = \frac{w}{k}(kQ_j) + \frac{w'}{k}T_j - rw'y_{..}$$

In this case,

$$P_j = \frac{0.0750}{3}(3Q_j) + \frac{0.00415}{3}T_j - 3 \times 0.00415 \times 47.926$$

$$= 0.0250(3Q_j) + 0.00138T_j - 0.5967$$

and

$$\hat{\tau}_j = \frac{3}{0.31203}(0.6040P_j - 0.0708\Sigma P_{j2})$$

$$= 5.80P_j - 0.68\Sigma P_{j2}$$

The variance of a treatment difference utilizing both interblock and intrablock information is

$$\frac{2k}{\Delta'}B'_{21} = 11.61 \quad \text{if the treatments are 1st associates}$$

and

$$\frac{2k}{\Delta'}B'_{22} = 12.98 \quad \text{if the treatments are 2nd associates}$$

We note that the utilization of the interblock information has resulted in a trivial lowering of variance. In general, we would find out if such were the case before undertaking combined estimation.

27.6   THE ENUMERATION OF PARTIALLY BALANCED INCOMPLETE BLOCK DESIGNS

Partially balanced incomplete block designs include, as a special case, completely balanced incomplete block designs, and the same methods may be used for enumeration. A brief review only of these methods will be given, and the reader may refer to Bose and Nair [1] for a complete discussion.

27.6.1   Geometrical Configurations

Several designs arise by translation of geometrical configurations: e.g., the Desargue configuration of 2 triangles in perspective gives rise to a design for 10 treatments in blocks of 3. If we take any regular polyhedron and regard the points as treatments and the faces as blocks, we get a partially balanced incomplete block design. For example, with a cube (Figure 27) we get the design

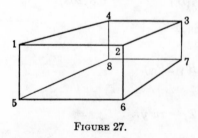

FIGURE 27.

$(1, 2, 3, 4)$, $(1, 2, 5, 6)$, $(1, 4, 5, 8)$, $(2, 3, 6, 7)$

$(3, 4, 7, 8)$, $(5, 6, 7, 8)$

In this case there are 3 classes of associates. Taking 1 as the fixed treatment, treatments 2, 4, and 5 are first associates occurring twice with treatment 1 in a block. Treatments 3, 6, and 8 are second associates occurring once with treatment 1 in a block, and treatment 7 is a third associate occurring not at all in a block with treatment 1. The parameters of the design are:

$$t = 8, \quad b = 6, \quad k = 4, \quad r = 3$$

$$\lambda_1 = 2, \quad n_1 = 3; \quad \lambda_2 = 1, \quad n_2 = 3; \quad \lambda_3 = 0, \quad n_3 = 1$$

$$p^1{}_{ij} = \begin{bmatrix} 0 & 2 & 0 \\ 2 & 0 & 1 \\ 0 & 1 & 0 \end{bmatrix}, \quad p^2{}_{ij} = \begin{bmatrix} 2 & 0 & 1 \\ 0 & 2 & 0 \\ 1 & 0 & 0 \end{bmatrix}, \quad p^3{}_{ij} = \begin{bmatrix} 0 & 3 & 0 \\ 3 & 0 & 0 \\ 0 & 0 & 0 \end{bmatrix}$$

$$\text{Efficiency factor} = \frac{14}{17}$$

This design may also be regarded as a 2^3 lattice in blocks of 2^2 plots.

The $k \times k$ simple lattice in a sense arises in this way, having parameters:

$$t = k^2, \quad b = 2k, \quad k = k, \quad r = 2$$

$$n_1 = 2(k - 1), \quad \lambda_1 = 1, \quad n_2 = (k - 1)^2, \quad \lambda_2 = 0$$

$$p^1{}_{ij} = \begin{pmatrix} k - 2 & k - 1 \\ k - 1 & (k - 1)(k - 2) \end{pmatrix}, \quad p^2{}_{ij} = \begin{pmatrix} 2 & 2(k - 2) \\ 2(k - 2) & (k - 2)^2 \end{pmatrix}$$

Any k^n quasifactorial design in blocks of k^{n-1} plots with n different replicates is a partially balanced incomplete block design. The design is a geometrical configuration one since it is obtainable by taking sets of $(n - 1)$-dimensional hyperplanes from an n-dimensional lattice.

27.6.2 Application of Finite Geometries

A general method of obtaining partially balanced incomplete block designs is to exclude from $EG(k, p^n)$ the origin $(0, 0, \cdots, 0)$ and regard the remaining points as treatments. We then take as blocks all the $(k - m)$ flats that do not contain the origin.

To obtain partially balanced incomplete block designs from $PG(k, p^n)$, we exclude any one point, say $(1, 0, 0, \cdots, 0)$, and regard the remaining points as treatments. Blocks are formed by taking all $(k - m)$ flats that do not contain the excluded point. We note in passing that, without excluding these points, and taking all $(k - m)$ flats as blocks, we obtained some of the completely balanced incomplete block designs of Chapter 26.

As examples, we quote the following from Bose and Nair's paper: [1]

*1. EG(k, p^n) with $k = 2$, $m = 1$.** The number of treatments is $s^2 - 1$, where $s = p^n$. The parameters of the design are found to be:

$$t = s^2 - 1, \quad b = s^2 - 1, \quad r = s, \quad k = s$$

$$\lambda_1 = 1, \quad n_1 = s^2 - s; \quad \lambda_2 = 0, \quad n_2 = s - 2$$

$$p^1{}_{ij} = \begin{pmatrix} (s-1)^2 & (s-2) \\ (s-2) & 0 \end{pmatrix}, \qquad p^2{}_{ij} = \begin{pmatrix} s^2 - s & 0 \\ 0 & s - 3 \end{pmatrix}$$

With $s = 2^2$, if the 15 treatments being denoted by (ij), $i, j = 0, 1, 2, 3$, excluding (00), the blocks are as shown in Table 27.6.

TABLE 27.6

(10, 11, 12, 13)	(20, 21, 22, 23)	(30, 31, 32, 33)
(01, 11, 21, 31)	(02, 12, 22, 32)	(03, 13, 23, 33)
(10, 01, 32, 23)	(20, 31, 02, 13)	(30, 21, 12, 03)
(10, 31, 22, 03)	(20, 01, 12, 33)	(30, 11, 02, 23)
(10, 21, 02, 33)	(20, 11, 32, 03)	(30, 01, 22, 13)

2. PG(k, p^n) with $k = 3$, $m = 1$. The parameters of the design are, with $s = p^n$, as follows:

$$t = s^3 + s^2 + s, \quad b = s^2, \quad r = s^2, \quad k = s^2 + s + 1$$

$$\lambda_1 = 3, \quad n_1 = s^3 + s^2; \quad \lambda_2 = 0, \quad n_2 = s - 1$$

$$p^1{}_{ij} = \begin{pmatrix} s^3 + s^2 - s & s - 1 \\ s - 1 & 0 \end{pmatrix}, \qquad p^2{}_{ij} = \begin{pmatrix} s^2 + s & 0 \\ 0 & s - 2 \end{pmatrix}$$

Similarly, we can cut out points of a particular m flat and take all $(m + 1)$ flats except those that contain the excluded m flat as blocks. For example, we may remove all points on a line from $PG(3, p^n)$ and

---

* It should be noted that k in $EG(k, p^n)$ bears no relationship to k the size of the block. Which k is meant is always clear from the context.

take as blocks all planes that do not contain the excluded line to give a design with the following parameters:

$$t = s^3 + s^2, \quad b = s^3 + s^2, \quad r = s^2 + s, \quad k = s^2 + s$$

$$\lambda_1 = s + 1, \quad n_1 = s^3; \quad \lambda_2 = s, \quad n_2 = s^2 - 1$$

$$p^1{}_{ij} = \begin{pmatrix} s^3 - s^2 & s^2 - 1 \\ s^2 - 1 & 0 \end{pmatrix}, \quad p^2{}_{ij} = \begin{pmatrix} s^3 & 0 \\ 0 & s^2 - 2 \end{pmatrix}$$

27.6.3 The Method of Differences

The reader should refer to Bose and Nair's paper for a description of this method. The designs are obtained by the use of moduls. An example is the design

$$(124) \quad (235) \quad (340) \quad (451) \quad (502) \quad (013)$$

for 6 treatments, denoted by 0, 1, 2, 3, 4, 5, in blocks of 3 plots, the parameters being

$$t = 6, \quad b = 6, \quad r = 3, \quad k = 3$$

$$\lambda_1 = 2, n_1 = 1, \quad \lambda_2 = 1, n_2 = 4$$

$$p^1{}_{ij} = \begin{pmatrix} 0 & 0 \\ 0 & 4 \end{pmatrix}, \quad p^2{}_{ij} = \begin{pmatrix} 0 & 2 \\ 2 & 2 \end{pmatrix}$$

This design is interesting mainly as a product of the method, it being generated by addition from the first block, the rule of addition being the ordinary one with reduction modulo 6.

27.6.4 Other Methods

Some simple ways of obtaining designs are as follows:

1. If $t = pq$, arrange the treatments in a $p \times q$ array, and take for the pq blocks each treatment and the treatments that occur with it in a row or in a column.

2. Using the same array, form pq blocks by taking all the treatments that occur in a row or a column with each treatment, excluding the treatment itself.

3. If $p = q$, a Latin square may be constructed, and all treatments having the same row, column, and letter as each treatment make up a block.

4. Given an incomplete block design, it can be inverted if treatments are renamed as blocks and blocks as treatments, and this sometimes gives another incomplete block design.

27.7 CONCLUSION

From the viewpoint of the experimenter, we may regard the incomplete block design problem as solved for all practical purposes with perhaps a few exceptions. The choice between various incomplete block designs and lattice designs is based primarily on the size of block desired and the number of replicates possible. With designs that have a low number of replicates, the efficiency factor is important, if there is doubt concerning the accuracy of the utilization of interblock information because of a low number of degrees of freedom for blocks.

The designs have been chosen primarily on the basis of the simplicity of the analysis. Many other designs which appear offhand to be reasonable are not practical on this basis. For example, a design for 50 treatments in blocks of 4 may be generated by taking as the initial block (0, 1, 2, 3) and adding (modulo 50) 1, 2, 3, $\cdots$, 49, respectively, to give 49 more blocks. Such a design is, however, difficult to analyze, because it is necessary to invert a 50×50 matrix, which is very tedious, even though the matrix is of a particular type, known as circulant.*

Further developments of partially balanced incomplete block designs are discussed by Rao [2] and Nair and Rao.[3,4] For example, other designs may be included in the class if the λ's are not restricted to be unequal.

REFERENCES

1. BOSE, R. C., and NAIR, K. R.   Partially balanced incomplete block designs. *Sankhyā*, **4**, 337–372, 1939.
2. RAO, C. R.   General methods of analysis for incomplete block designs. *Jour. Amer. Stat. Assoc.*, **42**, 541–561, 1947.
3. NAIR, K. R., and RAO, C. R.   A note on partially balanced incomplete block designs. *Sci. and Cult.*, **7**, 516, 1942.
4. NAIR, K. R., and RAO, C. R.   Incomplete block designs for experiments involving several groups of varieties. *Sci. and Cult.*, **7**, 625, 1942.

* Since writing the above, the author has found relatively simple solutions for this type of design, and the matter will be dealt with in a paper.

CHAPTER 28

Experiments on Infinite Populations
and Groups of Experiments

28.1 INTRODUCTION

We have considered the more important designs involving 1, 2, 3, or more factors from the point of view of both design and analysis. It should be noted, however, that we have always restricted ourselves to a discussion of the effect of the factors at the levels actually tested. There is a whole class of experiments which have the common feature that they involve factors or pseudofactors with a large, and often infinite, population of possible levels of the factors. For instance, we may take the 1-factor case, in which we are interested in the yields of a population of varieties of corn, but can, of course, test only a finite number of the varieties in an experiment. Again, for the 2-factor case, we might be interested in the differential effects of a number of nutrient treatments on a large population of varieties of corn. We can do no more than test the treatments on a sample of the population of varieties, but we are interested in the effects of the treatments on the whole population of varieties, possibly even more than in the effects of the treatments on the actual sample of varieties used in the experiment. For the 3-factor case, a typical and frequently occurring example is the comparison of a fixed set of varieties or treatments over a large population of places and a large population of years. The experiment we actually make must involve only a sample of the population of places and a sample of the population of years. The problems encountered have come to be known as the problems arising with a series of experiments (Cochran,[1] Yates and Cochran [2]). In this situation, the experimenter is often interested not only in the determination of effects for the individual experiments given by particular choices of place and year, but also in the effects for the population of possible years with a fixed place and the effects for the populations of possible years and possible places. In fact, the whole program of hybrid corn breeding in the United States is based on precisely this situation, and problems of design and analysis arise (cf. Federer and Sprague [3] for example). We shall endeavor in this chapter to give a unified discussion of this type of problem.

There are essentially two aspects: namely, the design of the whole experiment, which will include a discussion of the number of levels of factors that should be tested, and the interpretation of experimental results. It is intuitively clear that, in the absence of *a priori* information, the experiment actually made gives the best point estimate of a treatment effect for the whole population, even though this estimate is the estimated effect for the sample of levels actually used. In applying the estimate to the whole population of levels, we must take account of the fact that we have used only a sample of levels, and the error of the estimate will contain additional components of error. As a result, we shall become involved in the estimation and interpretation of components of variance. The estimation of components of variance was discussed in Chapter 6, and the reader may find it necessary to refer to that chapter.

The problems that arise are of very wide occurrence, and, although we shall couch them in agronomic terms, the reader should have no difficulty in translating the concepts into the language of engineering, psychology, education, and any other subject-matter field.

28.2 THE 1-FACTOR EXPERIMENT

Suppose we can obtain a new population of varieties of corn, for example, by breeding from a cross of two varieties of different geographic origin. We shall wish to determine characteristics of this population, and, confining ourselves to one attribute, say, yield, we shall wish to obtain knowledge on the distribution of the yields of the possible varieties that we can obtain by a particular breeding program. It is probably reasonable to assume that the yields of the possible varieties are distributed normally, and we would then wish to obtain an estimate of the mean μ and the variance σ^2_v of the distribution. To do this we shall perform the steps of the breeding program and obtain a random sample of, say, v of the possible varieties, which we shall test in a replicated experiment with randomized blocks. Insofar as the mean μ will depend markedly on the environment in which the varieties are grown, while the variance may be more stable, we shall concern ourselves mainly with the estimation of σ^2_v. Knowledge of σ^2_v is important, for we know that, if we adopt the rule of taking the top p percent of a random sample of size v of the varieties we generate, the selection being made on the basis of the observed means of the v varieties which are each subject to a variance of σ^2_e, then the difference between the true mean of the selected p percent and the mean of whole population will have an expectation of

$$\frac{K\sigma^2_v}{\sqrt{\sigma^2_e + \sigma^2_v}}$$

where K depends only on p and v (see Yates,[4] for example, or any text on selection in genetic material, such as Lush [5]). Given estimates of σ^2_v and σ^2_e, we can say whether it is worth our time to work on the population to extract the higher members. The formula we have given is also interesting in that it demonstrates the importance of reducing σ^2_e by the experimental design.

Suppose that we test the sample of v varieties with r randomized blocks of v plots. Assuming that the yields y_{ij} are given additively, we use the model

$$y_{ij} = \mu + b_i + v_j + e_{ij}$$

where

$i = $ block number $= 1, 2, \cdots, r$

$j = $ variety $\qquad = 1, 2, \cdots, v$

$v_j = $ normal independent random variables with mean zero and variance σ^2_v

and the e_{ij}'s are uncorrelated with a mean of zero and may be assumed to have constant variance σ^2.

We have found that the expectations of mean squares in the analysis of variance are as given in Table 28.1.

TABLE 28.1

Due to	df	Mean Square	Expectation of Mean Square
Blocks	$r - 1$		
Varieties	$v - 1$	V	$\sigma^2 + \dfrac{r}{v-1}\Sigma(v_j - \bar{v})^2$
Error	$(r-1)(v-1)$	E	σ^2

Since the v_j's are random variables from a normal distribution with variance σ^2_v, the expectations are

$$E(E) = \sigma^2$$

and

$$E(V) = \sigma^2 + r\sigma^2_v$$

so that

$$E\left(\frac{V - E}{r}\right) = \sigma^2_v$$

We may estimate σ^2 and σ^2_v by these equations. Under the infinite model, $(r-1)(v-1)E$ and $(v-1)V$ will follow χ^2 distributions independently. The variance of the estimate $\hat{\sigma}^2_v$ is then

$$\frac{2}{r^2}\left[\frac{(\sigma^2 + r\sigma^2_v)^2}{(v-1)} + \frac{(\sigma^2)^2}{(r-1)(v-1)}\right]$$

This formula may be used to estimate the number of varieties and replications that should be used to obtain a satisfactory estimate, given an idea of the values of σ^2 and σ^2_v that will be encountered. We gave a simple illustration of the use of this formula in Chapter 6.

The test of the hypothesis that $\sigma^2_v = 0$ is easily made by the F test. The same test may be obtained by applying the likelihood ratio criterion to the joint distribution of the y_{ij}'s under normality assumptions. A test of the hypothesis that $\sigma^2_v = k$, unequal to zero, does not appear to be obtainable easily. It is relatively easy to give a test of the hypothesis that σ^2_v/σ^2_e equals some constant, but such a hypothesis is not of practical interest, because σ^2_e is essentially a property of the measuring device, namely, the experiment, whereas σ^2_v is a property of the material being measured. We, therefore, expect σ^2_v to be relatively constant, while σ^2_e may vary with the type of experimental material (i.e., field plots in the present case) on which we obtain the measurements, and with the experimental design used.

If we were interested in the mean of the population of varieties, a problem of allocation of resources arises, because the variance of the observed mean about the true mean of the population, that is, the mean we would get if each member of the population were tested on the set of plots used, is

$$\frac{\sigma^2 + r\sigma^2_v}{rv} = \frac{\sigma^2_v}{v} + \frac{\sigma^2}{rv}$$

This formula is instructive in indicating that having considerable replication of a chosen sample of varieties is less important than choosing a large sample of varieties, and, consequently, having less replication per variety.

28.3 THE 2-FACTOR EXPERIMENT

An example of the type of problem we shall discuss is the testing of t treatments on a random sample of v varieties. There are several designs possible for such an experiment, and we shall first consider the case when randomized blocks of vt plots are used. The mathematical model we shall use is

$$y_{ijk} = \mu + b_i + t_j + v_k + (tv)_{jk} + e_{ijk} \tag{1}$$

$$i = \text{block number} \quad = 1, 2, \cdots, r$$

$$j = \text{treatment number} = 1, 2, \cdots, t$$

$$k = \text{variety number} \quad \doteq 1, 2, \cdots, v$$

and μ, b_i, and t_j are unknown constants, the other terms being random variables. The additive effect of treatment j in combination with variety k consists of 3 parts, t_j, v_k, and $(tv)_{jk}$, of which t_j is a fixed constant and the v_k's and $(tv)_{jk}$'s are random variables because we have taken a random sample of varieties. We may assume that the expectations of v_k and of $(tv)_{jk}$ are zero, so that t_j is the true effect of treatment j over the whole population of varieties. We shall assume the v_k's to be normally distributed with variance σ^2_v, and the $(tv)_{jk}$'s to be normally distributed with variance σ^2_{tv}, which does not depend on j or k. As usual, we may assume the e_{ijk}'s to be uncorrelated with mean zero and constant variance σ^2. We suppose that the object of the experiment is to obtain estimates of the differences between the t_j's and the errors of these estimates. The structure of the analysis of variance is given in Table 28.2.

TABLE 28.2 STRUCTURE OF ANALYSIS OF VARIANCE FOR RANDOMIZED BLOCK EXPERIMENT OF t TREATMENTS WITH A RANDOM SAMPLE OF v VARIETEIES

Due to	df	Mean Square	Expectation of Mean Square
Blocks	$r - 1$		
Treatments	$t - 1$	T	$\sigma^2 + r\sigma^2_{tv} + \dfrac{rv}{t-1}\Sigma(t_j - \bar{t})^2$
Varieties	$v - 1$	V	$\sigma^2 + r\sigma^2_{tv} + rt\sigma^2_v$
Treatments × varieties	$(t-1)(v-1)$	I	$\sigma^2 + r\sigma^2_{tv}$
Error	$(r-1)(tv-1)$	E	σ^2
Total	$rtv - 1$		

In writing down the expectations in the above analysis of variance, we have assumed that the $(tv)_{jk}$'s are normally and independently distributed around a mean of zero and with variance σ^2_{tv} (cf. Chapter 6). Since we have only a finite set of fixed treatments, it is reasonable to define the v_k's in such a way as to measure the differences between varieties averaged over this set of treatments. If we do this, the quantities $(tv)_{jk}$ are such that

$$\sum_j (tv)_{jk} = 0 \quad \text{for any } k$$

The expectation of the mean square for varieties should, therefore, be $\sigma^2 + rt\sigma^2_v$, the term in σ^2_{tv} dropping out, because the sum of squares for varieties is the sum of squares between variety totals with a certain divisor. This illustrates a generally applicable device, that, if we are considering a fixed set of levels of factor a with a random set of levels of factor b, the expectation of the sum of squares for factor b does not involve the interaction component of variance. In other words, the quantity $\sigma^2_b + \dfrac{1}{a}\sigma^2_{ab}$ should be replaced by σ^2_b, in the expectation of a mean square in which it occurs, if there is a finite number of levels of factor a.

If we wish to test for the existence of differences between the t_j's, that is, differences between treatments *averaged over all the possible varieties*, we shall use the criterion T/I. This criterion will be distributed under the null hypothesis, according to the F distribution, with $(t-1)$ and $(t-1)(v-1)$ degrees of freedom, because both treatment sum of squares and interaction sum of squares are distributed under the null hypothesis as $\chi^2(\sigma^2 + r\sigma^2_{tv})$ independently with the appropriate degrees of freedom. The plot errors are not independent as we have noted throughout this book, but all the knowledge we have suggests that we may ignore the dependence. It is also clear from the analysis of variance that we may test the hypothesis that σ^2_{tv} equals zero by comparing I/E with the appropriate F distribution.

For the reasons stated above, the hypothesis that there are no differences between the varieties averaged over the set of treatments is tested by comparing the criterion V/E with the appropriate F distribution. If the treatments are a random sample from an infinite population, the criterion V/I would be used to test the hypothesis that there are no differences between the varieties averaged over the population of treatments. If the treatments were a random sample from a population such that the t_j's are distributed with variance σ^2_t, the test with T/I would be a test of the null hypothesis that σ^2_t equals zero.

The best estimate of comparisons of the t_j's is given by the same comparison of the treatment means: that is, of the $y_{\cdot j\cdot}$'s. In any such comparison each $y_{\cdot j\cdot}$ has a variance of $\dfrac{1}{rv}(\sigma^2 + r\sigma^2_{tv})$ which equals $\dfrac{\sigma^2_{tv}}{v} + \dfrac{\sigma^2}{rv}$.

It may be noted that, if σ^2_{tv} is large relative to σ^2, it will be advisable to include a large number of varieties at the expense of the amount of replication, though a change in this direction will produce an increase in σ^2, because the block size will be correspondingly increased.

In fact, when an experiment apparently of the above type is performed, the experimenter has usually not selected a random sample of varieties, but a set that he considers worth examination. Frequently, however, he wishes to test hypotheses about treatment effects on a population of varieties, because he finds that treatment effects vary considerably over the varieties he used. He then takes the somewhat hazardous step of assuming that the varieties he used constitute a random sample of a population of varieties that he could have used, and wishes to talk not only about the varieties actually used but also about the whole population. This step is hazardous because the only definition we can accept of a random sample is a sample drawn with a device known to produce randomness, for example, a table of random numbers. It appears reasonable, however, to adopt this as a device to facilitate condensation of experimental results, providing the limitations are realized. As a result, the experimenter tends to be in the position of attempting to answer both of the following questions:

1. Are there differences between the treatments for the set of varieties used?
2. Are there differences between the treatments for the population of varieties of which the set used constitutes a random sample?

He also wishes to estimate treatment differences over both sets of situations. We have already discussed the test for question 2, and the test for question 1 is the comparison of T/E with the corresponding F distribution, as in the case of the ordinary factorial experiment. The estimate of a treatment comparison is the same for both cases, namely, the comparison of observed means, but the variance of each $y_{.j}$. for the population of varieties is $(\sigma^2 + r\sigma^2_{tv})/rv$, while the variance for the particular set of varieties is σ^2/rv. The error to be attached to an estimate depends on the use to which the estimate will be put. Let us suppose that the purpose of the experimenter is to predict the gain an individual farmer will make by using treatment 1 rather than treatment 0, and that the farmer is using a variety which is not one of those tested in the experiment, and one which may be assumed to be a random member of the population of varieties. Then the experimenter wishes to predict the quantity

$$X = t_1 - t_0 + (tv)_{1u} - (tv)_{0u} \tag{2}$$

where u denotes the number of the unknown variety y. The observed mean difference between treatment 1 and treatment 0 is $y_{\cdot1\cdot} - y_{\cdot0\cdot}$, and is an estimate of

$$(t_1 - t_0) + \frac{1}{v}\left[\sum_{k=1}^{v} (tv)_{1k} - \sum_{k=1}^{v} (tv)_{0k}\right] + \text{plot error} \qquad (3)$$

where the summation is over the varieties $(1, \cdots, v)$ tested, and the expectation of the square of the plot error is $2\sigma^2/rv$.

Therefore,

$$y_{\cdot1\cdot} - y_{\cdot0\cdot} = X + \frac{1}{v}\left[\sum_{k=1}^{v} (tv)_{1k} - \sum_{k=1}^{v} (tv)_{0k}\right]$$

$$- [(tv)_{1u} - (tv)_{0u}] + \text{plot error} \qquad (4)$$

so that

$$E[(y_{\cdot1\cdot} - y_{\cdot0\cdot}) - X]^2 = \frac{2\sigma^2}{rv} + \frac{2\sigma^2_{tv}}{v} + 2\sigma^2_{tv}$$

$$= 2\left[\frac{\sigma^2}{rv} + \sigma^2_{tv}\left(1 + \frac{1}{v}\right)\right] \qquad (5)$$

If we estimate σ^2 and σ^2_{tv} and substitute the estimates, we may say that the prediction of X is

$$y_{\cdot1\cdot} - y_{\cdot0\cdot} \pm \sqrt{2\left[\frac{\hat{\sigma}^2}{rv} + \hat{\sigma}^2_{tv}\left(1 + \frac{1}{v}\right)\right]}$$

and, if the numbers of degrees of freedom are sufficiently large, the interval

$$y_{\cdot1\cdot} - y_{\cdot0\cdot} \pm 1.96 \sqrt{2\left[\frac{\hat{\sigma}^2}{rv} + \hat{\sigma}^2_{tv}\left(1 + \frac{1}{v}\right)\right]}$$

will be an approximate 95 percent confidence interval on the true difference for the farmer. Reasoning of the above type is necessary if sound technological advice is to be given to users of the experimental results.

We will now consider the same pattern of treatment combinations but a different experimental arrangement. We will suppose that, for reasons of experimental technique, the experimental arrangement utilized split plots, and that treatments were applied to whole plots, each whole plot being split into v parts for the varieties. The structure of the analysis of variance for this case is given in Table 28.3, where σ^2_s is the split-plot error variance, and $\sigma^2_s + v\sigma^2_w$ is the whole-plot error variance.

TABLE 28.3 STRUCTURE OF ANALYSIS OF VARIANCE FOR SPLIT-PLOT EXPERIMENTS

Due to	df	Mean Square	Expectation of Mean Square
Blocks	$r-1$		
Treatments	$t-1$	T	$\sigma^2_s + v\sigma^2_w + r\sigma^2_{tv} + \dfrac{rv}{t-1}\Sigma(t_j - \bar{t})^2$
Error (whole plot)	$(r-1)(t-1)$	W	$\sigma^2_s + v\sigma^2_w$
Varieties	$v-1$	V	$\sigma^2_s + rt\sigma^2_v$
Treatments × varieties	$(t-1)(v-1)$	I	σ^2_s
Error (split plot)	$(r-1)t(v-1)$	S	σ^2_s
Total	$rtv-1$		

This case is instructive in two respects. First, the test of T/W with the F distribution does not test the hypothesis that the t_j's are equal. It will be remembered that, in our discussion of split-plot experiments, we noted that the criterion T/W could be used to test for differences in the treatments *averaged over the set of varieties used*, and, if the t_j's are defined for this set only, the term σ^2_{tv} does not appear. Now, however, the t_j's are defined to be averages over the whole population of varieties, and the existence of the term $r\sigma^2_{tv}$ in the expectation of T prevents our using the ratio T/W. Second, the test cannot be made by comparing T/I with the corresponding F distribution because of the presence of the term $v\sigma^2_w$ in the expectation of T. A third difference is that, if the treatments are a sample from an infinite population, we may use the criterion V/I to test the hypothesis that σ^2_v equals zero: that is, that there are no differences in the population of varieties when averaged over the population of treatments. The reason that we can make this test is that we have assumed that the yield of the combination of treatment j and variety k is expressible as

$$t_j + v_k + (tv)_{jk} + \text{error}$$

where the $(tv)_{jk}$'s are independent normal random variables with mean zero and variance σ^2_{tv}. Tests of the hypothesis that the t_j's are constant can be suggested on the basis of the expectations of the mean squares, on the lines suggested by Satterthwaite.[6] We have, for example,

$$E(T) = \sigma^2_s + v\sigma^2_w + r\sigma^2_{tv} + \frac{rv}{t-1}\Sigma(t_j - \bar{t})^2$$

$$E(W + I - S) = \sigma^2_s + v\sigma^2_w + \sigma^2_s + r\sigma^2_{tv} - \sigma^2_s$$

$$= \sigma^2_s + v\sigma^2_w + r\sigma^2_{tv}$$

so that the ratio $T/(W + I - S)$ could be used as a criterion if we knew ts distribution. Alternatively, as suggested by Cochran and Cox,[7] we have

$$E(T + S) = 2\sigma^2{}_s + v\sigma^2{}_w + r\sigma^2{}_{tv} + \frac{rv}{t - 1} \Sigma(t_j - \bar{t})^2$$

$$E(W + I) = 2\sigma^2{}_s + v\sigma^2{}_s + r\sigma^2{}_{tv}$$

so that we could use the criterion $(T + S)/(W + I)$, if we knew its distribution under the null hypothesis. We know that $(r - 1)(t - 1)W$ is distributed as $\chi^2(\sigma^2{}_s + v\sigma^2{}_w)$, $(t - 1)(v - 1)I$ as $\chi^2(\sigma^2{}_s + r\sigma^2{}_{tv})$, $(r - 1)t(v - 1)S$ as $\chi^2\sigma^2{}_s$, and so on, with the appropriate number of degrees of freedom for each χ^2, the distributions being independent. Now, if $n_1 E_1$ is distributed as $\chi^2\sigma^2{}_1$, and $n_2 E_2$ is distributed as $\chi^2\sigma^2{}_2$, then,

$$\text{var}(E_1) = 2\frac{(\sigma^2{}_1)^2}{n_1}, \qquad \text{var}(E_2) = 2\frac{(\sigma^2{}_2)^2}{n_2}$$

If E_1 and E_2 are distributed independently, then,

$$\text{var}(E_1 + E_2) = 2\left[\frac{(\sigma^2{}_1)^2}{n_1} + \frac{(\sigma^2{}_2)^2}{n_2}\right]$$

If we are to regard $(E_1 + E_2)$ as the numerator or denominator in an F test, then we should have

$$\text{var}(E_1 + E_2) = 2\frac{(\sigma^2{}_1 + \sigma^2{}_2)^2}{n}$$

where n is the degrees of freedom. We may, therefore, regard $n(E_1 + E_2)$ as being distributed approximately as $\chi^2{}_n(\sigma^2{}_1 + \sigma^2{}_2)$, the χ^2 having n degrees of freedom, if

$$n = 2\frac{(\sigma^2{}_1 + \sigma^2{}_2)^2}{V(E_1 + E_2)} = \frac{(\sigma^2{}_1 + \sigma^2{}_2)^2}{\dfrac{(\sigma^2{}_1)^2}{n_1} + \dfrac{(\sigma^2{}_2)^2}{n_2}}$$

Since we do not know $\sigma^2{}_1$ and $\sigma^2{}_2$, we replace them by their estimates E_1 and E_2, so that we assume as an approximation that $n(E_1 + E_2)$ is distributed as $\chi^2{}_n(\sigma^2{}_1 + \sigma^2{}_2)$, where

$$n = \frac{(E_1 + E_2)^2}{\dfrac{E^2_1}{n_1} + \dfrac{E^2_2}{n_2}}$$

In the present instance, we would test the hypothesis that the t_j's are equal by comparing the ratio $(T + S)/(W + I)$ with the F distribution with n_1 and n_2 degrees of freedom, where

and

$$n_1 = \frac{(T + S)^2}{\left[\dfrac{T^2}{t - 1} + \dfrac{S^2}{(r - 1)t(v - 1)}\right]}$$

$$n_2 = \frac{(W + I)^2}{\left[\dfrac{W^2}{(r - 1)(t - 1)} + \dfrac{I^2}{(t - 1)(v - 1)}\right]}$$

$$(6)$$

Alternatively, we may compare $T/(W + I - S)$ with the F distribution with n_1 and n_2 degrees of freedom, where

$$n_1 = t - 1$$

$$n_2 = \frac{(W + I - S)^2}{\dfrac{W^2}{(r - 1)(t - 1)} + \dfrac{I^2}{(t - 1)(v - 1)} + \dfrac{S^2}{(r - 1)t(v - 1)}} \qquad (7)$$

It is not known how reliable these tests are. It might be expected that the test based on $T/(W + I - S)$ would be better, in that the distributions of W, I, S are closer to normality than that of T because their numbers of degrees of freedom are larger. At best these tests are very crude. The results of Robbins and Pitman [8] may be used to give levels of significance with a bounded error, but the process is probably rather tedious.

A situation in which recourse must be had to the above test is the following. We wish to determine the effects of t treatments, which consist of different methods of cold storage, on the flavor of a food. A randomized block experiment of r blocks of t plots is used, and, in order to determine the flavor of the resulting food, the contents of each plot are divided into portions, one for each of j judges. The allocation of portions to judges is made at random. The scores of the judges are then subjected to the analysis of variance, though, before this is done, some *a priori* information on the additivity of scores is necessary. The analysis of variance has the form given in Table 28.4.

TABLE 28.4

Due to	df	Mean Square	Expectation of Mean Square
Replicates	$r - 1$		
Treatments	$t - 1$	T	$\sigma^2_s + j\sigma^2_w + r\sigma^2_{jt} + \dfrac{rj}{t-1}\Sigma(t_j - \bar{t})^2$
Error (plot)	$(r-1)(t-1)$	W	$\sigma^2_s + j\sigma^2_w$
Judges	$j-1$	J	$\sigma^2_s + rt\sigma^2_j$
Treatments × judges	$(t-1)(j-1)$	I	$\sigma^2_s + r\sigma^2_{jt}$
Error within judges	$(r-1)t(j-1)$	S	σ^2_s
Total	$rtj - 1$		

The significance of treatment effects for the set of judges used is given by the ordinary test: namely, to compare T/W with the F distribution with $(t-1)$ and $(r-1)(t-1)$ degrees of freedom. If it is assumed that the judges used are a random sample of a population of judges, it is necessary to test the null hypothesis that there are no treatment effects by the criterion $T/(W + J - S)$. It is usually found that judge-treatment interactions are considerable, and that, while there are highly significant treatment effects averaged over the set of judges actually used, the significance of treatment effects for the population of judges is much lower. Most of the difficulty appears to arise in practice, because the scores are not even approximately additive in mean, replicate, treatment, and judge effects, and this suggests that the scaling problem is all-important. A scale on which judge-treatment interactions are not small, relative to the error within judges, will be very insensitive to treatment effects, and will make the detection of effects very difficult. It is also likely that σ^2_{jt} and σ^2_s will not be homogeneous, some judges having little discriminatory power and good reproducibility and others the reverse. Even though the experimenter has not chosen judges at random, it does not appear satisfactory to consider tests and effects with the fixed set of judges, unless the same set of judges can be used for all experiments, because the experimenter will find that his experimental conclusions are not reproducible. The estimation of components of variance, even on a scale that is only roughly additive, is useful in that it gives an indication of the number of replicates and judges necessary, for the variance of a treatment mean is

$$\frac{1}{rj}(\sigma^2_s + j\sigma^2_w + r\sigma^2_{jt}) = \frac{\sigma^2_s}{rj} + \frac{\sigma^2_w}{r} + \frac{\sigma^2_{jt}}{j}$$

The dominant part of this variance is likely to be the term σ^2_{jt}/j, indicating that the number of judges should be large. In planning an experiment of this type, it is essential to obtain some prior notions about the components of variance, in order that the experiment may have adequate sensitivity. The difficulty will be encountered that any change in j, the number of judges, will have an effect on σ^2_s and σ^2_w, because, if the portion that the judge tastes is to be of constant size, an increase in j must be accompanied by an increase in the size of experimental unit and of σ^2_s and σ^2_w. It is believed, however, that the change in σ^2_s and σ^2_w will not be sufficiently large to vitiate completely a calculation of number of replicates and judges necessary, based on constant values for σ^2_s, σ^2_w and σ^2_{jt}. In the author's experience a very large number of experiments have been performed on this type of problem, which would not have been done had some examination of probable sensitivity been made.

28.4 THE DESIGN AND ANALYSIS OF A SINGLE SERIES OF EXPERIMENTS

A single series of experiments consists of an experiment repeated over a sample of a single population. For example, we may be interested in the responses of a crop to differing amounts of nutrients over a geographical area and, for that purpose, choose a random set of p locations, at each of which we have an experiment on the nutrients. There are essentially 4 cases, depending on the design of the individual experiment, in that the individual experiment may utilize a randomized block, Latin square, incomplete block, or split-plot design. The 4 cases differ only in minor but important respects, and we shall not discuss them all in full detail. In a single series of experiments we will generally be interested in both the individual experiments and in the series of experiments as a larger experiment.

We consider first the case of a randomized block experiment on t treatments in r blocks of t plots repeated over p places. The yields at the ith place will be given by the usual model

$$y_{ijk} = \mu_i + b_{ij} + t_{ik} + e_{ijk} \tag{8}$$

where

$\quad i$ = place $\qquad\qquad\qquad = 1, 2, \cdots, p$

$\quad j$ = block within place $= 1, 2, \cdots, r$

$\quad k$ = treatment $\qquad\qquad = 1, 2, \cdots, t$

$\quad b_{ij}$ = the effect of the jth block at the ith place

$\quad t_{ik}$ = the effect of the kth treatment at the ith place and the e_{ijk}'s are errors with mean zero, zero correlation (because of randomization) and constant variance σ^2_i.

We may perform the analysis of variance in the usual way for each place and obtain tests of significance and estimates of effects with errors, and this should be the first step in the analysis of the series of experiments. We shall then wish to test and estimate the treatment effects for the population of places of which we have a random sample. The model we may use for the whole set of experiments is

$$y_{ijk} = \mu + p_i + b_{ij} + t_k + (pt)_{ik} + e_{ijk} \qquad (9)$$

in which we have written

$$\mu_i = \mu + p_i$$

$$t_{ik} = t_k + (pt)_{ik}$$

The treatment effect at place i has been expressed as the sum of a component t_k, which is constant for all places, and a component $(pt)_{ik}$, which measures the deviation of the effect at place i from the mean effect over all possible places. By definition, the component $(pt)_{ik}$ has an expectation of zero, and we shall assume that its variance is σ^2_{tp}, independently of i and k. The e_{ijk}'s may be assumed to be approximately normally and independently distributed with mean zero and variance σ^2. Regarding the terms in the model apart from e_{ijk} as fixed variables, we have the ordinary general linear hypothesis model from which we derive the analysis of variance given in Table 28.5. In taking expecta-

TABLE 28.5 STRUCTURE OF ANALYSIS OF VARIANCE FOR AN EXPERIMENT
REPEATED OVER PLACES

Due to	df	Mean Square	Expectation of Mean Square
Blocks within places	$p(r - 1)$		
Places	$p - 1$	P	
Treatments	$t - 1$	T	$\sigma^2 + r\sigma^2_{tp} + \dfrac{rp}{t - 1}\Sigma(t_k - \bar{t})^2$
Treatment × places	$(t - 1)(p - 1)$	I	$\sigma^2 + r\sigma^2_{tp}$
Error	$p(r - 1)(t - 1)$	E	σ^2
Total	$prt - 1$		

tions, however, we utilize the assumption that the $(pt)_{ik}$'s have a variance of σ^2_{tp}.

The interpretation that is made of the analysis of variance is obvious from the expectation of the mean squares. We test the hypothesis that the t_k's are constant by the criterion T/I, and that the interactions are zero, that is, that σ^2_{tp} is zero, by the criterion I/E, in each case using the appropriate F distribution. The estimate of a treatment comparison will be the same comparison of the observed means, $y_{..k}$; and the variance of the observed comparison as an estimate of the comparison of the t_k's, that is, of the treatment effects *averaged over the population of places*, is proportional to

$$\frac{\sigma^2}{rp} + \frac{\sigma^2_{tp}}{p}$$

The variance of a comparison of the $y_{..k}$, as an estimate of the comparison of the treatment effects *averaged over the set of places actually used*, is σ^2/rp, the interaction component dropping out because of the restriction on the population about which the inference is made. The problem of allocation of resources may be discussed if the prime interest is the estimation of treatment differences for the population of places, for we may then suppose that the cost of the set of p experiments is proportional to

$$pC_p + rpC_1 = C_0$$

where C_1 is the cost of the experiments per plot, C_p is the additional cost per experiment (consisting of, for example, travel time to the different places), and C_0 is fixed. The optimum number of replicates at each place is given by

$$r = \sqrt{\frac{C_p \sigma^2}{C_1 \sigma^2_{tp}}}$$

and it may be noted that, with fixed costs, the optimum number of replicates per place decreases as σ^2_{tp} increases. In practice 2 replicates are desirable at each place, in order to provide an estimate of σ^2, and in many situations this is also the optimum number.

Assuming that the analysis for the individual experiments are valid, there are two possible difficulties which vitiate to a greater or less extent an interpretation based on the analysis of variance given in Table 28.5. The difficulties are:

1. That σ^2 is not constant.
2. That σ^2_{tp} depends on the combination of treatment and places.

The assumption that σ^2 is constant may be examined by Bartlett's test. It is possible that the variation in σ^2 is a result of non-additivity, and may be overcome by a transformation of the data, but, in general, σ^2 will vary from place to place because the experimental material is not of constant variability. This situation has been discussed by Cochran [1] and by Cochran and Cox,[7] but it is very complicated mathematically, and only very approximate solutions are available. Since the mean effect over all possible places would be estimated by $\hat{\gamma}$, which is the solution of the equation

$$\Sigma \frac{(\hat{\gamma}_i - \hat{\gamma})}{\left(\sigma^2_{tp} + \frac{\sigma^2_i}{r} \right)} = 0 \tag{10}$$

where $\hat{\gamma}_i$ is the estimate for the ith place, even if the σ^2_i's are heterogeneous, the unweighted average of the $\hat{\gamma}_i$'s will give a fairly good estimate of the mean γ for the whole population of places. Only if there are no interactions, would it be appropriate to weight each $\hat{\gamma}_i$ by its estimated error variance, say, s^2_i/r, and even then the s^2_i's should be based on 15 or more degrees of freedom for the weights to be sufficiently accurate.

The test of interaction of treatments and places is rendered complex by the occurrence of heterogeneity of error variance. A test may be derived by assuming that the variance of each treatment-place mean which is σ^2_i/r is known exactly. Then, if we denote r/σ^2_i by W_i, a test for interaction may be obtained (1) by minimizing the quantity

$$\sum_i W_i \sum_k (y_{i \cdot k} - \mu - p_i - t_k)^2$$

and obtaining I, and (2) by noting that I is distributed according to the χ^2 distribution with $(p - 1)(t - 1)$ degrees of freedom under the null hypothesis that interactions do not exist. Since we do not know the σ^2_i's, we use $w_i = r/s^2_i$, where s^2_i is the observed error variance, but, as a consequence, the quantity I is not distributed exactly as χ^2 with $(p - 1)(t - 1)$ degrees of freedom. Cochran and Cox [7] have stated that I is such that we may regard

$$\frac{(n - 4)(n - 2)}{n(n + t - 3)} I$$

as being distributed according to the χ^2 distribution with

$$(p - 1)(t - 1) \frac{(n - 4)}{(n + t - 3)}$$

degrees of freedom. Actually, I is equal to

$$\sum_i w_i \sum_k y^2_{i \cdot k} - \sum_i \frac{w_i Y^2_{i \cdot \cdot}}{t} - \sum_k \frac{\left(\sum_i w_i y_{i \cdot k}\right)^2}{w} + \frac{\left(\sum_i w_i Y_{i \cdot \cdot}\right)^2}{tw} \quad (11)$$

where

$$Y_{i \cdot \cdot} = \sum_k y_{i \cdot k} \quad \text{and} \quad w = \Sigma w_i$$

If there are differing numbers of replicates at each place, but the experimental error variances are constant, the above method may be used with $w_i = r_i$ and the quantity I will be distributed exactly as $\chi^2 \sigma^2$ with $(p - 1)(t - 1)$ degrees of freedom if there are no interactions. If the observed error mean squares and number of degrees of freedom are s^2_i and n_i, respectively, then, under the assumption of constant σ^2, the quantity $\Sigma n_i s^2_i$ is distributed as $\chi^2 \sigma^2$ with Σn_i degrees of freedom. We may, therefore, use the criterion

$$\frac{I}{(p - 1)(t - 1)} \bigg/ \frac{\Sigma n_i s^2_i}{\Sigma n_i}$$

which will be distributed exactly according to the F distribution with $(p - 1)(t - 1)$ and Σn_i degrees of freedom, if there is no interaction.

If there is heterogeneity of error variance but the interaction component σ^2_{tp} may be assumed to be homogeneous or if there are differing numbers of replicates, an approximate test of significance for the effects of treatments averaged over all places may be made by obtaining the analysis of variance of the treatment-place means indicated by Table 28.6.

TABLE 28.6   STRUCTURE OF ANALYSIS OF VARIANCE OF TREATMENT-PLACE MEANS

Due to	df	Expectation of Mean Square
Places	$p - 1$	
Treatments	$t - 1$	$\sigma^2_m + \sigma^2_{tp} + \frac{p}{t - 1} \Sigma(t_k - \bar{t})^2$
Treatments $\times$ places	$(p - 1)(t - 1)$	$\sigma^2_m + \sigma^2_{tp}$
Total	$pt - 1$	

In this table σ^2_m is equal to

$$\frac{1}{p}\left(\frac{\sigma^2_1}{r_1} + \frac{\sigma^2_2}{r_2} + \cdots + \frac{\sigma^2_p}{r_p}\right)$$

where σ^2_i is the error variance, and r_i the number of replicates at place i. Differences between the t_k's must be estimated by the differences of the means over places of place-treatment means, and each mean will have a variance of

$$\frac{(\sigma^2_m + \sigma^2_{tp})}{p}$$

The quantity σ^2_m will be estimated by

$$\frac{1}{p}\left(\frac{s^2_1}{r_1} + \frac{s^2_2}{r_2} + \cdots + \frac{s^2_p}{r_p}\right)$$

where the s^2_i's are the individual observed error mean squares.

Heterogeneity of interaction variance, that is, a dependence of σ^2_{tp} on place and treatment, is likely to be of frequent occurrence. For example, at one place, the experimental material may be unresponsive to all the treatments, while, at another place, there may be little response to a few of the treatments and very large responses to other treatments. Such situations will be brought to light by examination of the analyses of the individual experiments, and there will be little interest in an exact test of the hypothesis that all the t_j's are equal to a constant. The devices that may be suggested are the same ones we considered for individual experiments: namely, transformation of the data, or a partitioning of the treatment comparisons into orthogonal comparisons.

We have discussed only the case when the individual experiment is in randomized blocks. If the individual experiment is in Latin squares, the same considerations hold except that the sum of squares for rows within experiments and columns within experiments must be extracted, with a compensating change in the degrees of freedom for error. If the series of experiments consists of a number of small Latin squares, say, 4×4 squares, we shall be on rather uncertain ground if we use the analysis given above with weights equal to r/s^2_i. If the individual experiment is of lattice or incomplete block type, a weighted analysis of treatment means may be used to test for place-treatment interactions, in which each treatment mean is assumed to have a variance equal to $\frac{1}{2}$ of the average variance of a treatment difference (this is sometimes known as the "effective mean square"). If each experiment is of the split-plot type and both whole-plot and split-plot errors are homogeneous over places, the combined analysis of variance will consist of two portions: one for whole plots and one for split plots. If the split-plot factor is of the type discussed in Section 28.3, we shall have to use a similar device to test for the effects of the whole-plot factor.

28.5 A VARIETY TRIAL AT A RANDOM SAMPLE OF PLACES FOR A NUMBER OF YEARS

We shall consider the analysis of a trial on c varieties with r randomized blocks at each of a places in b years, and the model we shall use is the following:

$$y_{ijkl} = \mu + p_i + y_j + (py)_{ij} + v_k + (pv)_{ik} + (yv)_{jk} + (pyv)_{ijk}$$

$$+ r_{ijl} + e_{ijkl} \quad (12)$$

where

$$i = 1, 2, \cdots, a$$
$$j = 1, 2, \cdots, b$$
$$k = 1, 2, \cdots, c$$
$$l = 1, 2, \cdots, r$$

The results at any one place in any one year are qual to

$$[\mu + p_i + y_j + (py)_{ij}] + [v_k + (pv)_{ik} + (yv)_{jk} + (pyv)_{ijk}] + r_{ijl} + e_{ijkl}$$

which is analogous to the usual form for the single experiment of

$$y_{mn} = \mu + t_n + b_m + e_{mn}$$

We shall assume that

$$E(pv)_{ik} = E(yv)_{jk} = E(pyv)_{ijk} = 0$$

the expectation being taken over any one subscript. As a consequence the v_k's measure the differences between varieties averaged over all places and years. We shall also assume that

$$E(pv)^2_{ik} = \sigma^2_{pv}, \qquad E(p^2_i) = \sigma^2_p$$

$$E(yv)^2_{jk} = \sigma^2_{yv}, \qquad E(y^2_j) = \sigma^2_y$$

$$E(pyv)^2_{ijk} = \sigma^2_{pyv}, \qquad E(py)^2_{ij} = \sigma^2_{py}$$

and that the experiments are all subject to the same experimental error variance σ^2. Regardless of the distributions involved, we may make the analysis of variance given in Table 28.7.

TABLE 28.7 ANALYSIS OF VARIANCE OF GROUP OF EXPERIMENTS

Due to	df	Mean Square	Expectation of Mean Square
Places	$a-1$	P	$\sigma^2 + r + rb + rc\sigma^2{}_{py} + rbc\sigma^2{}_p$
Years	$b-1$	Y	$\sigma^2 + r + ra\sigma^2{}_{yv} + rc\sigma^2{}_{py} + rac\sigma^2{}_y$
Places × years	$(a-1)(b-1)$	PY	$\sigma^2 + r + rc\sigma^2{}_{py}$
Varieties	$c-1$	V	$\sigma^2 + r\sigma^2{}_{pyv} + ra\sigma^2{}_{yv} + rb\sigma^2{}_{pv} + \dfrac{rab}{c-1}\Sigma(v_k - \bar{v})^2$
Places × varieties	$(a-1)(c-1)$	PV	$\sigma^2 + r\sigma^2{}_{pyv} + rb\sigma^2{}_{pv}$
Years × varieties	$(b-1)(c-1)$	YV	$\sigma^2 + r\sigma^2{}_{pyv} + ra\sigma^2{}_{yv}$
Places × years × varieties	$(a-1)(b-1)(c-1)$	PYV	$\sigma^2 + r\sigma^2{}_{pyv}$
Replications	$ab(r-1)$		
Error	$ab(c-1)(r-1)$	E	σ^2
Total	$abcr-1$		

These expectations are easily checked by considering the mean square as a function of the y_{ijkl}'s. For example, PY is equal to

$$rc \sum_{ij} (y_{ij}.. - y_i... - y_{.j}.. + y....)^2$$

If we may assume normal distributions for each of the random variables in the model, we can write down immediately several tests of hypotheses.

Let us consider the hypothesis which may be of interest to the experimenter. The effect of variety k at place i in year j is

$$v_k + (pv)_{ik} + (yv)_{jk} + (pyv)_{ijk}$$

and the experimenter will be interested in the significance of combinations of the terms in this expression. He will certainly wish to test the hypothesis that the v_k's are equal, and, for that purpose, we may use a test analogous to the test given in the previous section: namely, to compare the criterion $V/(PV + YV - PYV)$ with the F distribution with $(c-1)$ and n degrees of freedom, where

$$n = \dfrac{(PV + YV - PYV)^2}{\dfrac{PV^2}{(a-1)(c-1)} + \dfrac{YV^2}{(b-1)(c-1)} + \dfrac{PYV^2}{(a-1)(b-1)(c-1)}} \tag{13}$$

The experimenter may also be interested in the differences between varieties for the set of places actually used and for all possible years. In terms of the v_k's, $(pv)_{ik}$'s, and so on, these differences are given by the differences of

$$v'_k = v_k + \frac{1}{a}\Sigma'(pv)_{ik}$$

where Σ' denotes summation over the sample of places, the other terms dropping out because we are considering all possible years. Insofar as we wish to talk about the set of places used, the terms $(pv)_{ik}$, where i takes the values for these places, are not random variables, because, with repetitions over the population of interest, we shall encounter the same variables each time. The test of the hypothesis that the v'_k's are constant may be obtained by noting that, if we had made an analysis of variance for this hypothesis, the quantity

$$\frac{\Sigma(v'_k - \bar{v}')^2}{c - 1}$$

would appear in Table 28.7, instead of

$$\frac{1}{a}\sigma^2_{pv} + \frac{\Sigma(v'_k - \bar{v}')^2}{c - 1}$$

The expectation of the variety mean square would turn out to be

$$\sigma^2 + r\sigma^2_{pyv} + ra\sigma^2_{yv} + \frac{rab}{c - 1}\Sigma(v'_k - \bar{v}')^2$$

To test the equality of the v'_k's, we take the criterion V/YV and compare it with the F distribution with $(c - 1)$ and $(b - 1)(c - 1)$ degrees of freedom. The hypothesis under test can perhaps be described more clearly in the form: Are there differences between varieties for this set of places that are consistent over all years?

We now make a list of the hypotheses that can be tested with a group of experiments of the type we have specified. It must be emphasized that by no means all of the hypotheses we shall mention are of practical interest, but our list will serve the purpose of indicating exactly what the possible test criteria in fact test. The multiplicity of hypotheses that can be tested is a possible source of some confusion, which we hope to remove. Possible questions and appropriate tests are:

1. Are there variety differences consistent over all places and years? The test criterion is given above.
2. Are there variety differences consistent over all years with this set of places? The test criterion is V/YV.
3. Are there variety differences consistent over all places with this set of years? The test criterion is V/PV.
4. Do the varieties interact with places consistently over all years? The test criterion is PV/PYV.

5. Do the varieties interact with years consistently over all the places? The test criterion is YV/PYV.
6. Is there an interaction of places, varieties, and years? The test criterion is PYV/E.
7. Are there variety effects averaged over this set of places and this set of years? The test criterion is V/E.
8. Are there variety-place interactions for this set of years? The test criterion is PV/E.
9. Are there variety-year interactions for this set of places? The test criterion is YV/E.

All of the above tests are not necessarily of interest, and, in fact, if the set of places was actually chosen at random, there can be little use for a test on the population consisting of the set of places actually used. In general, the most apt condensation of the results is a statement of the variance components with estimated errors. It may be noted that the sums of squares that do not contain fixed variables are distributed independently as χ^2(expectation of mean square) with the appropriate degrees of freedom for χ^2. If a component of variance is estimated by

$$\frac{1}{k}(S_1 - S_2)$$

where S_1 and S_2 are observed mean squares with n_1 and n_2 degrees of freedom, then the variance of the estimate is

$$\frac{1}{k^2}\left[2\frac{E^2(S_1)}{n_1} + 2\frac{E^2(S_2)}{n_2}\right]$$

where $E(S_i)$ is the expectation of S_i. The variance of $\frac{1}{k}(S_1 - S_2)$ may be estimated by

$$\frac{2}{k^2}\left(\frac{S^2_1}{n_1 + 2} + \frac{S^2_2}{n_2 + 2}\right) \quad \text{since} \quad E\left(\frac{S^2_i}{n_i + 2}\right) = \frac{E^2(S_i)}{n_i}$$

In the same way that there are a number of tests of hypotheses that can be made, there are a number of estimates that can be considered, though not many of them are of interest. We can estimate a varietal difference for the set of places and years actually used, for the set of places and all years, for the set of places and for a random year, and so on. The point estimate of the difference will be the same for all the possible circumstances mentioned, but the variance of the estimate will be different. The observed mean difference between two varieties, say, 1 and 2, is

$$D = \left[v_1 + \frac{1}{a} \sum_i{}' (pv)_{i1} + \frac{1}{b} \sum_j{}' (yv)_{j1} + \frac{1}{ab} \sum_{ij}{}' (pyv)_{ij1} + \frac{1}{rab} \sum_{ijl}{}' e_{ij1l} \right]$$

$$- \left[v_2 + \frac{1}{a} \sum_i{}' (pv)_{i2} + \frac{1}{b} \sum_j{}' (yv)_{j2} + \frac{1}{ab} \sum_{ij}{}' (pyv)_{ij2} + \frac{1}{rab} \sum_{ijl}{}' e_{ij2l} \right]$$

$$(14)$$

where Σ' denotes summation over the sets of i, j actually used in the experiment. Suppose we wish to estimate the difference of variety 1 and variety 2 for the set of places used over all possible years, that is, we wish to estimate

$$\theta = \left[v_1 + \frac{1}{a} \sum_i{}' (pv)_{i1} \right] - \left[v_2 + \frac{1}{a} \Sigma'(pv)_{i2} \right] \quad (15)$$

then,

$$E(D - \theta)^2 = 2 \left(\frac{\sigma^2{}_{yv}}{b} + \frac{\sigma^2{}_{pyv}}{ab} + \frac{\sigma^2}{rab} \right) \quad (16)$$

and the variance of D as an estimate of θ is estimated by $2 \dfrac{YV}{rab}$. Also, we may construct a confidence interval for θ in the usual way. As a second example, suppose we wish to estimate the gain in yield ϕ, which a randomly chosen farmer would obtain by using variety 1 rather than variety 2, say, in the next season. Then,

$$\phi = [v_1 + (pv)_{i1} + (yv)_{j1} + (pyv)_{ij1}] - [v_2 + (pv)_{i2} + (yv)_{j2} + (pyv)_{ij2}] \quad (17)$$

where i denotes the farmer's place, and j the next season which we assume to be a randomly chosen one. Then,

$$(D - \phi) = \frac{1}{a} \sum_i{}' (pv)_{i1} - \frac{1}{a} \sum_i{}' (pv)_{i2} + (pv)_{i1} - (pv)_{i2} + \text{etc.} \quad (18)$$

and

$$E(D - \phi)^2 = 2 \left[\sigma^2{}_{pv} \left(\frac{1}{a} + 1 \right) + \sigma^2{}_{yv} \left(\frac{1}{b} + 1 \right) \right.$$

$$\left. + \sigma^2{}_{pyv} \left(\frac{1}{ab} + 1 \right) + \frac{\sigma^2}{rab} \right] \quad (19)$$

The estimates of the variance components can be entered in this expression to give an estimated variance of D as an estimate of ϕ.

Finally, we may consider the problem of allocation of experimental resources for a group of experiments to provide an estimate of varietal differences for all possible places in the population and all years. The variance of each varietal mean for comparisons over this population is

$$\frac{1}{rab}(\sigma^2 + r\sigma^2_{pyv} + rb\sigma^2_{pv} + ra\sigma^2_{yv}) = \frac{\sigma^2}{rab} + \frac{\sigma^2_{pyv}}{ab} + \frac{\sigma^2_{pv}}{a} + \frac{\sigma^2_{yv}}{b}$$

In many investigations, it will be found that the best allocation consists of 2 replicates for each individual experiment to allow estimation of experimental error, and as many places and years as possible. Some knowledge of costs is necessary before a solution can be obtained, particularly as regards allocation between places and years. This formula is of some use in breeding programs, for example, in the selection of lines of corn for general distribution over an area. If we select the top p percent of a sample of V lines on the basis of their yields in a group of experiments with r randomized blocks at each of a places in each of b years, then the expected difference between the mean of all V lines and the mean of the selected p percent is

$$\frac{K\sigma^2_v}{\sqrt{\sigma^2_v + \frac{\sigma^2_{yv}}{b} + \frac{\sigma^2_{pv}}{a} + \frac{\sigma^2_{pyv}}{ab} + \frac{\sigma^2}{rab}}}$$

where σ^2_v is the variance of the population of lines, and K is a function of p and V, which is known (or calculable) if the distribution of yields of lines is assumed to be normal (cf. Federer and Sprague [3]).

28.6 DIFFICULTIES IN THE ANALYSIS OF A GROUP OF EXPERIMENTS

The difficulties that arise in practice can be listed by referring to the assumptions of the analyses given in the previous section. They are that the components of variance σ^2, σ^2_{pyv}, σ^2_{pv}, and σ^2_{yv} may not be homogeneous.

If the experimental error variances σ^2 vary from experiment to experiment, but we have, for each experiment, an estimate of σ^2, say, s^2_{ij}, based on 15 or more degrees of freedom, we may test the hypothesis that $\sigma^2_{pyv} = 0$ by a weighted analysis of the means for each place and year, using weights r/s^2_i. The test is analogous to the one we used for testing the hypothesis that σ^2_{pv} equals 0 for a single series of experiments. If all the other variance components are homogeneous, effects will be estimated from the variety-place-year means, and the variance of each variety-place-year mean is $\sigma^2_{pyv} + \sigma^2/r$. If the experimental error variances are heterogeneous, but σ^2_{pyv} is intermediate between or greater than the quantities σ^2/r, an unweighted analysis of variety-place-year means may be used to test approximately for variety-place or variety-year interactions, and for average varietal effects. The tests will be exactly the same in terms of mean squares as those given for the complete analysis in Table 28.7.

A frequent source of difficulty will be heterogeneity of the variance components σ^2_{yv} and σ^2_{pv}. An examination of the variety means by place and year may suggest the separation of the $(c - 1)$ degrees of freedom between varieties into sets which are homogeneous in these respects. A separate analysis would then be made for each set. The analysis for a set of $(t - 1)$ degrees of freedom will be of the form shown in Table 28.8.

TABLE 28.8

Due to	df	Expectation of Mean Square
Varietal comparisons	$t - 1$	$\sigma^2 + r\sigma^2_{pyv} + ra\sigma^2_{yv} + rb\sigma^2_{pv} + Q(t)$
Places × varieties	$(a - 1)(t - 1)$	$\sigma^2 + r\sigma^2_{pyv} + rb\sigma^2_{pv}$
Years × varieties	$(b - 1)(t - 1)$	$\sigma^2 + r\sigma^2_{pyv} + ra\sigma^2_{yv}$
Places × years × varieties	$(a - 1)(b - 1)(t - 1)$	$\sigma^2 + r\sigma^2_{pyv}$

The quantity $Q(t)$ is equal to $\dfrac{rab}{t - 1}$ (sum of squares of true values), and is zero only if the comparisons of the v_k's corresponding to the $(t - 1)$ degrees of freedom are all zero, and positive otherwise. An example of this method of analysis is given by Yates and Cochran.[2] A difficulty with this approach is that we may bias our conclusions considerably by choosing a method of analysis that seems reasonable in the light of the actual data.

REFERENCES

1. COCHRAN, W. G. Problems arising in the analysis of a series of similar experiments. *Suppl. Jour. Roy. Stat. Soc.*, **4**, 102–118, 1937.
2. YATES, F., and COCHRAN, W. G. The analysis of groups of experiments. *Jour. Agr. Sci.*, **28**, 556–580, 1938.
3. FEDERER, W. T., and SPRAGUE, G. F. A comparison of variance components in corn yield trials. *Jour. Amer. Soc. Agron.*, **39**, 453–463, 1947.
4. YATES, F. Modern experimental design and its function in plant selection. *Emp. Jour. Exp. Agr.*, **8**, 223–230, 1940.
5. LUSH, J. L. *Animal breeding plans.* Collegiate Press, Ames. 3rd ed., 1945.
6. SATTERTHWAITE, F. E. An approximate distribution of estimates of variance components. *Biometrics*, **2**, 110–114, 1946.
7. COCHRAN, W. G., and COX, G. M. *Experimental designs.* John Wiley & Sons, New York. 1950.
8. ROBBINS, H., and PITMAN, E. J. G. Application of method of mixtures to quadratic forms in normal variates. *Ann. Math. Stat.*, **20**, 552–560, 1949.

CHAPTER 29

Treatments Applied in Sequence

In this chapter we shall discuss situations in which treatments are applied in sequence to the experimental unit. We shall be concerned primarily with the case in which we are interested in the effects of each treatment in the sequence, which are assumed to be independent of the previous treatment. Some designs for this situation are known as cross-over or switch-over designs. The most complex problem is that of the long-term experiment, in which it is desired to compare, for example, continuous treatments, or several crop rotations, or sequences of agronomic practices. We shall discuss long-term experiments only to the extent of defining some of the problems and giving the more simple devices of design. The main distinction between the switch-over design and the long-term experiment is that, in the former case, we are interested in the effects of the treatments making up the sequence, whereas, in the latter, the effect of the whole sequence is of interest.

29.1   THE COMPARISON OF 3 TREATMENTS

Consider the following pattern for testing 3 nutritional treatments on the milk yield of dairy cows in which the total experimental time of 3 months is divided into 3 periods each of 1 month:

		Cow	
Period	1	2	3
I	*a*	*b*	*c*
II	*b*	*c*	*a*
III	*c*	*a*	*b*

The treatments are denoted by *a*, *b*, and *c*, and the whole pattern is a Latin square with periods as rows and cows as columns. We have noted that the Latin square design is effective in reducing the error of treatment comparisons by removing row and column effects. The above

594

pattern is very suitable for the problem, because differences between cows and differences between periods will be large, relative to the magnitudes of treatment effects which would be regarded as important. If we select cows that are similar in breed, age, and other characteristics and that started their lactation at about the same date, we may expect the differences between periods to be relatively constant over the cows selected. The error variance of the experiment will be expected to be correspondingly smaller than with a design that does not utilize the stratification by cows and periods. The pattern we have given is a valid design for the comparison of the 3 treatments if the effects of treatments are additive and if we select a random 3×3 Latin square. We have noted that a single 3×3 Latin square design is inadequate, so that a number of repetitions will be necessary. If r sets of 3 cows are used, with a random square for each set, and if the error variances are homogeneous between the sets, an analysis of variance of the form shown in Table 29.1 may be obtained.

TABLE 29.1 STRUCTURE OF ANALYSIS OF VARIANCE

Due to	df
Sets	$r - 1$
Cows within sets	$2r$
Periods within sets	$2r$
Treatments	2
Treatments by sets	$2(r - 1)$
Error within sets	$2r$
Total	$9r - 1$

The sum of squares for periods within each set must be isolated from the error, because we have a 3×3 Latin square for each set, and differences between periods within each set cannot have any effect on the estimates of the treatment effects or on the errors of the estimates. We may note in passing that, even if the periods are the same for the r sets of cows, and we are prepared to make the assumption that the period effects are the same in the r sets, we must not pool the sum of squares with $2(r - 1)$ degrees of freedom for periods by sets with the error, because the periods by sets sum of squares would be zero. It is easily verified, given the previous results on the characteristics of randomization procedures, that the expectation of the treatment mean square is equal to the expectation of the error mean square in the above analysis of variance under the null hypothesis and that the usual formulas hold for the variance of an estimated comparison. We make this remark because, on the basis of an infinite model, with constant period effects, the expected value of the mean square for periods by sets is equal to σ^2, which is the expectation of the error mean square above. This is an example of how the use of an infinite model can lead us astray. We may pool the sums of squares for treatments by repetitions and for error within repetitions only if we are prepared to assume that the treatment effects are the same in the r repetitions. If we do not pool these 2 components, the criterion (treatment mean square/error within repetitions mean square) tests the effects of treatments averaged over the sets of cows used.

So far we have not made any deviation from the normal use of the Latin square. The crucial condition for the design to be valid for the purpose at hand is that the treatments be additive in their effects for each combination of cow and period. Thus, if the basic yield of cow j in period i is x_{ij}, the yield under treatment k, say, y_{ijk}, is equal to $x_{ij} + t_k$. We regard the data for one Latin square as having arisen from the model

$$y_{ijk} = \mu + p_i + c_j + t_k + e_{ij} \tag{1}$$

where

$k = 1$ for a, 2 for b, 3 for c

μ = the effect common to all cow-period combinations

p_i = the effect common to all cows for period i

c_j = the effect common to all periods for cow j

t_k = the effect common to all cow-period combinations that receive treatment k

and

e_{ij} = the error

The practical obstacle we encounter with this design is that there may be residual effects, and the design we have used is not a valid one in this case. It is essential to use every possible device to ensure that there are no residual effects, the simplest one being to allow an interval between each experimental period during which we hope that residual effects of the treatments will be used up. However, even if the intervals chosen are long, the assumption that residual effects have been eliminated is a somewhat hazardous one, for the physiology of the cow is such that a whole lactation is, in a sense, a unit of biological activity. The question reduces to a consideration of the treatments in relation to the physiology of the animal; if, for instance, the treatments were different vitamins or amounts of vitamins, an interval of a certain length will probably be sufficient, whereas, if the treatments are number of times per day that access to water is allowed, the interval should probably be of a different length.

In view of these difficulties we may consider the design we have given from the point of view of residual effects. There are two essentially different Latin squares which we may obtain by randomization (Table 29.2).

TABLE 29.2

SQUARE I				SQUARE II			
	Cow				*Cow*		
Period	1	2	3	*Period*	1	2	3
I	*a*	*b*	*c*	I	*a*	*b*	*c*
II	*b*	*c*	*a*	II	*c*	*a*	*b*
III	*c*	*a*	*b*	III	*b*	*c*	*a*

We allow ourselves to obtain squares of type I or of type II, with a probability of $\frac{1}{2}$ for each. It may be noted, that in square I, treatment *b* always follows treatment *a* unless it is the first, treatment *c* always follows *b*, and treatment *a* always follows *c*. In square II, on the other hand, treatment *b* follows treatment *c*, treatment *c* follows treatment *a*, and treatment *a* follows treatment *b*. Our immediate reaction is that it would be wise to insist on an equal representation of the two types of square, for it would then be the case that any treatment follows the other 2 treatments with equal frequency. We find frequently that a design that looks balanced is better than one that is unbalanced, and so the modification is worth considering.

With this modification our randomization procedure will be to assign a square of type I or type II at random to *r* of the sets, with the stipulation that each type of square is represented equally frequently, and then randomize the allocation of sequences of treatments to the cows. In this way, we would generate $\dfrac{r!}{\left(\dfrac{r}{2}\right)!\left(\dfrac{r}{2}\right)!} 6^r$ possible allocations of sequences of treatments to cows. The interesting point is that we do not allow independent Latin squares from set to set, and might therefore suspect that the design is not valid. If we specify that a square is to be of type I, we can obtain any one of the 6 squares shown in Table 29.3.

TABLE 29.3

Period	I_1			I_2			I_3			I_4			I_5			I_6		
	1	2	3	1	2	3	1	2	3	1	2	3	1	2	3	1	2	3
I	a	b	c	a	c	b	b	c	a	b	a	c	c	a	b	c	b	a
II	b	c	a	b	a	c	c	a	b	c	b	a	a	b	c	a	c	b
III	c	a	b	c	b	a	a	b	c	a	c	b	b	c	a	b	a	c

For squares I_1, I_3, and I_5, the partition of the 9 cells of the square into 3 groups of those cells is the same, and both the treatment sum of squares and error sum of squares will be the same for all 3 squares, while, for squares I_2, I_4, and I_6, the treatment sum of squares will be the same and equal the error sum of squares for squares I_1, I_3, and I_5, and the error sum of squares will be the same for all 3 squares and equal to the treatment sum of squares for squares I_1, I_3, and I_5. Furthermore, the quantities δ_{ij}^k of Chapter 10 have the distributional properties necessary for a Latin square analysis. The analysis of variance given in Table 29.1 is therefore valid for this restricted randomization also. A practical example of this design is given by Cochran, Autrey, and Cannon.[1] With r small, it might well be advisable to test the hypothesis that treatments have no effect by the randomization test.

We now consider a further modification of the basic design. If we are able to perform only 4 repetitions, the number of degrees of freedom for error is 8, or 14 if we can assume the treatment effects to be constant over the 4 repetitions. If we assume that the periods are identical for the 4 repetitions, it might be reasonable under some circumstances to consider the set of 12 cows as a whole, and to assign the 6 possible sequences at random to the 12 cows, with the stipulation that each sequence is represented twice. If this were a valid design we would isolate 2 degrees of freedom for periods, 11 for cows, and 2 for treatments, leaving 20 degrees of freedom for error. To examine this design, we assume additivity of treatment effects as before, so that the yield from treatment k in period i from cow j is y_{ijk} equal to $x_{ij} + t_k$. The model may be written in the form

$$y_{ijk} = x.. + (x_i. - x..) + (x._j - x..) + t_k + (x_{ij} - x_i. - x._j + x..)$$

where the terms in order are the mean, the period effect, the cow effect, the treatment effect, and the error, and we may write this in the form

$$y_{ijk} = \mu + p_i + c_j + t_k + e_{ij}$$

It is possible that we can look at this design and state its properties. A rigorous examination is, however, the only reliable method of doing so, and is also of general interest. We shall number the sequences by s that can take the values 1 to 6, and are given by

$$s$$

Period	1	2	3	4	5	6
I	a	b	c	a	b	c
II	b	c	a	c	a	b
III	c	a	b	b	c	a

The experimental design is defined by the function δ_{sj} which is equal to 1 if sequence s (equals 1, $\cdots$, 6) is assigned to cow j (equals 1, 2, $\cdots$, 12), and zero otherwise. The function δ_{sj} has the properties, that

$$\delta_{sj} = 1 \quad \text{with probability } \tfrac{1}{6}$$
$$= 0 \quad \text{with probability } \tfrac{5}{6}$$

if

$$\delta_{sj} = 1 \quad \text{then} \quad \delta_{s'j} = 0 \quad \text{for all } s' \neq s$$

and

$$\delta_{sj'} = 1 \quad \text{with probability } \tfrac{1}{11}$$
$$= 0 \quad \text{with probability } \tfrac{10}{11} \left.\right\} \quad j' \neq j$$
$$\delta_{s'j'} = 1 \quad \text{with probability } \tfrac{2}{11}$$
$$= 0 \quad \text{with probability } \tfrac{9}{11}$$

This specification of the distribution of the δ_{sj}'s is sufficient for our purpose. Treatment comparisons are subject only to the errors e_{ij}, for we have ensured that each treatment occurs in each period and with each cow. The treatment total for treatment a is equal to

$$12\mu + 12t_1 + \sum_j \delta_{1j}e_{1j} + \sum_j \delta_{2j}e_{3j} + \sum_j \delta_{3j}e_{2j} + \sum_j \delta_{4j}e_{1j}$$
$$+ \sum_j \delta_{5j}e_{2j} + \sum_j \delta_{6j}e_{3j} \quad (2)$$

since, if sequence 1 is allocated to cow j, the contribution to the treatment total is e_{1j}, and so on.

It is easily verified that, if A, B, and C are the treatment totals, then

$$E[A - E(A)]^2 = \tfrac{24}{66} \sum_{ij} e^2{}_{ij}$$

$$E[A - E(A)][B - E(B)] = -\tfrac{12}{66} \sum_{ij} e^2{}_{ij}$$

$$E\left[\frac{(A^2 + B^2 + C^2)}{12} - \frac{(A + B + C)^2}{36}\right]$$

$$= \frac{6}{66} \sum_{ij} e^2{}_{ij} + 12\left[(t^2{}_1 + t^2{}_2 + t^2{}_3) - \frac{(t_1 + t_2 + t_3)^2}{3}\right]$$

By definition, a cow total is equal to $3\mu + 3c_i + (t_1 + t_2 + t_3)$, and differences between cow totals therefore measure cow effects only. Likewise, a period total is equal to $12\mu + 12p_i + 4(t_1 + t_2 + t_3)$, so that period differences contain none of the terms e_{ij}.

If we make the analysis of variance with structure

Due to	df
Cows	11
Periods	2
Treatments	2
Error	20
Total	35

the expectation of the error sum of squares is $\Sigma e^2{}_{ij}$ minus $\tfrac{6}{66}\Sigma e^2{}_{ij}$, or $\tfrac{60}{66}\Sigma e^2{}_{ij}$. The expectation of the treatment mean square in the absence of treatment effects is therefore equal to the expectation of the error mean square. If the true error mean square is σ^2, equal to $\tfrac{3}{66}\Sigma e^2{}_{ij}$, the variance of any comparison is obtained by regarding the treatment means as having a variance of $\sigma^2/12$, and applying the usual rules. For example,

$$E\left(\frac{A}{12} - \frac{B}{12}\right)^2 = \frac{1}{144}\left(\frac{24}{66}\Sigma e^2{}_{ij} + \frac{24}{66}\Sigma e^2{}_{ij} + \frac{24}{66}\Sigma e^2{}_{ij}\right) = \frac{1}{2}\left(\frac{1}{66}\Sigma e^2{}_{ij}\right)$$

$$= \frac{1}{6}\left(\frac{3}{66}\Sigma e^2{}_{ij}\right) = \frac{\sigma^2}{6} = \frac{\sigma^2}{12} + \frac{\sigma^2}{12}$$

29.2 THE CASE OF 4 TREATMENTS

The extension of the designs given earlier to the case of 4 treatments is straightforward. The design that has been suggested for this case

(Cochran [2]) is based on the three 4×4 squares in Table 29.4, which, when superimposed, give a completely orthogonal square.

TABLE 29.4

Period	Square I				Square II				Square III			
	1	2	3	4	5	6	7	8	9	10	11	12
I	a	b	c	d	a	b	c	d	a	b	c	d
II	b	a	d	c	c	d	a	b	d	c	b	a
III	c	d	a	b	d	c	b	a	b	a	d	c
IV	d	c	b	a	b	a	d	c	c	d	a	b

If we have 3 sets of 4 cows and we assign one of the 3 squares to each set at random, and then assign columns at random to cows within each set, we have a design in which each treatment is preceded by the other treatments with equal frequency.

To examine this design, we may denote the 12 sequences of treatments above by the numbers 1 to 12 and utilize the function δ_{sj} which equals unity if sequence s is allocated to cow j. For each square we would like to make the following partition in the analysis of variance:

Due to	df
Cows	3
Periods	3
Treatments	3
Error	6
Total	15

We shall consider the analysis of the first square and the first 4 sequences of treatments. The treatments will be assumed to be additive, so that, if the yield under a uniform treatment of cow j in period i is x_{ij}, the yield under treatment k is y_{ijk} equal to $y_{ij} + t_k$. We have, therefore, the identity

$$y_{ijk} = x.. + (x_i. - x..) + (x._j - x..) + t_k + (x_{ij} - x_i. - x._j + x..)$$

$$= \mu + p_i + c_j + t_k + e_{ij} \tag{3}$$

A period total is equal to $4\mu + 4p_i + \Sigma t_k$, so that the period sum of squares contains no treatment effects or errors, and similarly for the cow totals. The treatment totals are given by

$$A = 4\mu + 4t_1 + \sum_j \delta_{1j}e_{1j} + \sum_j \delta_{2j}e_{2j} + \sum_j \delta_{3j}e_{3j} + \sum_j \delta_{4j}e_{4j}$$

$$B = 4\mu + 4t_2 + \sum_j \delta_{1j}e_{2j} + \sum_j \delta_{2j}e_{1j} + \sum_j \delta_{3j}e_{4j} + \sum_j \delta_{4j}e_{3j}$$

$$C = 4\mu + 4t_3 + \sum_j \delta_{1j}e_{3j} + \sum_j \delta_{2j}e_{4j} + \sum_j \delta_{3j}e_{1j} + \sum_j \delta_{4j}e_{2j}$$ (4)

$$D = 4\mu + 4t_4 + \sum_j \delta_{1j}e_{4j} + \sum_j \delta_{2j}e_{3j} + \sum_j \delta_{3j}e_{2j} + \sum_j \delta_{4j}e_{1j}$$

where summation on j is from 1 to 4, over the 4 cows of the set.

The quantities δ_{sj} have the usual properties, namely:

$$\delta_{sj} = 1 \quad \text{with probability } \tfrac{1}{4}$$

$$= 0 \quad \text{with probability } \tfrac{3}{4}$$

if

$$\delta_{sj} = 1 \quad \text{then} \quad \delta_{sj'} = 0 \qquad j' \neq j$$

and

$$\delta_{s'j} = 0 \qquad s' \neq s$$

and

$$\delta_{s'j'} = 1 \quad \text{with probability } \tfrac{1}{3}, \qquad s' \neq s, \quad j' \neq j$$

The expectation of a treatment total is $4\mu + 4t_i$, so that the design gives unbiased estimates of treatment differences. The expectation of the square of a treatment total, apart from mean and treatment effect, is, for example,

$$E(A^2) = E\left[\sum_j (\delta_{1j}e_{1j} + \delta_{2j}e_{2j} + \delta_{3j}e_{3j} + \delta_{4j}e_{4j}) \right]^2$$

and, by utilizing the properties of the δ_{sj}, we find that

$$E(A^2) = \tfrac{1}{4} \sum_{ij} e^2{}_{ij} + \tfrac{1}{12} \sum_{ij} e^2{}_{ij} = \tfrac{4}{12} \sum_{ij} e^2{}_{ij}$$

The expectation of T the grand total contains no errors, so that the expectation of the treatment sum of squares is

$$E\left(\frac{A^2}{4} + \frac{B^2}{4} + \frac{C^2}{4} + \frac{D^2}{4} - \frac{T^2}{16} \right) = \frac{4}{12} \sum_{ij} e^2{}_{ij}$$

The expectation of the total sum of squares apart from treatment effects is $\sum_{ij} e^2{}_{ij}$, so that the expectation of the error sum of squares is, by subtraction, equal to $\frac{8}{12} \sum_{ij} e^2{}_{ij}$. The expectation of the treatment *mean* square in the absence of treatment effects is $\frac{1}{9} \sum_{ij} e^2{}_{ij}$ which is also equal to the expectation of the error *mean* square. The design is therefore *unbiased* in the sense in which the term is used in experimental design. This is in itself a curious fact, because we have not allowed the full randomization that we usually require with a Latin square. It turns out that the 24 possible randomizations will give equal sums of squares for treatments in sets of 4, there being only 6 different possible values. In a randomization test of the effects of the treatments, therefore, the minimum level of significance for an over-all test of treatment effects is $\frac{1}{6}$. All the results we have obtained above hold for the other 2 squares also. The minimum level of significance we can have for the 3 squares jointly is $\frac{1}{216}$.

We now consider treatment comparisons and, as an example, take $A - B$ for the first square,

$$(A - B) = 4(t_1 - t_2) + \sum_j \delta_{1j}(e_{1j} - e_{2j}) + \sum_j \delta_{2j}(e_{2j} - e_{1j})$$

$$+ \sum_j \delta_{3j}(e_{3j} - e_{4j}) + \sum_j \delta_{4j}(e_{4j} - e_{3j}) \quad (5)$$

The expectation of the square of the difference is

$$E(A - B)^2 = 16(t_1 - t_2)^2$$

$$+ \tfrac{2}{3} \sum_j (e^2{}_{1j} + e^2{}_{2j} + e^2{}_{3j} + e^2{}_{4j} - 2e_{1j}e_{2j} - 2e_{3j}e_{4j}) \quad (6)$$

For the second square, numbering the cows from 1 to 4 again,

$$E(A - B)^2 = 16(t_1 - t_2)^2$$

$$+ \tfrac{2}{3} \sum_j (e^2{}_{1j} + e^2{}_{2j} + e^2{}_{3j} + e^2{}_{4j} - 2e_{1j}e_{4j} - 2e_{2j}e_{3j}) \quad (7)$$

and, for the third square,

$$E(A - B)^2 = 16(t_1 - t_2)^2$$

$$+ \tfrac{2}{3} \sum_j (e^2{}_{1j} + e^2{}_{2j} + e^2{}_{3j} + e^2{}_{4j} - 2e_{1j}e_{3j} - 2e_{2j}e_{4j}) \quad (8)$$

We note, therefore, that the error of this difference depends on the square used and is not directly determinable from the expectation of the error mean square. We have, however, assigned the squares at random to the 3 sets of 4 cows, so that the above errors occur each with a frequency of $\frac{1}{3}$ for any one set of cows. The expectation of the squares error of $(A - B)$ from each set of cows is

$$\frac{2}{3} \sum_{ij} e^2_{ij} - \frac{2}{9} \sum_j (2e_{1j}e_{2j} + 2e_{3j}e_{4j} + 2e_{1j}e_{4j} + 2e_{2j}e_{3j}$$

$$+ 2e_{1j}e_{3j} + 2e_{2j}e_{4j})$$

which equals

$$\frac{2}{3} \sum_{ij} e^2_{ij} - \frac{2}{9} \sum_j [(e_{1j} + e_{2j} + e_{3j} + e_{4j})^2 - (e^2_{1j} + e^2_{2j} + e^2_{3j} + e^2_{4j})]$$

or   (9)

$$\frac{8}{9} \sum_{ij} e^2_{ij}$$

which is equal to 8(expectation of error mean square). It may further be verified that all treatment comparisons are estimated by the corresponding comparisons of treatment means, with error calculated in the usual way in terms of σ^2, the error variance.

The analysis of variance of the design will have the structure:

Due to	df
Periods within sets	9
Cows	11
Treatments	3
Treatments by sets	6
Error	18
Total	47

in which the terms are calculated in the usual way. In concluding the discussion of this design, it may be noted that the randomization of the allocation of squares to sets and sequences to cows is essential (or some other randomization scheme which generates the same population of possible patterns). It is also interesting to note that we may use any number of sets, providing that we allot each of the 3 squares to each set with a probability of $\frac{1}{3}$. From the point of view of estimation, it is not at all essential that the 3 possible squares be represented equally frequently, but it is essential that, in the population of possible randomizations for each set of cows, the 3 squares or squares derived from each by randomization of columns occur equally frequently. In other words, we can make reliable statements about the true treatment effects for the whole set of cows, if we take observations in this way.

29.3 RESIDUAL EFFECTS

We have seen that an essential part of the designs we have discussed in the two previous sections is the assumption that residual effects do not exist. In this section, we shall examine the effects of the presence of residual effects on interpretations made when there are assumed to be none. It will be of interest to note whether the balancing as regards preceding treatments serves any purpose at all.

We shall consider the design for 3 treatments with 2 squares, the one having the order of treatments opposite from the other, and shall assume that the true yields bear the relationships to each other shown in Table 29.5.

TABLE 29.5

Period	Sequence					
	1	2	3	4	5	6
I	a	b	c	a	b	c
II	$b + a'$	$c + b'$	$a + c'$	$c + a'$	$a + b'$	$b + c'$
III	$c + b'$	$a + c'$	$b + a'$	$b + c'$	$c + a'$	$a + b'$

If the analysis derived for the case when there are no residual effects is used, the expectation of the mean square for treatments within sets with 4 degrees of freedom is

$$\sigma^2 + \frac{3}{2}\left[(a^2 + b^2 + c^2) - \frac{(a + b + c)^2}{3} \right]$$

$$+ \frac{2}{3}\left[(a'^2 + b'^2 + c'^2) - \frac{(a' + b' + c')^2}{3} \right]$$

$$+ \tfrac{1}{3}[a(b' + c' - 2a') + b(c' + a' - 2b') + c(a' + b' - 2c')]$$

and of the error mean square within sets is

$$\sigma^2 + \frac{1}{3}\left[a'^2 + b'^2 + c'^2 - \frac{(a' + b' + c')^2}{3} \right]$$

The expectation of the sum of squares for treatment effects averaged over the 2 sets is likewise a complex expression. There does not appear to be any way of estimating the direct effects if residual effects are present. The sole advantage of the balancing is that a comparison of observed treatment totals is a comparison of ($6 \times$ direct effect $- 2 \times$ residual effect), so that we still have a comparison of the effects of the treatments, and we are not measuring a linear combination of the direct effects of one treatment and residual effects of others.

We make note of this, because we may modify the model we used in the absence of residual effects

$$y_{ijk} = \mu + p_i + c_j + t_k + e_{ij}$$

simply by adding a further term, say, r_l which denotes the additive effect on y_{ijk} if treatment k is preceded by treatment l, giving the model

$$y_{ijk} = \mu + p_i + c_j + t_k + r_l + e_{ij}$$

If, as we can with most experimental designs, and indeed for the present design with no residual effects, we assume as a device that the e_{ij}'s are normally and independently distributed with mean zero and variance σ^2, we can derive least squares estimates of the t_k's and r_l's. This procedure is subject essentially to the same difficulties as those we mentioned in Chapter 8 for the covariance technique. The reader may verify if he desires that this procedure does not lead to estimates that have a variance which may be estimated, in the sense that we estimate the variance of treatment comparisons in the ordinary randomized block or Latin square experiment. The difficulty about the assumption of normality of the errors is that we cannot specify accurately the population we are discussing. The procedure we follow, in the absence of residual effects, leads to statements of treatment effects on the cows actually used, and only on those cows. If we broaden the experiment by drawing sets of cows from a population by a random device, we can make statements about that population on the lines of Chapter 28.

The first problem when residual effects are known to be present is one of definition of what we mean by an assessment of the effect of the treatment. In the case of the hypothetical cow experiments discussed earlier in the chapter, we can regard the effect of a treatment as being made up of its direct effect in the period of application, plus the first-period residual effect, plus the second-period residual effect, and so on, weighted in some desired way. For example, if the lactation period consists of the 3 periods, and the treatment is applied continuously, we might expect to obtain 3 times the direct effect plus twice the first-period residual effect plus the second-period residual effect. Even if we could devise a design that would estimate direct effects, first-period residual effects, and second-period residual effects, however, this would be a most unsatisfactory way of estimating the effect of the treatment applied over the whole period, for we assume additivity of the effect of a treatment and its residual effect. A treatment applied for one period might well have a considerable residual effect if another treatment is applied in the second period, and no residual effect when the treatment in the second period is the same. It does not seem possible to avoid the conclusion that, if we wish to assess effects of treatments applied for a certain period, we must apply the treatments for the whole of that period. Having done so and kept a record of the response (i.e., yield) at regular intervals, we would then examine the records and abstract any measure we desire from the whole time-yield relationship. A basic assumption in the switch-over design is that the effect of a treatment is the same in all the periods in which it may be applied. This may perhaps be true of some characteristics of the animal, such as vitamin content of the blood, but is very unlikely to be true, for example, in the case of yield of milk. On all scores, therefore, the use of the switch-over design for the type of problem considered here is questionable. The utility of the switch-over design, or, in fact, of any design that involves different treatments on the same experimental unit, is limited because of the necessity of constant treatment effects and zero residual effects.

There are no new problems of design, though there may be difficulties of analysis when the treatments are applied for the whole period of interest.

29.4 LONG-TERM AGRICULTURAL EXPERIMENTS

The most extensive discussion of this subject is that of Cochran.[2] The most important types of problem are (1) the comparison of different rotations, for example, a 2-year rotation of crops, say, corn and oats repeated indefinitely, and a 3-year rotation of crops, say, corn, corn and oats repeated indefinitely, and (2) the comparison of agronomic practices on a fixed rotation. Combinations of these two types of problem are of frequent occurrence.

The basic point in the design of these experiments is that we can sample only the number of years that the experiment is performed, and, in general, experience indicates that, in matters of crop yield or the effectiveness of agronomic practices, the year-to-year variations in the effects are considerable and often larger in magnitude than plot-to-plot variations within a year. For this reason, it is essential that every crop of the rotations under comparison, or every phase of the agronomic practices, be represented by a plot every year. Thus, if we are comparing 2 rotations $COCO \cdots$ and $CCOCCO \cdots$, it is necessary to have multiples of a set of 5 plots with the treatments shown in Table 29.6.

TABLE 29.6

Plot

Year	1	2	3	4	5
1	C	O	C	C	O
2	O	C	C	O	C
3	C	O	O	C	C
4	O	C	C	C	O
5	C	O	C	O	C
6	O	C	O	C	C

In the same way, if some of the agronomic treatments are to be applied at fixed intervals, all the possible phases of the application of treatments must be represented in each year. In other words, for any year there must be a plot receiving the treatment in that year, a plot that received the treatment in the previous year, a plot that received the treatment 2 years previously, and so on. These considerations come directly from the fact that we may expect years to have large effects. In the same way, we can say that replication other than by phase in any one year is not of great importance, and frequently 2 replicates will be sufficient.

Cochran [2] and Crowther and Cochran [3] give examples of the various types of design and their analyses, and the interested reader may refer to these papers. We shall merely consider some of the difficulties that are inherent in the structure of the data which will be obtained.

After a long-term experiment has been performed for a long period of time, say, 25 years, we are presented with the history of each plot in terms of treatments and yields. The first problem is to decide how we wish to characterize the sequence of yields. From some points of view, an expression of trends in terms of orthogonal polynomials, by the linear trend, the quadratic trend, the cubic trend, and so on, is suitable, and this was the method used first by Fisher,[4] by Cochran,[2] and by Crowther and Cochran.[3] This procedure is not particularly satisfactory and has not been successful in the somewhat similar problems of the analysis of economic time series. It does not give a representation of the yield-time relationship which can be extrapolated to succeeding years. One of the important problems in assessing different crop rotations is to determine the limiting yields: that is, the yields of the crops of the rotation after the rotation has experienced, say, 20 or 30 cycles. For this purpose orthogonal polynomials are not satisfactory. The linear trend may be a reasonable representation of the change in yields over a relatively short period only at the beginning of the cycles of the rotation or after the cycles are producing little further changes. A further reason that militates against the use of orthogonal polynomials is that it is difficult to think of a mechanism which would result in a polynomial relationship of yields to time.

A second problem in the analysis of yields for each plot is that there may be correlation among the errors from year to year. The situation is entirely different from the 1-year agricultural experiment, for which the main errors are the plot errors and randomization is designed to estimate their effects. We may imagine that the true relationship of the yields of a crop of the rotation to time for a plot is given by a function, and that the observed values deviate from this function by an error. These errors will tend to be correlated, and some data give a strong indication of such an effect. An approach to the analysis of simple long-term experiments from this point of view is under way. Another difficulty which is certain to arise is the one discussed in the earlier parts of this chapter: namely, that simple analyses of variance involving years are useful only if we can assume that there are no residual effects of crops or treatments as the case may be. The existence of residual effects of crops and agronomic treatments is usually the main reason for performing long-term experiments.

REFERENCES

1. COCHRAN, W. G., AUTREY, K. M., and CANNON, C. Y. A double change-over design for dairy cattle feeding experiments. *Jour. Dairy Sci.*, **24**, 937–951, 1941.
2. COCHRAN, W. G. Long-term agricultural experiments. *Suppl. Jour. Roy. Stat. Soc.*, **6**, 104–148, 1939.
3. CROWTHER, F., and COCHRAN, W. G. Rotation experiments with cotton in the Sudan Gezira. *Jour. Agr. Sci.*, **32**, 390–405, 1942.
4. FISHER, R. A. Studies in crop variation I. An examination of the yield of dressed grain from Broadbalk. *Jour. Agr. Sci.*, **11**, 107–135, 1920.

TABLE I VARIANCE RATIO

10% Points of e^{2z}

n_2	n_1									
	1	2	3	4	5	6	8	12	24	∞
1	39.86	49.50	53.59	55.83	57.24	58.20	59.44	60.70	62.00	63.33
2	8.53	9.00	9.16	9.24	9.29	9.33	9.37	9.41	9.45	9.49
3	5.54	5.46	5.39	5.34	5.31	5.28	5.25	5.22	5.18	5.13
4	4.54	4.32	4.19	4.11	4.05	4.01	3.95	3.90	3.83	3.76
5	4.06	3.78	3.62	3.52	3.45	3.40	3.34	3.27	3.19	3.10
6	3.78	3.46	3.29	3.18	3.11	3.05	2.98	2.90	2.82	2.72
7	3.59	3.26	3.07	2.96	2.88	2.83	2.75	2.67	2.58	2.47
8	3.46	3.11	2.92	2.81	2.73	2.67	2.59	2.50	2.40	2.29
9	3.36	3.01	2.81	2.69	2.61	2.55	2.47	2.38	2.28	2.16
10	3.28	2.92	2.73	2.61	2.52	2.46	2.38	2.28	2.18	2.06
11	3.23	2.86	2.66	2.54	2.45	2.39	2.30	2.21	2.10	1.97
12	3.18	2.81	2.61	2.48	2.39	2.33	2.24	2.15	2.04	1.90
13	3.14	2.76	2.56	2.43	2.35	2.28	2.20	2.10	1.98	1.85
14	3.10	2.73	2.52	2.39	2.31	2.24	2.15	2.05	1.94	1.80
15	3.07	2.70	2.49	2.36	2.27	2.21	2.12	2.02	1.90	1.76
16	3.05	2.67	2.46	2.33	2.24	2.18	2.09	1.99	1.87	1.72
17	3.03	2.64	2.44	2.31	2.22	2.15	2.06	1.96	1.84	1.69
18	3.01	2.62	2.42	2.29	2.20	2.13	2.04	1.93	1.81	1.66
19	2.99	2.61	2.40	2.27	2.18	2.11	2.02	1.91	1.79	1.63
20	2.97	2.59	2.38	2.25	2.16	2.09	2.00	1.89	1.77	1.61
21	2.96	2.57	2.36	2.23	2.14	2.08	1.98	1.88	1.75	1.59
22	2.95	2.56	2.35	2.22	2.13	2.06	1.97	1.86	1.73	1.57
23	2.94	2.55	2.34	2.21	2.11	2.05	1.95	1.84	1.72	1.55
24	2.93	2.54	2.33	2.19	2.10	2.04	1.94	1.83	1.70	1.53
25	2.92	2.53	2.32	2.18	2.09	2.02	1.93	1.82	1.69	1.52
26	2.91	2.52	2.31	2.17	2.08	2.01	1.92	1.81	1.68	1.50
27	2.90	2.51	2.30	2.17	2.07	2.00	1.91	1.80	1.67	1.49
28	2.89	2.50	2.29	2.16	2.06	2.00	1.90	1.79	1.66	1.48
29	2.89	2.50	2.28	2.15	2.06	1.99	1.89	1.78	1.65	1.47
30	2.88	2.49	2.28	2.14	2.05	1.98	1.88	1.77	1.64	1.46
40	2.84	2.44	2.23	2.09	2.00	1.93	1.83	1.71	1.57	1.38
60	2.79	2.39	2.18	2.04	1.95	1.87	1.77	1.66	1.51	1.29
120	2.75	2.35	2.13	1.99	1.90	1.82	1.72	1.60	1.45	1.19
∞	2.71	2.30	2.08	1.94	1.85	1.77	1.67	1.55	1.38	1.00

Lower 10% points are found by interchange of n_1 and n_2; i.e., n_1 must always correspond with the greater mean square.

Table I is reprinted from Table V of Fisher and Yates: *Statistical Tables for Biological, Agricultural, and Medical Research*, Oliver and Boyd Ltd., Edinburgh, by permission of the authors and publishers.

TABLE I VARIANCE RATIO (*Continued*)

5% Points of e^{2z}

n_2	n_1									
	1	2	3	4	5	6	8	12	24	∞
1	161.4	199.5	215.7	224.6	230.2	234.0	238.9	243.9	249.0	254.3
2	18.51	19.00	19.16	19.25	19.30	19.33	19.37	19.41	19.45	19.50
3	10.13	9.55	9.28	9.12	9.01	8.94	8.84	8.74	8.64	8.53
4	7.71	6.94	6.59	6.39	6.26	6.16	6.04	5.91	5.77	5.63
5	6.61	5.79	5.41	5.19	5.05	4.95	4.82	4.68	4.53	4.36
6	5.99	5.14	4.76	4.53	4.39	4.28	4.15	4.00	3.84	3.67
7	5.59	4.74	4.35	4.12	3.97	3.87	3.73	3.57	3.41	3.23
8	5.32	4.46	4.07	3.84	3.69	3.58	3.44	3.28	3.12	2.93
9	5.12	4.26	3.86	3.63	3.48	3.37	3.23	3.07	2.90	2.71
10	4.96	4.10	3.71	3.48	3.33	3.22	3.07	2.91	2.74	2.54
11	4.84	3.98	3.59	3.36	3.20	3.09	2.95	2.79	2.61	2.40
12	4.75	3.88	3.49	3.26	3.11	3.00	2.85	2.69	2.50	2.30
13	4.67	3.80	3.41	3.18	3.02	2.92	2.77	2.60	2.42	2.21
14	4.60	3.74	3.34	3.11	2.96	2.85	2.70	2.53	2.35	2.13
15	4.54	3.68	3.29	3.06	2.90	2.79	2.64	2.48	2.29	2.07
16	4.49	3.63	3.24	3.01	2.85	2.74	2.59	2.42	2.24	2.01
17	4.45	3.59	3.20	2.96	2.81	2.70	2.55	2.38	2.19	1.96
18	4.41	3.55	3.16	2.93	2.77	2.66	2.51	2.34	2.15	1.92
19	4.38	3.52	3.13	2.90	2.74	2.63	2.48	2.31	2.11	1.88
20	4.35	3.49	3.10	2.87	2.71	2.60	2.45	2.28	2.08	1.84
21	4.32	3.47	3.07	2.84	2.68	2.57	2.42	2.25	2.05	1.81
22	4.30	3.44	3.05	2.82	2.66	2.55	2.40	2.23	2.03	1.78
23	4.28	3.42	3.03	2.80	2.64	2.53	2.38	2.20	2.00	1.76
24	4.26	3.40	3.01	2.78	2.62	2.51	2.36	2.18	1.98	1.73
25	4.24	3.38	2.99	2.76	2.60	2.49	2.34	2.16	1.96	1.71
26	4.22	3.37	2.98	2.74	2.59	2.47	2.32	2.15	1.95	1.69
27	4.21	3.35	2.96	2.73	2.57	2.46	2.30	2.13	1.93	1.67
28	4.20	3.34	2.95	2.71	2.56	2.44	2.29	2.12	1.91	1.65
29	4.18	3.33	2.93	2.70	2.54	2.43	2.28	2.10	1.90	1.64
30	4.17	3.32	2.92	2.69	2.53	2.42	2.27	2.09	1.89	1.62
40	4.08	3.23	2.84	2.61	2.45	2.34	2.18	2.00	1.79	1.51
60	4.00	3.15	2.76	2.52	2.37	2.25	2.10	1.92	1.70	1.39
120	3.92	3.07	2.68	2.45	2.29	2.17	2.02	1.83	1.61	1.25
∞	3.84	2.99	2.60	2.37	2.21	2.09	1.94	1.75	1.52	1.00

Lower 5% points are found by interchange of n_1 and n_2: i.e., n_1 must always correspond with the greater mean square.

Table I Variance Ratio (*Continued*)

1% Points of e^{2z}

n_2	n_1									
	1	2	3	4	5	6	8	12	24	∞
1	4052	4999	5403	5625	5764	5859	5981	6106	6234	6366
2	98.49	99.01	99.17	99.25	99.30	99.33	99.36	99.42	99.46	99.50
3	34.12	30.81	29.46	28.71	28.24	27.91	27.49	27.05	26.60	26.12
4	21.20	18.00	16.69	15.98	15.52	15.21	14.80	14.37	13.93	13.46
5	16.26	13.27	12.06	11.39	10.97	10.67	10.27	9.89	9.47	9.02
6	13.74	10.92	9.78	9.15	8.75	8.47	8.10	7.72	7.31	6.88
7	12.25	9.55	8.45	7.85	7.46	7.19	6.84	6.47	6.07	5.65
8	11.26	8.65	7.59	7.01	6.63	6.37	6.03	5.67	5.28	4.86
9	10.56	8.02	6.99	6.42	6.06	5.80	5.47	5.11	4.73	4.31
10	10.04	7.56	6.55	5.99	5.64	5.39	5.06	4.71	4.33	3.91
11	9.65	7.20	6.22	5.67	5.32	5.07	4.74	4.40	4.02	3.60
12	9.33	6.93	5.95	5.41	5.06	4.82	4.50	4.16	3.78	3.36
13	9.07	6.70	5.74	5.20	4.86	4.62	4.30	3.96	3.59	3.16
14	8.86	6.51	5.56	5.03	4.69	4.46	4.14	3.80	3.43	3.00
15	8.68	6.36	5.42	4.89	4.56	4.32	4.00	3.67	3.29	2.87
16	8.53	6.23	5.29	4.77	4.44	4.20	3.89	3.55	3.18	2.75
17	8.40	6.11	5.18	4.67	4.34	4.10	3.79	3.45	3.08	2.65
18	8.28	6.01	5.09	4.58	4.25	4.01	3.71	3.37	3.00	2.57
19	8.18	5.93	5.01	4.50	4.17	3.94	3.63	3.30	2.92	2.49
20	8.10	5.85	4.94	4.43	4.10	3.87	3.56	3.23	2.86	2.42
21	8.02	5.78	4.87	4.37	4.04	3.81	3.51	3.17	2.80	2.36
22	7.94	5.72	4.82	4.31	3.99	3.76	3.45	3.12	2.75	2.31
23	7.88	5.66	4.76	4.26	3.94	3.71	3.41	3.07	2.70	2.26
24	7.82	5.61	4.72	4.22	3.90	3.67	3.36	3.03	2.66	2.21
25	7.77	5.57	4.68	4.18	3.86	3.63	3.32	2.99	2.62	2.17
26	7.72	5.53	4.64	4.14	3.82	3.59	3.29	2.96	2.58	2.13
27	7.68	5.49	4.60	4.11	3.78	3.56	3.26	2.93	2.55	2.10
28	7.64	5.45	4.57	4.07	3.75	3.53	3.23	2.90	2.52	2.06
29	7.60	5.42	4.54	4.04	3.73	3.50	3.20	2.87	2.49	2.03
30	7.56	5.39	4.51	4.02	3.70	3.47	3.17	2.84	2.47	2.01
40	7.31	5.18	4.31	3.83	3.51	3.29	2.99	2.66	2.29	1.80
60	7.08	4.98	4.13	3.65	3.34	3.12	2.82	2.50	2.12	1.60
120	6.85	4.79	3.95	3.48	3.17	2.96	2.66	2.34	1.95	1.38
∞	6.64	4.60	3.78	3.32	3.02	2.80	2.51	2.18	1.79	1.00

Lower 1% points are found by interchange of n_1 and n_2: i.e., n_1 must always correspond with the greater mean square.

TABLE II   TABLE OF $E^2_{0.01}$ AND THE CORRESPONDING VALUES OF P_{II}

$f_1 = 1$

f_2	$E^2_{0.01}$	ϕ									
		1	1.5	2	2.5	3	4	5	6	7	8
2	0.980	0.970	0.947	0.914	0.874	0.828	0.720	0.602	0.484	0.373	0.277
4	0.841	0.949	0.885	0.784	0.651	0.501	0.233	0.077	0.018	0.003	
6	0.696	0.934	0.839	0.687	0.498	0.312	0.076	0.010	0.001		
7	0.636	0.928	0.822	0.652	0.447	0.258	0.049	0.006			
8	0.585	0.924	0.808	0.624	0.409	0.221	0.034	0.002			
9	0.540	0.920	0.796	0.601	0.379	0.193	0.025	0.001			
10	0.501	0.916	0.786	0.582	0.355	0.172	0.019	0.001			
11	0.467	0.913	0.777	0.567	0.336	0.156	0.015				
12	0.437	0.911	0.770	0.553	0.320	0.144	0.012				
13	0.411	0.909	0.763	0.542	0.307	0.133	0.010				
14	0.388	0.907	0.758	0.532	0.296	0.125	0.009				
15	0.367	0.905	0.753	0.523	0.286	0.118	0.008				
16	0.348	0.904	0.749	0.516	0.278	0.112	0.007				
17	0.331	0.902	0.745	0.509	0.271	0.107	0.006				
18	0.315	0.901	0.741	0.503	0.264	0.103	0.006				
19	0.301	0.900	0.738	0.498	0.259	0.099	0.005				
20	0.288	0.899	0.735	0.493	0.254	0.096	0.005				
21	0.276	0.898	0.732	0.488	0.249	0.093	0.004				
22	0.265	0.897	0.730	0.484	0.245	0.090	0.004				
23	0.255	0.896	0.728	0.481	0.241	0.088	0.004				
24	0.246	0.896	0.726	0.477	0.238	0.086	0.004				
25	0.237	0.895	0.724	0.474	0.235	0.084	0.004				
26	0.229	0.894	0.722	0.471	0.232	0.082	0.003				
27	0.221	0.894	0.720	0.469	0.229	0.081	0.003				
28	0.214	0.893	0.718	0.466	0.227	0.079	0.003				
29	0.212	0.893	0.717	0.464	0.225	0.078	0.003				
30	0.201	0.892	0.716	0.462	0.223	0.077	0.003				
60	0.106	0.885	0.696	0.430	0.194	0.061	0.002				
∞		0.877	0.675	0.400	0.169	0.048	0.001				

Table II is taken from *Statistical Research Memoirs*, Vol. II, by kind permission of Professor E. S. Pearson.

TABLE II   TABLE OF $E^2_{0.01}$ AND THE CORRESPONDING VALUES OF P_{II} (*Continued*)

$f_1 = 2$

f_2	$E^2_{0.01}$	ϕ									
		1	1.5	2	2.5	3	4	5	6	7	8
2	0.990	0.975	0.957	0.932	0.901	0.865	0.779	0.680	0.577	0.475	0.379
4	0.900	0.957	0.901	0.810	0.685	0.540	0.266	0.095	0.024	0.004	0.001
6	0.785	0.941	0.850	0.695	0.498	0.305	0.068	0.007			
7	0.732	0.934	0.828	0.649	0.431	0.235	0.035	0.004			
8	0.684	0.929	0.809	0.611	0.379	0.187	0.021	0.001			
9	0.641	0.924	0.793	0.579	0.338	0.152	0.013				
10	0.602	0.920	0.779	0.552	0.306	0.127	0.008				
11	0.567	0.916	0.767	0.528	0.278	0.108	0.006				
12	0.536	0.912	0.756	0.508	0.255	0.093	0.005				
13	0.508	0.909	0.746	0.491	0.237	0.082	0.003				
14	0.482	0.907	0.738	0.476	0.223	0.074	0.002				
15	0.459	0.904	0.730	0.463	0.211	0.066	0.002				
16	0.438	0.902	0.723	0.452	0.201	0.060	0.001				
17	0.418	0.900	0.717	0.442	0.193	0.055	0.001				
18	0.401	0.898	0.711	0.433	0.185	0.051	0.001				
19	0.384	0.896	0.706	0.424	0.177	0.048	0.001				
20	0.369	0.895	0.701	0.417	0.170	0.045	0.001				
21	0.355	0.894	0.697	0.410	0.165	0.042	0.001				
22	0.342	0.893	0.693	0.404	0.160	0.040	0.001				
23	0.330	0.891	0.690	0.399	0.155	0.038					
24	0.319	0.890	0.686	0.394	0.151	0.036					
25	0.308	0.889	0.683	0.389	0.148	0.035					
26	0.298	0.888	0.680	0.385	0.144	0.034					
27	0.289	0.887	0.678	0.381	0.141	0.032					
28	0.280	0.886	0.675	0.377	0.138	0.031					
29	0.272	0.886	0.672	0.373	0.136	0.030					
30	0.264	0.885	0.670	0.370	0.134	0.029					
60	0.142	0.873	0.637	0.324	0.102	0.019					
∞		0.860	0.601	0.279	0.076	0.011					

TABLE II   TABLE OF $E^2_{0.01}$ AND THE CORRESPONDING VALUES OF P_{II} *(Continued)*

$f_1 = 3$

f_2	$E^2_{0.01}$	ϕ									
		1	1.5	2	2.5	3	4	5	6	7	8
2	0.993	0.977	0.961	0.939	0.911	0.878	0.800	0.709	0.612	0.515	0.421
4	0.926	0.959	0.907	0.818	0.695	0.552	0.276	0.100	0.026	0.005	0.001
6	0.830	0.943	0.850	0.691	0.486	0.290	0.059	0.006			
7	0.784	0.936	0.825	0.636	0.408	0.210	0.025	0.002			
8	0.740	0.929	0.803	0.590	0.347	0.158	0.014				
9	0.700	0.923	0.783	0.550	0.299	0.120	0.008				
10	0.663	0.918	0.765	0.517	0.261	0.094	0.004				
11	0.629	0.913	0.749	0.487	0.231	0.075	0.002				
12	0.598	0.909	0.735	0.463	0.206	0.062	0.001				
13	0.570	0.906	0.723	0.441	0.186	0.051	0.001				
14	0.544	0.902	0.711	0.422	0.170	0.044	0.001				
15	0.520	0.899	0.701	0.406	0.156	0.038	0.001				
16	0.498	0.896	0.692	0.391	0.145	0.033					
17	0.478	0.893	0.683	0.378	0.135	0.029					
18	0.459	0.891	0.676	0.367	0.126	0.026					
19	0.442	0.889	0.669	0.356	0.119	0.023					
20	0.426	0.887	0.662	0.347	0.112	0.021					
21	0.410	0.885	0.656	0.339	0.107	0.019					
22	0.396	0.883	0.651	0.331	0.102	0.017					
23	0.383	0.881	0.646	0.324	0.098	0.016					
24	0.371	0.880	0.641	0.318	0.094	0.015					
25	0.359	0.879	0.637	0.312	0.090	0.014					
26	0.349	0.877	0.633	0.307	0.087	0.013					
27	0.338	0.876	0.629	0.302	0.084	0.012					
28	0.329	0.875	0.625	0.297	0.081	0.012					
29	0.319	0.874	0.622	0.293	0.079	0.011					
30	0.311	0.872	0.619	0.289	0.077	0.011					
60	0.171	0.856	0.571	0.233	0.050	0.005					
∞		0.836	0.519	0.182	0.030	0.002					

TABLE II TABLE OF $E^2_{0.01}$ AND THE CORRESPONDING VALUES OF P_{II} (*Continued*)

$f_1 = 4$

f_2	$E^2_{0.01}$	ϕ									
		1	1.5	2	2.5	3	4	5	6	7	8
2	0.995	0.978	0.962	0.942	0.915	0.884	0.810	0.724	0.631	0.536	0.444
4	0.941	0.960	0.909	0.822	0.700	0.557	0.280	0.102	0.027	0.005	0.001
6	0.859	0.943	0.849	0.685	0.475	0.277	0.053	0.005			
7	0.818	0.936	0.821	0.624	0.389	0.191	0.018				
8	0.778	0.928	0.796	0.571	0.322	0.136	0.010				
9	0.741	0.922	0.773	0.526	0.269	0.098	0.003				
10	0.706	0.916	0.752	0.487	0.227	0.073	0.002				
11	0.673	0.911	0.733	0.453	0.195	0.055	0.001				
12	0.643	0.906	0.716	0.424	0.169	0.042	0.001				
13	0.616	0.901	0.700	0.398	0.148	0.034					
14	0.590	0.897	0.687	0.376	0.131	0.028					
15	0.566	0.893	0.674	0.357	0.117	0.022					
16	0.544	0.890	0.662	0.340	0.106	0.018					
17	0.523	0.886	0.652	0.325	0.096	0.015					
18	0.504	0.883	0.642	0.312	0.088	0.013					
19	0.486	0.880	0.633	0.301	0.081	0.011					
20	0.470	0.878	0.625	0.290	0.075	0.010					
21	0.454	0.876	0.618	0.280	0.070	0.009					
22	0.440	0.873	0.611	0.272	0.066	0.008					
23	0.426	0.871	0.604	0.264	0.062	0.007					
24	0.413	0.869	0.598	0.257	0.059	0.006					
25	0.401	0.867	0.593	0.250	0.056	0.006					
26	0.389	0.865	0.588	0.244	0.053	0.005					
27	0.378	0.864	0.583	0.239	0.050	0.005					
28	0.368	0.862	0.578	0.234	0.048	0.005					
29	0.358	0.861	0.574	0.229	0.046	0.004					
30	0.349	0.860	0.570	0.225	0.044	0.004					
60	0.196	0.837	0.509	0.165	0.024	0.001					
∞		0.810	0.443	0.115	0.011						

TABLE II   TABLE OF $E^2_{0.01}$ AND THE CORRESPONDING VALUES OF P_{II} (*Continued*)

$f_1 = 5$

f_2	$E^2_{0.01}$	ϕ									
		1	1.5	2	2.5	3	4	5	6	7	8
2	0.996	0.978	0.964	0.944	0.918	0.888	0.817	0.733	0.642	0.549	0.458
4	0.951	0.961	0.910	0.824	0.702	0.559	0.282	0.103	0.027	0.005	0.001
6	0.879	0.943	0.848	0.679	0.466	0.266	0.048	0.004			
7	0.842	0.935	0.818	0.614	0.394	0.177	0.014				
8	0.806	0.928	0.790	0.556	0.301	0.121	0.007				
9	0.771	0.920	0.764	0.505	0.245	0.083	0.003				
10	0.738	0.914	0.740	0.461	0.201	0.058	0.001				
11	0.707	0.908	0.718	0.424	0.168	0.042					
12	0.679	0.902	0.699	0.391	0.141	0.031					
13	0.652	0.897	0.681	0.363	0.120	0.023					
14	0.626	0.892	0.664	0.339	0.104	0.018					
15	0.603	0.888	0.649	0.318	0.090	0.014					
16	0.581	0.883	0.636	0.299	0.079	0.011					
17	0.561	0.880	0.624	0.283	0.071	0.009					
18	0.541	0.876	0.612	0.269	0.063	0.007					
19	0.523	0.873	0.602	0.256	0.057	0.006					
20	0.506	0.870	0.592	0.245	0.052	0.005					
21	0.490	0.867	0.583	0.234	0.047	0.004					
22	0.475	0.864	0.575	0.225	0.044	0.004					
23	0.461	0.861	0.567	0.217	0.040	0.003					
24	0.448	0.859	0.560	0.210	0.037	0.003					
25	0.435	0.857	0.553	0.203	0.035	0.003					
26	0.423	0.855	0.547	0.196	0.033	0.002					
27	0.412	0.853	0.541	0.190	0.031	0.002					
28	0.401	0.851	0.536	0.185	0.029	0.002					
29	0.391	0.849	0.531	0.180	0.027	0.002					
30	0.381	0.847	0.526	0.176	0.026	0.002					
60	0.218	0.819	0.452	0.116	0.011						
∞		0.784	0.373	0.070	0.004						

TABLE II   TABLE OF $E^2_{0.01}$ AND THE CORRESPONDING VALUES OF P_{II} (*Continued*)

$f_1 = 6$

f_2	$E^2_{0.01}$	ϕ									
		1	1.5	2	2.5	3	4	5	6	7	8
2	0.997	0.978	0.964	0.945	0.920	0.891	0.821	0.739	0.650	0.558	0.468
4	0.958	0.962	0.911	0.825	0.704	0.560	0.283	0.104	0.027	0.005	0.001
6	0.894	0.944	0.847	0.675	0.459	0.258	0.044	0.003			
7	0.860	0.935	0.815	0.605	0.362	0.166	0.011				
8	0.827	0.927	0.784	0.543	0.285	0.109	0.006				
9	0.795	0.919	0.756	0.488	0.226	0.071	0.003				
10	0.764	0.912	0.730	0.441	0.181	0.048	0.001				
11	0.734	0.905	0.706	0.400	0.147	0.033					
12	0.707	0.899	0.683	0.365	0.120	0.023					
13	0.681	0.893	0.663	0.334	0.100	0.017					
14	0.656	0.888	0.645	0.308	0.084	0.013					
15	0.633	0.882	0.628	0.286	0.071	0.009					
16	0.612	0.878	0.612	0.266	0.061	0.007					
17	0.591	0.873	0.598	0.249	0.053	0.005					
18	0.572	0.869	0.585	0.233	0.046	0.004					
19	0.554	0.865	0.573	0.220	0.041	0.003					
20	0.537	0.862	0.562	0.208	0.036	0.003					
21	0.521	0.858	0.552	0.198	0.033	0.002					
22	0.506	0.855	0.542	0.188	0.029	0.002					
23	0.492	0.852	0.533	0.180	0.027	0.002					
24	0.478	0.849	0.524	0.172	0.024	0.001					
25	0.465	0.846	0.517	0.165	0.022	0.001					
26	0.453	0.844	0.510	0.159	0.020	0.001					
27	0.442	0.842	0.503	0.153	0.019	0.001					
28	0.430	0.839	0.497	0.147	0.017	0.001					
29	0.420	0.837	0.491	0.142	0.016	0.001					
30	0.410	0.835	0.486	0.138	0.015	0.001					
60	0.238	0.801	0.401	0.081	0.006						
∞		0.755	0.311	0.042	0.001						

TABLE II   TABLE OF $E^2_{0.01}$ AND THE CORRESPONDING VALUES OF P_{II} (*Continued*)

$f_1 = 7$

f_2	$E^2_{0.01}$	ϕ									
		1	1.5	2	2.5	3	4	5	6	7	8
2	0.997	0.979	0.965	0.946	0.922	0.893	0.824	0.743	0.655	0.564	0.475
4	0.963	0.962	0.912	0.826	0.705	0.561	0.283	0.104	0.027	0.005	0.001
6	0.906	0.944	0.845	0.671	0.452	0.251	0.041	0.003			
7	0.875	0.935	0.812	0.598	0.351	0.158	0.009				
8	0.844	0.926	0.779	0.532	0.272	0.100	0.005				
9	0.814	0.918	0.749	0.474	0.211	0.063	0.002				
10	0.785	0.910	0.720	0.423	0.166	0.041	0.001				
11	0.757	0.903	0.694	0.379	0.131	0.027					
12	0.730	0.896	0.670	0.342	0.105	0.018					
13	0.705	0.889	0.648	0.310	0.085	0.013					
14	0.681	0.883	0.627	0.283	0.069	0.009					
15	0.659	0.878	0.608	0.259	0.057	0.007					
16	0.638	0.872	0.591	0.238	0.048	0.004					
17	0.618	0.868	0.575	0.220	0.041	0.003					
18	0.599	0.863	0.561	0.205	0.035	0.002					
19	0.581	0.859	0.548	0.191	0.030	0.002					
20	0.564	0.854	0.535	0.179	0.026	0.002					
21	0.548	0.851	0.524	0.168	0.023	0.001					
22	0.533	0.847	0.513	0.159	0.020	0.001					
23	0.519	0.844	0.503	0.150	0.018	0.001					
24	0.505	0.840	0.494	0.143	0.016	0.001					
25	0.492	0.837	0.485	0.136	0.015	0.001					
26	0.479	0.834	0.477	0.130	0.013						
27	0.468	0.831	0.470	0.124	0.012						
28	0.456	0.829	0.463	0.119	0.011						
29	0.446	0.826	0.456	0.114	0.010						
30	0.435	0.824	0.450	0.110	0.009						
60	0.256	0.783	0.355	0.056	0.003						
∞		0.729	0.256	0.024							

TABLE II TABLE OF $E^2_{0.01}$ AND THE CORRESPONDING VALUES OF P_{II} (*Continued*)

$f_1 = 8$

f_2	$E^2_{0.01}$	ϕ									
		1	1.5	2	2.5	3	4	5	6	7	8
2	0.997	0.979	0.965	0.946	0.923	0.894	0.826	0.746	0.659	0.569	0.481
4	0.967	0.962	0.912	0.826	0.705	0.562	0.284	0.104	0.027	0.005	0.001
6	0.915	0.944	0.844	0.668	0.447	0.246	0.039	0.003			
7	0.887	0.934	0.809	0.592	0.343	0.151	0.007				
8	0.858	0.925	0.775	0.522	0.261	0.093	0.004				
9	0.829	0.917	0.743	0.461	0.199	0.056					
10	0.802	0.908	0.712	0.408	0.153	0.035					
11	0.775	0.901	0.684	0.363	0.118	0.022					
12	0.750	0.893	0.658	0.324	0.092	0.014					
13	0.726	0.886	0.634	0.290	0.073	0.009					
14	0.703	0.880	0.612	0.261	0.058	0.006					
15	0.681	0.874	0.591	0.237	0.047	0.004					
16	0.660	0.868	0.573	0.216	0.039	0.003					
17	0.641	0.862	0.555	0.197	0.032	0.002					
18	0.622	0.857	0.539	0.181	0.027	0.002					
19	0.605	0.852	0.525	0.168	0.023	0.001					
20	0.588	0.848	0.511	0.156	0.019	0.001					
21	0.572	0.843	0.499	0.145	0.017	0.001					
22	0.557	0.839	0.487	0.135	0.014						
23	0.542	0.835	0.476	0.127	0.012						
24	0.529	0.832	0.466	0.119	0.011						
25	0.515	0.828	0.456	0.113	0.010						
26	0.503	0.825	0.447	0.107	0.009						
27	0.491	0.822	0.439	0.101	0.008						
28	0.480	0.819	0.432	0.096	0.007						
29	0.469	0.816	0.425	0.092	0.006						
30	0.458	0.813	0.418	0.088	0.006						
60	0.274	0.766	0.315	0.039	0.001						
∞		0.702	0.211	0.014							

TABLE III   TABLE OF $E^2_{0.05}$ AND THE CORRESPONDING VALUES OF P_{II}

$f_1 = 1$

f_2	$E^2_{0.05}$	φ									
		1	1.5	2	2.5	3	4	5	6	7	8
2	0.903	0.862	0.763	0.643	0.517	0.395	0.200	0.083	0.028	0.008	0.002
4	0.658	0.805	0.631	0.428	0.247	0.120	0.016	0.001			
6	0.500	0.777	0.570	0.343	0.164	0.061	0.004				
7	0.444	0.768	0.552	0.319	0.144	0.050	0.003				
8	0.399	0.761	0.537	0.302	0.129	0.041	0.002				
9	0.362	0.756	0.526	0.288	0.119	0.036	0.001				
10	0.332	0.751	0.517	0.278	0.111	0.032	0.001				
11	0.306	0.747	0.510	0.269	0.105	0.029	0.001				
12	0.284	0.744	0.504	0.262	0.100	0.027	0.001				
13	0.264	0.741	0.499	0.256	0.096	0.025	0.001				
14	0.247	0.739	0.494	0.251	0.093	0.024	0.001				
15	0.232	0.737	0.490	0.247	0.090	0.023					
16	0.219	0.735	0.487	0.243	0.087	0.022					
17	0.207	0.734	0.484	0.240	0.085	0.021					
18	0.197	0.732	0.481	0.237	0.084	0.020					
19	0.187	0.731	0.479	0.235	0.082	0.020					
20	0.179	0.730	0.477	0.233	0.081	0.019					
21	0.171	0.729	0.475	0.231	0.079	0.019					
22	0.164	0.728	0.473	0.229	0.078	0.018					
23	0.157	0.727	0.471	0.227	0.077	0.018					
24	0.151	0.726	0.470	0.226	0.076	0.018					
25	0.145	0.725	0.468	0.224	0.075	0.017					
26	0.140	0.725	0.467	0.223	0.075	0.017					
27	0.135	0.724	0.466	0.222	0.074	0.017					
28	0.130	0.723	0.465	0.221	0.073	0.017					
29	0.126	0.723	0.464	0.220	0.073	0.017					
30	0.122	0.722	0.463	0.219	0.072	0.016					
60	0.063	0.715	0.450	0.205	0.065	0.014					
∞		0.707	0.437	0.193	0.058	0.011					

Table III is taken from *Statistical Research Memoirs*, Vol. II, by kind permission of Professor E. S. Pearson.

TABLE III   TABLE OF $E^2_{0.05}$ AND THE CORRESPONDING VALUES OF P_{II} (*Continued*)

$f_1 = 2$

f_2	$E^2_{0.05}$	ϕ									
		1	1.5	2	2.5	3	4	5	6	7	8
2	0.950	0.881	0.803	0.704	0.595	0.484	0.286	0.146	0.064	0.024	0.008
4	0.776	0.824	0.661	0.460	0.272	0.135	0.020	0.001			
6	0.632	0.789	0.579	0.340	0.153	0.052	0.002				
7	0.575	0.777	0.551	0.304	0.124	0.037	0.001				
8	0.527	0.767	0.530	0.277	0.104	0.027	0.001				
9	0.486	0.759	0.513	0.257	0.090	0.022					
10	0.451	0.752	0.498	0.241	0.080	0.017					
11	0.420	0.747	0.486	0.228	0.072	0.015					
12	0.393	0.742	0.476	0.217	0.066	0.013					
13	0.369	0.737	0.468	0.208	0.061	0.011					
14	0.348	0.734	0.461	0.201	0.057	0.010					
15	0.329	0.730	0.454	0.195	0.054	0.009					
16	0.312	0.727	0.448	0.189	0.051	0.008					
17	0.297	0.725	0.443	0.184	0.048	0.008					
18	0.283	0.722	0.439	0.180	0.046	0.007					
19	0.270	0.720	0.435	0.177	0.044	0.007					
20	0.259	0.718	0.431	0.173	0.043	0.006					
21	0.248	0.717	0.428	0.170	0.042	0.006					
22	0.238	0.715	0.425	0.168	0.040	0.006					
23	0.229	0.714	0.422	0.165	0.039	0.006					
24	0.221	0.712	0.420	0.163	0.038	0.005					
25	0.213	0.711	0.417	0.161	0.037	0.005					
26	0.206	0.710	0.415	0.159	0.037	0.005					
27	0.199	0.709	0.413	0.157	0.036	0.005					
28	0.193	0.708	0.411	0.155	0.035	0.005					
29	0.187	0.707	0.410	0.154	0.035	0.004					
30	0.181	0.706	0.408	0.153	0.034	0.004					
60	0.095	0.692	0.384	0.134	0.027	0.003					
∞		0.678	0.362	0.117	0.021	0.002					

TABLE III   TABLE OF $E^2_{0.05}$ AND THE CORRESPONDING VALUES OF P_{II} (*Continued*)

$f_1 = 3$

f_2	$E^2_{0.05}$	ϕ									
		1	1.5	2	2.5	3	4	5	6	7	8
2	0.966	0.888	0.817	0.726	0.624	0.519	0.324	0.177	0.084	0.035	0.013
4	0.832	0.830	0.670	0.468	0.278	0.139	0.020	0.001			
6	0.704	0.791	0.574	0.326	0.139	0.044	0.002				
7	0.651	0.776	0.540	0.283	0.106	0.028					
8	0.604	0.764	0.513	0.251	0.084	0.018					
9	0.563	0.754	0.491	0.226	0.068	0.013					
10	0.527	0.745	0.472	0.206	0.057	0.010					
11	0.495	0.738	0.457	0.190	0.049	0.008					
12	0.466	0.731	0.444	0.178	0.043	0.006					
13	0.440	0.726	0.433	0.167	0.038	0.005					
14	0.418	0.721	0.422	0.158	0.035	0.004					
15	0.397	0.716	0.414	0.151	0.032	0.004					
16	0.378	0.712	0.406	0.144	0.029	0.003					
17	0.361	0.709	0.399	0.139	0.027	0.003					
18	0.345	0.705	0.393	0.134	0.025	0.002					
19	0.331	0.702	0.388	0.130	0.024	0.002					
20	0.317	0.700	0.383	0.126	0.022	0.002					
21	0.305	0.697	0.379	0.123	0.021	0.002					
22	0.294	0.695	0.375	0.119	0.020	0.002					
23	0.283	0.693	0.371	0.117	0.019	0.002					
24	0.273	0.691	0.367	0.114	0.019	0.001					
25	0.264	0.689	0.364	0.112	0.018	0.001					
26	0.255	0.687	0.361	0.110	0.017	0.001					
27	0.248	0.686	0.359	0.108	0.017	0.001					
28	0.240	0.684	0.356	0.106	0.016	0.001					
29	0.233	0.683	0.354	0.105	0.016	0.001					
30	0.226	0.682	0.352	0.103	0.015	0.001					
60	0.121	0.662	0.320	0.083	0.010	0.001					
∞		0.642	0.289	0.067	0.007						

TABLE III TABLE OF $E^2_{0.05}$ AND THE CORRESPONDING VALUES OF P_{II} (Continued)

$f_1 = 4$

f_2	$E^2_{0.05}$	ϕ									
		1	1.5	2	2.5	3	4	5	6	7	8
2	0.975	0.892	0.824	0.738	0.640	0.537	0.345	0.195	0.097	0.043	0.017
4	0.865	0.833	0.673	0.471	0.279	0.139	0.020	0.001			
6	0.751	0.791	0.567	0.314	0.128	0.038	0.001				
7	0.702	0.774	0.529	0.265	0.092	0.022					
8	0.657	0.760	0.497	0.229	0.069	0.013					
9	0.618	0.748	0.471	0.201	0.054	0.008					
10	0.582	0.738	0.449	0.179	0.043	0.006					
11	0.550	0.729	0.430	0.161	0.035	0.004					
12	0.521	0.721	0.414	0.148	0.030	0.003					
13	0.494	0.714	0.401	0.136	0.025	0.002					
14	0.471	0.708	0.389	0.127	0.022	0.002					
15	0.449	0.702	0.378	0.119	0.019	0.002					
16	0.429	0.697	0.369	0.112	0.017	0.001					
17	0.411	0.693	0.361	0.106	0.016	0.001					
18	0.394	0.689	0.354	0.101	0.014	0.001					
19	0.379	0.685	0.347	0.097	0.013	0.001					
20	0.364	0.681	0.341	0.093	0.012	0.001					
21	0.351	0.678	0.335	0.089	0.011	0.001					
22	0.339	0.675	0.331	0.086	0.010	0.001					
23	0.327	0.672	0.326	0.083	0.010						
24	0.316	0.670	0.322	0.080	0.009						
25	0.306	0.668	0.318	0.078	0.009						
26	0.297	0.665	0.315	0.076	0.008						
27	0.288	0.663	0.312	0.074	0.008						
28	0.279	0.661	0.309	0.072	0.008						
29	0.272	0.660	0.306	0.071	0.007						
30	0.264	0.658	0.303	0.069	0.007						
60	0.144	0.632	0.265	0.049	0.004						
∞		0.604	0.227	0.036	0.002						

TABLE III TABLE OF $E^2_{0.05}$ AND THE CORRESPONDING VALUES OF P_{II} (*Continued*)

$f_1 = 5$

f_2	$E^2_{0.05}$	ϕ									
		1	1.5	2	2.5	3	4	5	6	7	8
2	0.980	0.894	0.828	0.745	0.649	0.549	0.359	0.207	0.106	0.048	0.019
4	0.887	0.835	0.675	0.473	0.280	0.138	0.020	0.001			
6	0.785	0.790	0.561	0.304	0.119	0.033	0.001				
7	0.739	0.772	0.519	0.251	0.082	0.018					
8	0.697	0.756	0.483	0.211	0.059	0.010					
9	0.659	0.743	0.454	0.181	0.044	0.006					
10	0.625	0.731	0.429	0.158	0.033	0.004					
11	0.593	0.720	0.408	0.140	0.026	0.002					
12	0.564	0.711	0.390	0.125	0.021	0.002					
13	0.538	0.703	0.374	0.113	0.017	0.001					
14	0.514	0.695	0.360	0.103	0.015	0.001					
15	0.492	0.689	0.348	0.095	0.012	0.001					
16	0.471	0.683	0.338	0.088	0.011	0.001					
17	0.452	0.678	0.328	0.083	0.009						
18	0.435	0.673	0.320	0.078	0.008						
19	0.419	0.668	0.312	0.073	0.007						
20	0.404	0.664	0.305	0.069	0.007						
21	0.390	0.660	0.299	0.066	0.006						
22	0.377	0.656	0.294	0.063	0.006						
23	0.365	0.653	0.288	0.060	0.005						
24	0.353	0.650	0.284	0.058	0.005						
25	0.342	0.647	0.279	0.056	0.005						
26	0.332	0.644	0.275	0.054	0.004						
27	0.323	0.642	0.272	0.052	0.004						
28	0.314	0.640	0.268	0.050	0.004						
29	0.305	0.637	0.265	0.049	0.003						
30	0.297	0.635	0.262	0.048	0.003						
60	0.165	0.604	0.219	0.031	0.001						
∞		0.567	0.177	0.019	0.001						

TABLE III   TABLE OF $E^2_{0.05}$ AND THE CORRESPONDING VALUES OF P_{II} (*Continued*)

$f_1 = 6$

f_2	$E^2_{0.05}$	ϕ									
		1	1.5	2	2.5	3	4	5	6	7	8
2	0.983	0.895	0.831	0.749	0.656	0.557	0.368	0.216	0.112	0.052	0.022
4	0.902	0.836	0.677	0.473	0.280	0.138	0.019	0.001			
6	0.811	0.789	0.556	0.296	0.113	0.030	0.001				
7	0.768	0.769	0.510	0.239	0.074	0.015					
8	0.729	0.753	0.472	0.198	0.051	0.008					
9	0.692	0.738	0.440	0.166	0.037	0.005					
10	0.659	0.725	0.412	0.142	0.027	0.003					
11	0.628	0.713	0.389	0.123	0.020	0.002					
12	0.600	0.702	0.369	0.108	0.016	0.001					
13	0.574	0.693	0.351	0.096	0.012	0.001					
14	0.550	0.685	0.336	0.086	0.010	0.001					
15	0.527	0.677	0.323	0.078	0.008						
16	0.507	0.669	0.311	0.071	0.007						
17	0.488	0.663	0.301	0.065	0.006						
18	0.470	0.657	0.291	0.061	0.005						
19	0.454	0.652	0.283	0.056	0.004						
20	0.438	0.648	0.276	0.053	0.004						
21	0.424	0.644	0.269	0.050	0.003						
22	0.410	0.639	0.262	0.047	0.003						
23	0.397	0.635	0.257	0.045	0.003						
24	0.385	0.632	0.252	0.043	0.003						
25	0.374	0.629	0.247	0.041	0.002						
26	0.363	0.625	0.242	0.039	0.002						
27	0.353	0.623	0.238	0.037	0.002						
28	0.344	0.620	0.234	0.036	0.002						
29	0.335	0.617	0.231	0.034	0.002						
30	0.326	0.615	0.228	0.033	0.002						
60	0.184	0.576	0.181	0.019	0.001						
∞		0.532	0.138	0.010							

TABLE III TABLE OF $E^2_{0.05}$ AND THE CORRESPONDING VALUES OF P_{II} (*Continued*)

$f_1 = 7$

f_2	$E^2_{0.05}$	ϕ									
		1	1.5	2	2.5	3	4	5	6	7	8
2	0.986	0.896	0.833	0.753	0.660	0.563	0.374	0.222	0.117	0.055	0.023
4	0.914	0.837	0.678	0.474	0.280	0.138	0.019	0.001			
6	0.831	0.788	0.552	0.289	0.108	0.028	0.001				
7	0.791	0.767	0.503	0.230	0.068	0.013					
8	0.754	0.749	0.462	0.187	0.046	0.007					
9	0.719	0.733	0.427	0.154	0.031	0.004					
10	0.687	0.719	0.398	0.129	0.022	0.002					
11	0.657	0.706	0.373	0.110	0.016	0.001					
12	0.630	0.695	0.351	0.094	0.012	0.001					
13	0.604	0.684	0.332	0.082	0.009						
14	0.580	0.675	0.316	0.073	0.007						
15	0.558	0.667	0.301	0.065	0.006						
16	0.538	0.659	0.289	0.058	0.005						
17	0.518	0.652	0.277	0.053	0.004						
18	0.501	0.645	0.267	0.048	0.003						
19	0.484	0.639	0.258	0.044	0.003						
20	0.468	0.634	0.250	0.041	0.002						
21	0.453	0.629	0.243	0.038	0.002						
22	0.439	0.624	0.236	0.036	0.002						
23	0.426	0.619	0.230	0.034	0.002						
24	0.414	0.615	0.224	0.032	0.001						
25	0.402	0.611	0.219	0.030	0.001						
26	0.391	0.607	0.215	0.028	0.001						
27	0.381	0.604	0.210	0.027	0.001						
28	0.371	0.601	0.206	0.026	0.001						
29	0.362	0.598	0.202	0.024	0.001						
30	0.353	0.595	0.199	0.023	0.001						
60	0.202	0.550	0.150	0.012							
∞		0.498	0.105	0.005							

TABLE III TABLE OF $E^2_{0.05}$ AND THE CORRESPONDING VALUES OF P_{II} (*Continued*)

$f_1 = 8$

f_2	$E^2_{0.05}$	ϕ									
		1	1.5	2	2.5	3	4	5	6	7	8
2	0.987	0.897	0.835	0.755	0.664	0.567	0.380	0.227	0.121	0.057	0.024
4	0.924	0.838	0.678	0.474	0.279	0.137	0.019	0.001			
6	0.847	0.787	0.548	0.284	0.103	0.026	0.001				
7	0.810	0.765	0.497	0.222	0.064	0.012					
8	0.775	0.746	0.454	0.178	0.041	0.006					
9	0.742	0.729	0.417	0.144	0.028	0.003					
10	0.711	0.714	0.386	0.119	0.019	0.001					
11	0.682	0.700	0.359	0.099	0.013	0.001					
12	0.655	0.688	0.336	0.084	0.009						
13	0.630	0.677	0.316	0.072	0.007						
14	0.607	0.666	0.298	0.062	0.005						
15	0.585	0.657	0.283	0.055	0.004						
16	0.564	0.648	0.269	0.048	0.003						
17	0.545	0.641	0.257	0.043	0.003						
18	0.527	0.634	0.247	0.039	0.002						
19	0.510	0.627	0.237	0.035	0.002						
20	0.495	0.620	0.228	0.032	0.001						
21	0.480	0.615	0.220	0.030	0.001						
22	0.466	0.609	0.213	0.027	0.001						
23	0.452	0.604	0.207	0.025	0.001						
24	0.440	0.600	0.201	0.024	0.001						
25	0.428	0.595	0.196	0.022	0.001						
26	0.417	0.591	0.191	0.021	0.001						
27	0.406	0.588	0.186	0.020	0.001						
28	0.396	0.584	0.182	0.019							
29	0.386	0.581	0.178	0.018							
30	0.377	0.578	0.175	0.017							
60	0.219	0.527	0.125	0.008							
∞		0.466	0.081	0.003							

Index